HOLTMATH 10

Bye   Dale   Doran   Midyette   Teshima

Holt, Rinehart and Winston of Canada, Limited

Authors
Marshall P. Bye/Calgary, Alberta
William A. Dale/School District #71, Courtenay,
British Columbia
Kevin Doran/Peel Board of Education
Robert Midyette/Calgary Board of Education
Roger Teshima/Calgary Board of Education

Reviewing Consultants
George Ditto/Calgary Board of Education
Ronald Scoins/University of Waterloo

Director, Art and Design   Mary Opper
Art Director   Sandra Quigley
Design by Julia Naimska
Assembly and technical art by David Hunter
Cover by Tiit Telmet

Executive Editor   Ken Leland
Developmental Editor   Colin Garnham
Senior Production Editor   Sharon Dzubinsky
Assistant Production Editor   Sharon Tomas

Canadian Cataloguing in Publication Data
Holtmath 10

For use in grade 10.
Includes index.
ISBN 0-03-921961-5

1. Mathematics - 1961-   - Juvenile literature.
I. Bye, Marshall P., 1928-

QA107.B95 1987   510   C86-094800-5

Printed in Canada
 2 3 4 5   91 90 89

Acknowledgements
P. 45 "Life on the Mississippi" Reprinted from THE
SHRINKING MISSISSIPPI by Mark Twain. Published by
Harper & Row, Publishers, Inc.

Acknowledgements

Photograph Credits
P. 4 Canadian National Exhibition, Toronto, ON. P. 30 Mil-
ler Services Ltd., Roberts M10132X. P. 38 Chicago Bulls.
P. 58 Miller Services Ltd., NASA AS10-34-5013. P. 64 Miller
Services Ltd., Roberts I6848. P. 84 Miller Services Ltd.,
W. Wittman 141-3. P. 124 Miller Services Ltd., Lambert
LS17588R. P. 184 Miller Services Ltd., Roberts P8166T.
P. 194 Miller Services Ltd., W.R. McCullagh B8-10. P. 249
M.C. Escher Waterfall 1961. Collection Haags Gemeente-
museum — The Hague. © M.C. Escher Heirs c/o Cordon
Art — Baarn — Holland. P. 282 Miller Services Ltd., Cam-
erique C1134. P. 320 Miller Services Ltd., Lambert LF7310.
P. 358 Aerial View of Giza, Dynasty IV, Courtesy, Museum of
Fine Arts, Boston.

Every reasonable effort has been made to trace the owners of
copyrighted material and to make due acknowledgement. Any
errors or omissions drawn to our attention will be gladly recti-
fied in future editions.

The authors of HOLTMATH wish to thank the following
teachers and the students at these schools for their invaluable
comments and suggestions during the pilot testing of these
texts.

Brian Dyrkach
Spruce Grove Composite High School
Spruce Grove, Alberta

Carson McIntosh
Saunders Secondary School
London, Ontario

Adam J. Smith
Gordon Graydon M.S.S.
Mississauga, Ontario

Frank Visser
James Fowler High School
Calgary, Alberta

CONTENTS

VARIATIONS IN COMPUTERS

The programs in the pupil text are written for use with Apple computers. The same programs can be run on Commodore and Radio Shack TRS-80 models if the following changes are made.

1. All programs should begin with the statement NEW to clear the memory.

2. All programs should be proceeded by:
HOME — for Apple
SHIFT/CLR — for Commodore
CLEAR — for TRS-80.

3. RETURN is used on both Apple and Commodore models; ENTER is used for TRS-80.

4. When the TRS-80 is turned on, the letters CASS appear on the screen. Press the key L before starting to type in the program.

5. The exponent symbols are keyed and displayed as follows:

Computer	Key	Display
Apple	∧	∧
Commodore	↑	↑
TRS-80	↑	[

FOREWORD TO THE STUDENT AND TEACHER

There are several unique features that we, the authors, have included in this book. We feel that a word of explanation about each is desirable.

The Calculator

The calculator, when used appropriately, helps to foster exploration and experimentation, assists in the development and reinforcement of concepts, and facilitates and encourages problem solving. We believe that each student should have a calculator readily available. In the text, we suggest specific instances where a calculator might be used to solve problems and to assist in the development of concepts, but it is not intended that the use of the calculator be restricted to these cases only. At the discretion of the teacher, it is recommended that students be encouraged to use calculators more generally, especially in those cases where the emphasis is not on manual calculation skills but rather on thinking, planning, or understanding in a problem-solving situation. Though we believe the student should learn when it is useful and desirable to use a calculator, the calculator is not a replacement for the learning of basic facts and mental computation.

Problem Solving

The problem-solving process developed in this book is useful in learning mathematics as well as in solving problems. It is a way of thinking through new concepts and ideas logically. To assist students in developing the ability to solve problems in the broadest sense, we emphasize problem solving in four different modes.

a. In the display for most of the lessons there is a description of a practical situation in which mathematics can be used to solve a problem. This lends credibility to the "need" for the mathematics about to be developed by indicating where and how such a concept or skill is used.

b. In the exercises, more practical problems are presented for solution based on the skills developed in the display. We endeavor to pose the problems in a "real-life" context.

c. A four-step problem-solving model is developed in Chapter 2. It is suggested that this procedure be used with all types of problems. The handling of routine-type problems using algorithms is just another strategy to be employed. Scattered throughout the text are specific "process" problems which can be solved using one or more of the strategies outlined in Chapter 2. These problems are identified by a coloured exercise number.

d. Some problems require an "insight" or a change in your normal thought pattern in order to solve them. They are not designed to be "tricky" but rather to require the student to have some special inspiration, insight, or hunch. While some may be solved using the problem-solving model presented in Chapter 2, all can be solved using a creative mental leap. Typically, problems of this type are presented in the Brainticklers.

Historical Notes

Mathematics is the product of the efforts of men and women throughout history. We believe mathematics is more interesting when students know something about the lives and times of these people. At times we encourage the readers to extend their knowledge of mathematicians through a section titled "Using the Library".

We hope you enjoy developing your skills and learning about mathematics in the year ahead.

The Authors.
M. P. Bye
W. A. Dale
K. Doran
R. Midyette
R. Teshima

SYMBOLS

h	hours	P(x)	probability of x
α	proportional to	$\sqrt{x}$	square root of a number
{}	the set of	$\triangle$	triangle
$\because$	since	A	area
$\therefore$	therefore	P	perimeter
|	such that	C	circumference
ϵ	belongs to	V	volume
N	set of Natural numbers	S.A.	surface area
W	set of Whole numbers	$\pm$	plus or minus
I	set of Integers	L.S.	left side of an equation
^+Q	positive Rational numbers	R.S.	right side of an equation
^-Q	negative Rational numbers	U	universal set
Q	set of all Rational numbers	$\subset$	is contained in
$\overline{Q}$	set of all Irrational numbers	$\cup$	union
R	set of all Real numbers	$\cap$	intersection
$>$	greater than	$\varnothing$	null set
$<$	less than	$a:b$	ratio of a to b
$\geq$	greater than or equal to	$\cong$	congruent to
$\leq$	less than or equal to	$\sim$	similar
$\neq$	does not equal	$\doteq$	approximately
$f(x)$	the value of an expression at x	$\llcorner$	right angle
°C	degrees Celsius	$\angle$	angle
$\rightarrow$	maps onto	$\overline{AB}$	line segment AB or measure of line AB
π	approximately 3.141 592	$\overleftrightarrow{AB}$	line AB
$\|x\|$	absolute value (magnitude) of x	$\overrightarrow{AB}$	ray AB
...	and so on	$\|\|$	parallel to
$\frown$	arc	$\perp$	perpendicular to
(x, y)	ordered pair		

NUMBER SYSTEMS

Tune Up

1. Examine the pattern. Find the sum of the 61st row.

Row 1	3
Row 2	$3 - 3$
Row 3	$3 - 3 + 3$
Row 4	$3 - 3 + 3 - 3$
Row 5	$3 - 3 + 3 - 3 + 3$

2. Match the number of the item in Column A with the best description in Column B.

A	**B**
i) 1, 3, 5, 7	**a.** prime number
ii) 57	**b.** whole number
iii) 2, 4, 6, 8	**c.** perfect square
iv) 13	**d.** perfect cube
v) 0	**e.** composite number
vi) 1331	**f.** consecutive numbers
vii) $1 + 3 + 5 + 7$	**g.** consecutive odd numbers
viii) 13, 14, 15	**h.** consecutive even numbers

3. It requires 1386 digits to consecutively number the pages of a book.
a. How many pages does the book have?
b. How many times is the digit 6 printed?

4. Find the least whole number by which 150 should be multiplied so that the product is
a. a perfect square.
b. a perfect cube.

5.　　A grand old leader
　　　　　called Lief,
　　ate sixty-four dollars
　　　　worth of beef,
　each roast cost eleven,
　each steak cost seven,
　how much did he eat
　that grand old chief?

6. Given that n is an integer.
a. What is the greatest integer less than n?
b. What is the least integer greater than n?

7. Many prime numbers can be written in the form $2^n - 1$, where n is a natural number. For instance, $3 = 2^2 - 1$. Find three other prime numbers that can be written in this form.

8. A perfect number is a number that is the sum of its factors. For instance, $6 = 1 + 2 + 3$. Find three other perfect numbers.

1·1 Natural and Whole Numbers

The cost for the Alpha Computer Company to manufacture 45 computers on Monday, 65 on Tuesday, 110 on Wednesday, 105 on Thursday, and 75 on Friday was $30 000 per day. Each computer was sold for $500.

Example 1

Find the value of the computers produced that week.

Number of Units × Unit Value = Total Value
$$400 \times 500 = 200\ 000$$

The total value of the computers is $200 000.

Example 2

Find the profit for the Alpha Computer Company.

Profit = Total Value − Cost of Production
Profit = 200 000 − (30 000 × 5)
= 200 000 − 150 000
= 50 000

The profit is $50 000.

Example 3

If each employee works 35 h/week, and the company records 1435 h of work per week, then find the number of employees in the company.

Number of Employees = Total Hours Worked ÷ Hours in a Work Week
= 1435 ÷ 35
= 41

There are 41 employees in the company.

The numbers used to solve these and many other problems are elements of the infinite sets called the **natural** numbers (N) and the **whole** numbers (W).

$$N = \{1, 2, 3, \dots\} \qquad W = \{0, 1, 2, 3, \dots\}$$

Exercises

1. Evaluate. Use a calculator if one is available.
a. $756 + 382 + 967$
b. $36 - 24 + 16 - 8 + 12$
c. $10\ 001 - 4987$
d. $7395 - 5688 + 623$
e. $3285 - 621 - 846$
f. $1 + 2 + 3 + 4 + \dots + 50$
g. $1 + 3 + 5 + 7 + \dots + 21$
h. $2 + 4 + 6 + 8 + \dots + 22$

2. Compute.
a. $5 \times 5 \times 5$ b. 61×38
c. 4321×795 d. $721 \div 7$
e. $0 \div 3249$ f. $5720 \div 11$
g. $2381 \times 65 \times 38 \times 0 \times 43$

3. If the Alpha Computer Company manufactures the same number of computers every week, then find the total value of the computers produced in one year.

4. Which whole number is not a natural number?

5. Alpha Computer's sales representative drove 165 km on Monday, 362 km on Tuesday, 68 km on Wednesday, 287 km on Thursday, and 158 km on Friday.
a. Find the total distance travelled during this week.
b. Find the average distance travelled each day.

6. For any element in the set of natural numbers, describe how to find its successor.

1·2 Operations with Integers

The set of whole numbers can be extended to include numbers that represent opposites, gains and losses, or temperatures above and below freezing. The result is the set of **integers**.

$$I = \{\ldots, -3, -2, -1, 0, 1, 2, 3, \ldots\}$$

Example

The freezer temperature in an ice-cream truck was reduced from 20°C to −10°C in 6 h.

a. Find the total temperature change.
Temperature change is the difference between the final temperature and the initial temperature.

$$-10 - 20 = -30$$

The total temperature change is −30°C.

b. Find the average hourly rate of temperature change.
Average rate of temperature change is the total temperature change divided by the time for the change.

$$-30 \div 6 = -5$$

The average rate of temperature change is −5°C/h.

Exercises

1. Evaluate. Use a calculator if one is available.
a. $-12 + (-16)$
b. $-3 - 4$
c. $-14 - 7$
d. $10 - 20$
e. $-65 + 13$
f. $-8 - 5 - 2$
g. $-21 + 6 - 18$
h. $-25 - 37$
i. $-38 - (-17)$
j. $-43 + (-9) - 35$

2. Evaluate. Use a calculator if one is available.
a. -32×5
b. $-19 \times (-6)$
c. $-18 \div (-9)$
d. $33 \times (-6)$
e. $-217 \div 7$
f. $-3055 \div 65$
g. $-1 \times (-1) \times (-1)$
h. $-2 \times (-2) \times (-2) \times (-2)$

3. Find the difference between Monday's temperatures and Tuesday's temperatures.
a. 0°C, −37°C
b. −12°C, −52°C
c. 14°C, −3°C
d. 20°C, −47°C

4. On the morning of 1943 01 22, Spearfish, South Dakota, experienced a record temperature change from −20°C to 8°C in 2 min.
a. Find the total temperature change.
b. Find the average temperature change each minute.

5. The number 64 is both a perfect square and a perfect cube because 64 is 4^3 and also 8^2. Find two other integers that are also perfect squares and perfect cubes.

6. It took 30 min to submerge an oil-drilling rig so that its supporting legs reached the ocean floor off Newfoundland. The rate of descent of the rig was −6 m/min. After every 2 min of descent, a pause of 5 min was needed to stabilize the rig. Find the depth of the ocean where the rig was placed.

Braintickler

Two numbers are said to be **friendly** numbers if each is the sum of the factors of the other. For example, 284 and 220 are friendly numbers since the factors of 220 are 1, 2, 4, 5, 10, 11, 20, 22, 44, 55, and 110 and this sum is 284; while the factors of 284 are 1, 2, 4, 71, and 142 and this sum is 220. In recent years, as many as 60 pairs of friendly numbers have been found. Find one such pair.

1·3 Operations with Rational Numbers

While the use of metric units has decreased everyday use of fractions and increased the use of decimals, there are still many uses for fractions.

The set of integers is **closed** under addition, subtraction, and multiplication. However, division does not always produce another integer. The set of all quotients in the form $\frac{a}{b}$, where a and b are both integers and $b \neq 0$, is the set of **rational** numbers.

$$Q = \{\frac{a}{b} \mid a, b \in I; b \neq 0\}$$

The set of all numbers   such that   belongs to

Example

Four members of a photography club organized a picture-framing booth for a charity carnival. Catalia worked at the booth for $2\frac{2}{3}$ h, Anne-Missa for $2\frac{1}{3}$ h, Owen for $1\frac{3}{4}$ h, and Chong-min for $3\frac{2}{3}$ h.

a. How long was the booth open?

$$2\frac{2}{3} + 2\frac{1}{3} + 1\frac{3}{4} + 3\frac{2}{3}$$
$$= \frac{8}{3} + \frac{7}{3} + \frac{7}{4} + \frac{11}{3}$$
$$= \frac{32}{12} + \frac{28}{12} + \frac{21}{12} + \frac{44}{12}$$
$$= \frac{125}{12}$$
$$= 10\frac{5}{12}$$

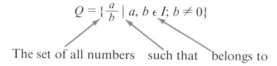

Change to improper fractions.

Find a least common denominator.

The club operated the booth for $10\frac{5}{12}$ h.

b. How long was the booth closed if the carnival ran for 12 h?

$$12 - 10\frac{5}{12} = 12 - \frac{125}{12}$$
$$= \frac{144}{12} - \frac{125}{12}$$
$$= \frac{19}{12}$$

The booth was closed for $1\frac{7}{12}$ h or 1 h 35 min.

c. For what fraction of the time did Chong-min work?

$$3\frac{2}{3} \div 10\frac{5}{12} = \frac{11}{3} \div \frac{125}{12}$$
$$= \frac{11}{3} \times \frac{12}{125}$$
$$= \frac{44}{125}$$

To divide by a fraction, multiply by the reciprocal of the divisor.

Chong-min worked for $\frac{44}{125}$ of the time the booth was open.

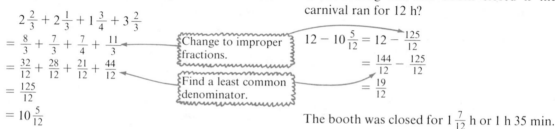

Exercises

1. Find the least common denominator for each set of fractions. The first one is done as an example.

$\frac{1}{4}, \frac{1}{10}, \frac{1}{5}$

Multiples of 4 are: {4, 8, 12, 16, 20, 24, ...}.
Multiples of 10 are: {10, 20, 30, 40, ...}.
Multiples of 5 are: {5, 10, 15, 20, 25, 30, ...}.
The least common denominator is 20.

a. $\frac{1}{2}, \frac{1}{3}, \frac{1}{5}$ **b.** $\frac{2}{5}, \frac{3}{7}, \frac{1}{9}$

c. $\frac{3}{8}, \frac{5}{12}, \frac{6}{17}$ **d.** $\frac{2}{9}, \frac{1}{9}, \frac{5}{8}$

2. Express each in lowest terms.

a. $\frac{-3}{6}$ **b.** $\frac{4}{12}$ **c.** $\frac{-5}{45}$

d. $\frac{-7}{-28}$ **e.** $-\left(\frac{-6}{-36}\right)$ **f.** $\frac{-17}{51}$

3. Calculate.

a. $\frac{7}{15} + \frac{8}{15}$ **b.** $\frac{-1}{8} + \frac{3}{8}$

c. $\frac{3}{5} - \frac{9}{5}$ **d.** $\frac{-7}{12} - \left(\frac{-5}{12}\right)$

e. $\frac{1}{2} - \left(\frac{-2}{3}\right)$ **f.** $2\frac{3}{4} + \frac{3}{8}$

g. $-5\frac{1}{2} + 3\frac{1}{4}$ **h.** $-3\frac{1}{5} - 1\frac{2}{3}$

4. Rewrite each fraction with a denominator of 12.

a. $\frac{1}{3}$ **b.** $\frac{2}{8}$ **c.** $\frac{5}{6}$

5. Refer to the example in the display. Find the total hours worked by these people.
a. Catalia and Owen
b. Anne-Missa and Chong-min
c. Catalia, Anne-Missa, and Owen

6. How much longer did Chong-min work than Owen?

7. If $\frac{1}{10}$ of the people attending a carnival at Sidney High were teachers, $\frac{1}{5}$ were parents, and $\frac{1}{4}$ were children not attending the school, then what fraction of the attendance were students attending the school?

8. Calculate.

a. $\left(\frac{2}{3}\right)\left(\frac{3}{5}\right)$ **b.** $\left(\frac{3}{4}\right)\left(\frac{2}{3}\right)$

c. $\left(\frac{-4}{9}\right)\left(\frac{3}{16}\right)$ **d.** $\left(\frac{2}{9}\right)\left(\frac{5}{11}\right)$

e. $\left(\frac{-1}{3}\right)\left(\frac{-7}{8}\right)$ **f.** $\left(\frac{3}{7}\right)\left(\frac{-7}{5}\right)\left(\frac{1}{9}\right)$

9. Calculate.

a. $\left(\frac{5}{8}\right)\left(1\frac{1}{4}\right)$ **b.** $\left(\frac{-6}{5}\right)\left(2\frac{3}{11}\right)$

c. $\left(-4\frac{2}{9}\right)\left(\frac{-3}{19}\right)$ **d.** $\left(-5\frac{1}{4}\right)\left(-20\right)\left(-10\frac{1}{3}\right)$

e. $\left(23\frac{3}{7}\right)\left(-3\frac{1}{2}\right)$ **f.** $\left(-18\frac{3}{16}\right)\left(-\frac{32}{97}\right)$

10. Write the reciprocal of each.

a. -5 **b.** $\frac{3}{2}$ **c.** $2\frac{1}{9}$

d. $-6\frac{4}{5}$ **e.** $\frac{-3}{4}$ **f.** 5

11. If $1\frac{1}{2}$ hens lay $1\frac{1}{2}$ eggs in $1\frac{1}{2}$ d, then how many eggs will 10 hens lay in 10 d?

12. Calculate.

a. $\frac{3}{5} \div 5$ **b.** $5 \div \frac{3}{5}$

c. $-10 \div \frac{2}{3}$ **d.** $\frac{0}{4} \div \frac{3}{4}$

e. $-\frac{3}{4} \div (-9)$ **f.** $\frac{-3}{7} \div \frac{9}{14}$

g. $\frac{-5}{8} \div 2\frac{7}{8}$ **h.** $5\frac{2}{9} \div \left(-6\frac{1}{3}\right)$

i. $\frac{5}{11} \div \frac{11}{5} \div \frac{-5}{11}$ **j.** $6\frac{1}{4} \div \left(-\frac{5}{4}\right) \div \frac{5}{26}$

k. $-13\frac{1}{3} \div 1\frac{7}{9} \div \left(-3\frac{1}{5}\right)$

Using the Library

The sinking of the *Titanic* caused people to rethink many ideas about mapping. It was decided that the open seas should be carefully charted and the location of all icebergs should be tracked. Research the sinking of the *Titanic* and write a report that answers these questions.

a. Why do we need maps?
b. How is the position of an iceberg recorded?
c. What is meant by the terms latitude and longitude?
d. How would you define the Prime Meridian and the Equator?

1·4 Order of Operations

In order to win a contest, Lance had to answer the following three skill-testing questions correctly. The calculations Lance made are shown. Did he win?

Question 1

$15 \times 3 - 20 \div 5 + 7$
$= 45 - 4 + 7$
$= 41 + 7$
$= 48$

Question 2

$-6 + [4(3 - 7) - 8] \div (-6)$
$= -6 + [4(-4) - 8] \div (-6)$
$= -6 + [-16 - 8] \div (-6)$
$= -6 + [-24] \div (-6)$
$= -6 + 4$
$= -2$

Question 3

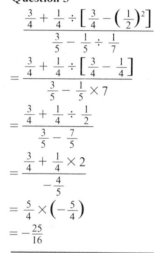

$$\frac{\frac{3}{4} + \frac{1}{4} \div \left[\frac{3}{4} - \left(\frac{1}{2}\right)^2\right]}{\frac{3}{5} - \frac{1}{5} \div \frac{1}{7}}$$

$$= \frac{\frac{3}{4} + \frac{1}{4} \div \left[\frac{3}{4} - \frac{1}{4}\right]}{\frac{3}{5} - \frac{1}{5} \times 7}$$

$$= \frac{\frac{3}{4} + \frac{1}{4} \div \frac{1}{2}}{\frac{3}{5} - \frac{7}{5}}$$

$$= \frac{\frac{3}{4} + \frac{1}{4} \times 2}{-\frac{4}{5}}$$

$$= \frac{5}{4} \times \left(-\frac{5}{4}\right)$$

$$= -\frac{25}{16}$$

> The fraction bar indicates that the numerator and the denominator must be evaluated independently.

> **Order of Operations**
>
> 1. Perform operations in brackets first.
>
> 2. Evaluate powers.
>
> 3. Do division and multiplication in order from left to right.
>
> 4. Do addition and subtraction in order from left to right.

Exercises

1. Explain why it is necessary that the same order of operations be used by all people performing calculations.

2. Calculate.
a. $(32 + 14) - 18$
b. $27 - (13 + 5)$
c. $14 - 5 \times 2$
d. $3 - 8 \div 4$
e. $5 + 3 \times 5$
f. $19 - 3 \times 4 \div 3$
g. $\frac{7 \times 3}{8 - 1}$
h. $\frac{15 + 12}{5 + 4}$
i. $[10 - (15 \div 3)] \times 4$
j. $\{3^2[48 \div (12 + 2^2)]\}$
k. $45 - 36 \div 9 + 3 \times 2$
l. $42 \div 7 \times 3(12 - 12)$

3. Calculate.
a. $-5 + 7 - 8$
b. $-5 + (-3) - 4$
c. $(-1)^3 + 1$
d. $(-1)^4 + 1$
e. $(-3 + 2)^2 \div (-1)$
f. $(-4)^2 + 4 \div (-2)$
g. $14 \div (-7) - 5$
h. $-12 \div (-2)2 + 2$
i. $\frac{-18 + (-6)}{-9 + 3}$
j. $\frac{-36 \div (-6)}{2 \div (-4)}$

4. Evaluate. Write the answer in lowest terms and with positive denominators.
a. $\frac{-16}{4} + \frac{4}{-2}$
b. $\frac{-8}{5} \div \frac{8}{5}$
c. $\frac{1}{4} + \frac{-1}{2}$
d. $\frac{3}{4} \div \frac{5}{4} + \frac{2}{5}$
e. $\frac{1}{8} \times \frac{4}{3} - \frac{1}{6}$
f. $\frac{1}{5} + \frac{4}{5} \times 5$
g. $\frac{-2}{9} \div \frac{4}{9} - \frac{1}{2}$
h. $\frac{0}{-3} \div \left(\frac{-7}{3}\right) + \frac{4}{27}$

5. A soaring hang glider lost 32 m, gained 65 m, and then lost 48 m. Find the glider's final height compared to the starting position. (*Hint:* Draw a diagram.)

6. Three bank accounts showed these changes over a week.

Account	Balance Monday	Amount Deposited During Week
A	200	−50
B	730	190
C	127	−106

Which expression represents the total amount in all three accounts at the end of the week?
a. $(200 - 150) + (730 - 920) + (127 - 21)$
b. $(200 - 150) + (920 - 730) + (21 - 127)$
c. $(150 - 200) + (920 - 730) + (21 - 127)$
d. $(200 - 150) + (920 - 730) + (127 - 21)$
e. $(200 - 50) + (730 + 190) + (127 - 106)$

7. A farmer started with 4 ha in oats. The next year the amount of land in oats was increased by the square of the original area. The third year, the farmer reduced oat seeding by three times the starting area. How many hectares were planted the third year?

8. Calculate.
a. $-(-1)^4$
b. $5(-2)^3$
c. $-3(6 - (-2)^2)$
d. $4(3)^2 - 4(3) - 5$
e. $9(5) - 8^2 + 2^3$
f. $\dfrac{2^3 \div 4 + 2}{3^2 - 1}$
g. $\dfrac{2(5) + 3(3)^2 - 1}{2^2 + 2}$
h. $\dfrac{-25 + (5)^2}{8^3 - 8^2 - 8 + 1}$
i. $(3^2 - 3)(3^2 + 3)$
j. $-\{-3[-4\{(-1)^2 - 3^2\} + 6] \div 2\}$

9. Perform the indicated operations.
a. $\left(\frac{1}{4}\right)^2 - \left(-\frac{1}{4}\right)^2$
b. $\frac{3}{4} - \left[\frac{1}{2}\{\left(\frac{1}{2}\right)^2 - \left(\frac{1}{4}\right)^2\}\right]$
c. $\left(\frac{5}{6} + \frac{1}{6} \div \frac{1}{3} + \frac{2}{3}\right)^2$
d. $-2 + \frac{1}{2} \div \frac{1}{2} \div \left(-\frac{1}{2}\right) \div \left(-\frac{1}{2}\right) + 2$
e. $-\{[-\frac{1}{2}(3^2 \div \frac{3}{2} + \frac{2}{5}) \div \left(-\frac{1}{25}\right)]\}$

10. A theatre sold 160 adult tickets at $5 each, 320 student tickets at $3.50 each, and 100 children's tickets at $2.25 each. The theatre management paid $200 each to 4 musicians, $40 each to 8 stagehands, $60 each to 2 electricians, and $44 each to 2 janitors. Which expression represents the total receipts after expenses?
a. $160(5) + 320(3.5) + 100(2.25) - 4(200) + 8(40) + 2(60) + 2(40)$
b. $160(5) + 320(3.5) + 100(2.25) - 16(344)$
c. $580(5 + 3.5 + 2.25) - [4(200) + 8(40) + 2(60) + 2(44)]$
d. $580(5 + 3.5 + 2.25) - 16(344)$
e. $160(5) + 320(3.5) + 100(2.25) - [4(200) + 8(40) + 2(60) + 2(44)]$

11. Calculate.
a. $2\frac{1}{2} \div \left(-3\frac{1}{2}\right) + 3\frac{1}{2}$
b. $3\frac{1}{5} + 2\frac{1}{5} \div \frac{5}{11} - 3\frac{1}{5} \times \left(-1\frac{1}{4}\right)$
c. $-4\frac{1}{2} \div \left(-\frac{3}{4} - \left(-2\frac{1}{4}\right)\right)$
d. $-1\frac{1}{2}\{-\frac{2}{3}[\frac{3}{2} \div \left(1\frac{1}{2} - 1\right)] + \frac{2}{3}\}$
e. $\dfrac{\left(3\frac{3}{4}\right)^2 \div -\left(1\frac{1}{2}\right)^3}{\left(3\frac{1}{2}\right)^2\left(2\frac{1}{7}\right)^2} + 1$

12. Make up a skill-testing question for use in a contest. Challenge five of your classmates to answer the question.

Braintickler

A weary traveller came to a fork in the road. One road led to Wondermath and the other led to Mathland. Standing guard at the fork were two guards. From experience, the traveller knew that one of the guards always told the truth and the other guard always lied. The traveller had to get home to Wondermath. The guards discussed the situation and allowed the traveller one question. What would the question have to be in order for the traveller to find his way home? Explain your reasoning.

1·5 Substitution

Algebra is a language used to communicate ideas about numbers and the relationships between them. Solutions to many problems can be found by substituting values for the variables in equations or formulas.

Example

A football field is enclosed by a track which is a semicircle in each end zone. The field, including end zones, is to be covered with Cosmo Turf that costs $35/m². Find the total cost of covering the field if the field, not including the end zones, is 100 m by 42 m. Recall that $\pi \doteq \frac{22}{7}$.

The total area to be covered, A, is the sum of the area of the field and the area of the end zones.

$$A = \frac{\pi r^2}{2} + \frac{\pi r^2}{2} + l \times w \qquad \text{Why do we use } \frac{\pi r^2}{2}\text{?}$$
$$= \pi r^2 + l \times w$$
$$= \frac{22}{7}(21)^2 + 100 \times 42$$
$$= 5586$$

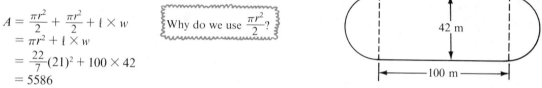

42 m

100 m

The total cost is the product of the total area and the cost per square metre of the turf.
Cost = (5586)(35)
     = 195 510

The total cost of the turf is $195 510.

Exercises

1. Evaluate each if $a = 5, b = -2$, and $c = 6$. Recall the order of operations.

a. $a + b \times c$ b. $a - c \div b$
c. $(a + b) \div c$ d. $a\{b[c(a - b)]\}$
e. $\dfrac{(a^2 - c^2)^2}{a^2 - b^2}$ f. $\dfrac{b^2 - c \div b - a}{c + b^2 \div a}$

2. A student's mark on a mathematics test was calculated using the formula $M = 150 - 5e$. Five marks were subtracted for each error, e. Calculate the marks for students having these numbers of errors. What happens if there are more than 30 errors?

a. 5   b. 7   c. 0
d. 10   e. 30   f. 13

3. Evaluate if $x = \frac{1}{2}, y = -\frac{1}{5}$, and $z = \frac{1}{7}$.

a. $\dfrac{x + y}{z}$ b. $\dfrac{x - z}{y}$ c. $x + y \div z$
d. $x^2 \div y^2$ e. $x + y \div z^2$ f. $x^3 \div y^2 + z$

4. An expression contains the variables x and y. When $x = 3$ and $y = 2$, the expression has a value of 4. When $x = 1$ and $y = 3$, the expression has a value of 1. Find the expression.

5. A stone is dropped into a well and reaches the water in $7\frac{1}{2}$ s. What is the speed of the stone when it hits the water and how far down is it to the water? Use the formula $d = \frac{1}{2}gt^2$, where d is the distance the stone falls in metres, g is 9.8 m/s², and t is the time in seconds. To find the speed, use $v = gt$, where v is the speed of the stone at impact.

6. The stalling speed of an aircraft, V_s, is calculated using the formula $V_s = V\sqrt{L}$. Find the stalling speed for each load factor, L, at a velocity, V, of 120 km/h.

a. 1.04   b. 1.15   c. 1.41
d. 2   e. 2.5   f. 3.75

1·6 Conversion of Fractions to Decimals

A hockey league announced the five most accurate shooters for a season. The ratio of goals scored to shots on goal gives the shooting accuracy. The ratios are converted to decimals for ease of comparison.

Player	Goals Scored	Shots Made	Calculation	Shooting Accuracy
1	66	198	66 ÷ 198	$0.\overline{3}$
2	65	200	65 ÷ 200	0.325
3	63	198	63 ÷ 198	$0.3\overline{18}$
4	56	225	56 ÷ 225	$0.248\overline{8}$
5	22	99	22 ÷ 99	$0.\overline{2}$

$0.\overline{3}$ is a way of writing 0.333... .

> To convert a fraction to a decimal, divide the numerator by the denominator.

The decimal $0.\overline{3}$ is a **repeating** decimal, while 0.325 is a **terminating** decimal.
The **period** of any decimal is the block of repeating decimals and the **length** of the period is the number of digits in the period.

Exercises

1. Identify the period in each repeating decimal.
a. $0.\overline{17}$ **b.** $4.2\overline{3}$ **c.** $-7.2\overline{543}$
d. $10.\overline{007}$ **e.** $-1.0\overline{97}$ **f.** $16.02\overline{07}$

2. Write each repeating decimal in short form.
a. 9.777 ...   **b.** 36.035 35 ...   **c.** −271.876 876 ...

3. Copy and complete the table. The first row is completed for you.

Fraction	Decimal	Period	Length of Period
$\frac{7}{9}$	$0.\overline{7}$	7	1
$\frac{7}{11}$			
$\frac{7}{99}$			
$\frac{99}{7}$			
$\frac{7}{24}$			
$\frac{4}{111}$			

4. Copy and complete the table. Give the decimal form of the shooting accuracy for each player listed.

Player	Goals	Shots	Accuracy
MacDonald	66	272	
Rota	42	173	
Gretzky	71	348	
Larmer	80	195	

5. Which is the more economical buy?
a. 42 g for $1.75 or 36 g for $1.52
b. 25 L for $12.48 or 36 L for $18.04
c. 470 kg for $57.81 or 172 kg for $21.07
d. 55.5 mL for $1.06 or 37.9 mL for $0.72
e. 472 mg for $22.80 or 350 mg for $16.77

6. The fraction $\frac{1}{19}$ has 18 repeating decimals. Using only a calculator, find the 18 digits.

1·7 Conversion of Decimals to Fractions

Any rational number can be expressed as a terminating or repeating decimal. As a result, all terminating and repeating decimals can be written as rational numbers.

Example 1

Drytown discovered during their last thunderstorm that 0.7 mm of rain fell in the first minute, 0.07 mm in the second, and 0.007 mm in the third. If this uniform rate of reduced rainfall continued, then what fraction will represent the total amount of rain that fell?

$0.7 + 0.07 + 0.007 + \ldots = 0.\overline{7}$

Let $n = 0.77\overline{7}$

$10n = 7.77\overline{7}$

Multiply by 10 to place the decimal at the end of the first period.

$\underline{-\ 1n = 0.77\overline{7}}$

Subtract to eliminate the repeating decimals.

$9n = 7$

$n = \dfrac{7}{9}$

The total rainfall will be $\dfrac{7}{9}$ mm.

Example 2

The Great Start Gold Miners removed $\dfrac{8}{10}$ t of gold in the first month of operation, $\dfrac{3}{100}$ t the second month, and $\dfrac{3}{1000}$ t the third month. If this steady rate of reduced yield continues, then what fraction will represent the amount of gold extracted from the mine?

$\dfrac{8}{10} + \dfrac{3}{100} + \dfrac{3}{1000} + \ldots = 0.8 + 0.03 + 0.003 + \ldots$
$= 0.8\overline{3}$

Let $n = 0.83\overline{3}$

$100n = 83.3\overline{3}$
$\underline{-\ 10n = \ \ 8.3\overline{3}}$

Multiply by 100, and then 10, to place the decimal point at the end of the first period, and the beginning of the first period.

$90n = 75$

Subtract to eliminate the repeating decimals.

$n = \dfrac{75}{90}$

The total gold taken from the mine is $\dfrac{5}{6}$ t.

Exercises

1. Express each as a fraction in lowest terms.

a. 0.4   b. 0.52   c. 2.25
d. −0.002   e. 0.625   f. 0.045

2. Multiply each by 10, 100, and 1000.

a. $0.\overline{6}$ b. $2.5\overline{3}$ c. $-8.7\overline{2}$
d. $0.\overline{9}$ e. $0.0\overline{4}$ f. $-12.\overline{12}$
g. $-13.\overline{78}$ h. $-1.00\overline{1}$ i. $0.312\,\overline{45}$

3. Perform the indicated operations.
a. $10x - x$ **b.** $100x - x$ **c.** $1000x - 100x$

4. Convert each to a fraction in lowest terms.
a. $0.\overline{1}$ **b.** $0.\overline{3}$ **c.** $0.\overline{5}$
d. $0.\overline{7}$ **e.** $1.\overline{6}$ **f.** $4.\overline{2}$

5. After a severe thunderstorm, the level of the water at the mouth of the Fraser River increased by $\frac{7}{10}$ cm the first hour, $\frac{7}{100}$ cm the second hour, and $\frac{7}{1000}$ cm the third hour. If the river continued to rise at this rate, then what is the maximum increase in the height of the water?

6. A snowstorm in Regina dropped $\frac{3}{5}$ m of snow the first day, $\frac{1}{20}$ m the second day, and $\frac{1}{200}$ m the third day. If the steady rate of declining snowfall continues indefinitely, then what fraction would represent the total depth of snow?

7. A nuclear rocket achieved $\frac{2}{10}$ the speed of light, c, in one hour, $\frac{27}{100}c$ in the second hour, and $\frac{277}{1000}c$ in the third hour. What fraction will represent the speed of the rocket if this declining rate of increased velocity continues indefinitely? Have you done a similar problem?

8. Convert each decimal to a fraction in lowest terms.
a. $0.\overline{21}$ **b.** $0.4\overline{5}$ **c.** $0.\overline{127}$
d. $1.3\overline{2}$ **e.** $-7.6\overline{1}$ **f.** $0.4\overline{2}$
g. $-4.9\overline{1}$ **h.** $3.63\overline{7}$ **i.** $0.95\overline{8}$
j. $0.39\overline{67}$ **k.** $0.8\overline{235}$ **l.** $-0.69\overline{1\,25}$

9. Find the digit in the one hundredth place to the right of the decimal point of $\frac{4}{11}$.

10. Find the 100th digit to the right of the decimal point of $\frac{3}{7}$.

11. A rubber ball is dropped from a height of 30 m. If it rebounds 0.1 of the distance of each prior fall, then how far will it travel before coming to rest? (Assume no air resistance.) Can you make this into a problem similar to one done earlier?

12. Explain why the length of the period of $\frac{a}{b}$ where $a, b \in N$ is less than b.

13. A pendulum swings 20 cm from right to left. On each swing it travels 0.01 of the distance of the previous swing. How far will it travel before coming to rest?

14. A rubber ball is dropped from a height of 72 m. On each bounce it rebounds 0.3 of the distance of each prior fall. Find the total distance the ball will travel.

15. The first wave from a passing ship caused a moored boat to move up and down 40 cm. Each successive wave moved the boat 0.8 of the distance travelled due to the previous wave. Find a fraction to represent how far the boat will move.

16. A steel ball drops 60 cm. On each bounce it rebounds $\frac{1}{10}$ as far as it dropped. Find a fraction to represent how far the ball has fallen.

17. An annual plant grows, reproduces, and dies in a single year. A population survey revealed that a rare annual variety was only reproducing 85% of the number of plants from the previous year. If the original population was 3000 plants, then how many plants would have lived before the variety became extinct?

18. The initial shock wave from an explosion caused dust particles to move up and down 3 mm. Each following wave moved the particles $\frac{1}{9}$ the distance moved by the previous wave. How far will the particles travel before the dust settles?

19. When any two rational numbers are multiplied together, the result is a rational number.
a. Multiply $0.\overline{1}$ and $0.\overline{3}$ on a calculator, as best you can, and record the resultant decimal.
b. Does this appear to be a repeating decimal?
c. In your own words, explain the fact that although the calculator does not appear to give a repeating decimal, this product is in fact a repeating decimal.

1·8 Rational Number Properties

In this section, we summarize the properties of the sets of numbers. We also will solve problems related to the properties and the sets of numbers. You may use the four-step problem-solving model to Understand the Problem, Develop a Plan to solve the problem, Carry Out the Plan, and Look Back on what you have done to see that the problem has been solved correctly.

Exercises

1. Copy and complete the table by indicating which properties hold for each set of numbers.

Properties	Natural Numbers	Whole Numbers	Integers	Rational Numbers
Closure under i) addition ii) multiplication iii) subtraction iv) division				
Associative under i) addition ii) multiplication iii) subtraction iv) division				
Commutative under i) addition ii) multiplication iii) subtraction iv) division				
Identity element for i) addition ii) multiplication				
Inverse element for i) addition ii) multiplication				
Density				
Distributive				

2. Explain, and give an example or a counter-example for each property in Exercise 1.

3. Construct a table similar to the one in Exercise 1 for each set of numbers.
a. $\{-2, -1, 0, 1, 2\}$ **b.** $\{0, 2, 4, 6, \ldots\}$
c. $\{1, 3, 5, \ldots\}$ **d.** $\left\{\frac{1}{2}, \frac{1}{4}, \frac{1}{6}, \frac{1}{8}, \frac{1}{10}, \ldots\right\}$
e. $\{0, 1\}$ **f.** $\left\{\frac{2}{7}, \frac{4}{7}, \frac{6}{7}\right\}$

4. Calculate each mentally. Name the property which made your calculation easier.
a. $0.95(43 + 17) + 0.05(43 + 17)$
b. $31.5(100 - 81) + 68.5(19)$
c. $0.17(36.7) + 0.61(36.7) + 0.22(36.7)$

5. Name the property of the rational numbers illustrated.

a. $6 + 4 = 4 + 6$ **b.** $\frac{1}{2} + 0 = \frac{1}{2}$
c. $-8 \times 1 = -8$ **d.** $\frac{31}{7} \times \frac{7}{31} = 1$
e. $\frac{9}{10} \times \frac{3}{8} = \frac{3}{8} \times \frac{9}{10}$ **f.** $-21 + 0 = -21$
g. $\frac{1}{2} < \frac{3}{4} < \frac{9}{10}$ **h.** $17 + (-17) = 0$
i. $0.31 < 0.312 < 0.313$ **j.** $-\frac{1}{2} \times \frac{3}{4} = \frac{3}{4} \times -\frac{1}{2}$
k. $8(6 + \frac{3}{4}) = 8 \times 6 + 8 \times \frac{3}{4}$

6. State whether each set of numbers is closed under subtraction.
a. natural numbers   **b.** whole numbers
c. integers   **d.** rational numbers

7. State whether each set of numbers is closed under division.

a. natural numbers **b.** whole numbers
c. integers **d.** rational numbers

8. Find a rational number between each pair of numbers.

a. $\frac{1}{16}, \frac{1}{32}$ **b.** $\frac{6}{25}, \frac{19}{75}$

c. $\frac{5}{6}, \frac{25}{31}$ **d.** $\frac{23}{56}, \frac{3}{7}$

9. Write the reciprocal of each.

a. $-\frac{12}{7}$ **b.** $\frac{5}{9}$ **c.** 0.8

d. 10.27 **e.** $-3\frac{4}{5}$ **f.** -1

10. State how to find each.
a. the next consecutive integer after n
b. the previous integer before n
c. the next consecutive integer after $n + 2$
d. the next consecutive odd integer after n
e. the next consecutive even integer after n
f. the product of two consecutive integers
g. the sum of two consecutive integers
h. the average of two consecutive integers

11. Add.
a. 0.111 111 111...
   0.777 777 777...

b. 2.333 333...
   1.666 666...

12. Subtract.
a. 8.897 897...
   4.564 564...

b. 0.321 321...
   1.210 210...

13. Multiply. Can you find a pattern?
a. 0.444 444...
   $\times$ 3

b. 0.444 444...
   $\times$ 0.3

c. 0.271 271...
   $\times$ 3

d. 2.271 271...
   $\times$ 0.3

e. 0.272 727...
   $\times$ 0.3

f. 0.111 111...
   $\times$ 0.333 333...

14. Multiply using the distributive property.
a. $5(n + 1)$ **b.** $-3(x + 3)$
c. $n(n + 4)$ **d.** $x(2 + 3)$
e. $8(x + y)$ **f.** $-5x(x^2 + x + 7)$

15. Find two rational numbers whose sum equals their product. An example is given.
$$6 + 1\frac{1}{5} = 6 \times 1\frac{1}{5}$$

16. Goldbach's Conjecture states that any even number greater than four can be expressed as the sum of two prime numbers. No one has been able to prove this or to find an even number that cannot be written as the sum of two prime numbers.
a. Write 36 and 48 as the sum of two prime numbers.
b. Is it possible for a prime number to be written as the sum of two prime numbers? Explain.
c. Are there any odd numbers that can be written as the sum of two prime numbers?

Historical Note

Algebra of Classes
The concept of the algebra of classes is fundamental in the study of logic. Leibniz developed some of the elementary algebra of classes. Using modern notation, if A and B are two classes of objects, then $A \cap B$, called the intersection of set A and set B, represents the objects belonging to both set A and set B. $A \cup B$ is called the union of set A and set B and represents the objects belonging to either set A or set B.

The algebra of classes can be illustrated graphically using **Venn diagrams**, named after the mathematician John Venn (1834-1923), where each class is represented by a different region. Use the library to write a brief biography of John Venn, along with his most significant contributions to the field of mathematics.

1·9 Properties of Irrational Numbers

Recall that the decimal representation of any number either repeats or terminates. Any number that does not repeat, and does not terminate, is an **irrational** number. One such number appears to be $\sqrt{2}$, which has a decimal equivalent of 1.414 213 562 ... .

An irrational number is a number that cannot be written in the form $\frac{a}{b}$, where a and $b \in I$, and $b \neq 0$.

Irrational numbers can be located on a number line. For example, locate $\sqrt{2}$.

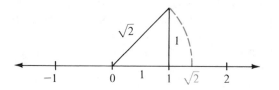

Using the Pythagorean Relation, a length equal to $\sqrt{2}$ can be found.

A calculator cannot be used to prove that $\sqrt{2}$ is an irrational number since a sequence of repeating digits may occur farther along in the decimal equivalent. The following is a proof that $\sqrt{2}$ is an irrational number.

Let $\sqrt{2} = \frac{a}{b}$, where a, $b \in I$, $b \neq 0$, and $\frac{a}{b}$ is a rational number in lowest terms.
$\sqrt{2} \times \sqrt{2} = 2$ because of the product of roots.
$\therefore \frac{a}{b} \times \frac{a}{b} = 2$ by substitution.
  or $\frac{a^2}{b^2} = 2$
     $a^2 = 2b^2$ by cross multiplication.

Since b^2 is multiplied by 2, $2b^2$ is an even product.
$\therefore a^2$ must also be an even number, and a must be an even number.
Since a is even, let $a = 2n$, where n is any integer.
$\therefore (2n)^2 = 2b^2$
   $4n^2 = 2b^2$
$\therefore b^2$ must also be even, and b is even.

However, this contradicts the original statement that $\frac{a}{b}$ is in lowest terms, because if both a and b are even, then 2 is a factor of both terms and the fraction could then be reduced.
$\therefore \sqrt{2}$ is irrational.

Exercises

1. State whether each number is rational or irrational.

a. 0.739 8$\overline{42}$
b. 0.246 810 121...
c. 0.888...
d. $\sqrt{121}$
e. $\sqrt{5}$
f. $3 + \sqrt{3}$
g. $16 - \sqrt{16}$
h. 0.254
i. $3\sqrt{19}$
j. 2.121 121 112...
k. 10.249 162 536...
l. -17.135 791 113...

2. Use the Pythagorean Relation to find the length of the third side of each right triangle.

a.
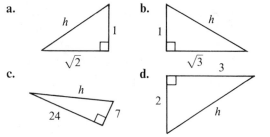

b.

c.

d.

3. Copy and complete the steps to prove that $\sqrt{3}$ is irrational.

$\sqrt{3} = \dfrac{a}{b}$ $a, b \in I, b \neq 0,$ and $\dfrac{a}{b}$ has no common factors.

$\sqrt{3} \times \sqrt{3} = 3$ ▆▆▆▆▆

$\blacksquare \times \dfrac{a}{b} = 3$ ▆▆▆▆▆

$\dfrac{\blacksquare}{\blacksquare} = 3$ Multiplication of rationals.

$a^2 = 3b^2$ The right member has 3 as a factor.

Let $a = 3n$ ▆▆▆▆▆

$\therefore (\blacksquare n)^2 = 3\blacksquare$

$3n^2 = \blacksquare$ The left member has 3 as a factor.

Therefore, ▆▆▆▆▆▆

Conclusion: ▆▆▆▆▆▆

So, $\sqrt{3}$ cannot be written in the form ▆▆▆.

$\therefore \sqrt{3}$ is ▆▆▆▆.

4. Prove that $\sqrt{7}$ is irrational.

5. Prove that $\sqrt{13}$ is irrational.

6. Name two integers that each irrational lies between.

a. $\sqrt{17}$ **b.** $\sqrt{35}$ **c.** $\sqrt{7}$
d. $-\sqrt{43}$ **e.** $-\sqrt{67}$ **f.** $\sqrt{29}$

7. Find an irrational number between each pair of rationals.

a. $0.\overline{37}$ and $0.37\overline{37}$ **b.** $4.\overline{123}$ and $4.1\overline{23}$

8. Given a rational number, $a = 6.3$, and an irrational number, $b = 3.303\ 003\ 000\ 300\ldots$, find two irrational numbers between a and b.

9. The bottom of a ladder is 3 m from a wall which is at right angles to the ground. If the ladder touches the wall at a point 3 m above the ground, then how long is the ladder?

10. Do these properties hold in the set of irrationals? Give a specific example. For example, the commutative property holds for the irrationals as $\sqrt{3} + \sqrt{2} = \sqrt{2} + \sqrt{3}$ and $\sqrt{3} \times \sqrt{2} = \sqrt{2} \times \sqrt{3}$.

a. density **b.** identity
c. distributive **d.** closure

11. A guy wire from the top of a transmission tower is 22 m long. The perpendicular tower is 18 m high. The guy wire is pulled straight and attached to the ground. How far is the point of attachment from the base of the tower?

12. Two sides of a right triangular bracket are each 8 cm long. How long is the third side?

13. A plane flies 30 km north, then 7 km east, then south to a point 14 km northeast of the starting point. How far south did the plane fly?

14. A circular screen is to be placed in a square storm drain. Find the diameter of the screen if the area of the storm drain opening is 13 m².

15. A crane operator wanted to know if the boom could be lowered to the horizontal without hitting a wall 14.2 m from the base of the boom. The cables supporting the boom were each 10 m long. Can it be done?

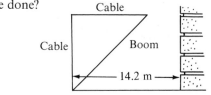

16. Using a calculator with a $\boxed{\sqrt{}}$ key, find the value of $\sqrt{13}$.
a. Is the number shown on the calculator rational or irrational?
b. Is $\sqrt{13}$ rational or irrational?
c. Is it possible for a number to be both rational and irrational? Explain.

1·10 Properties of Real Numbers

The need for different sets of numbers varies with each job or task. A scientist or engineer may have a need for irrational numbers, while a sports reporter or accountant may only require the rational numbers. Whatever the task may be, the appropriate numbers may be selected from the set of **real** numbers.

The Venn diagram illustrates the relation between the sets of numbers which make up the real numbers.

Real Numbers (*R*)

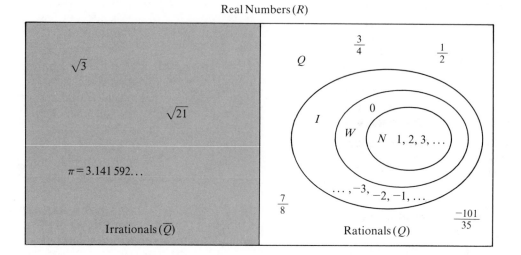

Exercises

1. For the operations of addition and multiplication, set up a table for the six sets of numbers presented in this chapter. Test whether the properties given in Exericse 1 of Section 1·8 hold.

2. State whether each is true or false. The first one is done as an example.

$I \subset Q$ ⟮Read "*I* is contained in *Q*".⟯

Since all integers can be written in the form $\frac{a}{b}$, all integers are rational numbers. Therefore, this is a true statement.

a. $Q \subset W$ **b.** $W \subset I$ **c.** $N \subset I$ **d.** $\overline{Q} \subset I$
e. $I \subset \overline{Q}$ **f.** $Q \subset \overline{Q}$ **g.** $N \subset \overline{Q}$ **h.** $\overline{Q} \subset R$
i. $Q \subset N$ **j.** $N \subset R$ **k.** $I \subset R$ **l.** $I \subset N$

3. Draw a Venn diagram to illustrate each.
a. $N \subset W \subset I$ **b.** $W \subset I \subset Q$ **c.** $I \subset Q \subset R$
d. $W \subset Q \subset R$ **e.** $N \subset W \subset I \subset Q \subset R$

4. State whether each is true or false. Provide an example or counterexample for each.
a. The even integers are closed with respect to addition.
b. Every element in *I* has an identity element under multiplication.
c. Multiplication distributes over subtraction with the whole numbers.
d. The natural numbers are closed with respect to addition.
e. The integers are closed with respect to division.
f. Every element in *W* has an inverse under addition.
g. Every element in *R* has an inverse under multiplication.
h. Every element in *R* has an inverse under addition.
i. Every element in *N* has an identity element under addition.
j. Every element in *W* has an identity element under addition.

1·11 Solving Equations I

To solve any equation, the variable must be isolated on one side of the equation. This often requires performing one or more operations on both sides of the equation.

Example

Solve for x.

a. $x - 250 = 1050$

$x - 250 + 250 = 1050 + 250$
$x = 1300$

Check:
L.S. $= 1300 - 250$ R.S. $= 1050$
$= 1050$
∴It checks.

b. $x + 4x + 8x = 208$

$13x = 208$
$\dfrac{13x}{13} = \dfrac{208}{13}$
$x = 16$

c. $6x - 2(2x + 5) = 20$

$6x - 4x - 10 = 20$
$2x - 10 = 20$
$2x = 30$
$x = 15$

d. $\dfrac{x}{5} - 5 = \dfrac{2}{3}$

$15\left(\dfrac{x}{5} - 5\right) = 15\left(\dfrac{2}{3}\right)$ Multiply by the least common denominator.
$3x - 75 = 10$
$3x = 85$
$x = 28\dfrac{1}{3}$

Exercises

1. Solve and check each equation. $x \in Q$.

a. $x - 3 = 12$
b. $x - 5 = 16$
c. $5x = 35$
d. $\dfrac{x}{2} = 32$
e. $5x + 2 = 12$
f. $-3x + 4 = 28$
g. $4 + x = 16$
h. $\dfrac{1}{2}x + 12 = 12$

2. Solve and check. $x \in Q$

a. $2x - 1 = x + 6$
b. $7x - 5 = 4x + 7$
c. $2x - 3 = 12 - x$
d. $4x + 1 = 7x - 8$
e. $5x + 3 = x + 4$
f. $2x - 1 = 4x - 2$
g. $2x - 5 = -9x$
h. $\dfrac{x+1}{2} = \dfrac{x+3}{3}$
i. $\dfrac{2x+5}{2} = \dfrac{2x+10}{4}$
j. $\dfrac{x-5}{2} = \dfrac{3(x-5)}{4}$
k. $2 - \dfrac{5}{6} = \dfrac{2}{3} + x$
l. $3(x - 2) = 9(x + 2)$
m. $4x + 6 + x = -10 + x$
n. $5x - (2 \times 8) = 2x - 16$
o. $5(x + 4) = 3x + 10$
p. $3 - (x + 2) = 5 + 3(x + 2)$
q. $13 - (2x + 2) = 2(x + 2) + 3x$
r. $3x + 4 = 18 - x + 5.9 - 6x$

3. Solve for x.

a. $2x - 5 = 13$
b. $16 - x = 27$
c. $\dfrac{x}{4} - 3 = 9$
d. $0.2x - 0.7 = 3$
e. $\dfrac{3}{4}x = 0.9$
f. $0.9 = \dfrac{5x}{2}$
g. $3x + 2 = 9$
h. $2x - 0.4 = 18.2$

4. Solve and check.

a. $2x - (x - 1) = 5$
b. $7 = 5 - (x - 3)$
c. $3x - 2(x + 3) = 15$
d. $(3x + 4) - (x - 2) = 10$
e. $\dfrac{x}{3} + \dfrac{x}{7} = 12$
f. $\dfrac{3x}{5} + \dfrac{x}{3} = 28$
g. $\dfrac{x}{6} - \dfrac{2x}{3} = -3$
h. $\dfrac{5x-3}{2} - \dfrac{3x-2}{3} = 22$

5. Copy and complete these statements.
a. Addition Property — If equals are added to equals, the sums are ▮▮▮▮▮.
b. Subtraction Property — If equals are ▮▮▮▮▮ from ▮▮▮▮▮, the differences are ▮▮▮▮▮.
c. Multiplication Property — ▮▮▮▮▮
d. Division Property — ▮▮▮▮▮

1·12 Solving Equations II

Equations can be used to solve problems. The facts in a problem are translated into an equation, and the equation is solved. Equations containing a variable on each side of the equal sign may require more than one operation before the variable is isolated.

Example

Computsales sold 250 computers more than five times the national, weekly average. Compuworld sold 50 computers less than 10 times the national average. If both outlets sold the same number of computers, then find the national average.

Let n represent the national average.
Number sold by Computsales is $5n + 250$.
Number sold by Compuworld is $10n - 50$.

$$10n - 50 = 5n + 250$$
$$10n - 5n - 50 = 5n - 5n + 250 \quad \text{Move all the variables to one side of the equation.}$$
$$5n - 50 = 250$$
$$5n = 300$$
$$n = 60$$

The national average is 60 computers sold.

Exercises

1. Find a number which is 22 more than its opposite. (Remember: $-x$ is the opposite of x.)

2. When the Canadians, Banting and Best, discovered insulin in 1921, Banting was fifteen years less than twice Best's age. In 1941, when Banting was killed in a Second World War plane crash, Best was thirty-five years more than $\frac{1}{7}$ of Banting's age. How old were these medical researchers in 1921?

3. The perimeter of a rectangle is 52 cm. Three times its length is 6 cm more than 6 times its width. Find the dimensions of the rectangle.

4. If the airspeed of a plane is increased by 65 km/h, then it would be 615 km/h. Find the airspeed.

5. The measure of one angle of a triangle is twice the measure of a second angle and six times the measure of the third. Find the measure of each angle of the triangle.

6. Find two consecutive odd integers whose sum is 376.

7. The memory capacity of Computer A is four times that of Computer B, while Computer C has twice the memory capacity of Computer A. What is the memory capacity of each computer if the total capacity of the three computers is 208 k?

8. As a hockey player, Meegan received $3 for every goal, but was fined $2 for every shot wide of the goal, and was fined $0.50 for every shot that hit the goal post. After 31 shots, she "broke even". How many goals did she get?

9. In 1793, the Seminaire de Quebec had been in existence 26 times longer than Kings College in Windsor, Nova Scotia. In 1888, the Seminaire de Quebec was $2\frac{1}{4}$ times as old as Kings College. In what year was each college founded?

10. How much oil must be added to 24.5 L of gasoline to make a mixture that is 2% oil?

1·13 Solving Problems Using Formulas

Applied mathematicians and scientists are often required to derive formulas in which a stated variable is expressed in terms of other variables.

Example

The formula, $v = \sqrt{\dfrac{E}{d}}$, relates the velocity of sound, v, the elastic modulus of the medium in which it travels, E, and the density of the medium, d. Rewrite the formula in terms of d.

$$v = \sqrt{\frac{E}{d}}$$
$$v^2 = \frac{E}{d}$$
$$v^2 \times d = \frac{E}{d} \times d$$
$$v^2 d = E$$
$$d = \frac{E}{v^2}$$

> Square both sides to eliminate the square root sign.

Exercises

1. Isolate either a, b, or c in each.

a. $a - x = y$ **b.** $x + a = t$

c. $2a = r$ **d.** $-5a + x = y$

e. $at = d$ **f.** $b - 3d = 2d$

g. $5(c - 2) = d$ **h.** $mt = c + t$

i. $x - a = 3x$ **j.** $A = \pi - 2c$

k. $\dfrac{a + m}{4} = n$ **l.** $-b = h - 7b$

m. $\dfrac{s + r + c}{2} = 2c$ **n.** $\dfrac{a - t}{a} = 3t$

o. $\dfrac{\pi + b}{x} = \dfrac{3}{2}$ **p.** $\dfrac{2(x - y)}{a} = \dfrac{a}{8(x - y)}$

2. Copy and complete to solve for a.
The first one is partially completed for you.

$$\frac{4}{2a - 4} = \frac{9}{b}$$
$$(2a - 4)\left(\frac{4}{2a - 4}\right) = \frac{9}{b}(\rule{1.5cm}{0.4pt})$$
$$\blacksquare \times 4 = \frac{18a - 36}{b} \times b$$
$$4b = 18a - 36$$
$$4b + \blacksquare = 18a - 36 + \blacksquare$$
$$\frac{\rule{1cm}{0.4pt}}{\rule{1cm}{0.4pt}} = a$$

a. $\dfrac{3}{a} = \dfrac{b}{12}$ **b.** $\dfrac{1}{a - 6} = \dfrac{b - 3}{9}$

3. Solve for the indicated variable.

a. $A = bh;\ h$ **b.** $d = vt;\ t$

c. $p = \dfrac{k}{v};\ k$ **d.** $n = \dfrac{F}{R};\ R$

e. $E = IR;\ I$ **f.** $V = lwh;\ w$

g. $C = 2\pi r;\ \pi$ **h.** $A = \dfrac{bh}{2};\ h$

i. $F = ma;\ a$ **j.** $I = p + prt;\ t$

k. $a = \dfrac{v^2}{r};\ v$ **l.** $x = \dfrac{Fl}{YA};\ l$

m. $v = \sqrt{2gh};\ g$ **n.** $W = J(H_1 - H_2);\ H_2$

o. $c = \dfrac{Q}{v_1 - v_2};\ v_2$ **p.** $\dfrac{1}{f} = \dfrac{1}{v} - \dfrac{1}{u};\ f$

q. $E = mc^2;\ c$ **r.** $T = 2\pi\sqrt{\dfrac{l}{g}};\ l$

4. A used-car dealer always marked up her cost 30% to reach the retail price. Due to poor sales, a discount of 10% on the selling price was offered. Find the cost of a car that sold for $2925.

5. Three business partners agreed to divide their annual profits in the ratio of 2:3:5. Find each partner's share if the annual profit is $13 750.

6. A trapezoid has an area of 416 cm². If it has a height of 16 cm and a base length of 20 cm, then find the length of the second base.

1·14 Percent

The word **percent** means "per hundred" and implies a ratio whose second term is 100. This means that 90% can be written as 90:100 or $\frac{90}{100}$.

Example 1

A concert, held at Phoenix High School, sold all 650 tickets available. If 12% of the tickets were bought by students from Phoenix High School, then how many students at the concert attend Phoenix High School?

12% of 650 is the number of students from Phoenix High School.
Let n represent the number of students from Phoenix High School.

$n = \frac{12}{100} \times 650$ ⎰ Recall that "of"
⎱ means "multiply".
$\quad = 78$

Therefore, 78 students from Phoenix High School attended the concert.

Example 2

The students at the concert accounted for 8% of Phoenix High School's total student population. Find how many students attend Phoenix High School.

8% of the student population is 78.
Let n represent the number of students at Phoenix High School.
8% of n is 78.

$\frac{8}{100} \times n = 78$

$\qquad n = 975$

Therefore, 975 students attend Phoenix High School.

Example 3

Each ticket to the concert cost $25. The same ticket cost $23 last year. Find the percent increase in the price of a ticket during the year.

Percent increase $= \frac{\text{Cost this year} - \text{Cost last year}}{\text{Cost last year}} \times 100$

$\qquad\qquad\quad = \frac{25 - 23}{23} \times 100$

$\qquad\qquad\quad \doteq 8.7$

Therefore, the percent increase is approximately 8.7%.

Exercises

1. Convert these percents to decimals and then to fractions in lowest terms.

a. 16% **b.** 69% **c.** 320%

d. 1% **e.** $\frac{1}{2}$% **f.** 0.003%

2. Find the number of students from each school attending the concert mentioned in Example 1 in the display, if

a. 8% of the students are from Central.

b. 20% are from Western.

c. 16% are from Northern.

d. 14% are from Eastern.
e. 6% are from Southern.
f. 24% are from Highland.

3. Find the total population for each school if the numbers in Exercise 2 represent the following percent of all the students attending each school.

a. Central 5% **b.** Western 15%
c. Northern 8% **d.** Eastern 10%
e. Southern 4% **f.** Highland 13%

4. The concert organizers debated the ticket price. What would have been the percent increase in each case if the price had been set at each?

a. $24 **b.** $24.50 **c.** $25.50
d. $26 **e.** $30 **f.** $32

5. Find the value of each.

a. $18\frac{1}{2}$% of 200 **b.** 37% of 85
c. 44% of some number is 319.
d. $37\frac{1}{2}$% of some number is 9.
e. 14 is what percent of 91?
f. 27 is what percent of 162?

6. Simple interest can be found using the formula $I = prt$, where I is the interest (earned or payed), p is the principal (loaned or borrowed), r is the rate of interest, and t is the time (expressed in years). Find the interest earned for each. Use a calculator if one is available.

a. $12 000 at 14% for 2 a
b. $75 000 at 16% for 5 a
c. $48 000 at $10\frac{1}{2}$% for 25 a
d. $3800 at $12\frac{1}{4}$% for 6 months

7. During an average day, a person breathes about 11.33 m³ of air. If 21% of this air is oxygen, then what is the volume of oxygen taken into the lungs?

8. If an 82 kg person has 32.8 kg of muscle, then what percent is muscle?

9. If the mass of a human brain is approximately 2.5% of the total body mass, then what is the mass of a person whose brain measures 1.7 kg?

For Exercises 10 to 12, use this equation:
Net Price = Marked Price − Retail Discount.

10. The marked price of a radio headset is $172.50. The store offers a 20% discount. Find the net price of the radio.

11. An item is advertised as selling at a discount of 25%. If the net price is $42, then what is the marked price?

12. A tennis racquet priced at $36 is reduced by 40%. Since it did not sell, it was reduced by 10% of the sale price. Find the total amount the tennis racquet was reduced and the final sale price.

13. A dining room set priced at $960 was reduced by 35%. It was then reduced by 20% of the sale price before it sold. Find the total amount the dining room set was reduced and the final sale price.

14. A store manager uses this rule to calculate the single discount that is equivalent to two successive discounts.
"A single discount is the difference between the sum of the individual discounts, and the product of the individual discounts."
Find the single discount that the store manager could offer instead of the two individual discounts. The first one is done as an example.

A 40% discount followed by a 10% discount.
$(0.4 + 0.1) - (0.4 \times 0.1)$
46% is the single equivalent discount.

a. A discount of 35% followed by a discount of 20%.
b. A discount of 45% followed by a discount of 5%.
c. A discount of 27.5% followed by a discount of 10%.
d. A discount of 60% followed by a discount of 15%.
e. A discount of 35% followed by a discount of 7%.

For Exercises 15 and 16, use this equation:
Invoice Price = List Price − Discount

15. A wholesaler plans to buy an item listed at $1200. If there are simultaneous trade discounts of 30%, 20%, and 10%, then find the invoice price.

16. Find the single rate of discount equivalent to successive discount rates of 40%, 30%, and 15%.

For Exercises 17 to 20, use this formula:
Selling Price = Cost Price + Mark Up

17. If 2 L of milk costs a merchant $1.80, then find the selling price if the mark up is 20% of the original cost.

18. A merchant purchased an article for $260. If the article sells for $390, then find
a. the mark up.
b. the mark up as a percent of cost.

19. Alpha Appliance buys refrigerators at a cost of $580 each. The mark up is 25% of cost.
a. Find the selling price.
b. Find the rate of mark up on the selling price.

20. Given the cost price and the rate of mark up on the cost price, find each.
 i) the actual mark up
 ii) the selling price
 iii) the mark up as a percent of the selling price
a. $300, 12%   **b.** $12.75, 10%
c. $42.50, 16%   **d.** $25.44, $66\frac{2}{3}$%
e. $5.20, 5%   **f.** $15.50, 35%

For Exercises 21 and 22, use this equation:
Net Proceeds = Gross Proceeds − (Commission + Expenses)

21. An orchardist sent a shipment of fruit to an agent who sold them for $12 400. If the delivery charges were $650, the storage and handling charges were $540, and the agent received a commission of 11%, then find the net proceeds of the sale.

22. An agent sold a shipment of fish and charged the company $21 300. Of this amount, $10 019.10 was for freight and storage, and the rest was commission at the rate of 9.3% on the gross proceeds. Find each.
a. the gross proceeds   **b.** the net proceeds

23. Find the rate of simple interest for each.
a. Charles borrows $900 and repays it in 8 monthly instalments of $140 each.
b. Julie borrows $1300 and repays it in 18 monthly instalments of $95 each.
c. Jason borrows $5500 and repays it in 12 monthly instalments of $550 each.

24. In the case of compound interest, interest is paid on interest earned. The table illustrates compound interest earned every six months (semiannually) on $100 deposited at 12%/a. Copy and complete the table for 6 interest periods. Use a calculator if one is available.

Interest Period	1	2	3 ...
Principal	$100	$106	$112.36...
Rate	0.12	0.12	0.12...
Time	0.5	0.5	0.5...
Interest	$6	$6.36	$6.74...
Amount	$106	$112.36	$119.10...

25. The formula $A = p\left(1 + \dfrac{r}{n}\right)^{nt}$ gives the amount, A, of a principal, p, invested at a rate of interest, r, where n represents the number of times the interest is compounded during the year, and t is the number of years of the investment. Find the following amounts. Use a calculator if one is available.
a. $2000 invested at 10% compounded semiannually for 20 a
b. $16 000 borrowed at 12% compounded quarterly for 10 a
c. $300 000 loaned at 14.5% compounded annually for 20 a

Calculator keying sequence:

Repeat $(nt - 1)$ times.

1·15 Proportion

A **proportion** is an equation which states that two ratios are equal. For example, $\frac{7}{3}$ and $\frac{21}{9}$ are two equivalent ratios, and $\frac{7}{3} = \frac{21}{9}$. This can also be written as $7:3 = 21:9$.

The first and last terms in any proportion are the **extremes**, or the first and fourth proportionals respectively. The middle terms are called the **means**, or the second and third proportionals.

In a proportion, the product of the means equals the product of the extremes.

If $\frac{a}{b} = \frac{c}{d}$, then $bc = ad$.

If the second and third proportionals are equal, as in $4:a = a:16$, then a is the **mean proportional** between 4 and 16.

Example

A machine produces nails at a rate of 500/min. How many nails will this machine produce in one hour?

$$\frac{500}{1} = \frac{n}{60}$$
$$n = 30\ 000$$

The product of the means equals the product of the extremes.

This machine will produce 30 000 nails in one hour.

Exercises

1. Solve for the variable.

a. $4:8 = x:12$ **b.** $17:23 = 34:x$

c. $x:64 = 24:56$ **d.** $\frac{18}{x} = \frac{9}{5}$

e. $\frac{5}{2} = \frac{m-3}{4}$ **f.** $\frac{3}{7} = \frac{2}{5(r+1)}$

g. $12:8 = 2x + 1:3x - 2$

2. Find the missing proportional.
a. the first proportional of 20, 30, and 10
b. the third proportional of 3, 15, and n
c. the fourth proportional of 3.2, 6.7, and 16
d. the mean proportional between 5 and 125
e. the second proportional of 4, 30, and 25

3. Find an equation for the indicated variable.

a. $\frac{A}{A_1} = \frac{\ell w}{\ell_1 w_1}; w$ **b.** $\frac{C}{C_1} = \frac{r}{r_1}; C_1$

c. $\frac{r}{E} = \frac{e}{r_1 + r}; r$ **d.** $\frac{T}{s} = \frac{C}{sR + r}; R$

4. Find two numbers whose difference is 10 and whose ratio is 3:2.

5. Two mechanics agreed to repair an engine for $360. If one worked 3 h and the other worked 5 h, then how much should each mechanic receive?

6. A fishing boat used 9.1 L of gasoline while trolling for 2 h. How much gasoline will be needed for 32 h of trolling?

7. A car dealer bought a car from a customer. She marked up the price of the car 60% from her purchase price but found that the car did not sell. She then marked the car down 40% and sold it. Did she make a profit? What percent did she gain or lose?

8. The ratio of the numerator of a fraction to its denominator is 5:7. If 3 is added to the numerator and 3 subtracted from the denominator, the ratio becomes 4:5. Find the original fraction.

9. If 2 cm represents 65 km on a map, and a satellite photo shows a rectangular ground area to be 18.5 cm by 26.3 cm, then find the area shown in the photo to the nearest square kilometre.

1·16 The Real Number Line

The real number system is said to be ordered because for every pair of elements, a and b, either $a < b$, $a = b$, or $a > b$. This principle can be used to determine the range of an answer in many problems.

Example 1

Each of three generators at a dam site produces power at the following times during the morning. Generator 1 produces power from 01:00 to 09:00, Generator 2 produces power from 05:00 to 10:00, and Generator 3 from 07:00 to 12:00. Graph the intersection of the times to show the peak power production time.

Generator 1 Time		$\{t \mid 1 \le t \le 9\}$
Generator 2 Time		$\{t \mid 5 \le t \le 10\}$
Generator 3 Time		$\{t \mid 7 \le t \le 12\}$
Intersection Time		$\{t \mid 7 \le t \le 9\}$

The peak power production time is from 07:00 to 09:00.

Example 2

A city engineer reported that 10 kPa more than twice the normal water pressure would result in water pressure ranging from 410 to 450 kPa. Find the range of normal water pressure.

Let p represent the normal water pressure.

$$410 \le 2p + 10 \le 450$$
$$410 - 10 \le 2p + 10 - 10 \le 450 - 10 \qquad \text{Isolate the variable.}$$
$$400 \le 2p \le 440$$
$$\frac{400}{2} \le \frac{2p}{2} \le \frac{440}{2}$$
$$200 \le p \le 220$$

Normal water pressure ranges from 200 kPa to 220 kPa.

Example 3

Solve the inequality. $-x - 7 > -4$, $x \in R$

$$-x - 7 > -4$$
$$-x - 7 + 7 > -4 + 7 \qquad \text{When multiplying or dividing both sides of an}$$
$$(-1)-x < 3(-1) \qquad\qquad \text{inequality by a negative number, reverse the}$$
$$x < -3 \qquad\qquad\qquad\quad \text{direction of the inequality.}$$

24

Exercises

1. Arrange in order from least to greatest.

a. $-1, \sqrt{2}, \frac{-1}{2}, 4\frac{3}{7}, -1.3, -1.414$

b. $\frac{7}{13}, \frac{8}{11}, \frac{7}{8}, \frac{5}{6}, \frac{11}{15}, \frac{5}{9}, \frac{6}{7}$

c. $0.45, 0.45\overline{3}, 0.453\,453, 0.4534, 0.453\,453, 0.453$

d. $0.010\,010\,001\ldots, 0.010\,101\,101\,110\ldots,$
$0.011\,011\,101\,111\ldots, 0.101\,101\,110\ldots, 0.010$

e. $0.581\,81, 0.58, 0.581\,811\,811\,181\ldots,$
$0.581\,581\,158\,111\ldots$

2. Use $>$, $<$, or $=$ to make each statement true.

a. $\frac{5}{4} \bullet \frac{3}{4}$ **b.** $\frac{3}{5} \bullet \frac{4}{7}$ **c.** $-\frac{2}{3} \bullet -\frac{7}{11}$

3. Graph each set where $x \in I$.

a. $\{x \mid x \le 7\}$ **b.** $\{x \mid 3x \le 12\}$
c. $\{x \mid x > -2\}$ **d.** $\{x \mid x \ge 0\}$
e. $\{x \mid 2x < -7\}$ **f.** $\{x \mid -4x > 5\}$

4. Graph each set where $x \in I$.

a. $\{x \mid x > 4\}$ **b.** $\{x \mid 3x \le -12\}$
c. $\{x \mid -3x \ge 6\}$ **d.** $\{x \mid -5x < 10\}$

5. Graph each set where $n \in R$. The first one is done as an example.

$\{n \mid 4 \le n \le 7\}$

a. $\{n \mid -5 < n \le 0\}$ **b.** $\{n \mid -3 \le n \le 2\}$
c. $\{n \mid 8 > n \ge -3\}$ **d.** $\{n \mid -1 \le n < 5\}$
e. $\{n \mid -10 \le n \le 10\}$ **f.** $\{n \mid -3 \ge n \ge -7\}$

6. Graph each set where $x \in R$. The first one is done as an example.

$\{x \mid x < 0 \text{ or } x \ge 3\}$

a. $\{x \mid x \ge 3 \text{ or } x < -2\}$
b. $\{x \mid x \le -1 \text{ or } x \ge 3\}$
c. $\{x \mid x \le \frac{-1}{2} \text{ or } x > \frac{3}{4}\}$

7. Power consumption in a city during low consumption periods ranged from 2 MW to 8 MW. During peak consumption periods, the range was from 10 MW to 12 MW. Graph these ranges on the same real number line.

8. The water in the spillway of a dam flowed from 0 kL to 2 kL per second during the dry season and from 8 kL to 15 kL per second during the rainy season. Graph these ranges on the same real number line.

9. Graph each set where $x \in R$. The first one is done as an example.

$\{x \mid x \le 7 \text{ and } x > 2\}$

a. $\{x \mid x > -3 \text{ and } x < 10\}$
b. $\{x \mid x \le -1 \text{ and } x \ge -5\}$
c. $\{x \mid x \ge 0 \text{ and } x \le 9\}$
d. $\{x \mid -3 \le x < 66\}$

10. If 100 kg of corn are distributed among 100 people so that each woman receives 3 kg, each man 2 kg, and each child 0.5 kg, then how many men, women, and children are there?

11. Thirty years of Canadian meteorological studies produced the following sets of data about selected Canadian cities. Graph the intersection of the data in each.

a. mean daily maximum temperatures in °C

Saskatoon	-13.5 to 25.9
Edmonton	-10.1 to 23.4
London	-2.2 to 26.4

b. mean wind speeds in metres per second

Victoria	3.9 to 5.5
Penticton	2.7 to 5.1
Charlottetown	6.3 to 9.4

12. The range of ages of the guests at a family reunion are as follows. The children range from 1 a to 25 a, the parents range from 21 a to 45 a, and the grandparents were from 48 a to 84 a. Graph the intersection of their ages.

13. Solve and graph the solution set. $x \in R$ (*Hint:* Isolate the variable.)

a. $-6 \le x + 2 \le 4$ **b.** $6 < x - 3 < 9$
c. $1 \le 3x - 5 < 10$ **d.** $5 \ge 2 - x \ge -5$
e. $\{x \mid -2 \le 2 - x < 0\}$ **f.** $\{x \mid 1 < \frac{2x - 2}{2} \le 4\}$
g. $\{x \mid 3(x + 2) \le 12\}$ **h.** $\{x \mid -2(x - 5) < 6\}$
i. $\{x \mid 0.5 < -2.5 - 1.5x \le 3.5\}$
j. $\{x \mid 2x - 1 < 3x + 5 < 2x + 10\}$

1·17 Computer Application — Order of Operations

A local service station ran a contest. In order to collect a prize, contestants had to answer this skill-testing question. $12 + 8 \times 3 - 10 \div 5$

Ming and her father both worked out the question and arrived at different answers. Ming's answer was 34, while her father's was 10. Who was correct? Recalling the order of operations, we see that Ming had the correct answer.

Example

Clear the memory of the computer and write a program to evaluate each expression.

a. $15 \times 36 \div 12$ **b.** $6 + 12 \times 4$ **c.** $7^3 \times 28 \div 14$

```
NEW
10 REM A PROGRAM TO EVALUATE EXPRESSIONS
20 PRINT 15 * 36 / 12
30 PRINT 6 + 12 * 4
40 PRINT 7 ∧ 3 * 28 / 14
50 END
```

Exercises

1. List the order of operations.

2. What symbol stands for each in the BASIC language?
a. an exponent   **b.** addition
c. multiplication   **d.** division

3. Enter the program shown in the display into a computer.

a. Evaluate each expression before running the program.
b. Record the computer's output for each expression.
c. Compare your answers and the computer's answers. Are they the same?

4. What is the purpose of entering the NEW statement at the beginning of the program in the display?

5. What is the purpose of the print command shown in lines 20, 30, and 40?

6. When you ran the program in the display, line 10 was not printed on the screen. Why not?

7. Modify line 30 of the program in the display so that the computer will find the sum of 6 and 12 before multiplying by 4.

8. The advancing technology of computers continues to change many lives. The introduction of computer-assisted machinery has allowed factories to increase production, while at the same time reducing costs. One cost reduction is due to the elimination of assembly-line jobs that can be done by computer-operated equipment. Present arguments, both for and against, the continual introduction and upgrading of computer technology in the workplace.

1·18 Chapter Review

1. Calculate.
a. $851 + 379 - 642$
b. $46 \div 2 + 16$
c. $472 \times 369 \times 0 \times 389$
d. 17×17
e. $50 + 60 + 70 + 80 + \ldots + 150$

2. Evaluate each if $x = -2$, $y = -6$, and $z = -3$.
a. $x + y + z$
b. xyz
c. xz^2
d. $x - y \div z$

3. A batter bolt sells for $0.69. Find the value of each day's production and the value of a week's production, if 4600 are produced on Monday, 8752 on Tuesday, 9563 on Wednesday, 10 320 on Thursday, and 5679 on Friday.

4. A biologist in Algonquin Provincial Park noticed these changes in the number of blackflies for a ten-year period. $-15\,135$, -9299, $-12\,643$, $-26\,366$, $-46\,429$, $-30\,884$, $-29\,876$, $-22\,841$, $-25\,790$, and $-22\,568$. Find the total change in the number of blackflies.

5. A ferry, which is the only link between Vancouver and Denman Islands, made four round trips. It carried 15 cars on its first trip to Vancouver Island and returned with 2 cars. It then carried 14 cars and returned with 5, then carried 8 cars and returned with 10, and finally carried 6 cars and returned with 4. How did the final number of cars on Denman Island compare with the number of cars before the first trip?

6. Evaluate each if $a = -5$, $b = -2$, $c = 10$, and $d = 0$.
a. $a - c + d$
b. $\dfrac{ab + bd}{ab}$
c. $\dfrac{abcd}{abc}$
d. $\dfrac{a + c}{b}$

7. Ms. Karnak drove to work at an average speed of 55 km/h for 1.5 h. Taking the same route home she drove at an average speed of 42 km/h. How far was she from home 1.5 h after leaving work?

8. Larry, Moe, and Curly decided to split a pizza which cost $7.20. Larry took $\frac{1}{4}$, Moe took $\frac{1}{2}$ of the remaining pizza, and Curly took $\frac{1}{2}$ of what was left.
a. How should the total cost be divided so that each pays for the amount taken?
b. Can the remaining pizza be divided so that each person finishes with the same amount?

9. Simple interest is calculated using the formula $I = prt$, where p is the principal amount invested, r is the rate of interest, and t is the time in years that the money is invested. Find the interest earned in each.
a. $p = \$6000$, $r = 11\%$, $t = 7$ a
b. $p = \$470\,000$, $r = 12.5\%$, $t = 3$ months
c. $p = \$25\,000$, $r = 14\%$, $t = 30$ weeks

10. Convert each decimal to a fraction in lowest terms.
a. $0.\overline{4}$
b. 0.27
c. $0.8\overline{2}$
d. $0.35\overline{8}$

11. A pumping station filled 0.7 of a reservoir the first hour, 0.07 the second hour, and 0.007 the third hour. If this uniformly reducing rate continues, then find a fraction to represent how much of the reservoir will be filled.

12. A human body contains approximately 5.7 L of blood. A blood donor usually gives 500 mL of blood. What percent of the total blood of a donor is given?

13. Use the formula $A = p(1 + \dfrac{r}{n})^{nt}$ and a calculator, if one is available, to find the amount earned in each investment.
a. $60 000 at 12.25% compounded semiannually for 4 a
b. $10 000 at 1% compounded quarterly for 2 a

14. A ramp in a parking lot rises 4 m and is 12.4 m long. Find the horizontal distance covered by the ramp.

1·19 Chapter Test

1. Evaluate the expression $3a - 2b$ for $a = 16$ and $b = 11$.

2. Find the total receipts from ticket sales to a movie which sold 345 adult tickets for $4.50 each, 450 student tickets for $3.50 each, and 64 children's tickets for $3.00 each.

3. Calculate.
a. $-16 - (-23)$ **b.** $47 \times (-3) - 2$
c. $-75 \div (-15)$ **d.** $-8 + (-2) - 43$

4. Evaluate $3x - 4y^2$ for $x = -7$ and $y = -2$.

5. Calculate.
a. $\frac{-3}{11} + \frac{5}{7}$ **b.** $\left(-5\frac{1}{2}\right)\left(3\frac{1}{8}\right)$ **c.** $4\frac{1}{2} \div \left(-3\frac{1}{6}\right)$

6. Write the reciprocal of $-2\frac{1}{6}$.

7. Evaluate.
a. $-21 \times 5 \div (-15) \times 3$
b. $\frac{1}{10}\left\{\frac{1}{4}\left[\frac{-1}{5}\left(\frac{2}{3} \div \frac{1}{15}\right)2\right]\right\}$

8. Convert $\frac{17}{999}$ to a decimal.

9. A motor-driven pump discharges 2500 L of water in 2.25 min. How long will the pump take to discharge 50 000 L of water?

10. Find the simple interest earned on a $12 000 investment at 11.5%/a over 5 a.

11. Convert each decimal to a fraction.
a. $0.\overline{23}$ **b.** $0.58\overline{1}$

12. Solve.
a. 27% of 640
b. 32% of what number is 6?
c. 10 is what percent of 350?

13. Find a rational number that lies between $\frac{1}{5}$ and $\frac{1}{6}$.

14. Expand. $-8(a + b)$

15. Simplify. $4a - 2(2a + 6)$

16. Solve. $10 = 6 - (x + 2)$

17. Solve to find the value of r.
$$\frac{5r - 2}{4} = \frac{6r - 8}{2}$$

18. Find two numbers whose sum is 12 and whose ratio is 4:3.

19. Solve for a. $\frac{\pi + c}{a} = \frac{5}{7}$

20. Find the single discount equivalent to a discount of 35% followed by a discount of 12%.

21. A pressure gauge reads 65 on a scale of 0-250. Find the same pressure reading using a scale of 0-100.

22. Find the measure of the third side of the right triangle.

8 m

5 m

23. An aircraft is 10 000 m high and 150 000 m horizontally from the end of a runway. Find the length of the flight path to the end of the runway.

24. Is the statement $N \subset \overline{Q}$ true?

25. Name the property of R illustrated by each example.
a. $-\frac{7}{5} \times -\frac{5}{7} = 1$ **b.** $6 \times 0 = 0$
c. $\sqrt{2}(\sqrt{3} + 7) = \sqrt{6} + 7\sqrt{2}$

26. Graph. $\{x \mid x \le -1 \text{ or } x > 0, x \in R\}$

27. Graph. $\{x \mid -12 \le x \le 0 \text{ and } -3 < x < 5, x \in Q\}$

CHAPTER TWO

PROBLEM SOLVING

Tune Up

1. How many times can five be subtracted from thirty-eight?

2. A hammer and a bag of nails sell for eleven dollars. If they are sold separately, then the hammer costs ten dollars more than the bag of nails. Find the cost of one bag of nails.

3. What can you put into an empty wooden 20 g box to make it lighter?

4. What number comes next?
3, 4, 7, 16, 43, ■

5. What number comes next?
10, 40, 90, 60, 10, 40, ■

6. Three baseball fans ordered one hotdog each. Two take mustard and two take relish. The one taking no relish takes no mustard. The one taking no mustard takes no onions. What did each fan have on their hotdog?

7. Part of Pascal's triangle is shown.

```
        1
       1  1
      1  2  1
     1  3  3  1
    1  4  6  4  1
```

If Pascal's triangle was extended indefinitely, then find the second number in the tenth row.

8. The reading area in a Grade 1 class has five chairs arranged in a straight line. There is a red chair, a white chair, a blue chair, an orange chair, and a green chair. How can the chairs be arranged so that neither an orange chair nor a green chair is next to a white chair, neither an orange chair nor a green chair is next to a red chair, neither a white chair nor an orange chair is next to a blue chair, and the red chair is to the right of the blue chair.

9. If D divides $\overline{BC}$ in the ratio 2:1, then what is the ratio of the area of $\triangle ABD$ and $\triangle ADC$?

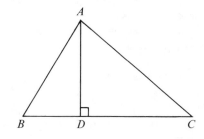

10. Thirty-two tennis players of equal ability enter a tennis tournament. The event is a "knock-out" competition where the loser of a match is eliminated from the competition. How many matches will have to be played in order to find a winner?

11. What is the one's digit in the product
123 456 789 × 987 654 321 × 111 111?

2·1 Problem Solving— A Model and Strategies

Mathematics can help us to interpret a problem, organize the data, and obtain a solution. The process of problem solving can be organized into a series of steps.

Understand the Problem
- Note key words and phrases.
- Identify the important facts.
a. State what is given.
b. State what is wanted.
c. Omit irrelevant information.

Develop and Carry Out a Plan
- Look for patterns.
- Guess and check.
- Use direct computation.
- Draw a diagram.
- Tables and graphs.
- Solve a simpler problem.
- Use reasoning.
- Work backwards to a solution.

Look Back
- Write a conclusion.
- Make sure that the answer is reasonable.
- If necessary, explain your solution.
- Make and solve similar problems.
- Solve the problem a different way.
- Is there more than one answer?

Example

A student bought a used car for $600, sold it for $700, bought it back for $800, and then sold it again for $900. How much money did the student make or lose overall?

1. Understand the Problem
a. The student paid $600 and $800 for the car on two separate occasions.
b. The student received $700 and $900 for the car on two separate occasions.

2. Develop a Plan
Decide which method will yield an answer. One possible method is direct computation.

3. Carry Out the Plan
Let the receiving of money be represented by positive integers.
Let the spending of money be represented by negative integers.
$$-600 + 700 - 800 + 900 = -1400 + 1600$$
$$= 200$$

4. Look Back
a. Write a conclusion.
The student made $200 on the transactions.
b. Does the answer make sense?
c. Are there other possible solutions?
d. Can you think of a similar problem?

Exercises

1. Answer the questions found under the Look Back section of the example in the display.

For each of the following problems,
a. list the known facts.
b. state what is required to solve the problem.
c. choose a plan to solve the problem.
d. state your reason for choosing that plan.
e. carry out your plan to get a solution.
f. check the reasonableness of your answer.
g. state a conclusion.

2. A yacht was bought for $110 000, sold for $95 000, bought back for $112 000, and sold again for $135 000. How much money did the original buyer make or lose in this series of transactions?

3. A gaggle of geese was chased by a bale of turtles. If there are 58 legs and 36 eyes for all the animals, then how many of each kind of animal are there?

4. Thirty-six barriers of equal size are used to construct a rectangular enclosure for sheep. Find the arrangement of the barriers that will provide the sheep with the greatest grazing area.

5. Styrofoam balls are glued together to form various crystal models. They are stacked in pyramid-like piles. If 4 balls are stacked with 2 on each side, 10 balls are stacked with 3 on each side, and 35 balls are stacked with 5 on each side, then how many balls could be stacked with 11 on each side?

6. How can a board 14 cm by 6 cm be cut into two equal pieces to cover completely a hole 21 cm by 4 cm?

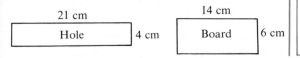

7. A Canadian politician spent one fifth of her life as a child, one tenth as a teenager, one twelfth as a political-science student, one half as a member of the government, and the last seven years retired on her ranch in Alberta. How old is she now?

8. If 5 students eat 5 hotdogs in 5 min, then how long will it take 100 students to eat 100 hotdogs?

9. Armand wanted only math students to know his seven-digit phone number. He announced that his number has the same first three numbers as everyone in the class, the last two digits are the same digit, and when multiplied gave the fourth digit. The sum of the last four digits is 15. What are the last four digits?

10. Sam went to purchase doughnuts for three friends. Upon returning he gave each of his friends, one at a time, half the doughnuts he had then and two more doughnuts besides. He finished with one doughnut. How many doughnuts did he originally purchase?

11. Kwei-lin has ten identical coins and five choices as to where to hide the coins. Is it possible for her to put a different number of coins in each hiding spot? Explain.

12. How many squares are there in this diagram?

Using the Library

Have you ever wondered how mathematicians tackle problems in science, the humanities, or even world affairs? Write a short essay on the use of mathematical models that reflect "real-life" problems. One reference that you may wish to use is *Math and Aftermath*, Hooke, R. and Shaffer, D. Walker and Co., 1966.

2·2 Classifying Information

Some problems will give irrelevant, extraneous, or even redundant information. In these cases, it is important that you read through the given information and find the information that is necessary to solve the problem.

Example

A passenger train leaves Winnipeg at 13:35 bound for Regina. There are 40 coaches, each carrying 30 passengers. The train had already travelled 2528 km from Montreal. The train arrived at Regina at 21:05 the same day, after having made two 15 min stops, one at Brandon and one at Broadview. Regina is 3102 km from Montreal. The adult fare to Regina is $46.20, while a child's fare is $23.10. What was the average speed of the train, while in motion, from Winnipeg to Regina, and what was the total fare collected for this trip?

1. Understand the Problem
a. The distance from Montreal to Winnipeg is 2528 km, while the distance from Regina to Montreal is 3102 km.
The train left Winnipeg at 13:35 and arrived in Regina at 21:05 after two 15 min stops.
There are 40 coaches with 30 passengers on each or 1200 passengers.
The adult fare for the trip is $46.20, while a child's fare is $23.10.
b. We are required to find the average moving speed of the train and the total fare collected.
c. We do not need the information on where the train stopped to answer either of these questions.
d. A diagram could be drawn to show the given information.

2. Develop a Plan
i) To find the average speed of the train, find the total distance the train travelled and divide this total by the total time the train was moving.
ii) To find the total fare collected for the trip, find the sum of the children's fares collected and the adults' fares collected.

3. Carry Out the Plan
i) The total distance travelled by the train is $3102 - 2528$ or 574 km.
The total time for the trip is $21:05 - 13:35$ or 7.5 h. Since there were two 15 min stops, the total time the train moved was 7 h.

$$\text{Average Speed} = \frac{\text{Distance}}{\text{Time}}$$
$$= \frac{574}{7}$$
$$= 82$$

ii) Since we do not know the number of adults that travelled on the trip or the number of children on the trip, the total fare collected cannot be determined.

4. Look Back
i) The average speed of the train while in motion was 82 km/h. Does this answer make sense? Explain.
ii) Why is it important to know when there is not enough information given by a problem?

Exercises

1. Answer the questions posed in the Look Back section of the example in the display.

For Exercises 2 to 5, what additional information is needed to solve the problem?

2. Halley's Comet reached its perihelion on February 9, 1986. When will this recurring comet reach its next perihelion?

3. A crane operator works a 40 h week. Time and a half is paid for overtime. How many hours of overtime were worked during a week if the operator earned $920?

4. A pickle-packing plant bottles pickles in jars having a 4 cm radius. If 10 jars hold one batch of pickles, then how tall are the jars?

5. How many spherical marbles having a diameter of 1 cm does it take to fill a bucket?

Solve each of the following. List the information **not** required to solve each problem.

6. The Sky Hawks parachute team was formed in 1971 to give public demonstrations of parachute techniques. A typical year for the team involves in excess of 2000 jumps, before an estimated two million spectators. A normal jump altitude is 3 km. Using an altimeter and a stopwatch, a parachutist free falls for 45 s, attaining speeds of more than 320 km/h. At 670 m, the main parachute is opened allowing the jumper to control the descent to a pinpoint landing. Find the height of a normal free fall.

7. The Nordic Tak Shop employs 8 people with a weekly payroll of $3500. Sales on ski equipment take place February 1 and April 1. On February 1, the owner offers a discount of 20% on all items. On April 1, a further 30% discount is offered on all unsold items. A pair of skis will sell for $350 on January 1. The successive discounts are equal to a single discount of what percent?

Analyse each of the following problems. If it contains **sufficient** information and nothing extraneous, then solve it. If it contains **extraneous** information, then discard the extra facts and solve it. If it contains **contradictory** information, then label it insoluble. If it contains **insufficient** information, then label it indeterminate.

8. Mrs. Kew is putting a fence around her rectangular city lot. The lot is 17 m x 40 m. The fence will have two 140 cm gates and one 3 m gate for a driveway. The fence costs $8.25/m, each small gate costs $8.50, and the large gate costs $15.75. What is the total cost if there is a charge of $3.75/m for installation, including gate spaces?

9. John's service station sells only two kinds of gasoline: regular and unleaded. Yesterday, he sold 10 000 L of regular and 12 000 L of unleaded for $4500. Today he sold 12 000 L of regular and 14 400 L of unleaded for $5000. If he charged identical prices on both days, how much did each kind of gas cost per litre?

10. Last week Milos spent $88 to buy a number of shirts on sale for $8 each and several pairs of jeans at $16 each. If the same number of shirts and twice the number of jeans were bought, there would have been 13 items. Find the number of pairs of jeans bought and the number of shirts bought.

11. Norma moved from Ontario to Northern Alberta. In Toronto she kept a 50% antifreeze solution in her car which protected her car to $-37°C$. She had to increase the strength to 70% to give her car protection to $-64°C$. How much pure antifreeze should she add to 15 L of a 50% solution to obtain a 70% solution?

12. When Ban drove the 420 km from Toronto to Ottawa, he averaged 70 km/h. During the trip he drove 2 h on icy roads and 4 h on dry roads. Assuming that he drove at a steady rate in each case, how fast did he travel on each type of road surface?

2·3 Look for Patterns

In Section 2·1, several different strategies for solving problems were suggested. One of those strategies is Looking for Patterns. This section will introduce some of the reasons for choosing this particular strategy. However, many of the exercises can be solved using other strategies. The other strategies should be explored in the Look Back section of your solution.

Example

People taking shortcuts through a park create pathways. Two paths will meet at one point, three paths will meet at a maximum of three points, and so on. The Parks Commission has decided to put a fountain at each point of intersection of the paths. Find the maximum number of fountains necessary for nine intersecting paths.

1. Understand the Problem
a. The more paths there are, the larger the number of intersecting points.
b. We are required to find the maximum number of fountains for 9 intersecting paths.
c. We do not need the information that the Parks Commission is making the decision.

2. Develop a Plan
a. One possibility is to draw all possible intersecting paths. But, the diagram could become very complicated after 5 or 6 paths. Therefore, this is not an efficient plan.
b. Create a table and look for patterns using simpler intersecting diagrams.

3. Carry Out the Plan

Number of Paths	2	3	4	5	6 ...
Number of Fountains	1	3	6	10	15 ...

From the table, notice that the difference between consecutive numbers of fountains is 2, 3, 4, 5, and so on. Using this pattern, the table can be completed.

Number of Paths (n)	2	3	4	5	6	7	8	9
Number of Fountains (f)	1	3	6	10	15	21	28	36

4. Look Back
The maximum number of fountains is 36.
This pattern can be generalized into a formula. If n is the maximum number of paths, then
$$f(n) = \frac{n^2 - n}{2}$$

Exercises

1. If the maximum number of drinking fountains in the display was found to be -36, then would this be a reasonable answer? Explain.

2. Straight-line conductors are embedded in a circuit board. A terminal is made at each point of intersection.

a. What is the maximum number of terminals in a board having 37 conductors?
b. What is the minimum number of terminals possible?

3. Amoebas reproduce by splitting into 2 parts after a few days. If one amoeba divided 8 times, then how many amoebas will there be after 8 divisions?

4. The distance between any two consecutive coils in a Gastropod shell is equal to the distance between the next larger spiral. That is, if the first spiral distance is 1 cm and the second spiral distance is 2 cm, then the third spiral distance is 3 cm. The pattern continues $1, 2, 3, 5, 8, \ldots$. What is the tenth spiral distance?

5. When a skydiver jumps from a plane, the distance in metres dropped during each successive second is approximately 4, 14, 24, 34, and so on. What is the total distance fallen after 20 s of free fall?

6. In bowling, 10 pins are set up with one pin in the first row, 2 pins in the second row, 3 in the third row, and 4 in the fourth row. If the pins were set up in the same manner in a game of Super Bowl with 30 rows of pins, then how many pins would you have to knock over for a strike?

7. Students decided to build a row of beans for a fund-raising stunt. On the first day, one bean was used to start the row. On the second day, 2 beans were added. On the third day, 4 beans were added, and so on for 25 school days.
a. How many beans did students have to bring on the 25th day? Use a calculator if one is available.
b. If each bean raised 1¢ for the fund, then how much money was raised?
c. If each bean was 1 cm in length, then how long was the row of beans?

8. The three-digit number 576 can be rearranged to produce 5 other three-digit numbers. Which of the following is the sum of the six different numbers?
a. 3996   **b.** 3948   **c.** 3997   **d.** 3850

9. The Kamloops' variety shop makes sales every day for one month. The amounts are $10 the first day, $20 the second day, $30 the third day, and so on. How much money does the store receive in the month of July?

10. A farmer had a piece of property in the shape shown. His will set out that the property was to be divided equally among his four children so that each had the same area and same shape of land. How was this done?

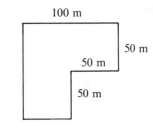

11. How many different meeting rooms can be made in a hotel convention hall if partitions can divide the length into thirds and the width into quarters?

12. A printer charges $35 for 100 pamphlets, $43 for 200 pamphlets, $51 for 300 pamphlets, and so on. How much will 2000 pamphlets cost at this rate?

13. One generation ago you had two ancestors. How many ancestors did you have 15 generations ago?

14. Divide each number of the sequence 5, 8, 13, 21, 34, 55, 89, 144, ... by 4 and record the remainders. State the pattern you discovered. This pattern was first discovered by the 18th-century mathematician Joseph Lagrange.

15. What is the sum of the labelled vertices in the Star of David shown?

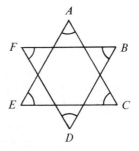

2·4 Checking a Solution

In some problems, listing the known facts will not always help to develop a plan. In this case, it is often necessary to guess a solution based on all the known facts and check this solution against the facts. If the guessed solution proves to be incorrect, then the guess should be modified to account for the inconsistency.

Example

There are three houses in a row on the same side of Main Street. The Browns, the Greys, and the Whites live in the houses. The Greys live next to the Whites and own a parrot, while the Browns own a dog. The baker does not live in the house to the left or own a dog, and the engineer does not live next to the baker. But, the lawyer's neighbour owns a parrot. Find where each family lives and the occupation of the wage earner in each household.

1. Understand the Problem

a. The Greys live next to the Whites.
The Browns own a dog and the Greys own a parrot.
The baker does not live in the house on the left.
The engineer does not live next to the baker.
The lawyer's neighbour owns a parrot.
The baker does not own a dog.

b. Find where each family lives and the occupation of the wage earner.

2. Develop a Plan

Because of the complexity of the known facts, no pattern can be discovered easily. As a result, guess a solution based on some reasoning and check the solution against all the known facts.

3. Carry Out the Plan

Using the information given in the Understand the Problem section, we can try these solutions.

First Guess

GREYS	WHITES	BROWNS
engineer	lawyer	baker
parrot		dog

Fact 6 contradicts this guess.

Second Guess

BROWNS	GREYS	WHITES
engineer	lawyer	baker
dog	parrot	

Fact 5 contradicts this guess.

Third Guess

BROWNS	WHITES	GREYS
engineer	lawyer	baker
dog		parrot

4. Look Back

The Browns live in the house to the left, own a dog, and the wage earner is an engineer. The Whites live in the middle house, do not have a pet, and the wage earner is a lawyer. The Greys live in the house to the right, own a parrot, and the wage earner is a baker.

Check that the answer does not contradict any of the facts by once again reviewing the facts against the solution. This final check should eliminate any doubt that you may have.

Exercises

1. The approach to the problem in the display started with Fact 1. Describe another approach using the guess-and-check process.

2. Three scientists, McKay, Eng, and Torrini, all live in Metro Toronto. Three construction workers also named McKay, Eng, and Torrini live in Metro Toronto. The scientist Eng and the carpenter live in Etobicoke, the scientist Torrini and the ironworker live in Scarborough, while the scientist McKay and the electrician live between these two boroughs. The carpenter's namesake earns $25 000/a. The electrician earns exactly two thirds of the scientist living nearest him. The construction worker McKay beats the ironworker at pool. What is the name of the electrician?

3. A clever chandelier shipper pays his packers $5 per chandelier safely packed and fines his packers $7 for every broken chandelier. Knowing his workers well, the shipper has chosen the rates so that a packer just breaks even after handling 24 chandeliers. How many chandeliers does the packer safely pack?

4. Eight club members went oyster picking. They returned and pooled their catch before dividing it equally among themselves. One member said it would be most fair to share by families instead of by individuals. Since there were 2 Armstrong brothers and 2 Maynes sisters, a redivision by families would have increased their share by 3 oysters. Enter Fred, President of the club. Although he couldn't help pick oysters, he was determined that he was entitled to share in the catch. All agreed and each gave Fred one oyster, making equal shares all around. How many oysters did the club members pick?

5. The people of Namned Island conducted business by barter. Two shovels could be exchanged for 3 fishing rods and a hatchet; and 25 pears could be exchanged for 3 shovels, 2 hatchets, and a fishing rod combined. How many pears would be exchanged for each article separately?

6. A group of friends went out to lunch and told the waiter to make one bill for the meal. The bill came to $60 and they agreed to split it equally. It was discovered that two of the party had left without paying. The remaining people had to pay an extra $2.50. How many people were in the group originally?

7. Friendly Square has one house on each of its four sides. The sides of the Square are called North, South, East, and West. The homeowners are Mr. Upton, Mr. Leftbank, Miss Rightside, and Ms. Downey. Their occupations are artist, lawyer, actor, and doctor (not necessarily in that order). The resident on the south side of the Square knows nothing about law. The doctor lives opposite Mr. Upton; the actor lives opposite Ms. Downey; Mr. Upton has never been in a play and has hired his lawyer neighbour to represent him. Miss Rightside is the actor's left-hand neighbour. The resident on the west side of the square travels frequently. Draw Friendly Square placing each resident and their occupation on the correct sides.

8. What is the sum?
$$400 - 399 + 398 - 397 + \ldots + 2 - 1$$

Historical Note

Lise Meitner (1878-1968)
Meitner obtained her doctorate degree in Physics at the University of Vienna in 1906. She attended Max Planck's lectures in Berlin and joined Otto Hahn in radioactivity research in 1907.

Over the next thirty years she distinguished herself in nuclear research.

In 1938, she left Nazi Germany to settle in Sweden. In January 1939, she described the process by which lighter barium was produced in neutron bombarded uranium. She proposed the term "nuclear fission" for this process.

Lise retired to England in 1960 and shared the Enrico Fermi Award with Otto Hahn and Fritz Strassmann in 1966.

Research what the term "nuclear fission" means.

2·5 Direct Computation

An expression or equation can sometimes be generated and evaluated directly from the information presented in a problem. The evaluation of the expression or equation will be the solution to the problem.

Example

Four fifths of the 1900 fans attending a basketball game have played basketball previously. Of these fans, five eighths played as a member of a team. Of those fans that played for a team, one half still play the game. Find the number of fans that have played basketball for a team and still play.

1. Understand the Problem

a. $\frac{4}{5}$ of the fans played basketball.

$\frac{5}{8}$ of these fans belonged to a team.

$\frac{1}{2}$ of those who played for a team, still play.

b. How many fans who played basketball for a team still play?

2. Develop a Plan

By recalling that "of" means to multiply, the solution can be obtained by calculating the fraction of the fans who still play and multiplying this fraction by the number of fans at the game.

3. Carry Out the Plan

$\frac{4}{5} \times \frac{5}{8} \times \frac{1}{2} = \frac{1}{4}$

$\frac{1}{4}$ of 1900 = 475

4. Look Back

Of the fans who played basketball for a team, 475 still play.

Exercises

1. In the Look Back section of your solution, you should check that your answer is reasonable and attempt to solve a related problem. Refer to the example in the display to answer each.
a. Is the answer reasonable? Explain.
b. If 1500 fans attended the game, then how many still play basketball?
c. What fraction of the fans played the game, but never belonged to a team?
d. Solve the problem another way. (*Hint:* Can you make a series of separate calculations?)

2. An expedition on a three-day crossing of Bathurst Island in the Arctic was hit by an earthquake at the end of the first day's travel. The team had enough fuel for 2 L per member and the quake destroyed $\frac{3}{4}$ of the fuel supply.
a. What fraction of the fuel supply (per member) was left?
b. Anything less than $\frac{2}{3}$ L per person will endanger the expedition. Should the expedition turn back?

3. Tickets on a draw are sold to raise funds. Wanetta sells $\frac{1}{2}$ of the total number of tickets, Sam sells $\frac{1}{2}$ of what is left after Wanetta's sales, Dino sells $\frac{1}{3}$ of the remaining tickets after Wanetta and Sam's sales, and Charlie sells the remainder of the tickets. What fraction of the total ticket sales does each make?

4. An employee earning $30 000/a is given the choice between two different two-year contracts. The first offer was a 9% increase the first year and no raise the second year. The second offer was a 4.5% raise each year. Which of the two contracts offered the greatest amount for the employee over the two years, and by how much?

5. An employee earns $450 per week. A pay cut of 10% is imposed. A month later a 10% cost of living raise is given the employee.
a. What is the employee's wage after the raise?
b. What percent cost of living raise would be needed to bring the employee's wage back to $450 per week?

6. A square walk-in closet requires 1.44 m² of floor tiles.
a. Can you stand in the centre of the closet and touch opposite walls at the same time? (*Hint:* Make an assumption about your own arm span.)
b. What are the dimensions of the closet?

7. A plane travelling at 900 km/h left Hackville, flew north for 45 min, west for 30 min, and landed at Weston.
a. What is the straight line distance from Hackville to Weston? Use a calculator if one is available.
b. If the plane consumed 1500 L of fuel for every hour of flight, then how much fuel was used on the flight from Hackville to Weston?

8. The sum of two numbers is 10 and their product is 20. Find the numbers.

9. Copy the nine digits 777 222 888. Cross out six of the nine digits so that the three digits that remain have a sum of 30. If there is no solution, explain why.

10. A crate contains less than 100 oranges. If the oranges are removed 2 or 4 at a time, there is 1 left over. If removed 3 at a time, there are none left over. If removed 5 or 6 at a time, there are three left over. How many oranges are in the crate?

11. The Kitamat Sailing Club decided to take 150 of its members on a thirty-day cruise. They took their own supplies and food to last for the entire trip. After ten days they rescued some shipwrecked fishermen. Due to the increased number of people, their supplies and food lasted only fifteen more days. How many fishermen did they rescue?

12. Sanjay knew that there were 7 red socks and 19 yellow socks in his drawer. What is the smallest number of socks that must be removed in order to ensure that he has a matching pair?

13. A teacher found that if she gave each student in the class 4 pencils, then she had 35 pencils left over. However, if she gave each student in the class 5 pencils, then there would be only 5 left over. How many pencils does she have and how many students are there in her class?

14. What number less than 510 leaves a remainder of 3 when divided by 7, 5 when divided by 11, and 6 when divided by 13?

15. A windshield cleaning solution contains 50% ethyl alcohol. How much water must be added to 6 L of this solution to reduce it to one which contains 25% alcohol?

16. How much water must be evaporated from 300 kg of a 2% salt solution to get a solution that is 3% salt?

2·6 Draw a Diagram

Drawing a diagram and placing the known information on that diagram is often useful in clarifying or solving a problem. This strategy is especially effective in deductive geometry, but it can be applied to many non-geometric problems.

Example

A plumber was called to repair a fountain located on a square platform. The platform was surrounded by a square moat 6 m wide. When the plumber arrived, she found two planks, each 6 m in length. How can the planks be positioned so that the plumber can cross the moat without getting wet?

1. Understand the Problem
a. The given information states that there is a square platform surrounded by a square moat. The moat is 6 m wide. The plumber has two planks, each 6 m in length.
b. We must find how the planks should be situated so that the plumber can cross to the platform without touching the water. The plank must overlap the platform and shore to make it secure.
c. The extraneous information is the fact that a plumber is required to fix a fountain on a platform.

2. Develop a Plan
This situation does not lend itself readily to an equation and it is difficult to picture mentally. As a result, a diagram will help us to solve the problem.

3. Carry Out the Plan
When a diagram is used, the given information should be placed on that diagram.

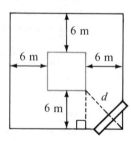

The distance from the corner of the platform to the corner of the moat can be found using the Pythagorean Relation.

$$6^2 + 6^2 = d^2$$
$$72 = d^2$$

Therefore, the distance from the corner of the platform to the corner of the moat is approximately 8.5 m.

The only way to get across the moat is to combine the boards. Therefore, place one board across a corner of the moat as shown in the diagram. This results in the centre of the board being 3 m from the corner of the moat. But $8.5 - 3 = 5.5$, which is the remaining distance to get to the platform. Because the second plank is 6 m in length, this plank will have one end on the first plank and the other end on the platform.

4. Look Back
Therefore, the two planks are combined in the manner shown in the diagram.

Exercises

1. A Parks Board planning engineer placed entrances at the four corners of a square park. City Council decided to enlarge the park to twice the size of the original and to retain its shape. How could the engineer lay out the new park and keep the entrances in the same places?

2. A cargo plane can hold 6 trucks and 7 jeeps or 8 trucks and 4 jeeps. If the plane is loaded with jeeps only, then what is the maximum number it can hold?

3. An orchardist, who had a passion for geometric planting patterns, planted 9 apple trees in ten rows with 3 in each row. Show how this was done.

4. A gardener planted 19 daffodil bulbs in a geometric pattern of 9 rows so that each row would have 5 daffodils. Show how it was done.

5. An aircraft flew south for 100 km, then flew east for 30 km, and then flew north for another 60 km. How far was the plane in a straight line from its starting point?

6. How many mirrors 3 cm by 4 cm can be placed on a rectangular area of a wall which is 10 cm by 16 cm?

7. How can a cake made in the shape of a cube be divided among 8 people so that each person receives the same amount of cake and icing?

8. Two skaters start at the same time from opposite sides of a canal frozen over with ice. The skaters travel at steady but different speeds. They first pass each other 250 m from one bank. They continue to the opposite bank without stopping and return immediately. They pass each other a second time when they are 300 m from the other bank. How wide is the canal?

9. The floor of a square convention centre can be divided into square display areas by partitions.
a. If the partitions can divide the sides into eighths, how many square display areas can be formed?
b. If the cost of renting the smallest square area is $1500, construct a table showing rental charges for all possible square display areas.

10. Ten men and two boys want to cross a river using a small rowboat. The boat can carry two boys or one man. How many times must the boat cross the river to get everyone on the other side?

11. Two circles with diameters of 4 cm intersect so that the two points of intersection and the centres of the circles are the vertices of a square. What is the area of the intersection of the interior of the circles?

12. If two circles of equal area are placed in a square having an area of 100 cm², then what is the maximum area they can cover?

13. Three vertical poles 25 m, 32 m, and 21 m high are placed in a straight line with the tallest pole between the other two. The distance between the shortest pole and the tallest pole is 60 m. The distance between the 25 m pole and the tallest pole is 24 m. Find the length of a wire antenna strung between the tops of the poles.

14. The manager of a food store gave instructions to cover half a display window with an area of 3 m². The window decorator followed the instructions and upon finishing the job discovered he still had a square window opening $\sqrt{6}$ m across. Draw a diagram to show how this was done.

15. If two squares of equal area are placed in a circle having a diameter of 30 mm, then what is the maximum area that they can cover?

2·7 Tables and Graphs

In some problems, relationships exist between pairs of numbers. In this case, a table of values and a graph, or an equation can be used to solve the problem.

Example

A Nordic cross-country skier is clocked at several points along a 30 km course. The times at the 5 km, 10 km, and 15 km check points were 15 min, 30 min, and 45 min, respectively. Assuming the skier maintains this steady pace, how long will he take to complete the race?

1. Understand the Problem
a. The total length of the course is 30 km. The rest of the information is displayed in the table.

b.

d (km)	t (min)
5	15
10	30
15	45

2. Develop a Plan
Because there is a relationship between pairs of numbers, a graph can be drawn.

3. Carry Out the Plan

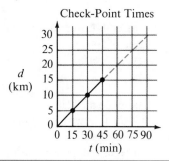

Check-Point Times

4. Look Back
The skier will take 90 min to complete the course.

This relationship between pairs of numbers also produces an equation; namely, $3d = t$.

$$\therefore t = 3(30)$$
$$= 90$$

Therefore, the original answer is verified.

Exercises

1. A ball is dropped from a height of 16 m. It hits the pavement in 2 s. Each time it hits the pavement, it rebounds to a height equal to half the distance from which it last fell. Each time it falls, it takes half the time of the last fall. What is the height of the ball after $5\frac{1}{4}$ s?

2. A swimmer competing in a 100 m breaststroke race covered 25 m in 9 s, 50 m in 23 s, and 75 m in 42 s. (*Hint:* A graph is often needed when an approximation is required.)
a. Approximately how long would it take to complete the race at this declining rate?
b. How far had the swimmer travelled in 30 s? 5 s?

3. Carbon 14 reverts to nitrogen at a steady rate with a half-life of 5500 a. Half-life is the time it takes for a radioactive substance to lose half its mass. What is the mass of Carbon 14 present in 100 g after these times?
a. 4000 a   **b.** 8000 a   **c.** 11 000 a   **d.** 20 000 a

4. Find approximate values for $\sqrt{3}$, $\sqrt{5}$, and $\sqrt{8}$ given that $\sqrt{0} = 0$, $\sqrt{1} = 1$, $\sqrt{4} = 2$, and $\sqrt{9} = 3$.

5. Find approximate values for $\sqrt[3]{4}$, $\sqrt[3]{5}$, and $\sqrt[3]{7}$ given that $\sqrt[3]{1} = 1$, $\sqrt[3]{8} = 2$, and $\sqrt[3]{27} = 3$.

6. How can a bill of $4.80 be paid using the same number of nickels, dimes, and quarters?

2·8 Solve a Simpler Problem

Sometimes a problem can be reduced to a simpler problem. This simpler problem often suggests a solution to the original problem.

Example

A customer at Stereomath was offered successive discounts of 16%, 8%, and 4%, in any order, on a $1299 sound system. In which order should the customer take the discounts in order to receive the lowest purchase price?

1. Understand the Problem
a. Successive discounts of 16%, 8%, and 4%.
b. What order should the customer take the discounts in order to receive the lowest purchase price?
c. The fact that the system costs $1299 is not important because we are concerned only with percent discounts.

2. Develop a Plan
Since the original list price is unimportant, a simpler list price could be used to make the calculations easier. For example, use an original list price of $100.

3. Carry Out the Plan
List Price $\times$ (1 − Percent Discount) = Sale Price
$100(1 - 0.08)(1 - 0.04)(1 - 0.16) = 74.19$
$100(1 - 0.16)(1 - 0.04)(1 - 0.08) = 74.19$
$100(1 - 0.04)(1 - 0.08)(1 - 0.16) = 74.19$

4. Look Back
A pattern has developed here. Using the Look for Patterns strategy, we can conclude that it does not matter what order the discounts are taken. This is a reasonable answer as the commutative property holds for multiplication.

Exercises

1. Could the problem in the display be answered using three simpler successive percent discounts?

2. Find the sum of the odd numbers up to 4001.

3. A supermarket clerk wants to build a square-based pyramid display of cans of soup. How many cans will be needed if the base of the pyramid has 15 cans along its edges?

4. A wire is strung to form a square antenna 40 m on each side. By joining the midpoints of each adjacent side, another square antenna is formed by wires. If this process is continued, what length of wire will be needed to form the fifth square?

5. How many diagonals can be drawn in a polygon of 14 sides? 15 sides? 20 sides?

6. Thirty members of two rugby teams shake hands at the end of the match. If each player shakes hands with each of the other players, including the members of their own team, how many handshakes will there be? (*Hint: A* shaking *B*'s hand is the same as *B* shaking *A*'s hand.)

7. An overfed seagull tried to fly from the water to its nest 18 m up a cliff. Experiencing difficulty it was only able to flap its wings for one minute and climbed 3 m in the air. During the next minute of rest, the gull descended 2 m. If the gull repeated its efforts, then how long would it take the bird to reach its nest?

2·9 Work Backwards to the Solution

The process of working backwards from a known condition to solve for an unknown condition is a useful strategy in many problems.

Example

A colony of bacteria double in size every hour. A biologist discovered that the container they were in was completely filled after 20 h. What fraction of the container was full after 16 h?

1. Understand the Problem
a. Bacteria population doubles every hour. The bacteria takes 20 h to fill the container completely.
b. Find the fraction of the jar full after 16 h.

2. Develop a Plan
Since the final result is given, we can work backwards from this final result to obtain the required fraction.

3. Carry Out the Plan
After 19 h, the container is $\frac{1}{2}$ of 1 or $\frac{1}{2}$ full.

After 18 h, the container is $\frac{1}{2}$ of $\frac{1}{2}$ or $\frac{1}{4}$ full.

After 17 h, the container is $\frac{1}{2}$ of $\frac{1}{4}$ or $\frac{1}{8}$ full.

After 16 h, the container is $\frac{1}{2}$ of $\frac{1}{8}$ or $\frac{1}{16}$ full.

4. Look Back
The container is $\frac{1}{16}$ full of bacteria after 16 h.

Can you find a pattern to the solution to find what fraction of the jar is full after 8 h?

Exercises

1. Answer the question asked in the Look Back section in the display.

2. An eggman sold Mrs. Parker half his supply of eggs. He then sold Mr. Nguyen half of his remaining stock. Mrs. Stein bought half of the remaining eggs. Finally, Mr. McTavish bought the last 24 eggs. How many eggs did the eggman have to start?

3. A dealer sold a radio to a stranger for $89 and was given a $100 bill as payment. The dealer, having no change, went next door and had the butcher change the bill. The stranger departed with the change and radio. Later, an excited butcher appeared, stating that the $100 bill was counterfeit. The dealer reimbursed the butcher with a legal $100 bill. How much had the dealer lost?

4. The receipts from a concert attended by 420 people were $1760. If adult tickets were $5 each and student tickets were $3 each, then how many adults and how many students attended the concert?

5. Dominic, Shauna, Bill, and Quanita were preparing for a cross-country ski race. Bill skied twice as far as Shauna. Quanita skied 10 km less than Bill. Shauna skied 8 km more than Dominic. Dominic skied 9 km. How far did each person ski?

6. Carlo was watching planes land at Pearson International Airport. He saw twice as many 767's as 747's. The number of 727's was 2 less than the 767's. There were four times as many 737's as 727's. Carlo saw sixteen 737's. In all, how many planes did he see land?

2·10 Make an Assumption and Draw a Conclusion

The following is an excerpt from Mark Twain's *Life on the Mississippi*.

... "In the space of one hundred and seventy-six years the Lower Mississippi has shortened itself two hundred and forty-two miles (389.45 km). That's an average of a trifle over one mile and a third (2.21 km) per year. Therefore, any calm person, who is not blind or idiotic, can see that in the Old Oolitic Silurian Period, just a million years ago next November, the Lower Mississippi River was upward of one million three hundred thousand miles (2 Mkm) long, and stuck out over the Gulf of Mexico like a fishing-rod. And by the same token any person can see that seven hundred and forty-two years from now the Lower Mississippi will be only a mile and three-quarters (2.82 km) long, and Cairo and New Orleans will have joined their streets together, and be plodding comfortably along under a single mayor and a mutual board of aldermen."

This humorous piece of literature focuses our attention on the fact that critical thinking is an essential skill in problem solving. Questionable or incorrect conclusions may be drawn from false assumptions made on information or data provided. The assumption that Mark Twain has made is that the Mississippi River has been shortening itself at a constant rate since its formation. This assumption leads to the rather humorous conclusion.

Exercises

Discover the hidden and/or false assumption and answer each of the following.

1. Three guests checking into a hotel pay $10 each for a room. Later, the desk clerk discovers a mistake has been made and instructs the bellhop to return $5 to the three guests. On the way to the room, the bellhop decides to return one dollar to each of the guests and keep two dollars for himself. Each guest received one dollar, making the total they paid $27. The two dollars the bellhop kept makes $29. What happened to the other dollar?

2. Two ski tracks are seen on a ski hill covered in snow. One track goes around a tree on the hill. The other track goes around the tree on the opposite side. Give as many different physical explanations to fit these facts as you can find.

3. If 92 players enter a tennis tournament for a singles championship, then how many games have to be played to determine the winner?

4. A gourmet cooking school invited guests to eat the food prepared during the final exam. The guests were asked to follow the rule that every two guests must share a plate of appetizers, every three must share a plate of entrees, every four a plate of the main course, and every five a plate of desserts. If there were 77 plates altogether, then how many guests were present?

5. Move only one toothpick to a new position to make a true sentence.

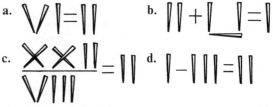

6. Describe the shape of an object if a light held under it casts a circular shadow on a ceiling. A light held directly in front casts a square shadow on a wall behind. A light held at the side of the object casts a triangular shadow on the opposite wall.

2·11 Use Reasoning

Using reasoning is a strategy similar to that of checking a solution. The difference here is that we take one or more known facts and draw conclusions, as opposed to drawing conclusions based on all the facts presented. We must then check the conclusion against all the known facts.

Example

Find the occupation of each person using the facts listed under the Understand the Problem Section.

1. Understand the Problem
a. The sun always shines on Bartok's birthday.
Lee and Stanton are neighbours and share a car pool to work.
Stanton makes more money than Pedersen.
The publisher has six children.
Lee beats Bartok regularly at tennis.
The engineer always walks to work.
The policeman does not live near the publisher.
The engineer likes classical music.
The only time the policeman met the grocer, he gave him a speeding ticket.
The policeman makes more money than the grocer or the publisher.
b. Find the occupation of each person.   **c.** Are any irrelevant facts listed here?

2. Develop a Plan
Take a subset of the known facts and draw a conclusion based on these facts. Check your conclusion against **all** the known facts to see if the conclusion is valid or not.

3. Carry Out the Plan

Fact	Lee and Stanton drive to work.
Fact	The engineer always walks to work.
Conclusion 1	Either Pedersen or Bartok is the engineer.
Implication	If Pedersen is the policeman, then Bartok is the engineer.
Result	Pedersen would make more money than Lee or Stanton.
Contradiction	Stanton makes more money than Pedersen.
Fact	Stanton makes more money than Pedersen.
Conclusion 2	Pedersen is the engineer.
Fact	The policeman does not live near the publisher.
Result	Either Lee is the policeman and Stanton the grocer, or Lee is the grocer and Stanton the policeman.
Contradiction	The policeman met the grocer for the first time when he gave him a speeding ticket and Lee and Stanton share a car pool.
Result	Neither Stanton nor Lee can be the policeman.
Result	Bartok is the policeman.
Fact	Lee beats Bartok regularly at tennis.
Result	Lee is the publisher by reason of the last contradiction.

4. Look Back
Lee is the publisher, Bartok is the policeman, Pedersen is the engineer, and Stanton is the grocer. Check the conclusion once more to ensure that your conclusion fits the facts.

Exercises

1. Answer the question asked in the Understand the Problem section of the display.

2. A 36-car train travelling along a single track meets a 40-car train going the opposite direction. Nearby is a siding that will hold only 30 cars. How did the trains manage to pass?

3. In a ship's flag locker, there are 20 red flags and 27 white flags. A flag officer reaches into the locker in the dark. How many flags must be removed to be sure of getting two flags the same colour?

4. A farmer had only 3 L and 5 L containers and a pail of milk. A neighbour asked for 4 L of milk. How did the farmer measure out the exact amount?

5. Three ships, a grain carrier, a tanker, and a container ship, are named the MacDonald, the Laurier, and the Borden, but not necessarily in that order. Their ports of departure and call are alphabetically listed as Bombay, Honolulu, Prince Rupert, Vancouver, Victoria, and Yokohama. Name the ships and their ports of departure and call using these facts.
a. The tanker passed the ship headed for Honolulu.
b. The Laurier arrived at Yokohama the same day the grain carrier left Prince Rupert.
c. The Borden left Victoria and did not sail for Bombay.
d. One of the other ships did set course for Bombay.

6. A coin collector complained that one of the nine coins he received was counterfeit. The coin was known to be slightly heavier than the other eight. Using only one equal arm balance and two trials, explain how the counterfeit coin could be found.

7. A farmer has hens and cows. There are 100 heads and 220 feet. How many hens and how many cows are there?

8. The flight-crew positions of Captain, Navigator, Flight Engineer, First Officer, and Attendant were held by Mr. Tidski, Miss Wong, Miss Lewis, Mr. Hohm, and Mr. Clarke, but not necessarily in that order. Name the flight-crew position each person holds.
a. The attendant is a bachelor.
b. Mr. Clarke is going to toast the bride when the Navigator and the First Officer get married.
c. The Navigator and Captain were roommates at university.
d. Mr. Tidski and Miss Wong have met only once, when Miss Wong sold him some property.
e. Mrs. Hohm was delighted to hear the Captain recommended her husband for a promotion.

9. Three people named Larry, Mary, and Terry work in a department store. They fill the positions of cashier, accountant, and clerk. A government auditor came in and wanted to find the accountant. She was given the following information to help her find the clerk.
a. If Terry is the cashier, then Mary is the clerk.
b. If Terry is the clerk, then Mary is the accountant.
c. If Mary is not the cashier, then Larry is the clerk.
d. If Larry is the accountant, then Terry is the clerk.
Who did the government auditor go to see?

10. Write your own question that can be solved using a series of facts. Challenge a classmate to answer your question while you answer theirs.

11. A tennis tournament contained 32 players and was a single knockout competition. In other words, once a player lost a game, they were eliminated. How many games are necessary to determine a winner? Solve this question in two different ways.

Braintickler

How can you group four nines so that they total 100?

47

2·12 Mixed Practice

The exercises in this section can be done using one or more of the problem-solving strategies presented in this chapter and in previous years. Before attempting any of the problems, review the strategies presented to date. The four-step problem-solving model is shown along with some hints for each step. Remember, any strategy that leads to the correct solution is a good strategy.

1. Understand the Problem
- Note key words.
- Restate the problem in your own words.
- State what is wanted.
- Identify extraneous, insufficient, or contradictory information.

2. Develop a Plan
Listed below are the strategies presented in this chapter. Add to this list any strategies that you know of, or feel are important, that have not been covered to date.
- Draw a diagram.
- Use reasoning.
- Look for a pattern.
- Guess and check.
- Solve a simpler problem.
- Direct computation.
- Use tables and graphs.
- Work backwards towards a solution.
- Use objects or manipulatives.
- Make an assumption and draw a conclusion.

3. Carry Out the Plan
Once a strategy has been decided upon, proceed to solve the problem.

4. Look Back
When the plan has been carried out, write a conclusion to the problem. You also should be prepared to explain your solution if necessary, make and solve similar problems, ensure that the answer is reasonable, check whether there is another way to solve the problem, and check whether there is another solution.

Exercises

1. The island of Notissap has a population of 19 531. News is distributed by word of mouth. Each person hearing news will tell it to 5 other people in 1 h and then tell no one else. How long did it take to pass a news item to all inhabitants of this island?

2. A businessman had to pay half of the money he had for a shipment of lettuce. He then had to pay $2000 in duties. He spent $\frac{1}{3}$ of the remaining money on a sales promotion and this left him with $24 000. With how much money did he start?

3. A group of people noted that all Edmontonians present were Albertans. All Albertans present were Canadians. There were thirty Edmontonians present. Five Canadians present were not Albertans. There were fifty-two Canadians in the group. How many Albertans were not Edmontonians?

4. Helen brought her golf foursome some Nanaimo bars that her husband had made. Ron ate half of them; Gwen ate half the remaining bars. Helen ate 1 and George put 1 away for later. There were no bars left. How many Nanaimo bars did Helen's husband send to the golf foursome?
Problem Extension:
If George put 3 bars away, then how many would Helen's husband have sent?

5. Five students compete in a music festival: Judy, Joanne, Darcy, Sandy, and Mai. Two attend Alpha High School and three attend Beta High School. Three are pianists and two are singers. Judy and Sandy attend the same school. Darcy and Mai attend different schools. Joanne and Darcy compete in the same event. Sandy and Mai compete in different events. The singer from Alpha High won first place. What is her name?

Problem Extension:

a. Name the students who attend Alpha High.

b. Name the students who attend Beta High.

c. Which students are pianists?

d. Which students are singers?

6. Four hikers were lost on a mountain. They pooled their food which consisted only of chocolate bars. Being tired, they all fell asleep. One hiker woke up very hungry and ate $\frac{1}{3}$ of the chocolate bars and went back to sleep. The second hiker woke up also very hungry and ate $\frac{1}{3}$ of the remaining chocolate bars and went back to sleep. The third hiker did the same. When the fourth hiker awoke, she took her rightful share of the remaining chocolate bars. This left 12 chocolate bars. With how many chocolate bars did the lost hikers begin?

7. Bill was jogging along the seawall at Qualicum Beach at a rate of 7 km/h. A cyclist passed him and disappeared around a bend in the pathway. From the moment the cyclist passed Bill until disappearing, he had jogged 10 paces. Bill continued on for 40 more paces to the bend in the pathway. How fast was the cyclist travelling?

8. A prospector set out in early spring to work in the Northlands. The first day he counted one black fly. On each of the following days, he counted four times as many as on the previous day.

a. At this rate, how many black flys did he count on the 7th day?

b. How many black flys were counted on the nth day and what was the total number of flies counted after n days?

9. Every hour on the hour a plane leaves Vancouver for Toronto and another leaves Toronto for Vancouver. The trip lasts 4 h. How many planes bound for Vancouver will a plane meet during its trip to Toronto?

10. A class of 30 students agreed that each person would send a Valentine card to every other person in the class. How many Valentine cards were required?

11. A flag maker had a choice of 8 different coloured cloths with which to make 2-coloured flags. How many different 2-coloured flags could be produced?

12. A course for a sailboat race was circular and had eight course markers equally spaced around it. All boats in a race line up at the first flag to start a race. Laurie took 15 min to get to the fourth flag. How long did it take her to complete the course if she sailed at the same rate?

13. Every day Wendy meets the bus and carries the incoming mail from the bus depot at 1st and Alder to the post office at 4th and Elm. To make her job interesting she decides to take a different route every day until she has travelled every route to the post office. If Wendy can only travel east and north, how many days will she take to cover all possible routes? (*Hint:* Make an assumption about the street names.)

14. The Calgary Rugby League held a lottery to raise funds. They sold 6975 tickets at $2 each. The league awarded 51 prizes. First prize was $1000, second prize was $500, third prize was $490, fourth prize was $480, and so on, with each subsequent prize worth $10 less than the one before. The 51st prize was worth $10. How much profit did the club make from the lottery?

15. If four years is added to three times Douglas' age, he will be as old as his forty-six year old father. How old is Douglas?

2·13 Computer Application — Rounding Numbers

In many disciplines, it is important to be able to approximate a numerical value with a certain degree of accuracy. Rounding numbers to the nearest specified value is one way of achieving this. Using the BASIC language, most computers will print only 8 significant digits and will simply cut off (truncate) all digits following. This truncation also occurs when the INTeger function (INT) is used in a program. For example, INT(9.9) returns 9.

Example

Mrs. Fremont's math class was asked to round any real number to a specified number of decimal places. Write a program to help Mrs. Fremont's math class.

Solve a simpler problem first.
State the purpose of the program.

Input the number to be rounded.

Round the number.
Print the result.

Does the user wish to round another number?

If yes, then goto line 20.
End when all numbers have been rounded.

```
10 REM A PROGRAM TO ROUND ANY
REAL NUMBER
15 REM TO THE NEAREST WHOLE
NUMBER
20 INPUT "NUMBER TO BE ROUND
ED ";X
30 LET ANS = INT(X + 0.5)
40 PRINT X; " ROUNDED IS ";
ANS
50 INPUT "ANOTHER NUMBER?
Y/N ";AN$
60 IF AN$ = "Y" THEN 20
99 END
```

Exercises

1. What is the purpose of lines 20, 30, and 60?

2. Copy and complete the program.

```
10 REM ROUND A REAL NUMBER
TO THE NEAREST TENTH
20 INPUT "▇▇▇▇▇▇ ";X
30 LET ANS = INT(10 * ▇▇▇
+ 0.5) / 10
40 PRINT ▇▇▇▇▇▇▇
50 INPUT "DO YOU WISH TO EN
TER ANOTHER NUMBER? Y/N";
AN$
60 IF ▇▇▇ = "Y" THEN ▇▇▇
99 END
```

3. It has been suggested that computers be used to record everyone's medical history, including what medication a person is using, the number of visits to a pharmacy, and even how healthy or sick a person is. Write a short essay to argue whether or not computers should be connected to medical establishments. Comment on the various ethical considerations; for example, a person's right to privacy, as well as the practicality of establishing such a system.

4. Write a program that will allow you to input a number and then round it to a specified value. (*Hint:* Use the four-step problem-solving model.)

2·14 Chapter Review

1. In the game of Blue Tick, a player chooses any three of the first seven positive integers to form a three-digit number. The second player tries to guess the chosen number by testing different three-digit numbers. Each guess receives a response such as "one ticket is not blue". This example means one of the three digits is correct, but does not occupy the correct position. A game was played in which the first four guesses were 372, 571, 567, and 456. The response to each guess was "one ticket is not blue". What was the chosen number?

2. A person ate 100 bonbons in five days. Each day six more bonbons than the previous day were consumed. How many bonbons were eaten on the fifth day?

3. How many boys would have to leave a bus containing 99 boys and one girl in order to reduce the percentage of boys to 98%?

4. A tugboat crew consists of a captain, an engineer, a cook, and a deckhand. Their names are Alfred, Bingo, Cedric, and Donovan, not necessarily in that order. Bingo is older than Alfred. The captain has no relatives in the crew. The cook and the deckhand are brothers. Bingo is Cedric's nephew. The deckhand is not the engineer's uncle. The engineer is not the cook's uncle. Name the position each man holds and state how they are related.

5. A grocer purchased a shipment of grapefruit at 3 for $1 and an equal number at 5 for $2. At what price must the grapefruit be sold for the grocer to break even?

6. What percent increase in wages must an employee receive to regain her original pay after getting a 20% cut in pay?

7. A wheel with a rubber tire has an outside diameter of 50 cm. When the radius has been decreased due to wear by 1 cm, by what percent will the number of revolutions of the wheel needed to travel one kilometre be increased?

8. Lisa and Larry started a race from opposite sides of the canal. After $2\frac{1}{2}$ min they passed each other at the centre of the canal. If they lost no time on their turns and they maintained their speed, then how many minutes after starting did they pass each other the second time?

9. If the sales tax on a purchase of $85 is $5.95, what will be the sales tax on a purchase of $200?

10. A micro-organism grows and then splits into two parts every 3 min, each new organism being the same size as the original. If one such organism is placed in a test tube, it takes 10 h to fill it. How long does it take to fill half the test tube?

11. A herd of elephants is chasing a mustering of storks. If there are 80 feet and 60 eyes for all the animals, then how many of each are there?

12. Find the sum of the numbers from 1 to 70.

13. Find the dimensions of a rectangular field that has a perimeter of 188 m and an area of 1920 m^2.

14. How can 19 musicians be positioned on a football field in 9 rows so that there are 5 musicians in each row?

15. The curator of Fort York arranges for a square-based pyramid of cannonballs to be placed at the entrance to the fort. How many cannonballs will be needed to build the pyramid having 8 balls along the solid base edge?

2·15 Chapter Test

1. List the four steps that might be applied in solving a problem.

2. How many different lecture rooms can be made in a hall if partitions divide the length into quarters and the width into fifths?

3. A group having dinner asked the waiter to make one bill for the meal. The bill came to $162. Later it was noted that four of the group had departed without paying their share. The remaining diners each had to pay an extra $6.75. How many people were in the group originally?

4. Discover the pattern to copy and complete the table.

$1 \times 2 = 2$ thus $(15)^2 = 225$
$2 \times 3 = 6$ thus $(25)^2 = 625$
$3 \times 4 = 12$ thus $(35)^2 = 1225$
$4 \times 5 = 20$ thus $(\blacksquare)^2 = 2025$
■■■■■ $(55)^2 = $ ■■
■■■■■ $(65)^2 = $ ■■
■■■■■ $(75)^2 = $ ■■
■■■■■ $(85)^2 = $ ■■
■■■■■ $(95)^2 = $ ■■
■■■■■ $(105)^2 = $ ■■

5. If Leah sold $\frac{1}{2}$ the hamburgers on the heat rack, Neil sold $\frac{1}{2}$ the remaining hamburgers, and Elaine sold $\frac{1}{3}$ of the rest leaving 11 burgers, then how many hamburgers were on the heat rack originally?

6. Write an equation as a model for each condition.
a. The difference between 61 and $4n$ is 85.
b. The value of (q) quarters and (n) nickels is $6.50.
c. The average velocity (v) is the ratio of distance (d) to time (t).

7. A log, 12 m long, was to be cut so that the shorter piece is 6 m less than five times the length of the longer piece. How long is the longer piece?

8. Predict the world population in the year 2000 A.D. based on the data provided.

Year	Estimate Population in Millions
1650	510
1700	625
1750	710
1800	910
1850	1130
1900	1600
1950	2510
1970	3575
1982	4600

9. What is the total percent discount resulting from three successive discounts of 25%, 15%, and 8%?

10. The total receipts from a concession stand where 46 hotdogs and pizzas were sold was $62. If a pizza sold for $2 and a hotdog sold for $1, then how many pizzas and how many hotdogs were sold?

11. What additional information is needed to solve this problem? How many jam jars will be needed to bottle 32 t of strawberries?

12. Two students agree to split an 80 mL milkshake evenly between them. They only had unmarked 50 mL and 30 mL containers with them. How could the students, using only these containers, evenly share the 80 mL of milkshake?

13. The Italian flag has three vertical bands each of a different colour. How many different flags could be made with five colours if two adjacent bands cannot be the same colour?

14. If 15 people eat 15 hotdogs in 15 min, then how long will it take 10 people to eat 10 hotdogs?

52

CHAPTER THREE

EXPONENTS AND RADICALS

Tune Up

1. Perform the indicated operations.

a. $9 - 6 \div 3 \times 2$ **b.** $5 + 7(-2) - 4$

c. $5 \times 15 \div 3 + (-7)$ **d.** $-15 - 3(5 - 7) + 5$

e. $8^2 - 5(3) + 7(-2)$ **f.** $6(7 - 2)^2 \div 15$

g. $28 + 14 \div 7 + 1$ **h.** $(3 \times 2 + 2)^2 \div 8 - 5$

i. $2 - [-3(4^2 - 13)^2 + 1] + 7$

j. $2 \times 3 + 12 \div 4 - 18 \div 6 + 3$

k. $(21 - 17)(4 + 1) \div 10(3 + 5)$

l. $\frac{-56}{-7} - 14(-2) - \frac{35}{-7}$

m. $8\left[\frac{1}{2}(3^2 - 7) - \frac{1}{4}(4^2 - 4) \right] + 1$

2. Using the Pythagorean Relation, solve for the length of the unknown side.

a.

b.

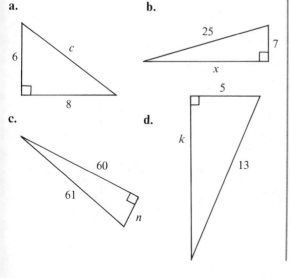

c.

d.

3. Perform the indicated operations.

a. $\frac{1}{2} + \frac{5}{6}$ **b.** $\frac{1}{8} \times \frac{3}{5}$

c. $\frac{3}{5} - \frac{2}{3}$ **d.** $\frac{4}{7} \div \frac{2}{3}$

e. $\frac{4}{9} + \frac{3}{5} \times \frac{1}{3}$ **f.** $\frac{7}{8} - \frac{1}{4} \div \frac{5}{6}$

g. $6\frac{1}{4} + 3\frac{3}{16} - 1\frac{7}{8}$

4. Solve. $x \in R$

a. $5x - 7 = 8$ **b.** $4x + 9 = 25$

c. $10x + 7 = 7x + 22$ **d.** $5x - 3 = 15 - 4x$

e. $\frac{x}{3} = -5$ **f.** $\frac{x}{2} + \frac{1}{4} = \frac{x}{4} + \frac{3}{2}$

g. $\frac{(x + 2)}{2} + \frac{x}{3} = 2$

h. $\frac{(x + 1)}{3} + \frac{(x - 1)}{2} = \frac{2}{3}$

5. If $a = 4$ and $b = 3$, then evaluate each expression.

a. $3a + 2b$ **b.** $4ab - 3a$

c. $\frac{2a - 5b}{a + b}$ **d.** $\frac{a + b}{a - b}$

6. Copy and complete.

a. The product of two positive and two negative numbers is a ▃▃▃▃▃▃ number.

b. The product of a positive and a negative number is a ▃▃▃▃▃▃ number.

3·1 Natural Number Exponents

An exponent is used to designate how many times a given base is used as a factor.

3^5 means 3 is used as a factor 5 times.

$3^5 = 3 \times 3 \times 3 \times 3 \times 3$

Number Bases	Variable Bases	Exponent Law $(m, n \in N)$
$(2^3)(2^4) = [(2)(2)(2)][(2)(2)(2)(2)]$ $= 2^{3+4}$ $= 2^7$	$(x^2)(x^3) = [(x)(x)][(x)(x)(x)]$ $= x^{2+3}$ $= x^5$	**Product Law** $(x^m)(x^n) = x^{m+n}$
$7^4 \div 7^2 = \dfrac{(7)(7)(7)(7)}{(7)(7)}$ $= 7^{4-2}$ $= 7^2$	$x^5 \div x^2 = \dfrac{(x)(x)(x)(x)(x)}{(x)(x)}$ $= x^{5-2}$ $= x^3$	**Quotient Law** $x^m \div x^n = x^{m-n}$ $(x \neq 0, m > n)$
$(2^2)^3 = [(2)(2)][(2)(2)][(2)(2)]$ $= 2^{(2)(3)}$ $= 2^6$	$(x^4)^2 = [(x)(x)(x)(x)][(x)(x)(x)(x)]$ $= x^{(4)(2)}$ $= x^8$	**Power of a Power** $(x^m)^n = x^{mn}$
$[(2)(7)]^3 = [(2)(7)][(2)(7)][(2)(7)]$ $= (2)(2)(2)(7)(7)(7)$ $= (2^3) \times (7^3)$	$(xy)^4 = (xy)(xy)(xy)(xy)$ $= [(x)(x)(x)(x)][(y)(y)(y)(y)]$ $= x^4 y^4$	**Power of a Product** $(xy)^m = x^m y^m$
$\left(\dfrac{3}{4}\right)^3 = \left(\dfrac{3}{4}\right)\left(\dfrac{3}{4}\right)\left(\dfrac{3}{4}\right)$ $= \dfrac{3^3}{4^3}$	$\left(\dfrac{x}{y}\right)^5 = \left(\dfrac{x}{y}\right)\left(\dfrac{x}{y}\right)\left(\dfrac{x}{y}\right)\left(\dfrac{x}{y}\right)\left(\dfrac{x}{y}\right)$ $= \dfrac{x^5}{y^5}$	**Power of a Quotient** $\left(\dfrac{x}{y}\right)^m = \dfrac{x^m}{y^m}$ $(y \neq 0)$

Using the exponent laws, it is often possible to simplify expressions involving exponents. Remember to follow the correct order of operations.

Example 1

Multiply. $(2ab)(-4a^2b^3)$

$(2ab)(-4a^2b^3) = (2)(-4)(a)(a^2)(b)(b^3)$
$\qquad\qquad\qquad = -8a^3b^4$

Example 2

Divide. $(12x^8) \div (2x^4)$

$(12x^8) \div (2x^4) = \dfrac{12x^8}{2x^4}$
$\qquad\qquad\qquad = 6x^4$

Example 3

Simplify. $\left(\dfrac{7x^4y^3}{21xy^2}\right)^2$

$\left(\dfrac{7x^4y^3}{21xy^2}\right)^2 = \left(\dfrac{x^3y}{3}\right)^2$
$\qquad\qquad\quad = \dfrac{x^6y^2}{9}$

Example 4

Write the product with a single base. $(a^{n+2})^3 \times (a^{m-1})^2$

$(a^{n+2})^3 \times (a^{m-1})^2 = a^{3n+6} \times a^{2m-2}$
$\qquad\qquad\qquad\qquad = a^{3n+2m+4}$

Exercises

1. Multiply. Use a calculator to evaluate where possible.

a. $(2^4)(2^7)$ **b.** $(3^9)(3^{14})$

c. $(p^4)(p^5)(p^6)$ **d.** $(m^7)(m^6)(m^2)$

e. $(4m^7)(6m^5)$ **f.** $(-3x^8)(-12x^7)$

g. $(r^n)(r^{2n})(r^{n+1})$ **h.** $(y^{a+2})(y^{a-2})(y^{5-a})$

2. Write the quotient as a power of one base. Evaluate where possible. The first one is done as an example.

$$\frac{a^4}{a^2} = a^2$$

a. $\dfrac{7^{15}}{7^{12}}$ **b.** $\dfrac{5^7}{5}$ **c.** $\dfrac{n^{17}}{n^{15}}$

d. $\dfrac{q^{23}}{q^7}$ **e.** $\dfrac{25s^{12}}{5s^6}$ **f.** $\dfrac{-56r^9}{8r^3}$

g. $\dfrac{z^{3b}}{z^b}$ **h.** $\dfrac{r^{2p-1}}{r^{p-3}}$ **i.** $\dfrac{-(m+n)^5}{(m+n)^2}$

3. Write each expression without brackets. Evaluate where possible.

a. $(2^3)^2$ **b.** $(5^2)^3$

c. $(-a^4)^5$ **d.** $(c^2)^{10}$

e. $(2x^3)^4$ **f.** $(-3a^5)^3$

g. $(q^x)^x$ **h.** $(s^{2s-1})^{2s+1}$

4. Write each expression without brackets.

a. $(a^2b^3)^3$ **b.** $(x^3y^4)^3$

c. $(xy^2)^4$ **d.** $(m^3n)^3$

e. $(-3p^2q^6)^4$ **f.** $(7x^7y^5z)^2$

g. $(k^bm^{2b})^4$ **h.** $(r^{2m+3}s^{2m-3})^{2m}$

5. Write each expression without brackets.

a. $\left(\dfrac{1}{2}\right)^4$ **b.** $\left(\dfrac{-3}{4}\right)^3$

c. $\left(\dfrac{x^4}{y^2}\right)^3$ **d.** $\left(\dfrac{b}{b+c}\right)^4$

e. $\left(\dfrac{5m^3}{2n^2}\right)^3$ **f.** $\left(\dfrac{-2r^5}{3s^3}\right)^3$

g. $\left(\dfrac{p}{q^2}\right)^n$ **h.** $\left(\dfrac{m^{2n+1}}{n^{3n-1}}\right)^{4n}$

6. Find the area of a square which has a side length of $2a^3$ units.

7. A rectangle has a length of $7k^3m^2$ units and a width of $2k^4m$ units. Find its area.

8. Simplify using the laws of exponents.

a. $(2x^2y^3)(3xy^4)$ **b.** $(5p^3q^2)(7pq^4)$

c. $(x^3y)(xy^2)(x^2y^2)$ **d.** $(4p^2q)(3r^2q)(-2p^2r^2)$

e. $\dfrac{(25x^2y^3)}{(5xy)}$ **f.** $\dfrac{(-27a^4b^2)}{(-9a^3b^2)}$

9. Perform the indicated operations. Write each expression without brackets.

a. $(xy)^3(x^2y)$ **b.** $(3a^2b^3c)^2(2a^2bc^2)^3$

c. $\dfrac{(x^5)^3(x^3)^5}{x^{10}}$ **d.** $\dfrac{(ab)^8}{(a^2b^2)^3}$

e. $\left(\dfrac{x^4y^2z}{xyz}\right)^3$ **f.** $\left(\dfrac{k^7m^2n^3}{k^6mn}\right)^4$

10. Evaluate if $p = -2$ and $q = 3$.

a. p^2q **b.** $-4pq^3$

c. $2p^2 + 3q$ **d.** $(2p - q)^3$

11. Express the product or quotient as a power with a single base.

a. $(c^{2m})(c^{3m})(c^m)$ **b.** $(h^{2k-1})(h^{2k+1})$

c. $\dfrac{(m)^{2a}}{(m^2)^a}$ **d.** $\dfrac{(a^m)^2(a^{m+1})^2}{(a^2)^m}$

e. $\left[\dfrac{(k^{2m})(k^{5m})}{k^{4m}}\right]^3$ **f.** $\dfrac{(z^{a+2b})^2(z^2)^a}{(z^b)^3}$

12. A triangle has a base length of $3(a+b)^3(b+c)^2$ units and its height is $7(a+b)^4(b+c)^5$ units. Find its area.

13. The area of a rectangle is $24p^5q^2r$ square units. If the length of the rectangle is $12p^3qr$ units, then find the width of the rectangle.

14. Find the value of 3^{3^3} and $(3^3)^3$.

15. Express as a single base by first expressing the numerator and denominator as a power of the number indicated. The first one is partially done for you.

a. $\dfrac{2^4 \times 4^7 \times 8^2}{16^3} = \dfrac{2^4 \times (2^2)^7 \times (2^3)^2}{(2^4)^3}$

b. $\dfrac{27^3 \times 9^2}{3^5 \times 81}$ as a power of 3

c. $\dfrac{4^3 \times 8^2}{16^2 \times 32^3}$ as a power of 2

16. What is the significance of the negative exponent in the solution to Exercise 15, part **c**?

55

3·2 Integral Exponents

Special meaning is given to powers with negative integral exponents. For example,

$$\frac{x^5}{x^8} = x^{5-8} \qquad \text{also} \qquad \frac{x^5}{x^8} = \frac{(x)(x)(x)(x)(x)}{(x)(x)(x)(x)(x)(x)(x)(x)}$$

$$= x^{-3} \qquad\qquad\qquad\qquad\qquad = \frac{1}{x^3}$$

Therefore, x^{-3} is the same as $\frac{1}{x^3}$.

$$\boxed{x^{-a} = \frac{1}{x^a},\ x \neq 0 \text{ or } \frac{1}{x^{-a}} = x^a,\ x \neq 0}$$

With this meaning, the exponent laws can be applied to any integral exponent. In the following, simplify the expression by writing the answer with positive exponents only and without brackets.

Example 1

Evaluate. 3^{-4}

$3^{-4} = \dfrac{1}{3^4}$

$\quad = \dfrac{1}{81}$

Example 2

Simplify. $x^2 y^{-3}$

$x^2 y^{-3} = \dfrac{x^2}{y^3}$

Example 3

Simplify. $\dfrac{3a^{-2}c}{b^{-3}}$

$\dfrac{3a^{-2}c}{b^{-3}} = \dfrac{3b^3 c}{a^2}$

Example 4

Evaluate. $\left(\dfrac{3}{5}\right)^{-1}$

$\left(\dfrac{3}{5}\right)^{-1} = \dfrac{3^{-1}}{5^{-1}}$

$\qquad = \dfrac{5}{3}$ or $1\dfrac{2}{3}$

Example 5

Simplify. $(x^{-3}y^{-2})^2 (x^2 y^{-1})^{-3}$

$(x^{-3}y^{-2})^2 (x^2 y^{-1})^{-3} = (x^{-6}y^{-4})(x^{-6}y^3)$

$\qquad\qquad\qquad\qquad = x^{-12}y^{-1}$

$\qquad\qquad\qquad\qquad = \dfrac{1}{x^{12}y}$

In a similar manner, we can find the value of x^0.

$$\frac{x^4}{x^4} = x^{4-4} \qquad\qquad \frac{x^4}{x^4} = \frac{(x)(x)(x)(x)}{(x)(x)(x)(x)}$$

$$= x^0 \qquad\qquad\qquad\qquad = 1$$

Therefore, $x^0 = 1$, where $x \neq 0$ and $x \in R$.

Example 6

Evaluate. $(2x)^0$

$(2x)^0 = 1$

Example 7

Calculate. $\dfrac{(p^2 q)^3}{p^6 q^3}$

$\dfrac{(p^2 q)^3}{p^6 q^3} = \dfrac{p^6 q^3}{p^6 q^3}$

$\qquad = p^0 q^0$

$\qquad = 1$

Exercises

1. Evaluate.

a. 2^{-3}

b. $\left(\frac{1}{2}\right)^{-1}$

c. 3^{-2}

d. -3^{-2}

e. $(-3)^{-2}$

f. $(-2)^0$

g. -2^0

h. $(5x^{-2})^0$

i. $\left(\frac{1}{3}\right)^{-3}$

j. $-\left(\frac{1}{5}\right)^{-2}$

k. $(0.1)^{-1}$

l. $(0.02)^{-2}$

2. Write each expression with positive exponents and without brackets.

a. x^{-2}

b. $\frac{1}{y^{-3}}$

c. $3y^{-4}$

d. $m^{-2}n^4$

e. $7a^{-3}b^2$

f. $-3x^{-1}$

g. $\frac{3b^{-2}}{m^{-2}}$

h. $\left(\frac{a}{b}\right)^{-2}$

3. Write each expression with positive exponents and without brackets.

a. $\frac{2m^{-3}n^{-2}}{k^{-2}p^{-4}}$

b. $\frac{1}{m^{-2}n^{-3}}$

c. $a^{-1}bc^{-1}$

d. $(3y)^{-2}$

e. $(2x^4y^{-3}z^0)^3$

f. $(-3ab^2)^{-3}$

g. $\frac{p^0}{m^{-1}n^{-2}}$

h. $\left(\frac{m}{p^2q}\right)^{-2}$

i. Which variables cannot be zero? Explain.

4. Simplify by writing the expression with positive exponents and without brackets.

a. $m^{-4}m^{-3}$

b. $(m^{-5}n^{-2})(m^{-1}n^3)$

c. $\frac{x^{-2}}{x^{-4}}$

d. $\frac{6p^6}{p^{-2}}$

e. $\frac{a^{-3}b^{-4}}{a^{-2}b}$

f. $\left(\frac{a^{-1}}{a^{-3}}\right)^3$

g. $\left(\frac{m^{-4}}{m^{-1}}\right)^{-2}$

h. $\frac{24m^5p^{-3}q^4}{-4m^3p^2q^{-2}}$

5. Simplify by writing the expression with positive exponents and without brackets.

a. $\frac{(2k^2m^{-3})^3}{(4k^{-2}m^{-1})^2}$

b. $\frac{(3a)^{-2}}{(4a)^{-1}}$

c. $\frac{(r^{-3}s^{-2})^{-2}}{(r^{-1}s^{-4})^{-1}}$

d. $\left(\frac{25m^{-4}n^{-3}}{-5m^{-1}n^{-5}}\right)^{-2}$

e. $\left(\frac{2x^{-1}}{y}\right)^{-2}$

f. $\frac{3^{-1}u^{-1}v^2}{2u^3v^{-4}}$

6. Simplify by writing each expression with positive exponents and without brackets.

a. $(56x^{-4}) \div (8x^{-3})(4x^{-2})$

b. $(8y^{-3})(5y^{-6}) \div (20y^{-12})$

c. $(4v^3w^2)^{-2} \div (2v^{-2}w^{-3})^3$

d. $\left(\frac{p}{q}\right)^{-1}\left(\frac{q}{r}\right)^{-2} \div \left(\frac{r}{p}\right)^{-1}$

e. $\left(\frac{a^2}{b}\right)^{-3} \div \left(\frac{b^2}{4}\right)$

f. $\left(\frac{x^{-3}y^{-2}}{z^3}\right)^{-2} \div \left(\frac{x^{-1}y^3}{z^2}\right)^{-3}$

7. Evaluate if $a = 2$ and $b = -1$.

a. a^{-2}

b. $-b^3$

c. $\left(\frac{b}{a}\right)^{-2}$

d. $b^{-2} + a^{-1}$

e. $(b^3a)^3$

f. $\left(\frac{1}{a}\right)^{-2} \times \left(\frac{3}{b}\right)^{-1}$

g. $(a - b)^{-3}$

h. $a^{-a} + b^{-b}$

8. Simplify. Express the answer with one base only.

a. $(x^{-2k})(x^{5k})$

b. $(x^{3r}) \div (x^{2r+1})$

c. $p^{3r-1} \times p^{2r+1}$

d. $(q^{2r+1})^2(q^{3-r})^3$

e. $\left(\frac{p^{5a+2}}{p^{3a-4}}\right)^a$

f. $\frac{(t^2)^{3-r}(t^3)^{r+1}}{t^{r+5}}$

9. What is the value of the one's digit in 2^{73}?

Historical Note

Hroswitha, the famous nun of Gandersheim, lived in the tenth century. During this era women were not allowed to learn to read or write. The only reason she was allowed to study mathematics was because she lived in a convent. She wrote about the Sun being the centre of the universe six hundred years before other scientists developed the idea. Seven hundred years before Newton was born, Hroswitha wrote about the force of gravity. She studied what we call "perfect" numbers and identified four of them. A perfect number is one which is the sum of its proper divisors. Six is a perfect number because its proper divisors are $1, 2$, and 3; $6 = 1 + 2 + 3$.

3·3 Scientific Notation

Very large or very small numbers are often written in scientific notation.
A number in scientific notation is the product of two factors:
  the first factor is a number, x, such that $1 \leq x < 10$, and
  the second factor is a power of 10.
For example, the distance from Earth to the Sun is approximately 150 000 000 km. This can be written in the following manner.

$$150\ 000\ 000 = 1.5 \times 10^8 \longleftarrow \text{Decimal point moved 8 places left.}$$

Decimal point moved 8 places left.

1 or greater but less than 10.

The average diameter of an atom is 0.000 000 021 cm.
In scientific notation this is

$$0.000\ 000\ 021 = 2.1 \times 10^{-8} \longleftarrow \text{Decimal moved 8 places right.}$$

Decimal point moved 8 places right.

1 or greater but less than 10.

The calculator uses scientific notation to store very large and very small numbers. Using a calculator enter 8 000 000 × 40 000. On the display you will see ∃·2　11. The calculator cannot display the answer 320 000 000 000 so it displays it in scientific notation.

Numbers less than one, such as 5.1×10^{-9}, are displayed as 5·1　−09.

Exercises

1. Express each in scientific notation.

a. 786	**b.** 67 400 000
c. 23	**d.** 546 200 000 000
e. 7.9	**f.** 20 030 000 000
g. 8600	**h.** 80 225 000 000 000
i. 0.0567	**j.** 0.000 000 000 23
k. 0.000 03	**l.** 0.000 000 000 000 7
m. 34 000	**n.** 0.002 15
o. 1.006	**p.** 0.1

2. Express each in standard notation.

a. 5.3×10^7	**b.** 2.58×10^{14}
c. 7.381×10^{-5}	**d.** 9×10^{-11}
e. 3.467×10	**f.** 4.92×10^0
g. 4.7392×10^{-1}	**h.** $3.874\ 567 \times 10^2$
i. 7.1×10^{-23}	**j.** 6×10^{-3}
k. 56.7×10^{-4}	**l.** 0.003×10^{-4}

3. Express each in both standard and scientific notation.

a. The mass of one molecule of water is about 3100×10^{-20} g.

b. The distance from the Sun to Neptune is about $0.000\ 478 \times 10^{13}$ km.

c. The distance from this solar system to the nearest star is about $41\ 600 \times 10^9$ km.

d. Helium has a half-life of $0.000\ 024 \times 10^{-26}$ s.

4. Show how these numbers would appear on a calculator if they were displayed in scientific notation.

a. 5.4×10^{15}	**b.** 7 610 000 000
c. 0.000 037	**d.** 6.98×10^{-53}

5. Which has the larger value, 2^{75} or 3^{50}? Do not use a calculator.

3·4 Calculations

Multiplication and division of numbers in scientific notation involve the laws of exponents.

$(5.7 \times 10^5)(1.2 \times 10^3) = (5.7 \times 1.2)(10^5 \times 10^3)$
$= 6.84 \times 10^8$

Many calculators allow you to enter a number in scientific notation by using the $\boxed{\text{EE}}$ key.

Example 1

Enter on your calculator.
a. 5.6×10^7 **b.** 3.62×10^{-3}

Enter   5.6 $\boxed{\text{EE}}$ 7   Enter   3.62 $\boxed{\text{EE}}$ $\boxed{+/-}$ 3
Display 5.6 $5.6\ 00$ $5.6\ 07$ Display 3.62 $3.62\ 00$ $3.62\ -00$ $3.62\ -03$

Example 2

Use your calculator to evaluate.
$(7.4 \times 10^{-5}) \times (8.1 \times 10^7)$

Enter	Display		Enter	Display
7.4	7.4	$\longrightarrow$	$\boxed{\text{EE}}$	7.4 00
$\boxed{+/-}$	7.4 -00	$\longrightarrow$	5	7.4 -05
$\boxed{\times}$	7.4 -05	$\longrightarrow$	8.1	8.1
EE	8.1 00	$\longrightarrow$	7	8.1 07
$\boxed{=}$	5.994 03			

which is 5.994×10^3.

Exercises

1. Calculate. Leave the answer in scientific notation.
a. $(6.4 \times 10^4) \times (5.0 \times 10^{12})$
b. $(5.6 \times 10^{12}) \times (2.0 \times 10^{-3})$
c. $(1.2 \times 10^3) \times (1.1 \times 10^{-12})$
d. $\dfrac{(1.2 \times 10^{13}) \times (5 \times 10^{15})}{6 \times 10^{11}}$
e. $\dfrac{(7 \times 10^{-3}) \times (8 \times 10^{-7})}{(1.4 \times 10^{-2}) \times (2 \times 10^{-1})}$ **f.** $\dfrac{(2.4 \times 10^{15})}{(6 \times 10^{-2})(8 \times 10^5)}$

2. Evaluate. Leave the answer in scientific notation.
a. $\dfrac{6000 \times 1500}{20 \times 300\ 000}$ **b.** $\dfrac{0.000\ 08 \times 0.003}{12\ 000}$
c. $\dfrac{1}{50\ 000 \times 0.0004}$ **d.** $\dfrac{560\ 000 \times 0.02}{0.008 \times 0.000\ 07}$
e. $\dfrac{36\ 000}{0.000\ 009 \times 2000}$ **f.** $\dfrac{35\ 080}{0.009 \div 5308}$

3. Check your answers to Exercise 1 using a calculator.

4. Write 24 using the same three digits but not using eights.

5. Express the answers in scientific notation.
a. If 6.02×10^{23} atoms of carbon have a mass of 12 g, then what is the mass of 1 atom?
b. If a space ship leaves Earth travelling at 120 000 km/h, then how far will it travel in 4000 h?
c. Pluto is 5.9×10^9 km from the Sun. If light travels at 300 000 km/s, then how long does it take light from the Sun to reach Pluto?
d. If the thickness of a piece of paper is 9×10^{-3} cm, then how many sheets of paper are in a book 5 cm thick?
e. If you spend 5 h/d and 200 d/a in school, then how many seconds are you in school during 12 a?

3·5 Introduction to Radicals

Irrational numbers are sometimes written in radical form; for example, $\sqrt{2}$ or $\sqrt[3]{5}$. Since 4 has two square roots, 2 or -2, we designate $\sqrt{4}$ as the **principal** (positive) square root. Radicals may be pure radicals such as $\sqrt{12}$ or mixed radicals such as $8\sqrt{2}$.

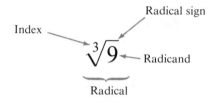

Some radicals can be evaluated exactly, while others can only be approximated.

Example 1

Evaluate each.

a. $\sqrt{64}$

Since $8 \times 8 = 64$, $\sqrt{64} = 8$.

b. $\sqrt[3]{125}$

Since $5 \times 5 \times 5$ has a value of 125, $\sqrt[3]{125} = 5$.

Example 2

Approximate each correct to one decimal place using a calculator.

a. $\sqrt{8}$

$8\ \boxed{\sqrt{}}\ \boxed{=}\ 2.8284271$

This value can be rounded to one decimal place to become 2.8.

b. $\sqrt[3]{50}$

$50\ \boxed{INV}\ \boxed{y^x}\ 3\ \boxed{=}\ 3.6840315$

This value can be rounded to one decimal place to become 3.7.

Example 3

Find a real number that represents $\sqrt{4} \times \sqrt{9}$.

$$\begin{aligned}\sqrt{4} \times \sqrt{9} &= 2 \times 3 \qquad \sqrt{4} \times \sqrt{9} = \sqrt{36}\\ &= 6 \qquad\qquad\qquad\quad\ = 6\end{aligned}$$

Therefore, $\sqrt{4} \times \sqrt{9} = \sqrt{36}$

Example 4

Find a real number that represents $\sqrt{7} \times \sqrt{5}$.

$$\begin{aligned}\text{Let } x &= \sqrt{7} \times \sqrt{5}\\ \therefore x^2 &= (\sqrt{7} \times \sqrt{5})(\sqrt{7} \times \sqrt{5})\\ &= \sqrt{7} \times \sqrt{7} \times \sqrt{5} \times \sqrt{5}\\ &= 35\\ \therefore x &= \sqrt{35}\end{aligned}$$

$$\boxed{\sqrt{ab} = \sqrt{a} \times \sqrt{b},\ a \geq 0 \text{ and } b \geq 0,\ a, b \in R.}$$

Example 5

Express $7\sqrt{3}$ as an entire radical.

$$\begin{aligned}7\sqrt{3} &= \sqrt{49} \times \sqrt{3}\\ &= \sqrt{147}\end{aligned}$$

Example 6

Express $3\sqrt{72}$ as a mixed radical.

$$\begin{aligned}3\sqrt{72} &= 3 \times \sqrt{36} \times \sqrt{2}\\ &= 3 \times 6 \times \sqrt{2}\\ &= 18\sqrt{2}\end{aligned}$$

Exercises

1. Evaluate each.

a. $\sqrt{3} \times \sqrt{3}$ **b.** $\sqrt{7} \times \sqrt{7}$ **c.** $\sqrt{20} \times \sqrt{5}$

d. $\sqrt{9} \times \sqrt{16}$ **e.** $\sqrt{24} \times \sqrt{6}$ **f.** $\sqrt{8} \times \sqrt{24.5}$

2. Evaluate each correct to two decimal places.

a. $\sqrt{144}$ **b.** $\sqrt{256}$ **c.** $\sqrt{225}$

d. $\sqrt{40}$ **e.** $\sqrt{70}$ **f.** $\sqrt{1000}$

g. $\sqrt{0.04}$ **h.** $\sqrt{0.009}$ **i.** $\sqrt{0.000\,049}$

3. Express each as a mixed radical in simplest form.

a. $\sqrt{8}$ **b.** $\sqrt{18}$ **c.** $\sqrt{32}$

d. $\sqrt{75}$ **e.** $\sqrt{96}$ **f.** $\sqrt{288}$

4. Express each as a mixed radical. Simplify by reducing the radical as much as possible.

a. $\sqrt{2x^2}$ **b.** $\sqrt{12x^4y}$ **c.** $\sqrt{27a^2b^3}$

d. $\sqrt{m^5n^3}$ **e.** $\sqrt{63k^6}$ **f.** $\sqrt{147a^9}$

g. $3\sqrt{25x^3}$ **h.** $2x\sqrt{44x^2}$

i. $4ab\sqrt{12a^5b^6}$ **j.** $7km^2\sqrt{k^2m^7}$

k. $\sqrt{44a^2b^3}$ **l.** $r^5s^2\sqrt{7r^2s^9}$

5. Express each as an entire radical.

a. $2\sqrt{3}$ **b.** $3\sqrt{5}$ **c.** $7\sqrt{6}$

d. $12\sqrt{7}$ **e.** $5\sqrt{11}$ **f.** $12\sqrt{2}$

g. $6\sqrt{6}$ **h.** $4\sqrt{14}$ **i.** $a\sqrt{2}$

6. Express each as an entire radical.

a. $ab^2\sqrt{3}$ **b.** $5xy\sqrt{2x}$ **c.** $2c\sqrt{3c}$

d. $\dfrac{4\sqrt{2}}{2}$ **e.** $\dfrac{5\sqrt{5}}{3}$ **f.** $\dfrac{3\sqrt{7}}{7}$

g. $\dfrac{x\sqrt{3x}}{\sqrt{2}}$ **h.** $\dfrac{a^2b\sqrt{2ab^2}}{b^2\sqrt{3a^2b}}$ **i.** $5r^3s\sqrt{2rs^2}$

7. Express each as a mixed radical in simplest form by reducing the radical as much as possible.

a. $2\sqrt{8}$ **b.** $3\sqrt{12}$ **c.** $5\sqrt{72}$

d. $2\sqrt{50}$ **e.** $4\sqrt{48}$ **f.** $5\sqrt{27}$

g. $4\sqrt{18}$ **h.** $7\sqrt{98}$ **i.** $3\sqrt{45}$

8. Use a calculator to verify.

a. $\sqrt{75} = 5\sqrt{3}$ **b.** $\sqrt{1620} = 18\sqrt{5}$

c. $\sqrt{1058} = 23\sqrt{2}$ **d.** $\sqrt{3971} = 19\sqrt{11}$

9. Simplify. The first one is done for you.

$$\sqrt[3]{24} = \sqrt[3]{8} \times \sqrt[3]{3}$$
$$= 2\sqrt[3]{3}$$

a. $\sqrt[3]{125}$ **b.** $\sqrt[4]{81}$ **c.** $\sqrt[3]{40}$

d. $\sqrt[4]{32}$ **e.** $\sqrt[3]{54}$ **f.** $\sqrt[4]{112}$

g. $\sqrt[3]{320}$ **h.** $\sqrt[4]{1250}$ **i.** $\sqrt[3]{320x^3y}$

10. Suggest why the radicand must be a positive number in $\sqrt{x}$.

11. A square has an area of 450 cm². What is the length of the side of the square?

12. A cube has a volume of 1400 m³. What is the length of each side of the cube?

13. The length of a rectangle is $\sqrt{5}$ cm and its width is $5\sqrt{12}$ cm. Without using a calculator, find its area.

14. The altitude of a triangle is $3\sqrt{12}$ cm and its base is $5\sqrt{12}$ cm. Without using a calculator, find its area.

15. Is $\sqrt{x^2} = |x|$ for all real values of x? Explain your answer.

16. The diagrams are a representation of 3^1, 3^2, and 3^3, constructed from small cubes.

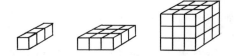

a. If each of these models were immersed in a can of paint and paint could only adhere to the outer faces, then how many faces would be covered with paint in each model? (A face is the square surface on each individual cube.)

b. Construct a model for 5^1, 5^2, and 5^3. If each of these models were immersed in paint, then how many faces would be covered with paint in each model?

c. Given models for n^1, n^2, and n^3, how many surfaces would be covered with paint in each model?

3·6 Adding and Subtracting Radicals

Addition and subtraction of radicals follows the same pattern as addition and subtraction of polynomials.

$$5x + 7x = (5 + 7)x \qquad\qquad 2\sqrt{3} + 4\sqrt{3} = (2 + 4)\sqrt{3}$$
$$= 12x \qquad\qquad\qquad\qquad\qquad = 6\sqrt{3}$$

Just as $2x + 3y$ cannot be combined because they are not "like" terms, $2\sqrt{3}$ cannot be combined with $4\sqrt{2}$ because they are not "like" radicals. Just as $2x$ cannot be added to $3x^2$ because they are not of the same degree, $2\sqrt{3}$ cannot be added to $5\sqrt[3]{3}$ because they do not have the same index.

In order to combine radicals using addition and subtraction, they must have the same index and be expressed using the same radicand.

Example 1

Add. $6\sqrt{2} + 5\sqrt{2}$

$$6\sqrt{2} + 5\sqrt{2} = (6 + 5)\sqrt{2}$$
$$= 11\sqrt{2}$$

Example 2

Subtract. $4\sqrt[3]{3} - 2\sqrt[3]{3}$

$$4\sqrt[3]{3} - 2\sqrt[3]{3} = (4 - 2)\sqrt[3]{3}$$
$$= 2\sqrt[3]{3}$$

Example 3

Add. $18\sqrt{2} + 12\sqrt[3]{3}$

Since the indexes are not the same, we cannot combine the radicals.

Example 4

Calculate. $4\sqrt{3} + 2\sqrt{6} - \sqrt{3} - 8\sqrt{6}$

$$4\sqrt{3} + 2\sqrt{6} - \sqrt{3} - 8\sqrt{6} = (4 - 1)\sqrt{3} + (2 - 8)\sqrt{6}$$
$$= 3\sqrt{3} - 6\sqrt{6}$$

Sometimes radicals have different radicands that, if simplified, allow the radicals to be added and subtracted.

Example 5

Add. $7\sqrt{2} + 3\sqrt{8}$

$7\sqrt{2} + 3\sqrt{8}$ has two different radicands but upon closer inspection:

$$3\sqrt{8} = 3\sqrt{4} \times \sqrt{2} \qquad\qquad \text{Hence, } 7\sqrt{2} + 3\sqrt{8} = 7\sqrt{2} + 6\sqrt{2}$$
$$= 3 \times 2 \times \sqrt{2} \qquad\qquad\qquad\qquad\qquad = 13\sqrt{2}$$
$$= 6\sqrt{2}$$

Exercises

1. Add or subtract where possible.

a. $3\sqrt{7} + 5\sqrt{7}$ **b.** $15\sqrt{11} - 18\sqrt{11}$

c. $23\sqrt{3} + 15\sqrt{3}$ **d.** $17\sqrt{6} - 12\sqrt{6}$

e. $19\sqrt{10} - 21\sqrt{10}$ **f.** $36\sqrt{15} + 73\sqrt{15}$

g. $9\sqrt[3]{2} - 4\sqrt[3]{2}$ **h.** $7\sqrt[4]{6} - 2\sqrt[4]{6}$

2. Perform the indicated operations.

a. $5\sqrt{3} - 8\sqrt{3} + 4\sqrt{3}$

b. $17\sqrt{11} + 5\sqrt{11} - 16\sqrt{11}$

c. $12\sqrt{10} + 15\sqrt{10} - 27\sqrt{10}$

d. $3\sqrt{6} - 9\sqrt{7} - 11\sqrt{6} + 11\sqrt{7}$

e. $5\sqrt{2} + 7\sqrt{5} - \sqrt{2} + 8\sqrt{5}$

f. $8\sqrt{13} - 7\sqrt{14} + 5\sqrt{15} - 6\sqrt{13} - 2\sqrt{15}$

3. Add or subtract. First express each entire radical as a mixed radical.

a. $\sqrt{250} - \sqrt{90}$ **b.** $\sqrt{50} + \sqrt{18}$

c. $\sqrt{28} + \sqrt{63}$ **d.** $\sqrt{99} - \sqrt{44}$

e. $\sqrt{20} - \sqrt{45} + \sqrt{80}$ **f.** $\sqrt{75} - \sqrt{27} - \sqrt{48}$

4. Perform the indicated operations.

a. $2\sqrt{40} + 3\sqrt{90}$ **b.** $2\sqrt{50} - \sqrt{18}$

c. $3\sqrt{98} - 4\sqrt{72}$ **d.** $4\sqrt{48} - \sqrt{3}$

e. $3\sqrt{28} - 2\sqrt{63} - 2\sqrt{112}$

f. $2\sqrt{24} + 3\sqrt{54} - 4\sqrt{96}$

g. $5\sqrt{80} - 10\sqrt{45} + 2\sqrt{125}$

h. $12\sqrt{52} - 2\sqrt{13} + 7\sqrt{117}$

5. Abbeyvale is 15 km due north of Bountyville. Charleston is 3 km south and 6 km west of Abbeyvale. How far is it to fly from Abbeyvale to Bountyville if you wish to pass over Charleston? Express your answer as both a mixed radical and a decimal correct to the nearest tenth.

6. Simplify by performing the indicated operations.

a. $8\sqrt{7} - 5\sqrt{8} + 3\sqrt{28} - 4\sqrt{2}$

b. $\sqrt{48} + 7\sqrt{12} - 6\sqrt{5} - 4\sqrt{20}$

c. $3\sqrt{18} + \sqrt{175} - 8\sqrt{98} + 4\sqrt{63}$

d. $4\sqrt{80} - 4\sqrt{48} - 5\sqrt{75} + 7\sqrt{20}$

e. $\sqrt{63} - (2\sqrt{44} - 3\sqrt{7} - 5\sqrt{99})$

7. Three sides of a triangle are $\sqrt{20}$ cm, $\sqrt{45}$ cm, and $\sqrt{80}$ cm in length. Find the perimeter of the triangle.

a. Express your answer as a mixed radical.

b. Express your answer as a decimal correct to one decimal place.

8. Simplify by collecting like radicals.

a. $3\sqrt{6x} - 7\sqrt{6x} + 4\sqrt{6x} - 2\sqrt{6x}$

b. $19\sqrt{7d} - 27\sqrt{5d} + 37\sqrt{5d} - 18\sqrt{7d}$

c. $2\sqrt{x^3} - 5\sqrt{x^3} + 3y\sqrt{y} - 2\sqrt{y^3}$

d. $2a\sqrt{54} + 3a\sqrt{24} - a\sqrt{96}$

e. $3\sqrt{5x^2} - 4x\sqrt{5} + 2\sqrt{45x^2}$

9. Simplify. Reduce where possible before collecting like terms.

a. $\dfrac{\sqrt{6}}{2} - \dfrac{\sqrt{6}}{4} + \dfrac{2\sqrt{6}}{5}$

b. $\dfrac{5\sqrt{63}}{7} - \dfrac{\sqrt{28}}{7}$

c. $\dfrac{\sqrt{8}}{2} + \dfrac{4\sqrt{50}}{5} - \dfrac{\sqrt{18}}{3}$

d. $\dfrac{2\sqrt{24}}{8} - \dfrac{5\sqrt{96}}{40} + \dfrac{3\sqrt{54}}{18}$

e. $\dfrac{2\sqrt{72}}{3} - \dfrac{4\sqrt{54}}{3} - \dfrac{3\sqrt{96}}{2} + \dfrac{6\sqrt{98}}{7}$

10. A mountain 2 km tall stands between two towns, Harz and Llama, which are both at the same elevation. Harz and Llama are both at the base of the mountain. If a tunnel were built through the mountain to connect the two towns, it would be 12 km long. If you tunnelled 4 km into the mountain from Harz, you would be directly below the mountain peak. To travel between the two towns one must climb directly over the mountain. How far is it from Harz to Llama over the mountaintop? Use a calculator, if one is available, to calculate the distance saved for the trip by building the tunnel.

11. A cow is tethered to a barn by a 30 m rope. The barn has dimensions of 15 m by 40 m. The cow is tied to a hook on the barn at a point 10 m from the corner on the 40 m side. Find the area that the cow may cover while grazing.

3·7 Multiplication of Radicals

Multiplication of radicals does not depend on having like radicands. However, they must be of the same index. Just as $3x$ and $2y$ can be multiplied to give a product of $6xy$, $3\sqrt{2}$ and $2\sqrt{3}$ can be multiplied to give a product of $(3 \times 2)(\sqrt{2} \times \sqrt{3})$ or $6\sqrt{6}$.

Example 1

The blueprint for an engineering project shows this rectangle. What value will the engineer find as the area of the rectangle correct to two decimal places?

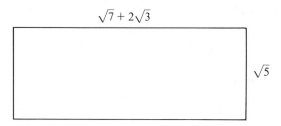

$\sqrt{7} + 2\sqrt{3}$

$\sqrt{5}$

The engineer decided to simplify the expression using the multiplication of radicals and then evaluate this expression correct to two decimal places.

Area = length × width
$$= \sqrt{5} \times \sqrt{7} + \sqrt{5} \times 2\sqrt{3}$$
$$= \sqrt{35} + 2\sqrt{15}$$

Use the distributive property.

A calculator can be used to evaluate the final expression.
The area is 5.916 + 7.746 or 13.662 cm².
Since the engineer only needs to have a value correct to two decimal places, the area is 13.66 cm². Why did the engineer round each part of the expression to find the final answer?

Example 2

Multiply. $(2\sqrt{5} - 3)(3\sqrt{5} + 2)$
$$= [(2)(3)][\sqrt{(5)(5)}] + (2)(2)(\sqrt{5}) + (-3)(3)(\sqrt{5}) + (-3)(2)$$
$$= 6\sqrt{25} + 4\sqrt{5} - 9\sqrt{5} - 6$$
$$= (6)(5) - 5\sqrt{5} - 6$$
$$= 24 - 5\sqrt{5}$$

Example 3

Remove the brackets. $(3\sqrt{p} - 2\sqrt{y})(3\sqrt{p} + 2\sqrt{y})$ $p, y > 0$
$$= (3)(3)(\sqrt{p})(\sqrt{p}) + (3)(2)(\sqrt{p})(\sqrt{y}) + (-2)(3)(\sqrt{y})(\sqrt{p}) + (-2)(2)(\sqrt{y})(\sqrt{y})$$
$$= 9\sqrt{p^2} + 6\sqrt{py} - 6\sqrt{py} - 4\sqrt{y^2}$$
$$= 9(p) - 4(y)$$
$$= 9p - 4y$$

Exercises

1. Multiply.

a. $(\sqrt{3})(\sqrt{7})$ **b.** $(\sqrt{6})(\sqrt{5})$

c. $(\sqrt{11})(\sqrt{13})$ **d.** $(\sqrt{2})(\sqrt{15})$

e. $(\sqrt{6})(\sqrt{17})$ **f.** $(\sqrt{3})(\sqrt{14})$

2. Multiply. Write the radical in lowest form.

a. $(\sqrt{12})(\sqrt{6})$ **b.** $(\sqrt{8})(\sqrt{12})$

c. $(\sqrt{15})(\sqrt{3})$ **d.** $(\sqrt{7})(\sqrt{21})$

e. $(\sqrt{10})(\sqrt{20})$ **f.** $(\sqrt{11})(\sqrt{11})$

3. Multiply. Reduce the radical to its lowest form.

a. $(3\sqrt{5})(5\sqrt{2})$ **b.** $(-5\sqrt{7})(3\sqrt{6})$

c. $(4\sqrt{3})(7\sqrt{17})$ **d.** $(3\sqrt{5})(7\sqrt{10})$

e. $(2\sqrt{24})(5\sqrt{6})$ **f.** $(-4\sqrt{18})(\sqrt{2})$

4. A land survey showed a park with the picnic area shaded.

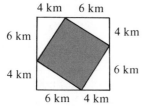

4 km   6 km

6 km   4 km

4 km   6 km

6 km   4 km

a. Calculate the length of each side of the shaded picnic area using radicals.

b. Calculate the area of the picnic area.

5. Remove the brackets. Simplify where possible.

a. $\sqrt{2}(\sqrt{5} + \sqrt{7})$ **b.** $\sqrt{7}(\sqrt{3} + 13)$

c. $2\sqrt{5}(\sqrt{3} - 2\sqrt{2})$ **d.** $\sqrt{13}(2\sqrt{3} - \sqrt{13})$

e. $3\sqrt{6}(2\sqrt{3} + 5\sqrt{4})$ **f.** $3\sqrt{3}(5\sqrt{15} - 2)$

6. Expand. Simplify where possible.

a. $(\sqrt{3} - 5)(\sqrt{2} + 6)$

b. $(\sqrt{5} - 3)(\sqrt{5} + 2)$

c. $(7 - \sqrt{11})(2 - 2\sqrt{11})$

d. $(\sqrt{5} - \sqrt{2})(\sqrt{3} + \sqrt{7})$

e. $(3 + 5\sqrt{2})(2 - 4\sqrt{2})$

7. Find the length of the diagonal of a rectangle if it has sides which are $\sqrt{14}$ units and $\sqrt{10}$ units respectively. (*Hint:* Use the Pythagorean relation.)

8. Multiply. Is there a pattern in the answers? If so, describe it.

a. $(2 - \sqrt{5})(2 + \sqrt{5})$

b. $(\sqrt{7} - 2)(\sqrt{7} + 2)$

c. $(2\sqrt{6} + 5)(2\sqrt{6} - 5)$

d. $(3\sqrt{5} - 2\sqrt{2})(3\sqrt{5} + 2\sqrt{2})$

e. $(4\sqrt{3} + 4\sqrt{2})(4\sqrt{3} - 4\sqrt{2})$

f. $(2\sqrt{11} - 6)(2\sqrt{11} + 6)$

The pairs of numbers above are called **conjugates** because their products are rational numbers rather than irrational numbers.

9. Write the conjugate of each.

a. $\sqrt{5} + 1$ **b.** $\sqrt{3} - \sqrt{6}$

c. $2\sqrt{7} - 8$ **d.** $5\sqrt{2} + 3\sqrt{7}$

10. The dimensions of a trapezoid are shown. Calculate the area and perimeter of the trapezoid. Express each in radical form and evaluate to the nearest tenth.

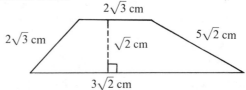

$2\sqrt{3}$ cm

$2\sqrt{3}$ cm $\sqrt{2}$ cm $5\sqrt{2}$ cm

$3\sqrt{2}$ cm

11. Find the square.

a. $(\sqrt{2} + 1)^2$ **b.** $(3 - \sqrt{5})^2$

c. $(3\sqrt{6} + \sqrt{2})^2$ **d.** $(5\sqrt{6} - 2\sqrt{3})^2$

e. $(2\sqrt{3} + 2)^2$ **f.** $(\sqrt{11} - \sqrt{5})^2$

g. $(3 + \sqrt{2} - \sqrt{3})^2$ **h.** $(\sqrt{2} + \sqrt{5} + \sqrt{10})^2$

i. $(3\sqrt{2} - \sqrt{6} + 1)^2$

12. Cube these irrational numbers.

a. $2\sqrt{3}$ **b.** $\sqrt{2} + 1$

c. $2 - \sqrt{5}$ **d.** $\sqrt{7} - 2\sqrt{3}$

13. A pup tent has a centre pole with a height of 1 m. If the material on the sides of the tent is stretched tight to the ground and is 2 m long on each side, what is the width of the floor of the tent?

14. What number can be multiplied by $(3\sqrt{2} - 3)$ to give a product of 3?

3·8 Dividing Radicals

Just as multiplication of radicals does not depend on having like radicals, neither does the division of radicals. For example, $\dfrac{\sqrt{100}}{\sqrt{4}}$ can be written as $\dfrac{10}{2}$ or 5 because $\sqrt{100}$ is 10 and $\sqrt{4}$ is 2. Similarly, $\sqrt{\dfrac{100}{4}}$ is the same as $\sqrt{25}$ which also has a value of 5. Therefore, $\dfrac{\sqrt{100}}{\sqrt{4}} = \sqrt{\dfrac{100}{4}} = 5$.

$$\boxed{\dfrac{\sqrt{a}}{\sqrt{b}} = \sqrt{\dfrac{a}{b}} \ , a \ge 0, b > 0, \text{ and } a, b \in R}$$

A radical expression is in simplified form when it is written without radicals in the denominator. This is called **rationalizing the denominator**.

Examples

Rationalize the denominator.

a. $\dfrac{10\sqrt{14}}{2\sqrt{2}} = \dfrac{10}{2} \times \sqrt{\dfrac{14}{2}}$
$= 5\sqrt{7}$

b. $\dfrac{3\sqrt{2}}{2\sqrt{3}} = \dfrac{3\sqrt{2} \times \sqrt{3}}{2\sqrt{3} \times \sqrt{3}}$
$= \dfrac{3\sqrt{6}}{6}$
$= \dfrac{\sqrt{6}}{2}$

$\dfrac{\sqrt{3}}{\sqrt{3}} = 1$

c. $\dfrac{\sqrt{6} - \sqrt{3}}{\sqrt{3}} = \dfrac{\sqrt{6} - \sqrt{3}}{\sqrt{3}} \times \dfrac{\sqrt{3}}{\sqrt{3}}$
$= \dfrac{\sqrt{18} - 3}{3}$
$= \dfrac{3(\sqrt{2} - 1)}{3}$
$= \sqrt{2} - 1$

Exercises

1. Evaluate each without using a calculator.

a. $\dfrac{\sqrt{99}}{\sqrt{11}}$ b. $\dfrac{\sqrt{48}}{\sqrt{3}}$ c. $\dfrac{\sqrt{250}}{\sqrt{10}}$

2. Express each with a rational denominator.

a. $\dfrac{\sqrt{15}}{\sqrt{3}}$ b. $\dfrac{\sqrt{28}}{\sqrt{14}}$ c. $\dfrac{\sqrt{18}}{\sqrt{2}}$

d. $\dfrac{\sqrt{72}}{\sqrt{18}}$ e. $\dfrac{5\sqrt{55}}{\sqrt{11}}$ f. $\dfrac{7\sqrt{26}}{\sqrt{13}}$

g. $\dfrac{12\sqrt{18}}{2\sqrt{3}}$ h. $\dfrac{16\sqrt{20}}{8\sqrt{4}}$ i. $\dfrac{-8\sqrt{30}}{6\sqrt{10}}$

3. Express each with a rational denominator.

a. $\dfrac{1}{\sqrt{3}}$ b. $\dfrac{5}{\sqrt{7}}$ c. $\dfrac{6}{\sqrt{2}}$

d. $\dfrac{14}{\sqrt{7}}$ e. $\dfrac{5\sqrt{2}}{4\sqrt{5}}$ f. $\dfrac{4\sqrt{3}}{\sqrt{5}}$

g. $\dfrac{5\sqrt{18}}{3\sqrt{10}}$ h. $\dfrac{6\sqrt{24}}{2\sqrt{18}}$ i. $\dfrac{5\sqrt{12}}{2\sqrt{8}}$

4. Using two lines, divide a square into four congruent parts so that the parts are neither squares, rectangles, nor triangles.

5. The volume of a cylinder is $\sqrt{180}$ cm³. If the area of the base is $\sqrt{5}$ cm², then find the height correct to one decimal place.

6. The volume of a cube is $\dfrac{\sqrt{150}}{\sqrt{6}}$ m³. Find the length of one side and the area of the base as a radical and a decimal correct to one decimal place.

7. Suggest two ways to add the following fractions. Add them and leave your answer with a rational denominator.

a. $\dfrac{3}{\sqrt{2}} + \dfrac{2}{\sqrt{3}}$ b. $\dfrac{\sqrt{5}}{\sqrt{75}} + \dfrac{\sqrt{2}}{\sqrt{8}}$

8. Rationalize the denominator.

a. $\dfrac{\sqrt{3} + 2}{\sqrt{3}}$ b. $\dfrac{\sqrt{5} - \sqrt{2}}{\sqrt{2}}$ c. $\dfrac{5\sqrt{10} - \sqrt{50}}{\sqrt{5}}$

Using the Library

Write a short essay discussing why there were relatively few women mathematicians before the twentieth century.

3·9 Binomial Denominators

When the denominator of an expression is a binomial with a radical in it, a different process has to be used to rationalize the denominator. Section 3·7 introduced the multiplication of conjugates to produce a rational number.

> The conjugate of $\sqrt{a}+\sqrt{b}$ is $\sqrt{a}-\sqrt{b}$.

Example

Rationalize each denominator.

a.
$$\frac{4}{2-\sqrt{3}} = \frac{4}{2-\sqrt{3}} \times \frac{2+\sqrt{3}}{2+\sqrt{3}}$$

$$\frac{2+\sqrt{3}}{2+\sqrt{3}} = 1$$

$$= \frac{8+4\sqrt{3}}{4+2\sqrt{3}-2\sqrt{3}-\sqrt{9}}$$

$$= \frac{8+4\sqrt{3}}{4-3}$$

$$= 8+4\sqrt{3}$$

b.
$$\frac{2+4\sqrt{3}}{1-\sqrt{3}} = \frac{2+4\sqrt{3}}{1-\sqrt{3}} \times \frac{1+\sqrt{3}}{1+\sqrt{3}}$$

$$= \frac{2+2\sqrt{3}+4\sqrt{3}+4\sqrt{9}}{1+\sqrt{3}-\sqrt{3}-\sqrt{9}}$$

$$= \frac{2+6\sqrt{3}+12}{1-3}$$

$$= \frac{14+6\sqrt{3}}{-2}$$

Factor and reduce.

$$= -7-3\sqrt{3}$$

Exercises

1. Mentally find the product. The first one is done for you.

$$(2-\sqrt{5})(2+\sqrt{5}) = 4-5$$
$$= -1$$

a. $(1+\sqrt{3})(1-\sqrt{3})$ **b.** $(4-\sqrt{3})(4+\sqrt{3})$
c. $(7-3\sqrt{2})(7+3\sqrt{2})$ **d.** $(3\sqrt{5}-8)(3\sqrt{5}+8)$

2. Rationalize the denominator.

a. $\dfrac{1}{1+\sqrt{2}}$ **b.** $\dfrac{-4}{3-\sqrt{2}}$ **c.** $\dfrac{5}{2+\sqrt{3}}$

d. $\dfrac{-6}{\sqrt{3}+1}$ **e.** $\dfrac{15}{\sqrt{7}+3}$ **f.** $\dfrac{-2}{\sqrt{5}-1}$

3. Rationalize the denominator.

a. $\dfrac{2\sqrt{3}}{5-3\sqrt{3}}$ **b.** $\dfrac{5\sqrt{2}}{3\sqrt{2}+4}$ **c.** $\dfrac{5\sqrt{7}}{5-\sqrt{11}}$

d. $\dfrac{4\sqrt{5}}{2\sqrt{5}+3}$ **e.** $\dfrac{4\sqrt{3}}{2\sqrt{3}+\sqrt{5}}$ **f.** $\dfrac{4\sqrt{2}}{\sqrt{2}-4\sqrt{5}}$

4. Rationalize the denominator.

$$\frac{7}{\sqrt{24}-\sqrt{18}}$$

Suggest a method for rationalizing the denominator that could be easier than multiplying by the conjugate.

5. Using your method from Exercise 4, rationalize the denominator.

a. $\dfrac{2}{\sqrt{8}-\sqrt{12}}$ **b.** $\dfrac{\sqrt{3}}{\sqrt{50}+\sqrt{75}}$

6. Obtain equivalent expressions by rationalizing the denominator. Reduce the resultant fraction where possible.

a. $\dfrac{2+\sqrt{3}}{1-\sqrt{3}}$ **b.** $\dfrac{5-\sqrt{5}}{3-2\sqrt{5}}$ **c.** $\dfrac{7\sqrt{2}-1}{3\sqrt{2}+1}$

7. Rationalize each denominator. Assume that all letters represent positive numbers and all denominators are not equal to zero.

a. $\dfrac{5a}{\sqrt{a}}$ **b.** $\dfrac{-3}{6-2\sqrt{b}}$ **c.** $\dfrac{\sqrt{x}}{1-2\sqrt{x}}$

3·10 Rational Number Exponents

Exponents that are rational numbers have a special meaning that is consistent with our understanding of irrational numbers.

Using the laws of exponents:

$(3^{\frac{1}{2}})(3^{\frac{1}{2}}) = 3^{\frac{1}{2} + \frac{1}{2}}$
$\qquad\qquad = 3^1$

$\{(x^m)(x^n) = x^{m+n}\}$

Therefore, $3^{\frac{1}{2}}$ must be the same as $\sqrt{3}$.

$(2^{\frac{2}{3}})(2^{\frac{2}{3}})(2^{\frac{2}{3}}) = 2^{\frac{2}{3} + \frac{2}{3} + \frac{2}{3}}$
$\qquad\qquad\qquad = 2^2$
$\qquad\qquad\qquad = 4$

Therefore $2^{\frac{2}{3}}$ is the same as $\sqrt[3]{4}$ or $\sqrt[3]{2^2}$.

Using radicals:

$(\sqrt{3})(\sqrt{3}) = \sqrt{(3)(3)}$
$\qquad\qquad = 3$

$(\sqrt[3]{4})(\sqrt[3]{4})(\sqrt[3]{4}) = \sqrt[3]{(4)(4)(4)}$
$\qquad\qquad\qquad = \sqrt[3]{64}$
$\qquad\qquad\qquad = 4$

$$x^{\frac{a}{b}} = \sqrt[b]{x^a} = (\sqrt[b]{x})^a, \text{ where } x \geq 0 \text{ if } b \text{ is even, } b \neq 0, \text{ and } a \text{ and } b \text{ are integers.}$$

It is often easier to evaluate $(\sqrt[b]{x})^a$ than $\sqrt[b]{x^a}$.

Example 1

Evaluate. $4^{\frac{5}{2}}$

$4^{\frac{5}{2}} = (\sqrt{4})^5 \quad$ or $\quad \sqrt{4^5} = \sqrt{1024}$
$\quad\; = 2^5 \qquad\qquad\qquad\quad = 32$
$\quad\; = 32$

Example 2

Write each as a radical and evaluate.

a. $(-27)^{\frac{2}{3}}$

$(-27)^{\frac{2}{3}} = (\sqrt[3]{-27})^2$
$\qquad\quad = 9$

b. $125^{-\frac{2}{3}}$

$125^{-\frac{2}{3}} = \dfrac{1}{125^{\frac{2}{3}}}$

$\qquad\quad = \dfrac{1}{(\sqrt[3]{125})^2}$

$\qquad\quad = \dfrac{1}{25}$

Generally, $9^{\frac{1}{2}}$ is referred to as the principal root of 9. All the laws of exponents that are true for integer exponents are also true for rational exponents.

Example 3

Evaluate. Round to one decimal place.

a. $(\sqrt[3]{45})^2$ b. $(45)^{\frac{1}{2}}$

a. 45 $\boxed{\text{INV}}$ $\boxed{y^x}$ 3 $\boxed{=}$ $\boxed{y^x}$ 2 $\boxed{=}$ $\text{12.65149} \doteq 12.7$

b. 45 $\boxed{\sqrt{}}$ $\boxed{y^x}$ 3 $\boxed{=}$ $\text{5.4870524} \doteq 5.5$

Example 4

Simplify. $\left(\dfrac{x^{\frac{1}{3}}}{y^{\frac{2}{3}}}\right)^3$

$\left(\dfrac{x^{\frac{1}{3}}}{y^{\frac{2}{3}}}\right)^3 = \dfrac{x^1}{y^2}$

Exercises

1. Express each as a radical in two ways. Assume that all variables are positive numbers.

a. $2^{\frac{1}{3}}$ **b.** $5^{\frac{2}{3}}$ **c.** $4^{\frac{1}{2}}$

d. $6^{-\frac{3}{4}}$ **e.** $8^{\frac{4}{7}}$ **f.** $4^{-\frac{5}{2}}$

g. $x^{\frac{3}{5}}$ **h.** $a^{-\frac{4}{3}}$ **i.** $y^{\frac{3}{8}}$

2. Express each with a positive exponent. Assume that all variables are positive numbers.

a. $\sqrt{14}$ **b.** $\sqrt{4^3}$ **c.** $\sqrt{6^5}$

d. $\sqrt[3]{7}$ **e.** $\sqrt[5]{2}$ **f.** $\sqrt[4]{3}$

g. $\sqrt[5]{x^2}$ **h.** $\sqrt[3]{c^7}$ **i.** $\sqrt[5]{q^3}$

3. Write each as a radical. Evaluate where possible.

a. $16^{\frac{1}{2}}$ **b.** $81^{\frac{1}{2}}$ **c.** $49^{\frac{1}{2}}$

d. $64^{-\frac{1}{2}}$ **e.** $49^{-\frac{1}{2}}$ **f.** $27^{\frac{1}{3}}$

g. $(-8)^{\frac{1}{3}}$ **h.** $16^{\frac{1}{4}}$ **i.** $32^{\frac{1}{5}}$

j. $(-125)^{\frac{1}{3}}$ **k.** $(-27)^{\frac{1}{3}}$ **l.** $243^{\frac{1}{5}}$

4. Evaluate.

a. $64^{\frac{2}{3}}$ **b.** $16^{\frac{3}{4}}$ **c.** $81^{\frac{3}{4}}$

d. $4^{\frac{5}{2}}$ **e.** $(-8)^{\frac{2}{3}}$ **f.** $(-27)^{\frac{4}{3}}$

g. $125^{\frac{2}{3}}$ **h.** $16^{\frac{5}{2}}$ **i.** $64^{\frac{5}{6}}$

5. Evaluate.

a. $16^{-\frac{3}{4}}$ **b.** $8^{-\frac{2}{3}}$ **c.** $81^{-\frac{1}{2}}$

d. $9^{-\frac{1}{2}}$ **e.** $100^{-\frac{1}{2}}$ **f.** $36^{-\frac{1}{2}}$

g. $64^{-\frac{5}{6}}$ **h.** $(-125)^{-\frac{2}{3}}$ **i.** $(-32)^{-\frac{3}{5}}$

j. $144^{-\frac{1}{2}}$ **k.** $(-27)^{-\frac{4}{3}}$ **l.** $(-343)^{-\frac{1}{3}}$

6. 27 raised to what exponent is $\frac{1}{9}$?

7. 256 raised to what exponent is $\frac{1}{64}$?

8. Evaluate.

a. $\left(\frac{1}{4}\right)^{-\frac{3}{2}}$ **b.** $\left(\frac{1}{27}\right)^{\frac{2}{3}}$ **c.** $\left(\frac{1}{81}\right)^{-\frac{3}{4}}$

d. $\left(\frac{9}{16}\right)^{-\frac{1}{2}}$ **e.** $\left(\frac{27}{8}\right)^{-\frac{2}{3}}$ **f.** $\left(\frac{100}{16}\right)^{\frac{1}{2}}$

g. $\left(\frac{243}{32}\right)^{-\frac{3}{5}}$ **h.** $\left(\frac{81}{16}\right)^{-\frac{1}{4}}$ **i.** $\left(\frac{-125}{8}\right)^{\frac{4}{3}}$

9. Evaluate. Round to one decimal place.

a. $30^{\frac{2}{3}}$ **b.** $90^{\frac{4}{3}}$ **c.** $156^{\frac{3}{4}}$

10. Evaluate.

a. $8^{\frac{1}{3}} - 16^0 + 4^2 - \left(\frac{1}{16}\right)^{-\frac{1}{4}} + (-3)^3$

b. $9^{\frac{1}{2}} + 16^{\frac{3}{4}} - \left(\frac{16}{81}\right)^{-\frac{1}{2}} + [(27)^2]^0 - \left(\frac{49}{16}\right)^{\frac{1}{2}}$

c. $4^{-\frac{1}{2}} - \left(\frac{8}{27}\right)^{-\frac{1}{3}} + 140^0 - [(-2)^3]^2 + \left(\frac{125}{8}\right)^{\frac{2}{3}}$

d. $\left(\frac{25}{16}\right)^{\frac{1}{2}} - 2^{-2} + \left(\frac{9}{4}\right)^{-\frac{1}{2}} - \left(\frac{1}{2}\right)^{-3} + (-3)^3$

11. Simplify by leaving your answer with only positive exponents. Assume all bases are positive numbers.

a. $(x^{\frac{2}{3}})(x^{\frac{5}{6}})$ **b.** $(p^0)^{\frac{2}{3}}$

c. $(r^{\frac{1}{5}})(r^{\frac{1}{4}})$ **d.** $(a^3b^4c)^{\frac{1}{2}}$

e. $(k)(k^{\frac{1}{4}})(k^{\frac{1}{2}})$ **f.** $(x^{\frac{1}{2}}y^{\frac{1}{4}})^{-4}$

g. $\dfrac{b^{\frac{1}{6}}}{b^{-\frac{1}{3}}}$ **h.** $\dfrac{(y^{-\frac{2}{3}})(y^{\frac{3}{4}})}{y^{\frac{1}{2}}}$

i. $(a^{\frac{1}{3}})(a^{\frac{2}{3}})$ **j.** $(k^4m^6n^2)^{\frac{3}{4}}$

k. $\dfrac{(r^4s^2)^{\frac{3}{2}}}{r^5s^5}$ **l.** $\dfrac{(c^{\frac{1}{3}})(c^{\frac{2}{5}})}{c^{\frac{2}{3}}}$

m. $\dfrac{(k^4m^6)^{-\frac{1}{2}}}{(k^{\frac{1}{2}}m^{-2})}$ **n.** $\dfrac{(a^2bc^3)^{\frac{1}{3}}}{(a^{-1}b^{-2}c)^{-\frac{1}{3}}}$

o. $(a^{\frac{1}{2}}b^{\frac{3}{4}})^{12}$ **p.** $(a^{\frac{1}{2}})(a^{\frac{3}{8}})(a^{-\frac{1}{4}})$

q. $\left(\dfrac{(c)(c^{\frac{3}{4}})}{(c^{\frac{1}{4}})(c^0)}\right)^2$ **r.** $\left[\left(\dfrac{rs^{\frac{1}{2}}}{t}\right)^{\frac{3}{2}}\right]^4$

s. $\left(\dfrac{(ab^{\frac{1}{2}})^{\frac{1}{2}}}{c}\right)^4$ **t.** $\dfrac{(63x^4)^{\frac{5}{2}}}{(28y^6)^{\frac{3}{2}}}$

12. Consider the following.
a. How many different ways can 1 marble be placed in 2 marble bags?
b. In how many different ways can 2 marbles be placed in 2 marble bags? (Each bag may hold 0, 1, or 2 marbles.)
c. Illustrate the various ways that 4 marbles can be placed in 2 marble bags.
d. In how many different ways can 10 marbles be placed in 2 marble bags?
e. In how many different ways can n marbles be placed in 2 marble bags?

3·11 Radical Equations

The solutions to equations containing radicals sometimes do not satisfy the original equation. Such a root is called an **extraneous root**.

Example

Solve.

a. $\sqrt{x+6} = 4$

$\sqrt{x+6} = 4$ Square both sides.
$x + 6 = 16$
$x = 10$

Check:

L.S.	R.S.
$\sqrt{10+6}$	4
$\sqrt{16}$	
4	

It checks, so the solution is $\{10\}$.

b. $\sqrt{x+2} = x$

$\sqrt{x+2} = x$ Square both sides.
$x + 2 = x^2$
$0 = x^2 - x - 2$
$0 = (x-2)(x+1)$
$x - 2 = 0$ or $x + 1 = 0$
$x = 2$ or -1

The solution is $\{2\}$. Why is -1 not a possible solution?

Exercises

1. Solve and check your solution. The first one is partially done for you.

a. $\sqrt{x} = 2$
$(\sqrt{x})^{\blacksquare} = (2)^{\blacksquare}$
$x = \blacksquare$
Solution is $\{\blacksquare\}$.

b. $\sqrt{x} = 5$

c. $\sqrt{p} = -4$

d. $-\sqrt{r} = 7$

e. $-\sqrt{n} = -3$

2. Solve. Check your solution. The first one is partially done for you.

a. $\sqrt{2x-3} = 5$
$(\sqrt{2x-3})^{\blacksquare} = \blacksquare^2$
$\blacksquare = 25$
$2x = 28$
Solution is $\{\blacksquare\}$.

b. $\sqrt{2y} = 2$

c. $\sqrt{x-1} = 2$

d. $\sqrt{3x+1} = 7$

e. $\sqrt{9a+1} - 8 = 0$

3. Find the solution set.

a. $\sqrt{2m+5} = 4$ **b.** $5\sqrt{3} = \sqrt{w}$

c. $\sqrt{4x-3} = \sqrt{3x+4}$ **d.** $3\sqrt{5} = \sqrt{2x+15}$

4. Explain why -1 cannot be a solution to part **b** of the example in the display.

5. Find the solution set.

a. $\sqrt{\dfrac{n-3}{2}} = 2\sqrt{2}$ **b.** $\sqrt{\dfrac{3x-5}{2}} = \sqrt{x+1}$

c. $\sqrt{\dfrac{4b}{3}} - 2 = 0$ **d.** $\sqrt{\dfrac{9x}{2}} - 6 = 0$

e. $\dfrac{\sqrt{4x-7}}{5} = \dfrac{\sqrt{5x+9}}{7}$

6. Solve. Identify the extraneous roots. What does "extraneous" mean?

a. $\sqrt{5x-6} = x$ **b.** $x = \sqrt{-3x-2}$

c. $x = \sqrt{5-4x}$ **d.** $\sqrt{6x-8} = x$

e. $2x = \sqrt{4x+3}$ **f.** $\sqrt{9x-2} = 3x$

g. $x = \sqrt{\dfrac{9x-5}{4}}$ **h.** $x = \sqrt{\dfrac{x+4}{3}}$

Braintickler

The letters below represent a sequence. Can you find the pattern or what they represent?

O, T, T, F, F, S, S, E, ...

3·12 Applications

The Pythagorean Relation, $c^2 = a^2 + b^2$, can be used to solve problems.

Example

Two cities, York and Villa, are connected by a straight road that is 10 km long and by a railroad track. To get to York from Villa by train, one must travel through Deer City which is 5 km east and 5 km north of York. How much farther is it to travel from York to Villa by train than by car?

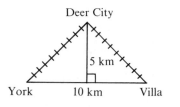

$$c^2 = a^2 + b^2$$
$$c^2 = 5^2 + 5^2$$
$$c = 5\sqrt{2}$$

The distance from York to Villa by train is ▬▬▬.

Exercises

1. Answer the following from the example in the display.
a. Identify the sides corresponding to a, b, and c in the diagram.
b. What is the distance from York to Deer City? from Deer City to Villa?
c. What is the distance from York to Villa by train? Round your answer to the nearest kilometre.
d. Answer the question from the example.

2. If the train travels twice as fast as the car, then which gets to York from Villa faster? Explain.

3. Find the value of the unknown side. Express your answer as a radical and as a decimal correct to one decimal place.

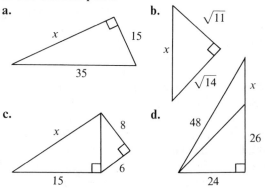

4. An empty lot measures 40 m by 50 m. How much shorter is it walking diagonally across the lot rather than walking the length and the width? Use a calculator to approximate your answer correct to one decimal place.

5. A circle is inscribed in a square.
a. Draw a diagram to show this.
b. Find the ratio of the areas.

6. The rectangular prism has sides of 3 cm, 4 cm, and 12 cm. Find the length of these diagonals.
a. $\overline{AC}$ **b.** $\overline{CF}$ **c.** $\overline{CE}$

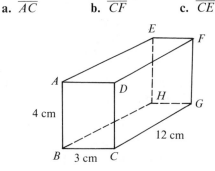

7. Find a real number which added to $\sqrt{15}$ gives $\sqrt{3}$.

8. What number multiplied by $2\sqrt{5} - 1$ equals -7?

3·13 Computer Application — Interest

Elizabeth wanted to invest the $1000 she had saved from her summer job. She decided to write a program to compare the amounts invested at simple interest or compound interest.

Elizabeth's Plan

Clear the screen and the memory.
State the purpose of the program.

Have the computer read the appropriate data.
Calculate the simple interest earned.
Calculate the total amount of the investment.
Input the data required.
Have the computer read the data for compound interest.
Calculate the interest earned.

Input the data required.
Print both results for comparison.

Elizabeth's Program

```
NEW:HOME
10 REM A PROGRAM TO COMPARE
INTEREST RATES
20 READ P, R, T
30 LET I = P * R * T
40 LET AS = P + I
50 DATA 1000, 0.1225, 5
55 REM COMPOUND INTEREST
60 READ P, R, N, T
70 LET AC = P * (1 + R / N) ^
(N * T)
80 DATA 1000, 0.1225, 4, 5
90 PRINT "SIMPLE INTEREST
GIVES "; AS
100 PRINT "COMPOUND
INTEREST GIVES "; AC
110 PRINT "DIFFERENCE IS ";
AC - AS
120 END
```

Exercises

1. What is the function of these lines?
a. line 20   **b.** line 60

2. What would be the order of operations if N * T in line 70 was not in brackets?

3. Predict what the difference in the interest will be when the program is RUN. Run the program to find the output. Was your prediction reasonable?

4. Predict what the output will be if lines 50 and 55 are interchanged. Run the program to check your prediction. Was your prediction reasonable?

5. What is the purpose of the semicolon in lines 90 and 100?

6. Modify the program from the display to compare the following.
a. the interest earned on $15 750
b. the interest earned at a rate of 11.5%

7. Modify the program in the display to compare the interest earned on $1000 compounded semi-annually and quarterly for 25 a.

8. Marvin Minsky, a leading computer expert, has been quoted as saying that "evolution leads to greater intelligence and there is nothing special about the human brain because it is basically a computer made out of muscle." This statement could lead to the belief that computers will evolve like the human brain. Is it possible to invent a computer that is capable of independent thought?

3·14 Chapter Review

1. Perform the indicated operations. Write the answer with positive exponents only.

a. $(4^5)(4^7)$ **b.** $(r^3)(r^7)(r^{10})$

c. $(3x^2)(2x^3)(5x^5)$ **d.** $(m^x)(m^y)(m^{x-y})$

e. $\dfrac{5^7}{5^8}$ **f.** $\dfrac{4x^7}{2x^5}$

g. $(2x^4y^6)^3$ **h.** $\dfrac{(6p^4q^2)^2}{(3p^2q^4)^3}$

2. Perform the indicated operations. Write the answer with positive exponents only.

a. $(m^{-2})(m^{-3})$ **b.** $(14a^2b^3)(7a^{-2}b^{-4})$

c. $\left(\dfrac{x^2}{y^{-3}}\right)^{-2}$ **d.** $\dfrac{2(abc)^{-4}}{(a^2b^3c)^{-3}}$

3. Evaluate.

a. 3^{-3} **b.** $-\left(\dfrac{3}{4}\right)^2$

c. $81^{\frac{3}{4}}$ **d.** $(0.004)^{-2}$

4. Evaluate. Where necessary, round to two decimal places.

a. $\sqrt{121}$ **b.** $\sqrt[3]{343}$ **c.** $\sqrt[4]{1296}$

d. $\sqrt{449}$ **e.** $\sqrt[3]{478}$ **f.** $\sqrt{812}$

g. $(\sqrt[3]{456})^2$ **h.** $178^{\frac{1}{2}}$ **i.** $89^{\frac{2}{3}}$

5. Evaluate if $a = -2$ and $b = 3$.

a. a^2b **b.** $a^{-2} + b$

c. $(a + b)^3$ **d.** $\sqrt{(-a)^2b^3}$

6. Write in scientific notation. Always leave the answer with a denominator of one.

a. 56 000   **b.** 0.003

c. 720 000 000   **d.** 56×10^{-3}

e. 0.04×10^{-5} **f.** $(8 \times 10^4)(4 \times 10^{-5})$

g. $\dfrac{1.2 \times 10^8}{6 \times 10^{-4}}$ **h.** $\dfrac{0.003 \times 96\,000}{160}$

7. Express in standard form.

a. 4.7×10^5 **b.** 5.3×10^{-2}

8. Express as mixed radicals.

a. $\sqrt{40}$ **b.** $\sqrt{162x^2}$

c. $\sqrt{1250}$ **d.** $\sqrt[3]{56x^4}$

9. Add or subtract. Reduce the radical first where necessary.

a. $5\sqrt{7} - \sqrt{7}$ **b.** $3\sqrt{2} + 15\sqrt{2}$

c. $\sqrt{27} + \sqrt{48}$ **d.** $\sqrt{500} - \sqrt{245}$

e. $3\sqrt{6} + 2\sqrt{5} - (4\sqrt{6} - \sqrt{5})$

f. $2\sqrt{28} - 2\sqrt{108} + \sqrt{175} - \sqrt{147}$

g. $2b\sqrt{a^3b} + a\sqrt{ab^3} - 4\sqrt{a^3b^3}$

10. Multiply.

a. $(\sqrt{3})(\sqrt{11})$ **b.** $(\sqrt{6})(\sqrt{18})$

c. $(3\sqrt{2})(-5\sqrt{6})$ **d.** $(-4\sqrt{3})(-5\sqrt{2})$

e. $3\sqrt{2}(\sqrt{2} + \sqrt{6})$ **f.** $5\sqrt{7}(2\sqrt{3} + 5\sqrt{2})$

g. $(5 + \sqrt{3})(2 - \sqrt{3})$ **h.** $(4\sqrt{2} - 3)(5\sqrt{3} - 2)$

i. $(\sqrt{6} - \sqrt{2} + \sqrt{3})^2$ **j.** $(3\sqrt{5} - 2)^2$

k. $(2\sqrt{a} + \sqrt{b})(3\sqrt{a} - \sqrt{b})$ $(a \geq 0, b \geq 0)$

11. The radius of a circle is $(4\sqrt{3} - \sqrt{3})$ cm. Calculate the area both as a radical and as a decimal correct to two decimal places. (*Hint:* Use $\pi = 3.14$.)

12. Rationalize the denominator.

a. $\dfrac{\sqrt{18}}{\sqrt{2}}$ **b.** $\dfrac{\sqrt{45}}{\sqrt{3}}$ **c.** $\dfrac{9\sqrt{12}}{3\sqrt{2}}$

d. $\dfrac{28\sqrt{50}}{7\sqrt{10}}$ **e.** $\dfrac{\sqrt{7}}{\sqrt{2}}$ **f.** $\dfrac{2\sqrt{14}}{3\sqrt{3}}$

g. $\dfrac{5\sqrt{3} + 2}{\sqrt{6}}$ **h.** $\dfrac{1 + \sqrt{3}}{1 - \sqrt{3}}$ **i.** $\dfrac{5 - \sqrt{7}}{2\sqrt{7} - 1}$

13. Express as a radical. Evaluate if possible.

a. $5^{\frac{2}{3}}$ **b.** $13^{\frac{3}{5}}$ **c.** $27^{\frac{1}{4}}$

d. $169^{\frac{3}{2}}$ **e.** $9^{-\frac{1}{2}}$ **f.** $49^{-\frac{1}{2}}$

14. Simplify. Leave the answer with positive exponents only. (Assume all bases are positive numbers.)

a. $(x^{\frac{1}{2}})(x^{\frac{1}{3}})(x^{\frac{5}{6}})$ **b.** $\dfrac{a^{\frac{1}{3}}}{a^{\frac{1}{12}}}$

c. $(b^{\frac{3}{4}})^{\frac{2}{3}}$ **d.** $(p^{\frac{1}{5}})(p^{\frac{1}{10}})$

e. $(a^{\frac{1}{2}}b^{\frac{1}{3}})^6$ **f.** $(r^{-\frac{1}{4}}s^{-\frac{2}{3}})^{\frac{1}{2}}$

g. $\left(\dfrac{m^{\frac{1}{2}}n^{\frac{3}{2}}}{m^{-\frac{1}{4}}n^{\frac{1}{2}}}\right)^{-2}$ **h.** $x^{\frac{1}{2}}(x^{\frac{1}{2}} + x)$

3·15 Chapter Test

1. Perform the indicated operations. Write the answer with positive exponents.

a. $(5^3)(5^8)$ **b.** $(m^7)(m^3)(m^4)$

c. $(5y^3)(3y^2)(2y)$ **d.** $(t^x)(t^{2x+y})(t^{x-2y})$

e. $\dfrac{33y^7}{11y^2}$ **f.** $\dfrac{4r^{a-2b}}{2r^{a+2b}}$

g. $\dfrac{(x^2y^3)^2}{(xy^2)^3}$ **h.** $\left(\dfrac{6a^8b^6c^7}{2a^2b^4c^9}\right)^2$

2. Perform the indicated operations. Write the answer with positive exponents.

a. $\dfrac{3x^{-2}y^3}{x^4y^2}$ **b.** $\dfrac{(5x)^{-2}}{(3x)^{-3}}$

c. $(a^{-1}b^{-1})^{-m}$ **d.** $(a^2b^{-2}c^3)^{-2}$

3. Evaluate.

a. 5^{-2} **b.** $(0.02)^{-2}$

c. $\left(\dfrac{1}{5}\right)^2\left(\dfrac{1}{5}\right)^{-4}$ **d.** $49^{\frac{3}{2}}$

e. $\left(\dfrac{8}{27}\right)^{-\frac{2}{3}}$ **f.** $\left(\dfrac{4}{25}\right)^{\frac{3}{2}}$

4. Evaluate if $p = -3$ and $q = 2$.

a. $p^2 - q$ **b.** $p^{-2}q$

c. $(q - p)^2$ **d.** $3p^2 - q^3$

5. Evaluate. Round to one decimal place.

a. $\sqrt[3]{84}$ **b.** $(\sqrt{156})^3$ **c.** $164^{\frac{2}{3}}$

6. Write in scientific notation. Leave the answer with a denominator of one.

a. 0.000 072   **b.** 830 000

c. 17   **d.** 870×10^{-4}

e. 0.013×10^8 **f.** $(5 \times 10^{-6})(3 \times 10^{-2})$

g. $\dfrac{5.6 \times 10^{-8}}{4 \times 10^5}$ **h.** $\dfrac{0.000\ 006}{1200 \times 0.0001}$

7. Express in standard notation.

a. 9.31×10^{-5} **b.** 1.2×10^6

8. A living cell (a general rectangle in shape) has a length of about 3×10^{-4} cm and a width and thickness about half its length.

a. Calculate the volume of 10^6 cells.

b. How many cells fill 1 mm³?

9. Express as mixed radicals.

a. $\sqrt{56}$ **b.** $\sqrt{108a^3b^2}$

c. $\sqrt{288}$ **d.** $\sqrt[4]{32y^6}$

10. Perform the indicated operation. Reduce the radical to its lowest form.

a. $7\sqrt{6} + 15\sqrt{6}$ **b.** $7\sqrt{3} - 15\sqrt{3}$

c. $2\sqrt{99} + 5\sqrt{44}$ **d.** $\sqrt{96} - \sqrt{24}$

e. $(5\sqrt{3} + 2\sqrt{2}) + (7\sqrt{3} - 4\sqrt{2})$

f. $5\sqrt{32} - 3\sqrt{63} + \sqrt{112} - \sqrt{162}$

g. $5xy\sqrt{xy} - 2\sqrt{x^3y^3} + 3x\sqrt{xy^3}$

11. Multiply. Reduce the radical to its lowest form.

a. $(\sqrt{2})(\sqrt{7})$ **b.** $(\sqrt{5})(\sqrt{10})$

c. $(4\sqrt{5})(-2\sqrt{3})$ **d.** $(-7\sqrt{3})(-6\sqrt{6})$

e. $4\sqrt{3}(2\sqrt{3} - 1)$ **f.** $3\sqrt{2}(4\sqrt{5} - \sqrt{6})$

12. The radius of a cone is $(\sqrt{6} + 2)$ cm. The height is $\sqrt{5}$ cm. Calculate the volume of the cone both as a radical and as a decimal correct to two decimal places.

13. Rationalize the denominator.

a. $\dfrac{\sqrt{20}}{\sqrt{2}}$ **b.** $\dfrac{\sqrt{39}}{\sqrt{3}}$ **c.** $\dfrac{12\sqrt{70}}{6\sqrt{10}}$

d. $\dfrac{57\sqrt{40}}{19\sqrt{5}}$ **e.** $\dfrac{\sqrt{6}}{\sqrt{7}}$ **f.** $\dfrac{5\sqrt{11}}{2\sqrt{5}}$

g. $\dfrac{5 - 2\sqrt{6}}{\sqrt{3}}$ **h.** $\dfrac{2 - 5\sqrt{2}}{3 + \sqrt{2}}$

i. $\dfrac{4\sqrt{7} + 2\sqrt{2}}{2\sqrt{7} - 3\sqrt{2}}$ **j.** $\dfrac{\sqrt{ab} + 3}{5 - 2\sqrt{ab}}$ $(a, b \geq 0)$

14. Express as a radical. Evaluate if possible.

a. $7^{\frac{1}{2}}$ **b.** $12^{\frac{2}{3}}$ **c.** $81^{\frac{3}{4}}$

d. $243^{\frac{3}{5}}$ **e.** $4^{-\frac{5}{2}}$ **f.** $64^{-\frac{2}{3}}$

15. Solve.

a. $\sqrt{n + 12} = 18$ **b.** $2\sqrt{y} - 3 = 5$

c. $\dfrac{\sqrt{r - 12}}{5} = 1$ **d.** $4\sqrt{n - 3} = 3\sqrt{n + 4}$

e. $\sqrt{x^2 + 7} = \sqrt{19}$ **f.** $n = \sqrt{\dfrac{7n + 3}{6}}$

Cumulative Review Chapters 1–3

1. The Alpha finance department issued a cheque in the amount of $383 375 for the purchase of 15 335 microcomputer chips.
a. Write the amount of the cheque in words.
b. What is the cost of one chip?

2. Alpha quality control rejected 16 computers on Monday, 5 on Tuesday, 2 on Wednesday, 8 on Thursday, and 14 on Friday. What is the total value of the computers rejected during the week if the value of one computer is $500?

3. Which whole number is not preceded by a whole number?

4. Which natural number is not preceded by a natural number?

5. Write the set of natural numbers greater than 17 but less than 26.

6. From the set of all natural numbers, remove all elements less than eleven and all those greater than seventeen.
a. Write the set of numbers that you have left.
b. How many prime numbers are in this set?

7. Seven friends exercise at the same health club. All are working out at the club today. However, all do not exercise in this club every day.
The first person exercises there every day.
The second person exercises there every other day.
The third person exercises there every three days.
The fourth person exercises there every four days.
The fifth person exercises there every five days.
The sixth person exercises there every six days.
The seventh person exercises there every seven days.
How many days from today will all appear in the health club on the same day?

8. Calculate.
a. $6 \times 6 \times 6$ **b.** 61×54
c. $2377 \times 63 \times 91 \times 0 \times 2$ **d.** $9119 \div 11$

9. Calculate.
a. $1 + 3 + 5 + 7 + \ldots + 21$
b. $2 + 4 + 6 + 8 + \ldots + 32$

10. Evaluate.
a. $-16 + (-21)$ **b.** $-4 - 3$
c. $-8 - 5 - 2$ **d.** $-36 - (-12)$
e. $-62 + (-9) - 27$ **f.** $-9 + 17 - (-24)$

11. Evaluate.
a. -16×5 **b.** $-21 \times -3 \times -2$
c. $-4690 \div 35$ **d.** $-1 \times -1 \times -1 \times -1 \times -1$

12. Given $x + (\blacksquare) = y$ for all pairs of natural numbers x and y. State a relation between x and y.

13. A submarine descended to 1100 m in 11 min.
a. Find an integer which best represents the depth of the submarine.
b. Find an integer which best represents the depth at the surface.
c. Find the rate of change in depth during the descent.

14. Lagrange's Theorem states that every natural number can be expressed as the sum of four or less perfect squares. For example,
$26 = 1 + 9 + 16 = 1 + 25$.
Express each of the following as the sum of four or fewer perfect squares.
a. 56   **b.** 110   **c.** 93   **d.** 145

15. The seven partners in a company equally shared a loss of $14 000 in their business.
a. Find an integer which best represents a loss of $14 000.
b. What operation would be used to find each partner's share of the loss?
c. Find each partner's share of the loss.

16. Copy and complete.
a. The product of two negative numbers is a ▬▬▬ number.
b. The quotient of a negative and a positive number is a ▬▬▬ number.

17. The formula $a = \dfrac{v-u}{t}$ describes the acceleration, a, of an object given the initial velocity, u, the final velocity, v, and the time, t, in seconds. Find the acceleration for each situation.

a. $v = 10$ m/s   b. $v = 0$ m/s
    $u = 20$ m/s $u = 300$ m/s
    $t = 30$ s $t = 30$ s
c. $v = 16$ m/s   d. $v = 5$ m/s
    $u = 5$ m/s $u = 0.3$ m/s
    $t = 11$ s $t = 8$ s

18. Calculate.

a. $\left(\dfrac{4}{3}\right)\left(\dfrac{3}{5}\right)$ b. $\left(\dfrac{-6}{7}\right)\left(\dfrac{49}{3}\right)$ c. $\left(-5\dfrac{1}{4}\right)(20)$

19. Write the reciprocal of each.

a. -7 b. $\dfrac{6}{7}$ c. $3\dfrac{1}{5}$

20. Evaluate each if $a = -4$, $b = -2$, $c = 0$, and $d = 5$.

a. $\dfrac{a+c}{b}$ b. $\dfrac{a+b-c+d}{a+b+c-d}$ c. $a^2 + b^2 - d^2$

21. Evaluate. Remember the order of operations.
a. $16 - [(3 \times 2) \div 6]$
b. $12 - 3 \times 4$
c. $6 \times 9 + 10 \div 2 \div 5$

22. Perform the indicated operations.

a. $\left(\dfrac{1}{3}\right)^2 - \left(\dfrac{1}{4}\right)$ b. $2\dfrac{5}{8} - 1\dfrac{1}{2}$ c. $2\dfrac{5}{8} + \left(-3\dfrac{1}{4}\right)$

23. Perform the indicated operations.

a. $2\dfrac{1}{2} \div \left(-2\dfrac{3}{4}\right)$ b. $3\dfrac{1}{5} \times 1\dfrac{2}{3}$

24. Express each as a decimal.

a. $\dfrac{3}{5}$ b. $\dfrac{7}{9}$ c. $\dfrac{67}{99}$ d. $\dfrac{2}{3}$

e. $\dfrac{8}{99}$ f. $\dfrac{450}{99}$ g. $\dfrac{111}{44}$ h. $\dfrac{235}{99}$

25. Evaluate if $x = \dfrac{1}{2}$ and $y = \dfrac{3}{4}$.

a. $\dfrac{x+y}{x}$ b. $\dfrac{x}{x+y}$

26. A Canadian, Cynthia Nichols, holds the swimming record for the fastest double crossing of the English Channel. She completed the round trip of 68 km in 19 h 12 min. Find her average speed.

27. Baseball pitchers can be ranked by the number of games won compared to the number of games pitched. Calculate, correct to three decimal places, each player's lifetime winning average.

Pitcher	Wins	Games
Cy Young	511	826
Walter Johnson	416	695
Grover Alexander	373	581
Christy Mathewson	373	561
James Galvin	365	674
Lefty Grove	300	441

28. The Gold and Silver point totals for gold and silver medal winners in the last four Olympic Games for the decathalon are shown in the table.

Gold	Silver
8193	8111
8454	8035
8618	8411
8495	8331

Rank the Gold/Silver ratios from least to greatest.

29. Convert each decimal to a fraction.

a. $0.3\overline{1}$ b. $0.0\overline{23}$ c. $0.012\overline{5}$

30. Convert $\dfrac{135}{100}$ to a percent.

31. Convert 736% to a decimal.

32. If the marked price on an item is $82.50, and the rate of discount is 25%, then find each.
a. the discount
b. the selling price

Cumulative Review Chapters 1-3

33. The batting averages for baseball teams are found using the ratio of the number of hits, H, to the number of times at bat, AB. Rank the following team batting averages from greatest to least.

Team	AB	H
Baltimore	5456	1374
Boston	5648	1594
Texas	5569	1452
Kansas City	5543	1487
Chicago	5513	1360
Toronto	5687	1555
New York	5661	1560
Minnesota	5562	1473
Detroit	5644	1529
California	5470	1363
Seattle	5546	1429
Oakland	5457	1415
Cleveland	5643	1498
Milwaukee	5511	1446

34. If the discount on an item is $80 on a marked price of $320, then find each.
a. the rate of discount
b. the selling price

35. If the discount on an item is $85 given a 16% rate of discount, then find each.
a. the marked price
b. the selling price

36. If the cost price of an item is $18 and the selling price is $27, then find each.
a. the profit
b. the rate of profit

37. A worker earns $10.25/h. She received a $0.50/h raise in pay. Find the percent increase in her hourly wage.

38. A suit which regularly sells for $250 is put on sale at a 20% discount. Find the sale price of the suit.

39. Calculate the amount of simple interest earned when $4000 is invested at an interest rate of 8% for 2 a.

40. Find the interest earned on $5000 invested at 8% compounded semiannually for 2 a.

41. Find the amount that will accumulate in an account at the end of 3 a if $1000 is deposited at 11% interest compounded semiannually.

42. Find the final amount of $6000 invested at 8% compounded quarterly for 2 a.

43. Find the single discount equivalent to a 40% and a 20% chain discount.

44. Name the property of rational numbers illustrated.
a. $-16 + 0 = -16$
b. $\frac{7}{5} \times \frac{5}{7} = 1$
c. $6 \times 2 = 2 \times 6$

45. Solve and check. $m \in Q$
a. $5m = 45$
b. $2m + 4 = -6$
c. $2m - 1 = m + 5$
d. $\frac{2m + 5}{2} = \frac{4m + 8}{4}$
e. $5(m - 4) = 3m + 12$
f. $2(m - 3) + 10 = 3m - 2(4m - 9)$
g. $\frac{m}{5} + \frac{m}{3} = 8$

46. How much oil must be added to 30 L of gasoline to make a mixture that is 1.5% oil?

47. Isolate the variable a in each.
a. $a - b = c$
b. $3a = d$
c. $5(a - 2) = x$
d. $\frac{a - t}{a} = 2t$

Cumulative Review Chapters 1–3

48. Solve for the indicated variable.
a. $A = \pi r^2$; r **b.** $pmr = 1$; m
c. $V = \frac{4}{3}\pi r^3$; r **d.** $\frac{1}{f} - \frac{1}{v} = \frac{-1}{u}$; v

49. Three dependents were to share in a $680 000 estate in the ratio of 5:3:2. Find each dependent's share in the estate.

50. Wings Airline was advised by a market analyst that an economy sale would sell three times as many economy seats as the number of business-class seats plus 4500 more for each month of the sale. First-class seat sales would drop to half the number of business class.
a. Write an inequality showing this relationship for a two-month sale.
b. Wings ran the sale for two months and sold 1000 first-class seats. How many of each kind of seat were sold and what was the total number of seats sold?

51. Use the Pythagorean Relation to find the length of the third side of each right triangle.
a.   **b.**

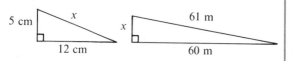

52. Simplify. Leave your answer in exponential form and with positive exponents.

a. $7^2 + 7^4$ **b.** $10^2 \div 10^2$ **c.** $\frac{4m^3n^2}{2m^2n^2}$

d. 4^{-2} **e.** $\left(-\frac{1}{3}\right)^{-2}$ **f.** $(x^2y^3c)^{-2}$

53. Evaluate each if $x = -3$ and $y = 3$.
a. $x^2 - y^2$ **b.** $\sqrt{(-x)^2 y^2}$

54. Express 57 000 000 in scientific notation.

55. Express 6.73×10^{-3} in standard form.

56. Express $\sqrt{48x^2y^3}$ as a mixed radical.

57. Simplify.
a. $4\sqrt{10} - 2\sqrt{10}$ **b.** $\sqrt{50} + \sqrt{162}$
c. $\sqrt{6} \times \sqrt{24}$ **d.** $-5\sqrt{3} \times -3\sqrt{2}$

58. Rationalize the denominator.
a. $\frac{\sqrt{5}}{\sqrt{3}}$ **b.** $\frac{1 + \sqrt{2}}{1 - \sqrt{2}}$

59. Solve.
a. $\sqrt{x - 4} = 2$ **b.** $\sqrt{\frac{x^2 - 9}{4}} = 2$

60. A tall mast displaying a warning sign at the centre of a circular sewage treatment pond was leaning precariously. The pond was exactly 50 m in diameter. A maintenance worker wanted to knot the end of a rope around the mast to straighten it. His rope was 51 m long and he had no boat. The worker was able to do the job without leaving the edge of the pond or getting wet. How was this done?

61. Find the missing number in this pattern.
4 6 2
6 8 6
5 ▮ 4

62. A couple agreed to meet for a date at 19:00. Unknown to each other, the boy's watch is 10 min slow and the girl's watch is 10 min fast. If the boy arrives for the date 10 min late by his watch, and the girl arrives 10 min early by her watch, then how many minutes will the girl have to wait for the boy?

63. The Skytrain route between X and Y has 16 trains in operation. How many trains pass while going from X to Y?

64. Al owes Bob $10, Bob owes Charles $8, Charles owes David $11, and David owes Al $3. Assuming all the debts are paid, what is the amount paid or received by each person?

CHAPTER FOUR

ALGEBRAIC EXPRESSIONS

Tune Up

1. Write each as a product of prime factors.
a. 32   **b.** 20   **c.** 5^3
d. $6x^2$ **e.** $2^2 3^3$ **f.** $-12a^2b^2$

2. Write each as a power with positive exponents.
a. $(5^3)(5^4)$ **b.** $6^4 \div 6$
c. $(2^2)(2^3)(2^5)$ **d.** $(3^2)^3 \div 3^4$

3. Name the like terms.
a. $5xy^2, 3xy, -2xy^2, 4xy^2$
b. $8p^2q, pq^3, 8pq, -pq^3$

4. Use the distributive property to expand.
a. $5(3x - 2)$ **b.** $-4(x + 7)$
c. $(2x - 5)(3)$ **d.** $3(2a - 5b + c)$

5. Find an expression for the perimeter of the quadrilateral. Evaluate it for $x = 3$ cm and $y = 4$ cm.

5x − 2y

2x + 3y

8x + 4y

10x − 6y

6. Perform the indicated operations and simplify by gathering like terms.
a. $8p - 3q + (2q - 5p)$
b. $(6a^2 - b) - (3a^2 + 4b)$
c. $5(2m + 4n) + 3(m - 2n)$

7. Evaluate each for $a = -3$, $b = 4$, and $c = 1$.
a. $4a - 3b + 2$
b. $a^2 + 2b^2 - 3ac$
c. $2(a - 3b) + 4(3a + b)$
d. $10(2a + b) - 8(5a - 4b)$

8. Multiply.
a. $(x - 3)(2x + 5)$ **b.** $(2x + 1)(2x + 1)$
c. $(5x - 2)(5x + 2)$ **d.** $(x - 3)(4y + 5)$

9. Divide.
a. $\dfrac{3a^2 - 12ab}{3a}$ **b.** $\dfrac{20p^2q + 36p^2q^2}{4pq}$

10. Factor completely.
a. $a^2 - b^2$ **b.** $x^2 - 11x - 12$
c. $36x^2 - 18xy$ **d.** $m^2 - 2m + 35$
e. $u^2 + 17uv + 16v^2$ **f.** $4p^2 - q^2$

4·1 Polynomials

A **term** is a number or letter standing alone or a combination of numbers and letters joined only by multiplication or division. An **algebraic expression** is comprised of one or more terms separated by addition or subtraction. The letters or **variables** represent unknown quantities.

These are examples of algebraic expressions.

$$15, \qquad -6x^2, \qquad 7x - 3\sqrt{5}, \qquad 12ab, \qquad \frac{a+b}{a-b}, \qquad x^2 - 6\sqrt{x}, \qquad 4x^2 - y^2 + \frac{x}{y}$$

The first expression consists only of a number called a **constant**. In the expression $12ab$, each individual term is the **coefficient** of the product of the other two individual terms. The number 12 is the **numerical coefficient** of ab; while a and b are the **literal coefficients**.

> A **polynomial** is an algebraic expression which contains one or more terms. The exponents of the variables in a polynomial are whole numbers.

Expressions with variables in the denominator, or variables with fractional exponents, are not polynomials.

Name	Number of Terms	Examples
*mono*mial	1	$6, \quad 5x, \quad -10x^3$
*bi*nomial	2	$2x - 9, \quad 3x^2 + 4y^2$
*tri*nomial	3	$a + 2b - c, \quad x^2 - 9x + 8$

Although there are specific names for polynomials with more than 3 terms, they are generally described as polynomials of four terms, five terms, six terms, etc.

Exercises

1. Copy and complete.
a. An expression containing 2 terms is called a ■■■■■.
b. The term $12x^2yz$ contains three ■■■■■.
c. In the polynomial $x^2 + 7$, the number 7 is referred to as a ■■■■■.

2. What is the numerical coefficient of x?
a. $23x$ 　　　　　 **b.** $-0.5x$
c. x 　　　　　　 **d.** $6\sqrt{2}x$
e. $24xy$ 　　　　 **f.** 4^3x
g. $\dfrac{5x}{3}$ 　　　　　 **h.** $\dfrac{3x+7}{2}$
i. $\dfrac{7-4x}{2}$ 　　　 **j.** $\dfrac{x^2+8x-3}{10}$

3. What is the coefficient of y?
a. $5xy$ 　　　　　 **b.** $-3x^2y$
c. xyz 　　　　　 **d.** $\dfrac{xy}{9}$

4. Which of the following are polynomials? For each polynomial, classify it according to the number of terms and write the constant term. For the others, tell why they are not polynomials.
a. $8x^3 - 6x + 3$ 　　　 **b.** $3x^2 + x$
c. $4\sqrt{x} - x$ 　　　　 **d.** 5
e. $15 - 3x + x^2$ 　　 **f.** $-6x^3$

> **Using the Library**
>
> A square is an example of an object in two dimensions. A cube is an example of a three-dimensional object. A cube is six two-dimensional squares connected at the vertices by line segments called **edges**. A **hypercube** is one representation of a four-dimensional object. It is two, three-dimensional cubes joined at the vertices. Using the library, find a picture of a hypercube, and give a brief explanation of why it is considered four-dimensional.

4·2 Evaluation of a Polynomial

An expression containing variables can be evaluated for specific values of the variables.

Paul's age can be represented by the expression $2x + 3$.
If $x = 6$, then he is $2(6) + 3$ or 15 a.

Example 1

Evaluate $6ab - 5bc$ for $a = 2$, $b = 3$, and $c = -6$.

$6ab - 5bc = 6(2)(3) - 5(3)(-6)$
$\qquad\qquad = 126$

Example 2

If $P(x) = 4x^2 - 5x + 3$, then find $P(2)$.

$P(2) = 4(2)^2 - 5(2) + 3$
$\qquad = 9$

> $P(2)$ means the value of $4x^2 - 5x + 3$ when $x = 2$.

Exercises

1. Evaluate each expression for $x = 3$.
a. $x - 6$ **b.** $2x + 8$
c. $3x - 4$ **d.** $12 - 5x$
e. $8(x + 1)$ **f.** $4x^2 - 16$
g. $-5x^2 + 2x - 4$ **h.** $x^4 - 8x^2 + 3x$

2. Evaluate each expression for $a = -2$, $b = 6$, and $c = 4$.
a. $a - 5bc$ **b.** $4a^2 - 3b^2$
c. $2ab + ac$ **d.** $a^2 - c^2 + 2bc$
e. $b^2 + a^3$ **f.** $c^4 - 8b + 5a^2$

3. If $P(x) = 3x^2 - 5x + 2$, then find the value of each.
a. $P(-3)$ **b.** $P(4)$
c. $P(0)$ **d.** $P(-2)$
e. $P(5)$ **f.** $P(2)$

4. The interest earned on an investment is given by the formula $I = prt$. If the principal, p, invested is $480, the rate, r, is 8.5%/a, and the time, t, is 3 a, then find the interest earned on this investment.

5. The area of a trapezoid is given by the formula $A = \frac{1}{2}(a + b)h$, where a and b are the lengths of the parallel sides and h is the perpendicular distance between them. Two parallel sides of a trapezoid are 8 cm and 14 cm in length, and they are 5 cm apart. What is the area of the trapezoid?

6. The distance, s, an object travels during free fall is given by the formula $s = 4.9t^2$. To the nearest tenth of a metre, find the distance an object will fall in 3.2 s.

7. The period, T, of a pendulum is given by the formula $T = 2\pi\sqrt{\frac{L}{9.8}}$, where L is the length of the pendulum in metres. Use a calculator to find the period of a pendulum whose length is 1.2 m.

8. A transit driver finds that on each stop, she either picks up 4 passengers or she picks up 2 people and lets off 3. If she begins her run with an empty bus, then what is the minimum number of stops she will make to have an empty bus again?

9. The sum of the angles, s, at the vertices of a polygon of n sides is given by the formula $s = 180(n - 2)$. What is the sum of the angles of a hexagon?

10. A number n is doubled, and then decreased by 4. Write the algebraic expression which represents this value. If the number is 8, then find the value of the expression.

11. Give a value of x such that the polynomial $x^2 - 4x + 4$ is a perfect square. a perfect cube.

12. What number, other than 1, is both a perfect square and a perfect cube?

4·3 Degree of a Polynomial

The **degree** of a polynomial in one variable is the highest power of any term contained in that polynomial. The degree of a constant term is zero.

First degree: $8x$, $5x - 12$, $\dfrac{3y}{5}$
Third degree: $5x^3$, $x^3 - 2x^2 + 8$

Second degree: $6x^2$, $9x^2 + 5x - 1$
Fourth degree: $-10x^4$, $5x^4 + 2x^3 + 1$

The degree of a term is the sum of all the exponents of all the variables contained in that term. For example, $5x^2y^3$ is of degree 5 because x is of degree 2 and y is of degree 3.

The degree of an expression is determined by the highest degree of any term contained in the expression.

Second degree: $x^2 + 5xy - 1$, $8y - 4z + 6yz$
Third degree: $10rt^2 + 2r + 5$, $4u^3 - u^2v + 5uv^2$
Fourth degree: $x^2 - 3x^3y$, $h^3 + h^2k^2$, $s^4 - 7s + 10t + t^4$

The degree of a polynomial in a specified variable is the greatest exponent for that variable.

$4x^2 - x + 8$
A second-degree polynomial in x.

$-3x^3y^2$
A third-degree polynomial in x.
A second-degree polynomial in y.
A fifth-degree polynomial.

Example 1

State the degree of the polynomial. Arrange the terms in decreasing order of degree.
a. $3x - 8x^2 + 1$

b. $6x^2y^2 + y^2 + 2x^3$

Second-degree polynomial.
$-8x^2 + 3x + 1$

Fourth-degree polynomial.
$6x^2y^2 + 2x^3 + y^2$

Example 2

State the degree of the polynomial, the degree of the polynomial in x, and arrange the terms in increasing order of degree in x.
a. $2x^3 + 5x^2y^3 - 6x$

b. $10 - x^4 + x^2y^2z$

Fifth-degree polynomial.
Third degree in x.
$6x + 5x^2y^3 + 2x^3$

Fifth-degree polynomial.
Fourth degree in x.
$10 + x^2y^2z - x^4$

Example 3

The lengths of the three sides of a triangle are $2a^2$, $7b$, and $3c - b$ units respectively.
a. Write an expression for the perimeter of the triangle.
b. State the degree of the expression.

a. The perimeter is the sum of the three sides of the triangle.
Therefore, the perimeter is $2a^2 + 6b + 3c$ units.
b. The expression is a second-degree polynomial.

Exercises

1. State the degree of each polynomial.
a. $2x^2 - 8x + 9$ **b.** $x^4 + 3x^2 - 6x - 12$
c. $x^2 - 4x^2y^2 + 5y^3$ **d.** $a^2b + a^3b^2 - ab^4c^2$

2. State the degree of each polynomial in x.
a. $5x^3 - 2x^2y^2$ **b.** $-3x^2 + xy^2 - 6y^4$
c. $15y - 8x$ **d.** $2y^2 + 6y - 15$

3. Arrange the terms in increasing order of degree in x.
a. $xy^2 + 5$ **b.** $4x^3 - x^2y^2 + 9$
c. $x^3y^2 + 8xy - 5x^2$ **d.** $x^2 - 4 + 5xy + 2x^3$

4. State the degree of the polynomial and arrange the terms in decreasing order of degree in x.
a. $5x^2 + x^3 - 6x + 8$ **b.** $2\sqrt{3} - x$
c. $10 - 2x^2 + 8x^4 - 3x^3$ **d.** 74
e. $14x + x^5$ **f.** $4x^3 + 7xy - x^2$
g. $xy^3 + 9x^4y - 5x^2y^2$
h. $6x^4 - 10y^4 + 3x^3y^3 - 2x$

5. Select the expressions which are third-degree polynomials. Identify these as monomials, binomials, or trinomials. Arrange the terms in increasing order of degree in x.
a. $3x^2 + 4x - 18$ **b.** $4x^2y + xy$
c. $-5xyz + 3y^2 + x^2$ **d.** $-2x + x^3 + 5$
e. $6x^2 + 3x^2y^2 - y^2$ **f.** $x^3 + 2x^2y - 7xy^2$
g. $10x^3$ **h.** $3xy + 8x^2 - 9y^2$

6. In a triangle, the shortest side is two more than half the length of the longest side. Write an expression for the length of the shortest side of the triangle using the variable k.

7. The length of a rectangle is 3 less than 5 times the width. If the length is represented by p, then write the expression which would represent the width of the rectangle.

8. If the length of the side of a square is x, then write an expression which would represent the doubling of the area of the square.

9. The lengths of the three sides of a triangle are represented by $5x - 3y$, $6x$, and $2y + 9$ units. How many terms would the most simplified expression for the perimeter of the triangle contain?

10. If the deposits made into a bank account are represented by $\$(2x - 3y)$, $\$(5x^2 + 8)$, and $\$(-4x + y)$, then of what degree would the expression be which represents the total of the deposits?

11. The letters S, Q, U, A, R, and I are printed on the sides of a cube. Copy and complete the blank sides of the cube.

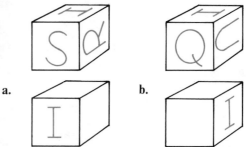

a.   **b.**

12. The journalism class of Westmew High produces the school paper. For the purpose of spacing words in a line, values are assigned to characters. The letters I, i, l, and the number 1 are each assigned a line-count value of 0.5. The capital letters M and W are assigned a line-count value of 2.5. The other capital letters, lower-case letters, digits, and spaces are assigned a line-count value of 1.0.
a. Determine the line-count value for WESTMEW HIGH WINS AWARD.
b. Can you think of a seven-letter word with a line-count value of 4.5?

13. Use the expression $8x^4 + 2x^2y^3 - xy^4$ to answer each.
a. What is the degree of this polynomial?
b. What is the numerical coefficient of the fourth-degree term?
c. What is the numerical coefficient of the third-degree term in y?
d. What is the numerical coefficient of the second-degree term in x?
e. Classify the polynomial according to the number of terms.

83

4·4 Addition and Subtraction of Polynomials

Monomials that contain exactly the same variables raised to the same degree are called **like terms**. Expressions containing like terms are **simplified** by collecting the like terms. These are examples of like terms: $3x^2$, $\sqrt{6x^2}$, $-2x^2$, $0.5x^2$.

Example 1

Simplify.

a. $12x + 5y - 3y - x$
$= 11x + 2y$

b. $6ab + bc + 2ab - 4bc$
$= 8ab - 3bc$

c. $(3x^2 - 8xy - 6y^2) + (x^2 + 4xy - 2y^2)$
$= 4x^2 - 4xy - 8y^2$

Example 2

Simplify.

a. $(-4x + 3y) - (2x - 5y)$
$= -4x + 3y - 2x + 5y$
$= -6x + 8y$

> To remove the second set of brackets, multiply each term by -1.

b. $(6p^2 - q^2) - (2p^2 + 5pq - 9q^2)$
$= 6p^2 - q^2 - 2p^2 - 5pq + 9q^2$
$= 4p^2 - 5pq + 8q^2$

Exercises

1. Identify the like terms.
a. $3a$, $5a^2$, $-9b$, $12ab$, $5a$, $7ab$, a^2
b. $8m^2$, $-15mn$, $2m^2n$, mn, $4m^2$
c. $5pk^2$, $22pk$, $3p^2k$, $-8pk$, $2p^2k^2$
d. $6x^2$, xy^2, $9x^2$, $14xy^2$, $-3y^2$

2. Simplify by collecting the like terms.
a. $3ab - 8bc + ab + 12bc - 6ab$
b. $8xy + 10xz - 3yz - 2xz + 14xy - yz$
c. $5m^2 - 8mn + 2n^2 - m^2 + 15mn$
d. $3x^2y^2 + 6x^2y - xy^2 + 6x^2y^2 - 9xy^2$
e. $5rt - 8st + 3rs + 13rs - 6rt + st$
f. $-8cw + 2cx + 3cw - 6cw - cx$
g. $3m^2 + 14mj - 5j^2 + 2mj - 6m^2$
h. $x^2y^2 - 4x^2y - xy^2 + 8x^2y + 3x^2y^2$
i. $14a^2 + 6ab - 7b^2c - a^2 + 3b^2c - 10ab$
j. $3p^3 + 9pq^2 - q^2 - 5pq^2 + 4p^3 - q^2$

3. Remove the brackets.
a. $-(4x + 6y)$ **b.** $-(-2a + 5b)$
c. $-(3x^2 + 9x - 15)$ **d.** $-(x^2 - y^2)$
e. $-(-5x^2 - 2xy + 16y^2)$
f. $-(8ab + 3bc - 5ac)$

4. Subtract the second polynomial from the first polynomial.
a. $5x - 2y$; $7x + 3y$
b. 15; $3a^2 - 4$
c. $6ab - 5bc + 12ac$; $-4ab - 2bc + 5ac$
d. $2x^2 + 14x - 9$; $3x^2 - x + 3$
e. $2r^2 - 3rs - 12s^2$; $5r^2 + rs + 2s^2$
f. $4x^2 + 5x - 8$; $6x^2 - 4x - 1$
g. $x^2 + 6$; $5x^2 + 3x - 8$
h. $6x^2 - 9x$; $15x - 6$
i. $-3y^2 + 2yz - 10z^2$; $y^2 + 5z^2$
j. $10x^3 + 2x + 18$; $4x^3 - 9x^2 + 3x - 2$

5. On the first day of their vacation, Bonny and Linda travelled $(3x + 2y)$ km. On the second and third days, they travelled $(4x - y)$ km. On the last day they travelled $(x + 4y)$ km. Find an expression for the total distance they travelled in the four days.

6. Add.

a. $6x - 3y$
$\quad 2x + 5y$

b. $2a + 3b$
$\quad a - 8b$

c. $14a - 2b + \ c$
$\quad -6a \qquad + 8c$

d. $4x^2 + 9x - 3$
$\quad 8x^2 - 2x + 7$

e. $4x + 15y - 8z$
$\quad x - \ 6y + 2z$
$\quad -8x - \ 3y + 4z$

f. $8a^2 - 10a - \ 5$
$\quad 5a^2 + \ 3a - \ 3$
$\quad -3a^2 - \ 8a + 22$

7. Simplify and evaluate the expression for $x = 3$, $y = -2$, and $z = 4$.
a. $(12x - 3y) + (5x + 2y)$
b. $(x + 4y - 5z) - (x + y + 3z)$
c. $(-6x + 8y + 4z) + (4x - 5y)$
d. $(2x + 15y) - (-2x + 3z)$
e. $(4x^2 + 5x - 1) - (x^2 - 9x + 7)$
f. $(x^2 + 6x - 5) - (2x^2 + 6x - 2)$
g. $(x^2 - 3xy - y^2) + (3x^2 + 5xy + y^2)$

8. Simplify. Write the expressions in descending order of degree in x.
a. $(6 - 2x + x^3) + (4x^2 + x - 3)$
b. $(x^4 - 2x^3 - 5) + (3x^2 + 2)$
c. $(15x + 6 - 2x^2) + (3x^2 + 4 - 9x)$
d. $(10 - 3x + 4x^2) + (-4x^2 + 8x - 5)$
e. $(7x - 4 + 2x^2) - (5x^2 - 8 + 3x)$
f. $(4x^2 + x - 8) - (7x + 2)$
g. $(1 + 3x^2 - 6x) - (8x^2 - 5x - 2)$

9. Simplify. State the degree of the simplified polynomial.
a. $(6x^2 + 3x + 4) + (x^2 - 3x - 1)$
b. $(-5x^2 + 11x + 8) + (5x^2 - 2x + 6)$
c. $(3x^2 - 2x - 18) - (8x^2 + x - 6)$
d. $(2x^2 + 7x + 3) - (2x^2 + 6x + 5)$
e. $(4x^2 - x + 2) + (-4x^2 + x + 2)$

10. The four sides of a quadrilateral have lengths of $6x - 15, 2x + 5, 4x - 3$, and $5x - 2$ units. Find an expression for the perimeter of the quadrilateral.

11. Lani's present age can be represented by the expression $2x^2 + 9x - 12$. Ramji's present age is given by the expression $4x^2 + 3x$. Find an expression for the sum of their ages in five years.

12. The following deposits were made into a bank account: $\$(5a + b)$, $\$(2a - 8b)$, and $\$(6a + 2b)$. If a withdrawal of $\$(4a + 5b)$ was made, then what would be the balance left in the account?

13. The perimeter of an isosceles triangle is $14a + 7b - 9c$ units. If the length of one of the two equal sides is $5a - b + 2c$ units, then find the length of the third side.

14. The smallest of three numbers is defined as x. The second number is 8 more than 3 times the smallest number. The third number is 5 less than twice the smallest number. Write an expression for the sum of the second and third numbers.

15. In a group of 15 coins, 14 have the same mass and one is a little lighter. Using a balance scale, what is the minimum number of trials required to positively identify the lighter coin?

16. Find the length of $\overline{AB}$ and $\overline{AC}$.

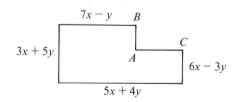

17. Copy and complete the table so that the third column contains the sum of the numbers in the first two columns and the third row contains the sum of the numbers in the first two rows.

		$3x$	$9x$
			$5x$
$7x$			

4·5 Multiplication of Polynomials I

Find the area of this rectangle.

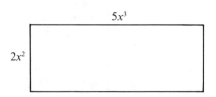

$5x^3$

$2x^2$

The area of the rectangle is found by using the formula $l \times w$.
Therefore, the area is $2x^2 \times 5x^3$ or $10x^5$ square units.

> To multiply two or more monomials, the numerical coefficients are multiplied and the literal coefficients are multiplied.

Example 1

Multiply.

a. $(5x^3)(3x^2y)$
$= (5)(3)(x^{3+2})y$
$= 15x^5y$

b. $(-2ab^4)(5a^2c^2)(-abc^3)$
$= 10(a^{1+2+1})(b^{4+1})(c^{2+3})$
$= 10a^4b^5c^5$

Example 2

Expand. Recall the distributive property.

a. $-2x(5x - 3y)$
$= -10x^2 + 6xy$

> "expand" means "multiply"

b. $4ab^2(2a^2 - ab - 7b^2)$
$= 8a^3b^2 - 4a^2b^3 - 28ab^4$

c. $6(5x^2 - 3y) + 4x(5x + y) = 30x^2 - 18y + 20x^2 + 4xy$
$= 50x^2 - 18y + 4xy$

> To multiply a monomial by a polynomial, use the distributive property and the rule for the multiplication of two monomials.

Example 3

Find an expression for $3(2x - 5y) - 4(x - 2y)$ if $x = 5m$ and $y = -2n$.

$3(2x - 5y) - 4(x - 2y) = 6x - 15y - 4x + 8y$
$= 2x - 7y$
$= 2(5m) - 7(-2n)$
$= 10m + 14n$

Exercises

1. Multiply.
a. $(2x)(5y)$ **b.** $(-7a)(-2c)$
c. $(2a^2)(6a)$ **d.** $(3x^2y^2)(4xy^3)$
e. $(a^3b^2)(-2a^2b)(-3a^2b^3)$
f. $(3x^4)(2x^3y^2)(-6xy^4)$
g. $(2pq)(-5p^2)(8p^3q^5)(pq^3)$
h. $(5r^3)(s^2)(3r^2s^2)(4rs^4)$

2. Expand.
a. $5a(a - 5b)$ **b.** $4p(m + 3n)$
c. $-3(6x - 2y)$ **d.** $8x(2x - 5)$
e. $-(10a - 2b)$ **f.** $3a^2(4a + 7b)$
g. $2a(4a^2 - a + 2)$ **h.** $-5x(2x^2 - xy + y^2)$
i. $3x(5 + x - 3x^2)$ **j.** $2x^2(3x^2 - 4x + 6)$
k. $-4p^2(13 + 6p - 5p^2)$

3. Multiply.
a. $(3x^2y)^2$ **b.** $(-2ab^3)^2$
c. $4x(xy)^2$ **d.** $-5x^2(x^3y)^2$
e. $5a^3b(2a)^2(4b^2)^2$ **f.** $3(x^3y)(4xy)^2$
g. $(2x^2y^2)^2(xy^3)^2$ **h.** $-2(p^2)^3(pq^2)^2$

4. Expand using the distributive property. Simplify by collecting like terms.
a. $7(2x - 3) + 2(4x + 1)$
b. $5(3a + 6b - c) + 4(a - b + 3c)$
c. $2(3p - 4q) - 5(2p + q)$
d. $8(3x - 2y) + 2(7x - 2y)$
e. $-3(a + 5b) + 3(2a - 10b)$

5. Expand and simplify.
a. $3(4a - b + 3c) + 2(6b - c)$
b. $7(8x + y) - 4(x - 3y + 2z)$
c. $5(2x^2 - 5x + 2) + 3(6x - 2)$
d. $12(3a - 2c) + 4(a + 6b) - 5(3a - c)$
e. $6(x + 4) - 3(x^2 + 2x + 5)$
f. $3(2x^2 - y^2) + 5(3x^2 + 2xy + y^2)$
g. $8(a^2 + 2ab - b^2) - 4(3ab - 5b^2)$

6. Expand and simplify.
a. $2x(8x + 1) - 3x(6x - 2)$
b. $12(2a - 3b) - 4a(b - 4)$
c. $5x(2x + 5) + 8x(x - 3)$
d. $-x(x^2 - 7x) + 6(2x^2 + 7x - 2)$
e. $a(2b - a) - 4b(9a + b)$

7. Evaluate each expression for $x = 5$.
a. $3(x + 2) + 4(x - 2)$
b. $8(x^2 - 6x + 3) + 2(5x - 2)$
c. $10(x^2 + 3x + 4) - 5(3 + x)$
d. $7(5x - 2) + 2(x^2 + 4)$
e. $4x(6x + 9) - 2x(8x + 13)$

8. Remove the brackets and simplify.
a. $3[2(x - 5) + 12]$
b. $2[4(2y - 3x) - 6(x + y)]$
c. $5a[8(b - 2c) + 2c]$
d. $18[2(5x - 3) - 3(3x - 7)]$
e. $2[4(6 - x) + 3] + 5[3(2x + 1)]$

9. One side of an equilateral triangle has a length of $4x - 3y$ units. Find an expression for the perimeter of this triangle.

10. The radius of a circle is $8a - 3b$ units. Find an expression for the circumference of the circle.

11. The length of a rectangle is increased by 5 units and the width decreased by 2 units. Find an expression for the perimeter of the new rectangle.

12. If you can only move downward or to the right, then how many different paths from point A to point B are possible?

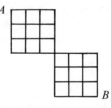

13. Find an expression for the perimeter of the rectangle.

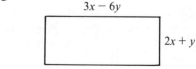

14. Simplify. State the degree of each polynomial.
a. $3x(5x^2 - 6x + 1)$
b. $x^4(2x^2 + 5)$
c. $-2x^2(6x^2 - 4)$

87

4·6 Multiplication of Polynomials II

Find the area of a rectangle whose dimensions are $2x + 5$ units and $x + 3$ units.

$2x$	$+$	5

	$2x$ + 5
x	$2x^2$ $\quad$ $5x$
$+$	
3	$6x$ $\qquad$ 15

The area of the large rectangle is the sum of the areas of the smaller rectangles.
$2x^2 + 5x + 6x + 15 = 2x^2 + 11x + 15$

The area of the rectangle is $2x^2 + 11x + 15$ square units.

Example 1

Multiply.

$(2a - 5b)(3a + 8b)$
$= 6a^2 + 16ab - 15ab - 40b^2$
$= 6a^2 + ab - 40b^2$

A reminder to multiply two binomials is to think of the word **FOIL**.
Each letter represents the terms which are to be multiplied.
F — first terms
O — outside terms
I — inside terms
L — last terms

When two polynomials are multiplied, each term in the first polynomial is multiplied by each term in the second polynomial.

The distributive property can be used to multiply polynomials containing three or more terms.

Example 2

Expand and simplify.

a. $(6x + 2)(x^2 - 5x - 5)$
$= 6x(x^2 - 5x - 5) + 2(x^2 - 5x - 5)$
$= 6x^3 - 30x^2 - 30x + 2x^2 - 10x - 10$
$= 6x^3 - 28x^2 - 40x - 10$

b. $(p - 3)(2p^2 + p - 1) - (4p - 1)(2p + 5)$
$= 2p^3 + p^2 - p - 6p^2 - 3p + 3 - [8p^2 + 20p - 2p - 5]$
$= 2p^3 - 5p^2 - 4p + 3 - 8p^2 - 18p + 5$
$= 2p^3 - 13p^2 - 22p + 8$

Example 3

Evaluate for $x = 2$.

$(2x + 1)(6x - 5) - 3(x^2 - 4)$
$= 12x^2 - 10x + 6x - 5 - 3x^2 + 12$
$= 9x^2 - 4x + 7$

Substitute $x = 2$.

$9x^2 - 4x + 7$
$= 9(2)^2 - 4(2) + 7$
$= 36 - 8 + 7$
$= 35$

$(2x + 1)(6x - 5) - 3(x^2 - 4)$
$= (5)(7) - 3(0)$
$= 35$
$\therefore$ It checks.

Exercises

1. Calculate the product of $(2x + 6)(x + 3)$ by finding the sum of the areas of each individual rectangle.

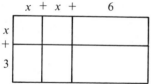

2. Calculate the product of $(x + 4)(x + 1)$ by finding the sum of the areas of each individual rectangle.

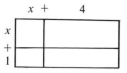

3. Calculate the product of $(2x + 1)(x + 2)$ by finding the area of the large rectangle.

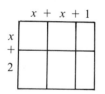

4. Using the diagram, copy and complete to find the shaded area.

$(x - 2)(x + 3) = x^{\blacksquare} + \blacksquare x - \blacksquare - \blacksquare = $ ▬▬▬

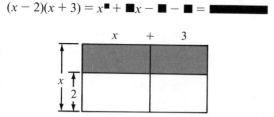

5. Expand and simplify by collecting like terms.
a. $(x + 6)(x - 8)$
b. $(x + 1)(x - 4)$
c. $(x + 9)(x - 3)$
d. $(x - 5)(x + 1)$
e. $(x - 7)(x + 2)$
f. $(x + 3)(x + 4)$
g. $(x - 5)(x - 1)$
h. $(x + 8)(x - 2)$
i. $(x - 4)(x + 10)$
j. $(x - 6)(x - 3)$

6. Expand and simplify.
a. $(2x + 3)(x + 5)$
b. $(x - 4)(5x + 1)$
c. $(8x + 5)(2x - 5)$
d. $(x + 6)(2x - 1)$
e. $(5x - 3)(4x - 7)$
f. $(9x + 8)(x - 2)$
g. $(3x + 1)(6x - 5)$
h. $(2x + 9)(x - 3)$
i. $(3x + 2)(4x + 3)$
j. $(6x - 1)(x + 4)$

7. A class of 22 students is arranged in a circle and assigned the numbers from 1 to 22. One student is selected to begin a count-off with every fourth student being eliminated. If this process leaves students numbered 9, 17, and 19, then which student began the count?

8. Expand and simplify.
a. $(x + 3y)(2x - 5y)$
b. $(x - 4y)(x - 2y)$
c. $(2x + y)(x + 6y)$
d. $(4a - b)(3a - b)$
e. $(5m - 6n)(2m + n)$
f. $(8p - q)(p + 2q)$

9. Expand and simplify.
a. $(2x + 5)(6x^2 - x + 2)$
b. $(x - 3)(2x^2 + 5x + 4)$
c. $(5t + 6)(t^2 - 3t + 2)$
d. $(n^2 + 4n)(2n^2 - n + 5)$
e. $(5x + 2y)(4x^2 - 3xy + y^2)$

10. Expand and simplify.
a. $(k + 5)(2k - 3) + (3k + 4)(2k - 1)$
b. $(4x - 1)(x - 2) + (3x + 5)(x - 1)$
c. $(x + 6)(x - 4) - (x + 1)(5x - 2)$
d. $(3p + 8)(2p - 3) - (p + 4)(3p - 2)$
e. $(10x - 7)(x + 1) + (3x - 5)(2x - 1)$
f. $(m - 5)(m - 4) - (2m + 3)(m + 2)$
g. $(3x + 1)(2x - 5) + (x + 6)(4x - 1)$
h. $(x + 2y)(x - 3y) + (x + 4y)(x + y)$

11. Find the area of this shape.

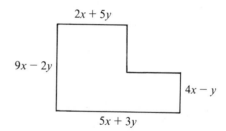

89

12. Find the area of a right triangle if the lengths of the perpendicular sides are $5x - 6y$ units and $2x + 3y$ units.

13. The width of a rectangle is 8 cm less than twice the length. Write an expression which represents the area of the rectangle.

14. Three numbers are related such that the second number is 5 more than twice the first number. Write an expression for the third number if it is equal to eight times the first number minus three times the second.

15. The first five rows of Pascal's Triangle are shown.

$$1$$
$$1 \quad 1$$
$$1 \quad 2 \quad 1$$
$$1 \quad 3 \quad 3 \quad 1$$
$$1 \quad 4 \quad 6 \quad 4 \quad 1$$

a. Multiply each and state a relation between the nth row of Pascal's Triangle and $(A + B)^n$.
i) $(A + B)^1$ ii) $(A + B)^2$ iii) $(A + B)^3$
b. Predict what $(A + B)^4$ will be.

16. Ali makes a down payment of \$125 on a Moped. He must then pay $\$(8x - 15)$ per month for the next $(3x + 4)$ months. Find an expression for the total amount paid.

17. Expand and simplify.
a. $3(2x + 5)(x - 4)$ **b.** $-2(6p - 1)(p + 2)$
c. $5(x + 3)(x - 6)$ **d.** $8(3 - x)(2 - 3x)$
e. $-3(2a + 1)(3a + 2)$ **f.** $4(5t - 12)(t + 3)$
g. $-2(4m - 3)(m + 2)$ **h.** $(5 + 2x)(3)(2 - x)$

18. Expand and simplify.
a. $4(x - 5)(2x + 1) - (x + 3)(x + 2)$
b. $2(4p - 3)(p - 1) + 3(p + 5)(2p - 3)$
c. $6(x - 2)(x - 1) + 2(2x - 1)(2x + 5)$
d. $(3x - 2)(2x - 9) - 4(x + 5)(x - 4)$

19. Expand and simplify.
a. $4x(3x^2 - 10) + (x - 2)(x^2 - 5x - 6)$
b. $3(n^2 + 8)(n - 6) - 5n^2(2n - 1)$
c. $(2x - 5)(3x^2 + x - 4) + 4x(x - 1)$
d. $12x^2(4 - x) + 3(x - 2)(x^2 + 4x - 2)$

20. Expand and simplify. Check using $x = -3$ and $y = 2$.
a. $(2x - 5)(x + 3) - 4(x^2 + 2)$
b. $2(x - 6)(5x - 1) + 8(3x - 1)$
c. $(y + 3)(y - 1) - 4(8y - 1)$
d. $4x(y + 2) - 5y(x - 3)$
e. $2(x^2 - 5y^2) + 3(x + y)(x + 2y)$

21. The height of a triangle is $6a - 2b$ units and its base is $a + 3b$ units. Find an expression which would represent the area of the triangle.

22. The length and width of rectangle A are $(2x - y)$ cm and $(4x + 3y)$ cm respectively. The length and width of rectangle B are $(x + 5y)$ cm and $(2x - 7y)$ cm respectively. Find an expression for the combined areas of the two rectangles.

23. Norm has collected the coins from the juice machine in the school cafeteria. He has found that there are only quarters, dimes, and nickels. Write an expression which would represent the total value of the coins.

24. A water storage tank can be filled in 3 h by one pipe and emptied by another in 5 h. If both pipes are left open at the same time, then how long will it take to fill the tank?

25. A tank can be filled in x h by one pipe and emptied by another in y h. If both pipes are left open at the same time, then at what rate is the tank filling?

26. Rowing upstream in a canoe, Kaori notices a log as it floats past her. She continues to paddle upstream for 20 min, turns around, and paddles downstream at the same rate through the water. When Kaori overtakes the log she had seen earlier, it is exactly 1 km downstream from the point where she had first sighted it. How fast is the current flowing?

27. Today Anil's age is m years and Jodi's age is n years. Write an expression which would represent the product of their ages in 5 a.

4·7 Special Products

The area model can be used to multiply these special binomials. Find the area of the square whose side length is $a + b$ units.

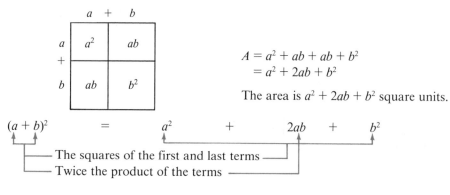

$$A = a^2 + ab + ab + b^2$$
$$= a^2 + 2ab + b^2$$

The area is $a^2 + 2ab + b^2$ square units.

$(a + b)^2 \quad = \quad a^2 \quad + \quad 2ab \quad + \quad b^2$

— The squares of the first and last terms —
— Twice the product of the terms —

$(a + b)^2 = a^2 + 2ab + b^2$ and $(a - b)^2 = a^2 - 2ab + b^2$

Example 1

Find the product.

$(2x + 5y)^2$
$= 4x^2 + 20xy + 25y^2$

Example 2

Simplify. $(2x - 1)^2 + (3x - 2)(x + 4)$
$= 4x^2 - 4x + 1 + 3x^2 + 10x - 8$
$= 7x^2 + 6x - 7$

This area model shows a method to find the product of $(a + b)$ and $(a - b)$.

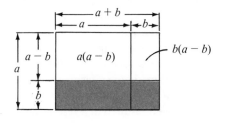

The area of the nonshaded rectangle whose dimensions are $(a + b)$ and $(a - b)$ is given by
$a(a - b) + b(a - b)$
$= a^2 - ab + ab - b^2$
$= a^2 - b^2$

$(a + b)(a - b) = a^2 - b^2$

Example 3

Find the product.

$(8a + 3b)(8a - 3b)$
$= 64a^2 - 9b^2$

Example 4

Expand and simplify. $(a + b + c)^2$

$(a + b + c)^2 = [(a + b) + c]^2$
$= (a + b)^2 + 2(a + b)c + c^2$
$= a^2 + 2ab + b^2 + 2ac + 2bc + c^2$
$= a^2 + b^2 + c^2 + 2ab + 2ac + 2bc$

Exercises

1. Calculate the area of the square whose sides are $2a + b$ units. Use the diagram as a guide.

$$2a \ + \ b$$

$2a$
$+$
b

2. Expand and simplify by collecting like terms.
a. $(x - 3)^2$ **b.** $(2p + 1)^2$
c. $(4x - 5)^2$ **d.** $(3x + 4)^2$
e. $(5n + 2)^2$ **f.** $(6y - 1)^2$
g. $(a + 8)^2$ **h.** $(9x - 2)^2$

3. Expand and simplify.
a. $(2b - 5)(2b + 5)$ **b.** $(6x + 1)(6x - 1)$
c. $(x + 3)(x - 3)$ **d.** $(9m - 2)(9m + 2)$
e. $(4q - 5)(4q + 5)$ **f.** $(3x - 8)(3x + 8)$

4. Expand and simplify. Check using $x = -2$ and $y = -3$.
a. $(5x - 2y)(5x + 2y)$ **b.** $(4x + y)^2$
c. $(3x + 4y)^2$ **d.** $(x - 2y)(x + 2y)$
e. $(8 - 3y)^2$ **f.** $(1 + 5x)^2$
g. $(2x - 9)(2x + 9)$ **h.** $(6x - 5y)^2$

5. If the height of a triangle is $5x + 3$ units and the base is the same length, then find the area of the triangle.

6. Multiply.
a. $3(x + 5)^2$ **b.** $2(2x - 3)^2$
c. $3a(a - 3)^2$ **d.** $6t(2t + 1)^2$
e. $4(3x - 1)(3x + 1)$ **f.** $-2(n - 2)(n + 2)$
g. $5k(k + 4)(k - 4)$ **h.** $3p(2p - 5)(2p + 5)$

7. Expand and simplify.
a. $(2x - 5)^2 - (x - 6)(x + 3)$
b. $(4y + 3)(4y - 3) - (2y - 3)^2$
c. $(a + 5)^2 + 3(2a - 5)^2$
d. $(6x + 5)(6x - 5) - 3(2x - 1)^2$

8. Expand and simplify.
a. $(r + 1)(r - 4)^2$ **b.** $(3x - 1)(2x + 1)^2$
c. $(2x + 5)(x - 4)^2$ **d.** $-6a(2a - 7)(2a + 7)$
e. $(8k - 3)(k + 4)(k - 4)$
f. $(2u + 5)(3u - 2)(3u + 2)$

9. Use the pattern for the expansion of the square of a binomial to expand and simplify.
a. $[(x + y) + z]^2$ **b.** $[(2x - y) - z]^2$
c. $[a + (b + 3c)]^2$ **d.** $[p - (q - 2r)]^2$
e. $[2u - (v + 3)]^2$ **f.** $[3m - n + 2p]^2$

10. A manufacturer has a cylinder with these dimensions.

Radius = $4x - 5$ units

Height = $2x + 9$ units

a. Find the volume of the closed cylinder.
$V = \pi r^2 h$
b. Find the surface area of the cylinder.
$S.A. = 2\pi r^2 + 2\pi rh$

Historical Note

Euclid (c. 300 B.C.)
Euclid is best known for his work on a book called *Elements*. His chief work is the first 13 chapters of this geometry text, which is the earliest surviving textbook on geometry.

    The **Euclidean Algorithm** for finding the greatest common divisor is so named because it is found at the start of Book VII of *Elements*. This algorithm is the foundation of several developments in modern mathematics. To find the greatest common divisor, divide the smaller number into the larger number. The remainder, if nonzero, now becomes the divisor and it is divided into the original divisor. This process is repeated until a remainder of zero is obtained. The divisor which resulted in a zero remainder is the greatest common divisor.

Example: 2016 and 1400
$\frac{2016}{1400} = 1 + \frac{616}{1400}; \quad \frac{1400}{616} = 2 + \frac{168}{616};$
$\frac{616}{168} = 3 + \frac{112}{168}; \quad \frac{168}{112} = 1 + \frac{56}{112}; \quad \frac{112}{56} = 2 + 0$

56 is the greatest common divisor.

Use this method to find the greatest common divisor.
a. 420 and 896   **b.** 4410 and 5544

4·8 Factors of a Monomial

When one of the factors of a monomial is given, the other factor can be determined by dividing the monomial by the given factor.

Example 1

Find the missing factor.

a. $270m^2n^5 = (15mn)(\blacksquare)$ $\qquad \dfrac{270m^2n^5}{15mn} = 18mn^4$

Therefore, $270m^2n^5 = (15mn)(18mn^4)$.

Recall the rules for division of exponents.

b. $-56a^5b^3 = (-4a^2b)(\blacksquare)$ $\qquad \dfrac{-56a^5b^3}{-4a^2b} = 14a^3b^2$

Therefore, $-56a^5b^3 = (-4a^2b)(14a^3b^2)$.

To determine the Greatest Common Factor (GCF) of a set of monomials, find the Greatest Common Factor of the numerical coefficients and of the literal coefficients.

Example 2

Find the GCF of each.

a. $12a$ and $15a^2b$

3 is the GCF of 12 and 15.
a is the GCF of a and a^2b.
Therefore, the GCF is $3a$.

b. $56x^2y^3$, $32xy^2$, and $16x^4y^4$

8 is the GCF of 56, 32, and 16.
xy^2 is the GCF of x^2y^3, xy^2, and x^4y^4.
Therefore, the GCF is $8xy^2$.

Exercises

1. Copy and complete to find the missing factor.
a. $48a^2b^2 = (6ab^2)(\blacksquare)$
b. $14x^4y^2 = (2x^3y)(\blacksquare)$
c. $-96m^3n^3 = (-8m)(\blacksquare)$
d. $135r^2s^3t^4 = (15rs^2t^2)(\blacksquare)$
e. $-18a^6b^2c^5 = (a^4bc^2)(\blacksquare)$
f. $360x^3y^2z = (24x^2z)(\blacksquare)$
g. $210pq^4 = (-14q^2)(\blacksquare)$

2. Find the GCF of each set of monomials.
a. 120, 180
b. $56x$, $104x^2$
c. $65a^3b$, $91ab^2$
d. $162y^2$, $54x^2$
e. $90x^3y^2$, $115x^2y$
f. $78a$, $156ab^2$
g. $315m^4n^2$, $1575mn^2$, $90m^2n^2$
h. $96s^3t^3$, $36s^4t^6$, $108st^5$

3. Find the least positive integer that gives a remainder of 4 when divided by 7 and gives a remainder of 5 when divided by 8.

4. If the condition "gives a remainder of 6 when divided by 9" is added to the conditions of Exercise 3, then find the least positive integer which satisfies all three conditions.

Braintickler

The number 7384 can be written in the form $7(1000) + 3(100) + 8(10) + 4$. The first two terms of this expression are divisible by 4 because both 1000 and 100 are divisible by 4. The number 7384 would be divisible by 4 if the last two digits as a number is divisible by 4. In this case, 84 is divisible by 4. Therefore, 7384 is divisible by 4.

Use this test to determine whether these numbers are divisible by 4.

a. 51 038
b. 428 396
c. 621 574
d. 109 356

4·9 Common Factor

To factor an expression, divide it into smaller terms or expressions, which, upon multiplication, yield the original expression.

One way to factor a polynomial is to find the GCF of all the terms of the polynomial. The polynomial is then written as a product of all its factors. This method is called **common factoring**.

For example, factor $18ab^2 - 12abc$.
The GCF of the numerical coefficients is 6.
The GCF of the literal coefficients is ab.
Therefore, $18ab^2 - 12abc = 6ab(3b - 2c)$.

Example 1

Factor.

$5a^2 + 20ab^2 - 80ab$
$= 5a(a + 4b^2 - 16b)$

Example 2

Express as a product.

$2x(x - 3y) + 9(x - 3y)$
$= (x - 3y)(2x + 9)$

> Some expressions have binomials and trinomials as the common factors.

Sometimes a factor cannot be found which is common to all the terms in the polynomial but only to some of them. Grouping these terms together, and finding the common factor of the smaller expressions, often leads to a binomial or trinomial that is a common factor.

Example 3

Factor.

a. $2ac - 6ab - 5bc + 15b^2$
$= (2ac - 6ab) - (5bc - 15b^2)$
$= 2a(c - 3b) - 5b(c - 3b)$
$= (c - 3b)(2a - 5b)$

b. $x - y - 3yz + 3xz$
$= (x - y) + (3xz - 3yz)$
$= (x - y) + 3z(x - y)$
$= (x - y)(1 + 3z)$

Exercises

1. Find the GCF.
a. $10x^2 + 5x$ **b.** $3a^2 - 6ab$
c. $8x^2 + 20xy$ **d.** $2x^2 + 8x$
e. $-6p^2 + 21pq$ **f.** $6a^3 - 12a^2b$
g. $4a^2 + 20$ **h.** $16x^2y + 6xy^2$

2. Find the width of each rectangle.

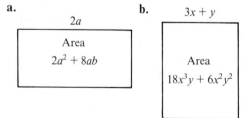
a.
$2a$
Area
$2a^2 + 8ab$

b.
$3x + y$
Area
$18x^3y + 6x^2y^2$

3. Factor.
a. $x^2 - xy + 6xz$
b. $6x^2 + 9x - 3y$
c. $10a + 2ab - 4ac$
d. $10a^2 - 15ab + 5a$
e. $-x^2y - 2xy^2 + xyz$
f. $4x^2y - 12y^2 - 2yz$

4. Express each as a product in the form (GCF)(polynomial).
a. $3x - 6y$ **b.** $5ap + 5aq$
c. $-8m - 24m^2x$ **d.** $5\pi r - 3\pi r^2$
e. $x^2y + xy^2 - xy$ **f.** $12 + 60ab$
g. $4x + 2(m + n)$ **h.** $x^2 - 6x(5a - b)$
i. $2mxy - 8nxy + 2xy$
j. $12a^2b^2 - 20ab^3 + 8ab^2$

5. Factor.

a. $2a(x + y) - 3b(x + y)$
b. $x(m + 5) - 3(m + 5)$
c. $a(2x - 1) + b(2x - 1)$
d. $a(3x + 1) - (3x + 1)$
e. $(x + 5) + y(x + 5)$
f. $6x^2(a - 2b) + 3(a - 2b)$
g. $15x(m + 4) - 5(m + 4)$
h. $x^3(4a - b) + x^2y(4a - b)$
i. $5a(x - 2) - 3b(x - 2) + (x - 2)$
j. $x(6x - 5) + y(6x - 5) - 6z(6x - 5)$

6. List the pairs of terms which contain a common factor and give the common factor.

a. $12x,\ 3y,\ 4xy^2$ **b.** $5p^2q,\ 2q,\ 8pq^2$
c. $6u^3v,\ 10u^2v,\ 9uv$ **d.** $5m^2n,\ 12m,\ 7mn^2$
e. $5ab^2,\ -15a^2b^2,\ 60b^3c^2$
f. $5(x - 2y),\ (x - 2y)(x + 2y),\ 3x(x + 2y)$
g. $6pq,\ 3(2p + 3q),\ 2p(p + 2q)(2p + 3q)$

7. Group and factor completely.

a. $m^2 + 6m + mn + 6n$
b. $x^2 - 2x + xy - 2y$
c. $5mn + 15m - 2n - 6$
d. $2xy + 6 - 12y - x$
e. $ay - 5y - 3a + 15$
f. $x^3 - 3x^2 + 2x - 6$
g. $4a^2 + ab^2 - 20ab - 5b^3$
h. $3a^3 - a^2b^2 + 24ab - 8b^3$
i. $15mn + 25m^2 - 10mn^2 - 6n^3$
j. $6pr + 12pq - 9qr - 18q^2$
k. $10x^2y + 40x^2 - 2xy^3 - 8xy^2$
l. $12ax^2 - 15a^2x + 8abx - 10a^2b$
m. $10m^2n + 5m^2 - 30mn - 15m$
n. $4p^2q^2 - 8p^3q - 24p^2q + 12pq^2$

8. Find an expression for the area of the shaded region. Write your answer in factored form. All measurements are made in centimetres.

a.   **b.**

$2(2x + 3)$

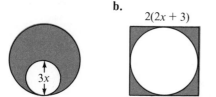

9. Find an expression for the combined area of the two triangles. (Leave your answer in factored form.)

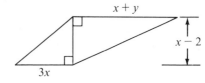

10. A worker is paid an hourly rate of $9.40 for a regular 35 h work week. Hourly pay for overtime is "time and a half". Write an expression for the pay a worker receives for N h of work in a week, where N is equal to or greater than 35.

11. On the first day of a sale, p record albums were sold for $7.98 each. On the second day, q albums were sold for the same price. Write an expression for the total income from the sale of the albums in the two days.

12. An owner is celebrating a grand opening at her new car dealership. The showroom can accommodate M people. She estimated that 2 out of every 5 people invited will attend. How many invitations should be sent?

13. Linda has accepted a sales position at an audio equipment store. She has a choice of either a straight commission of 7.5% of sales or a weekly wage of $60 plus a 3% commission. What is the minimum amount of merchandise she must sell in order that straight commission is more profitable?

14. A win earns a team 2 points, while a tie is worth 1 point. A team needs 40 points to proceed to the division A playoffs. The Cougars presently have 14 wins and 3 ties with 7 games remaining in the schedule. Make a list of the possible combinations of wins and ties which would allow them to make the playoffs.

15. A copying machine decreases the size of the copy to 0.95 of the original. If an original picture was 10 cm by 14 cm, then how many times was a copy made and used again to obtain a picture which is 12 cm long?

95

4·10 Factoring Trinomials I

The product of two binomials often results in a trinomial. By examining the product of two binomials, methods for factoring trinomials can be discovered.

$(x + 4)(x - 8) = x^2 - 4x - 32$ ◂——— Product of 4 and -8
                                  Sum of $4x$ and $-8x$

$$\boxed{(x + a)(x + b) = x^2 + (a + b)x + ab}$$

To factor a trinomial of the form $x^2 + bx + c$, two integers must be found such that their product is c and their sum is b. For example, find two factors for $x^2 + 10x - 56$.

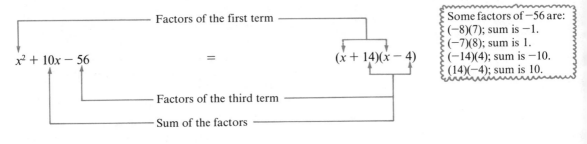

Factors of the first term

Some factors of -56 are:
$(-8)(7)$; sum is -1.
$(-7)(8)$; sum is 1.
$(-14)(4)$; sum is -10.
$(14)(-4)$; sum is 10.

$x^2 + 10x - 56 \qquad = \qquad (x + 14)(x - 4)$

Factors of the third term

Sum of the factors

Example 1

Factor.
a. $x^2 + 6x + 5$
$= (x + 1)(x + 5)$

Find factors of 5 whose sum is 6.

b. $x^2 - 4x - 12$
$= (x - 6)(x + 2)$

$-12 = (-6)(2)$
$(-6) + (2) = -4$

If the trinomial involves more than one variable, the same method can be used to factor the expression.

Example 2

Factor.
a. $x^2 + 2xy - 8y^2$
$= (x + 4y)(x - 2y)$

b. $m^2 - 7mn + 10n^2$
$= (m - 2n)(m - 5n)$

Example 3

Factor completely.
a. $2x^2 - 4x - 6$
$= 2(x^2 - 2x - 3)$
$= 2(x - 3)(x + 1)$

The terms of the original trinomial contain a common factor.

b. $x^4y - 3x^2y - 4y$
$= y(x^4 - 3x^2 - 4)$
$= y(x^2 - 4)(x^2 + 1)$

Example 4

Factor.
a. $p^4 - 5p^2 - 14$
$= (p^2 - 7)(p^2 + 2)$

b. $s^4 + 6s^2t - 27t^2$
$= (s^2 + 9t)(s^2 - 3t)$

Exercises

1. What two integers have
a. a sum of 7 and a product of 12?
b. a sum of 13 and a product of 36?
c. a sum of 1 and a product of -30?
d. a sum of -1 and a product of -30?
e. a sum of 16 and a product of 48?

2. Determine the two factors for each monomial in Column P whose sum is given in Column S.

	Column P	Column S
a.	$-56a^2$	$10a$
b.	$22x^2$	$-23x$
c.	$-6m^2$	$-m$
d.	$-12x^2$	$4x$
e.	$10p^2$	$7p$

3. Factor.
a. $x^2 + 4x + 3$ **b.** $a^2 - 7a + 6$
c. $y^2 + 3y - 18$ **d.** $x^2 - 4x - 12$
e. $x^2 - 13x + 22$ **f.** $b^2 + 7b - 18$
g. $x^2 + 3x - 28$ **h.** $a^2 - 22a + 21$
i. $p^2 - 6p - 16$ **j.** $x^2 + x - 30$
k. $t^2 + 9t + 20$ **l.** $u^2 - 16u - 36$

4. Express each as a product.
a. $x^2 - xy - 12y^2$ **b.** $a^2 + 7ab + 6b^2$
c. $p^2 + 13pq - 48q^2$ **d.** $m^2 + 11mn + 30n^2$
e. $x^2 - 10xz + 21z^2$ **f.** $a^2 - 18ad - 63d^2$
g. $x^2 + 11xy + 24y^2$ **h.** $x^2 - 8xy + 15y^2$
i. $r^2 - 7rs + 12s^2$ **j.** $a^2 + 4ab + 3b^2$
k. $p^2 + 6pq + 8q^2$ **l.** $u^2 + 8uv + 12v^2$

5. Factor completely. Use $x = 2$ to check parts **a** through **h.**
a. $3x^2 + 3x - 6$ **b.** $2x^2 + 6x - 20$
c. $ax^2 + 7ax + 12a$ **d.** $5x^2 + 20x + 15$
e. $2x^2 - 16x + 24$ **f.** $4x^2 - 12x - 16$
g. $-3x^2 + 6x + 45$ **h.** $2x^3 + 14x^2 + 12x$
i. $2r^3 + 10r^2s + 8rs^2$ **j.** $p^3 + 5p^2q - 24pq^2$

6. Factor completely.
a. $x^2y^2 + 2xy - 15$ **b.** $x^2 + 4xyz - 12y^2z^2$
c. $a^4 + 3a^2b + 2b^2$ **d.** $x^2y^2 - 10xy + 24$
e. $18 + 7mn - m^2n^2$ **f.** $a^2b^2 - 6abc - 16c^2$
g. $x^4y^2 + 12x^2y + 35$ **h.** $a^2 - 6abc - 16b^2c^2$

7. Find all integral values of p such that the trinomial is factorable.
a. $x^2 + px - 27$ **b.** $x^2 + px + 16$
c. $x^2 + px - 42$ **d.** $x^2 + px - 12$
e. $x^2 + px + 21$ **f.** $x^2 + px - 40$

8. Eighteen chairs are to be placed along the walls of a rectangular room. Along each wall are the same number of chairs. Describe how the arrangement is accomplished.

9. Factor completely.
a. $a^2 - 3a - 40$ **b.** $x^2 + 17xy + 30y^2$
c. $m^2n^2 - 4mn - 12$ **d.** $x^2 + 7xy - 27y^2$
e. $32 - 12x + x^2$ **f.** $a^2 - 10ab + 9b^2$
g. $x^2 - 20x + 36$ **h.** $x^2 + 10xy + 21y^2$
i. $b^2c^2 - 10bc - 24$ **j.** $2p^2 + 52p + 50$
k. $3a^2 - 21a - 24$ **l.** $-5x^2 - 10x + 15$
m. $x^3 - 2x^2 - 63x$ **n.** $2a^3 + 26a^2 + 60a$
o. $4p^2 - 24p + 32$ **p.** $-xa^2 + 10xa + 56x$
q. $3x^2 + 48xy - 108y^2$ **r.** $5n^2 + 75mn + 180m^2$

10. If the trinomial $x^2 - 6x + p$ is factorable, then give four different values of p and factor each trinomial.

11. Factor completely.
a. $x^4 - 3x^2 - 40$ **b.** $a^4 + 12a^2 + 20$
c. $m^4 + m^2 - 12$ **d.** $p^4 - 16p^2 - 36$
e. $k^4 - 16k^2 + 28$ **f.** $x^4 + 17x^2 + 42$
g. $a^4 - 4a^2b - 5b^2$ **h.** $r^4 - 13r^2t + 36t^2$
i. $u^4 - u^2v^2 - 30v^4$ **j.** $p^4 - 9p^2q^3 - 22q^6$

12. Two men agree to meet for lunch at 12:30. Unknown to each other, the first man's watch is 5 min slow and the second man's watch is 8 min fast. According to their own watches, both men are 5 min late. How long does one man have to wait for the other?

13. Amanda is required to take half a spoon full of medicine. The spoon is presently two thirds full and by using another empty spoon of the same size, she can measure and take her medicine. Describe how she might have made the measurements.

97

4·11 Factoring Trinomials II

To factor trinomials of the form $ax^2 + bx + c$, where $a \neq 1$, an additional step in the process of Section 4·10 will be considered. For example, factor $8x^2 + 6x - 5$.

$8x^2 + 6x - 5$

$(8x^2)(-5) = -40x^2$ Determine two factors of $-40x^2$ such that the sum of these factors is $6x$. The terms $-4x$ and $10x$ satisfy these conditions.

$8x^2 + 6x - 5$
$= 8x^2 - 4x + 10x - 5$ Substitute $-4x + 10x$ for $6x$.
$= (8x^2 - 4x) + (10x - 5)$
$= 4x(2x - 1) + 5(2x - 1)$ Notice the common factors.
$= (2x - 1)(4x + 5)$

Example 1

Factor. $12x^2 + 11x + 2$
$= 12x^2 + 3x + 8x + 2$
$= (12x^2 + 3x) + (8x + 2)$
$= 3x(4x + 1) + 2(4x + 1)$
$= (4x + 1)(3x + 2)$

Product $= 24x^2$
Sum $= 11x$
   $= 3x + 8x$

Example 2

Factor. $6x^2 - 17x + 10$

$6x^2 - 12x - 5x + 10$
$= 6x(x - 2) - 5(x - 2)$
$= (x - 2)(6x - 5)$

Example 3

Factor. $6x^2 + 27xy - 54y^2$
$= 3(2x^2 + 9xy - 18y^2)$
$= 3(2x - 3y)(x + 6y)$

Example 4

Factor. $2(a + 2b)^2 + 3(a + 2b) + 1$

Let $(a + 2b)$ be a single variable u.
$2u^2 + 3u + 1 = (2u + 1)(u + 1)$
Replace u by $a + 2b$.
$= (2(a + 2b) + 1)(a + 2b + 1)$

Exercises

1. Find two integers which satisfy the two conditions.

	Product	Sum		Product	Sum
a.	54	21	b.	−132	1
c.	144	−25	d.	−56	10

2. Find all integral values for p so that the expression is factorable. The first one is done as an example.

$2x^2 + px - 5$
The product of the decomposed factors must be -10.

$2 \times (-5) = -10$ $2 + (-5) = -3$
$-2 \times 5 = -10$ $-2 + 5 = 3$
$1 \times (-10) = -10$ $1 + (-10) = -9$
$-1 \times 10 = -10$ $-1 + 10 = 9$
Values for p are $\pm 3, \pm 9$.

a. $5x^2 + px + 2$ **b.** $6x^2 + px - 3$

3. Factor. The first one is partially done for you.
a. $3x^2 + 17x + 10$
$= 3x^2 + 15x + \blacksquare + 10$
$= 3x(\blacksquare + \blacksquare) + 2(\underline{\hphantom{xxxx}})$
$= (\blacksquare + \blacksquare)(3x + 2)$

b. $2x^2 + 5x + 2$ **c.** $3x^2 - 13x + 12$
d. $8x^2 - 2x - 15$ **e.** $6x^2 + 11x + 3$
f. $12x^2 + 20x + 3$ **g.** $6x^2 - 19x + 15$

4. Factor. The first one is done for you.

$3x^2 + xy - 30y^2$
$= 3x^2 + 10xy - 9xy - 30y^2$
$= x(3x + 10y) - 3y(3x + 10y)$
$= (3x + 10y)(x - 3y)$

a. $5x^2 - 24xy - 5y^2$ **b.** $2a^2 + 5ab + 2b^2$
c. $18m^2 - 9mn - 2n^2$ **d.** $12x^2 - 19xy + 5y^2$
e. $2x^2 - 17xy + 36y^2$ **f.** $15x^2 + 18xz + 3z^2$
g. $6a^2 + 17ab - 14b^2$ **h.** $10p^2 + 17pq - 6q^2$

5. Express each as a product.

a. $8x^2 - 10x - 12$ **b.** $5x^2y - 9xy - 2y$
c. $18x^2 - 15x + 3$ **d.** $60x^2 - 25x - 10$
e. $2ax^2 + 15ax + 18a$ **f.** $16x^3 - 28x^2 - 30x$
g. $9a^2 + 21ab - 60b^2$ **h.** $2p^3 - 10p^2q^2 - 12pq^3$

6. Factor.

a. $4(x + y)^2 - (x + y) - 3$
b. $2(2p + q)^2 - (2p + q) - 15$
c. $5(x - 3y)^2 + 8(x - 3y) - 4$
d. $6(a - b)^2 - (a - b) - 2$
e. $(m + 2n)^2 - 10(m + 2n) + 24$
f. $4(5x + y)^2 - 2(5x + y) - 6$
g. $12(a + b)^2 + 24(a + b) - 15$

7. Factor.

a. $20x^2 + 11x - 3$ **b.** $x^2 + 13x + 12$
c. $12x^2 - 16x - 3$ **d.** $x^2 - 12x + 27$
e. $4a^2 + 22a + 10$ **f.** $18 + 27x - 5x^2$
g. $6p^2 + 3p - 165$ **h.** $18x^2 + 17x - 15$
i. $10y^2 - 23y + 9$ **j.** $x^3 + 22x^2 + 40x$
k. $(p - q)^2 - 5(p - q) - 6$ **l.** $81x^2y - 72xy + 15y$

8. Find an expression for the length of the rectangle.

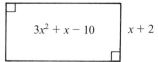

$3x^2 + x - 10$ $x + 2$

9. As Juan watched his father's red car circle the race track, he noticed that the number of other cars circling the track was equal to one half the cars in front of the red car, plus two thirds of the cars behind the same red car. How many cars were in the race?

10. Some trinomials of degree higher than 2 can be factored using the same process as in the display. Factor these trinomials. The first one is done as an example. Notice that each term has the same degree.

$2x^4 + 7x^2y^2 + 3y^4$
$= 2x^4 + 6x^2y^2 + x^2y^2 + 3y^4$
$= 2x^2(x^2 + 3y^2) + y^2(x^2 + 3y^2)$
$= (2x^2 + y^2)(x^2 + 3y^2)$

a. $4a^4 + 4a^2b^2 - 15b^4$
b. $3u^4 - 8u^2v^2 - 3v^4$
c. $5m^4 + 8m^2n^2 + 3n^4$
d. $12r^4 - 4r^2s^2 - 5s^4$
e. $6p^4 + 5p^2q^2 - 4q^4$
f. $2x^4 - 13x^2y^2 + 21y^4$
g. $16r^4 - 30r^2t^2 + 9t^4$
h. $2a^4 + 11a^2c^2 - 6c^4$

11. Factor each trinomial.

a. $15a^2 + a - 2$ **b.** $9x^2 - 24x + 16$
c. $2m^2 + mn - 10n^2$ **d.** $8p^4 + 6p^2q^2 + q^4$
e. $6r^2 - 11rs - 2s^2$ **f.** $6x^2 + 15xy - 9y^2$
g. $2a^2b^2 + 11abc + 12c^2$ **h.** $4m^3 - 18m^2n + 20mn^2$
i. $3(a + 3b)^2 - 2(a + 3b) - 1$
j. $5(2x - y)^2 + 7(2x - y) + 2$

12. The four letters $p, q, r,$ and s represent consecutive natural numbers. If the number represented by $10p + q$ is equal to the product of r and s, then what numbers do the letters $p, q, r,$ and s represent? There is more than one set of digits.

13. A candle is five times as long as another, but both burn in the same length of time. Both candles are lit at the same time. When the longer candle is half burned, how many times longer is it than the shorter candle?

14. Jason shared half his inheritance from his uncle's estate with the other four members of his family. He gave one quarter to his father, one third to his mother, one fifth to this sister, and $260 to his brother. How much did Jason inherit?

4·12 Difference of Two Squares

Find an expression for the area of the shaded region.

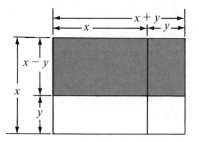

The larger shaded region has an area of $x(x-y)$ or $x^2 - xy$ square units.
The smaller shaded region has an area of $y(x-y)$ or $xy - y^2$ square units.

The combined area of the two regions is $(x^2 - xy) + (xy - y^2)$ or $x^2 - y^2$ square units.

The area of the shaded region is $(x+y)(x-y)$ or $x^2 - y^2$ square units.

The product of a sum and difference of two terms is equal to the difference of the squares of the two terms. Similarly, the difference of the squares of the two terms can be factored as the sum and difference of the square roots of the two terms.

$$x^2 - y^2 = (x+y)(x-y)$$

Example 1

Factor and check. $4x^2 - 25$
$= (2x - 5)(2x + 5)$

Check: $(2x - 5)(2x + 5)$
$\quad = 4x^2 + 10x - 10x - 25$
$\quad = 4x^2 - 25$ It checks.

Example 2

Factor. $18m^2 - 72n^2$

Check for a common factor first.
$= 18(m^2 - 4n^2)$
$= 18(m + 2n)(m - 2n)$

Example 3

Factor. $x^4 - 16y^8$
$= (x^2 + 4y^4)(x^2 - 4y^4)$

Check each factor to see if they also factor.
$= (x^2 + 4y^4)(x - 2y^2)(x + 2y^2)$

Example 4

Factor. $(a + b)^2 - c^2$

Let $a + b = x$.
$x^2 - c^2 = (x - c)(x + c)$
Replace x by $a + b$.
$= (a + b - c)(a + b + c)$

Example 5

Factor. $x^2 - (y - 4z)^2$

Let $y - 4z = c$.
$x^2 - c^2 = (x + c)(x - c)$
Replace c by $y - 4z$.
$= (x + y - 4z)(x - y + 4z)$

Example 6

Factor. $(a - 3b)^2 - (2a + b)^2$
$= [(a - 3b) + (2a + b)][(a - 3b) - (2a + b)]$
$= [a - 3b + 2a + b][a - 3b - 2a - b]$
$= -(3a - 2b)(a + 4b)$

Exercises

1. Copy and complete so that each polynomial is factored by the difference of two squares.

a. $9x^2 - \blacksquare = (\blacksquare + 4y)(\blacksquare - \blacksquare)$

b. $\blacksquare - 25 = (3x + \blacksquare)(\blacksquare - \blacksquare)$

c. $4p^2 - \blacksquare = (\blacksquare + \blacksquare)(\blacksquare - 9r)$

d. $8x^2 - \blacksquare = 2(\blacksquare + \blacksquare)(\blacksquare - 1)$

e. $\blacksquare - 3y^2 = 3(3x + \blacksquare)(\blacksquare - \blacksquare)$

f. $20x^2 - \blacksquare = 5(\blacksquare + 1)(\blacksquare - \blacksquare)$

2. Express each as a product. Check the factors to see if they can be factored again.

a. $16x^2 - 1$ **b.** $a^2 - 4b^2$

c. $81m^2 - 36n^2$ **d.** $x^2 - 9y^4$

e. $64 - p^2$ **f.** $49r^2 - 121s^2$

g. $4x^4 - 81$ **h.** $a^2 - b^2c^2$

i. $9a^2 - 100b^6$ **j.** $4x^8y^4 - 1$

k. $49 - 16d^6$ **l.** $144x^2 - 25$

m. $a^4 - 169$ **n.** $p^2q^4 - r^2$

3. Factor completely.

a. $12x^2 - 75$ **b.** $a^3 - ab^2$

c. $45m^2 - 20$ **d.** $6x^2 - 216y^4$

e. $x^3 - 64x$ **f.** $2x^4 - 450x^2$

g. $a^5 - a$ **h.** $128x^8 - 8x^2$

i. $2a^4 - 18a^2$ **j.** $12x^3y - 3xy$

4. Factor completely.

a. $x^4 - 1$ **b.** $81a^8 - 16b^4$

c. $a^4 - 81y^4$ **d.** $256x^{12} - y^8$

e. $p^4 - 81$ **f.** $x^4 - 16y^{16}$

g. $2x^8 - 2$ **h.** $16 - x^{12}$

5. Factor. Simplify where possible.

a. $(x + y)^2 - z^2$ **b.** $(3a + b)^2 - 4c^2$

c. $(x - 5y)^2 - 9z^4$ **d.** $(2a - 3b)^2 - b^2$

e. $(5x + y)^2 - 25y^2$ **f.** $x^2 - (3x + y)^2$

g. $9a^2 - (2b - 6c)^2$ **h.** $16 - (2x + 3)^2$

i. $m^2 - (m - 4n)^2$ **j.** $25x^2 - (4x + 9)^2$

k. $4 - (3x - 2)^2$ **l.** $36p^2 - (q + 4t)^2$

6. Factor. Simplify where possible.

a. $(2a + b)^2 - (a - 3b)^2$

b. $(3x + 2)^2 - (x + 4)^2$

c. $(p - 6q)^2 - (3p + q)^2$

d. $(x + 3)^2 - (5x - 2)^2$

e. $4(a + 4)^2 - (2a - 1)^2$

7. Use a variety of factoring skills to factor each expression completely.

a. $2x^4 - 7x^2 - 4$ **b.** $a^4 - 6a^2 - 27$

c. $3p^4 - p^2q^2 - 2q^4$ **d.** $3m^4 - 10m^2n^2 - 8n^4$

8. Factor. Check the factors to see if they factor.

a. $(x^2 + 3x)^2 - 4$ **b.** $(2a^2 - 5a)^2 - 4$

c. $(3p^2 - 4p)^2 - 16$ **d.** $25 - (7t + 2t^2)^2$

e. $9t^4 - (5t + 2)^2$ **f.** $m^4 - (n^2 - 2m^2)^2$

9. A bank offers a choice in its chequing accounts. You may select a monthly service charge of $3.00 plus $0.40 for each cheque written or a straight charge of $0.65 for each cheque.

a. If you average 6 cheques per month, then which plan would be the better choice?

b. At what point would the other choice be more economical?

10. Use a variety of factoring skills to factor each expression completely.

a. $45x^2 - 20$ **b.** $4p^2 - 4p - 15$

c. $64a^2 + 16ab + b^2$ **d.** $49m^4 - 16n^2$

e. $6u^2 - 7uv - 10v^2$ **f.** $48 - 72c + 27c^2$

g. $6a^3 + 20a^2 - 16a$ **h.** $12k^2 - 20k + 7$

i. $m^4 - (p^2 + 2q)^2$ **j.** $4x^4 - 15x^2 - 25$

k. $8p^2 - 44pq - 24q^2$ **l.** $9a^2b^2 - 64c^6$

m. $(2x + 5)^2 - 9$ **n.** $12m^2 + 17mn + 5n^2$

11. What is the volume of dirt, measured in cubic centimetres, contained in a hole that is 1 m deep, 3 m wide, and 4 m long?

12. The cost of 2 is $0.76. The cost of 12 is $1.52. The cost of 124 is $2.28. What is being purchased?

13. A thin pipe, 8 m in length, is cut and welded to form a cube. What would be the largest volume contained in the cube? Ignore the losses due to cuts being made.

14. Use factoring to calculate each. The first one is partially done for you.

a. $(98)(102) = (100 - 2)(100 + 2)$

$= \rule{2cm}{0.3cm}$

$= \rule{1.5cm}{0.3cm}$

b. $(85)(115)$ **c.** $(75)(125)$

d. $(950)(1050)$ **e.** $(55)(65)$

4·13 Perfect Trinomial Squares

Find an expression for the area of a square whose side lengths are given by the expression $2a + b$.

$$2a + \qquad b$$

	$2a +$	b
$2a$ +	$4a^2$	$2ab$
b	$2ab$	b^2

The area of the square is $(2a + b)(2a + b)$ or $4a^2 + 4ab + b^2$ square units.

A trinomial is classified as a perfect square when these conditions are met.

1. The first and last terms are perfect squares.

2. The middle term is equal to twice the product of the square roots of the first and last terms.

These trinomials are called **perfect trinomial squares**.

$$a^2 + 2ab + b^2 = (a + b)(a + b)$$

Example

Factor completely.

a. $16x^2 - 24x + 9$
$= (4x - 3)^2$

b. $49x^2 + 14xy + y^2$
$= (7x + y)^2$

c. $18x^2 + 60x + 50$
$= 2(9x^2 + 30x + 25)$
$= 2(3x + 5)^2$

Exercises

1. Copy and complete so that each trinomial is a perfect square.
a. $9x^2 + \blacksquare + 1$
b. $100a^2 - 60a + \blacksquare$
c. $36 + \blacksquare + x^2$
d. $4x^2 + 44x + \blacksquare$

2. Express each as a product.
a. $x^2 + 10x + 25$
b. $16a^2 + 24a + 9$
c. $x^2 - 2x + 1$
d. $64x^2 + 16x + 1$
e. $49y^2 - 56y + 16$
f. $9x^2 + 48x + 64$
g. $25x^2 + 20xy + 4y^2$
h. $9x^2 - 60xz + 100z^2$
i. $4a^2 + 36ac + 81c^2$
j. $36a^2b^2 - 12ab + 1$
k. $16 + 40pq + 25p^2q^2$
l. $9x^2 - 30xyz + 25y^2z^2$

3. Factor.
a. $2x^2 + 16x + 32$
b. $3a^2 - 18ab + 27b^2$
c. $x^2y + 10xy + 25y$
d. $18ax^2 + 48ax + 32a$
e. $-2x^2 - 4x - 2$
f. $6x^2 - 72xy + 216y^2$
g. $-50x^2 - 40x - 8$
h. $108 - 180p + 75p^2$

4. If the expression $9x^2 + 42x + 49$ represents the area of a square, then find an expression for the length of the sides of the square.

5. A bag contains 3 green, 3 yellow, and 3 red balls. If we must be certain to have at least one ball of each colour in the bag, then what is the largest number of balls that should be removed from the bag?

6. Factoring can be used to assist in calculations. Factor each to evaluate. The first one is partially completed for you.
a. $52^2 = (50 + 2)^2$
$= 2500 + \blacksquare + \blacksquare$
$= \blacksquare$
b. 27^2
c. 36^2
d. 112^2

102

4·14 Nested Form of a Polynomial

Polynomials are evaluated by substituting the values of the variables directly into the expression. The computation can often become complicated unless the expression is simplified first. The simplification can involve factoring.

Example 1

Evaluate $2a^2 + 5ab - 3b^2$ for $a = 18$ and $b = -7$.

$2a^2 + 5ab - 3b^2$
$= (2a - b)(a + 3b)$
$= [2(18) - (-7)][18 + 3(-7)]$
$= -129$

Factor the polynomial, then substitute the values for a and b.

Sometimes a polynomial can be grouped into smaller expressions, and these expressions can be factored.

Example 2

Evaluate $x^4 - 3x^3 + 2x^2 - 8x - 10$ for $x = 4$.

$x\{x^3 - 3x^2 + 2x - 8\} - 10$
$= x\{x[x^2 - 3x + 2] - 8\} - 10$
$= x\{x[x(x - 3) + 2] - 8\} - 10$
$= 4\{4[4(4 - 3) + 2] - 8\} - 10$
$= 54$

Group so that the variable x is the common factor.

This successive grouping and factoring of the polynomial results in a **nested form** of the polynomial. The advantage of evaluating an expression in its nested form is that calculations can be performed either mentally or using a calculator.

Exercises

1. Evaluate each polynomial for $x = 24$ and $y = 16$.
a. $x^2 + xy - 6y^2$ **b.** $2x^2 - xy - 15y^2$
c. $x^2 + 4xy + 4y^2$ **d.** $x^2 - 9y^2$
e. $3x^2 + 8xy + 5y^2$ **f.** $2x^2 - 12x + 18$

2. The profit made on ticket sales is determined by the number of tickets sold. If n is the number of tickets, then the profit is given by the expression $(350n - n^2)$ cents.
a. Use a calculator to determine the profit on the sale of 64 tickets.
b. Determine the profit on the sale of 120 tickets without using a calculator.

3. Think of any number, n. Subtract 8 from the number and multiply the result by 2. Add 7 to this result. Describe the next two steps that will lead to the original number.

4. Write each as a nested form of a polynomial. Evaluate each expression. Check your answer using a calculator.
a. $x^4 + 2x^3 - 5x^2 - 12$; $x = 4$
b. $2x^3 - 6x^2 + x + 4$; $x = 6$
c. $x^4 + 4x^3 - 2x^2 + x - 8$; $x = 3$
d. $3x^5 - 2x^3 + 5x^2 + x - 4$; $x = -2$
e. $-x^4 + 5x^3 - 4x^2 + 3x - 12$; $x = 2$
f. $2x^5 - x^3 + 4x^2 + 2x - 18$; $x = -1$

4·15 Division of Polynomials

In Chapter 3, the laws for the division of exponents were introduced. These same laws can be used to divide polynomials by both monomials and binomials.

When a polynomial is divided by a monomial, each term of the polynomial is divided by the monomial.

Example 1

Simplify by dividing.

a. $\dfrac{18x^2 - 10x}{2x}$

$= \dfrac{18x^2}{2x} - \dfrac{10x}{2x}$

$= 9x - 5$

b. $\dfrac{24a^2b^2 + 30ab^3 - 15a^2b^4}{3ab^2}$

$= \dfrac{24a^2b^2}{3ab^2} + \dfrac{30ab^3}{3ab^2} - \dfrac{15a^2b^4}{3ab^2}$

$= 8a + 10b - 5ab^2$

Recall: $\dfrac{x^m}{x^n} = x^{m-n}$

Dividing a polynomial by a binomial parallels the long-division process with numbers.

Example 2

Divide. $(3x^2 - 7x - 20) \div (x - 4)$

$$
\begin{array}{r}
3x + 5 \\
x - 4 \overline{)\, 3x^2 - 7x - 20} \\
3x^2 - 12x \\
\hline
5x - 20 \\
5x - 20 \\
\hline
0
\end{array}
$$

$(3x^2) \div (x) = 3x$

$(3x)(x - 4) = 3x^2 - 12x$

$(3x^2 - 7x) - (3x^2 - 12x) = 5x$

$(5x) \div (x) = 5$

$(5)(x - 4) = 5x - 20$

$(5x - 20) - (5x - 20) = 0$

Example 3

Divide. $(x^3 + 5x^2 - 12) \div (x + 2)$

Occasionally a polynomial may be without one or more terms, and for convenience, a term with a coefficient of zero is inserted as a placeholder.

$$
\begin{array}{r}
x^2 + 3x - 6 \\
x + 2 \overline{)\, x^3 + 5x^2 + 0x - 12} \\
x^3 + 2x^2 \\
\hline
3x^2 + 0x \\
3x^2 + 6x \\
\hline
-6x - 12 \\
-6x - 12 \\
\hline
0
\end{array}
$$

$0x$ is used as a placeholder.

Exercises

1. Divide.

a. $\dfrac{16x^3y^2}{12x^2y}$ **b.** $\dfrac{20a^6b^4}{35a^3b^6}$

c. $\dfrac{36x^5y^2z^3}{-18x^3yz^2}$ **d.** $\dfrac{8a^2b^4}{6a^4b^2}$

e. $\dfrac{-45pq^3}{30p^2q^3}$ **f.** $\dfrac{24xz^3}{20x^2y^2}$

g. $\dfrac{-42ab^5}{-18a^2b^2}$ **h.** $\dfrac{9x^3y}{9xy}$

i. $\dfrac{(3m^2)(4mn)}{6mn}$ **j.** $\dfrac{(-15u^3v)(3uv^3)}{9u^2v^2}$

k. $\dfrac{(4st^2)(-6s^2t^2)}{8s^4t}$ **l.** $\dfrac{(a^2b)(8b)(5a^2)}{10a^2b^2}$

2. Divide.

a. $\dfrac{5x-10}{5}$ **b.** $\dfrac{6x^2-18x}{6x}$

c. $\dfrac{3x^2+12x-6}{3}$ **d.** $\dfrac{8a+20b-4c}{4}$

e. $\dfrac{2a^3+16a^2-10a}{2a}$ **f.** $\dfrac{4x^3y-10x^2}{2x}$

g. $\dfrac{12a^4b^3-8a^2b^2}{4a^2b}$ **h.** $\dfrac{12x^2y+36xy^3-6xy}{6xy}$

i. $\dfrac{6x^3y+15x^2y^2-9xy^3}{3xy}$ **j.** $\dfrac{-12p^2+2pq+30p^2q}{-2p}$

3. The total cost of operating a car over a given period of time is given by the expression $\$(12x^3+40x^2+13x-30)$.

a. If the car has travelled $(2x+3)$ km, then find an expression for the cost of operating the car per kilometre.

b. If there are $(3x-2)$ weeks in the given time period, then find an expression for the cost of operating the car per week.

4. Divide.

a. $\dfrac{18x^2-3x-10}{3x+2}$ **b.** $\dfrac{4x^2+20x+25}{2x+5}$

c. $\dfrac{8x^2+6x-9}{4x-3}$ **d.** $\dfrac{18y^2-15y-25}{6y+5}$

e. $\dfrac{x^3-8}{x-2}$ **f.** $\dfrac{8a^3-32a+21}{2a-3}$

g. $\dfrac{8x^3+2x^2-61x+15}{x+3}$ **h.** $\dfrac{3x^3-2x^2-6x+4}{3x-2}$

i. $\dfrac{2x^3+6x^2+x+3}{x+3}$ **j.** $\dfrac{6x^3-2x^2+3x-1}{3x-1}$

k. $\dfrac{m^4-m^3+m^2-m}{m^2+1}$

l. $\dfrac{2x^5+2x^4-3x^3-3x^2+x+1}{2x^2-1}$

5. The area of a rectangle is given by the expression $2x^4+8x^3-3x^2-20x-5$. If the width of the rectangle is given by the expression $2x^2-5$, then find an expression for the length of the rectangle.

6. Carolyn conducted a survey at school. Her results are shown below. How many different students are accounted for in this survey?

86 students are enrolled in Mathematics.

45 students are enrolled in Physics.

65 students are enrolled in English.

50 students are enrolled in both Mathematics and English.

31 students are enrolled in both Mathematics and Physics.

20 students are enrolled in both English and Physics.

12 students are enrolled in all three.

7. A sum of $12x^2+11x-15$ dollars is to be divided equally among $3x+5$ people. Find an expression for how much money each person will receive.

8. A car travels at a rate of $(2x+5)$ km/h for a distance of $(8x^3-2x^2-61x-15)$ km. Find an expression for the length of time a car will travel to cover this distance.

9. Two bags each contain 3 green, 3 yellow, and 3 red balls. Without looking, the maximum number of balls is removed from the first bag while still being certain that it contains one of each colour. The balls which have been removed are placed in the second bag. Again, without looking, the smallest number of balls are transferred back to the first bag so that the first bag contains at least two balls of each colour. How many balls remain in the second bag?

10. The total value of $(x-8)$ cheques is given by the expression $\$(x^2+4x-96)$. Determine the average value of each cheque.

4·16 Zeros of a Polynomial

Sue challenged Christopher and Michael by saying: "I am thinking of a pair of numbers such that their product is zero. What can be said about the numbers?"

Christopher was the first to reply by saying: "Although I do not know what the two numbers are, I know that at least one of the numbers must be zero."

> If $(a)(b) = 0$, then $a = 0$, or $b = 0$, or $a = b = 0$.

Michael thought of a more intriguing problem. He wondered what the value for x is if one number is given by the expression $x + 3$, the other number by the expression $2x - 5$, and their product is zero.

Christopher volunteered the information that one or both expressions must equal zero.

Either $x + 3 = 0$ or $2x - 5 = 0$

$$x = -3 \qquad\qquad x = \frac{5}{2}$$

Therefore, the two values for x must be either -3 or $\frac{5}{2}$.

> **Zeros of a polynomial** are the values for the variable(s) that will make the polynomial equal to zero.

Example 1

Find the zeros of each polynomial. Begin by letting the polynomial equal zero.

a. $3x^2 - 10x + 8$

Let $3x^2 - 10x + 8 = 0$
$(3x - 4)(x - 2) = 0$
$3x - 4 = 0$ or $x - 2 = 0$
Either $x = \frac{4}{3}$ or $x = 2$.

The zeros are $\frac{4}{3}$ and 2.

b. $6x^2 + 15x$

Let $6x^2 + 15x = 0$
$3x(2x + 5) = 0$
$3x = 0$ or $2x + 5 = 0$
Either $x = 0$ or $x = -\frac{5}{2}$.

The zeros are 0 and $-\frac{5}{2}$.

Example 2

Find two positive integers such that the larger is 4 more than the smaller and the sum of their squares is 400.

Let the smaller number be x. Then the larger number is $x + 4$.

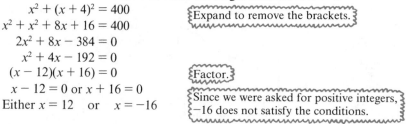

$$x^2 + (x + 4)^2 = 400$$
$$x^2 + x^2 + 8x + 16 = 400$$
$$2x^2 + 8x - 384 = 0$$
$$x^2 + 4x - 192 = 0$$
$$(x - 12)(x + 16) = 0$$
$$x - 12 = 0 \text{ or } x + 16 = 0$$
Either $x = 12$ or $x = -16$

> Expand to remove the brackets.

> Factor.

> Since we were asked for positive integers, -16 does not satisfy the conditions.

The smaller integer is 12. The larger integer is $x + 4$ or 16. Therefore, the two integers are 12 and 16.

Exercises

1. From the display, explain why Christopher is correct in his reasoning for Sue's problem.

2. If a number is multiplied by 5, the result is equal to zero. What number would make this statement true?

3. If $P(x) = x^2 - 2x - 8$, then find the value of each. Find the zeros of $P(x)$.

a. $P(-4)$ **b.** $P(-2)$ **c.** $P(0)$
d. $P(2)$ **e.** $P(4)$ **f.** $P(3)$

4. For what values of p will the polynomials equal zero?

a. $p + 2$ **b.** $4p$
c. $p(q - 2)$ **d.** $-2p(q + 5)$
e. $(p - 3)(q^2 + 1)$ **f.** $(5p + 2)(q^2 + 1)$

5. For what values of x will the polynomials equal zero?

a. $(x + 6)(x - 3)$ **b.** $(x - 5)(x + 1)$
c. $x(x + 10)$ **d.** $(2x - 7)(x + 5)$
e. $(4x - 3)(5x + 2)$ **f.** $(x + 6)(5x + 8)$
g. $3x(x - 5)$ **h.** $(x - 6)(2x + 1)$
i. $(6x + 5)(3x - 8)$ **j.** $-6x(5x - 3)$

6. Find the zeros of the polynomials.

a. $5x^2 + 10x$ **b.** $x^2 - 6x + 5$
c. $x^2 - 36$ **d.** $6x^2 - 20x$
e. $2x^2 - 5x - 3$ **f.** $3x^2 + 18x + 27$
g. $25x^2 - 16$ **h.** $4x^2 - 7x - 2$

7. Factor to find the value(s) for x that make each expression true.

a. $2x(3x - 5) - 8(3x - 5) = 0$
b. $5x(x - 8) + (x - 8) = 0$

8. The height, in metres, of a projectile above the ground is given by the formula $h = 12t - 3t^2$. At what time, t, is the object 9 m above the ground?

9. Find two positive integers such that one is 5 less than the other and their product is 104.

10. In a right triangle, the hypotenuse is 9 cm longer than the shortest side and the third side is 1 cm longer than the shortest side. Find the length of the hypotenuse.

11. Find the value(s) of the variable.
a. $3a - 12 = 0$ **b.** $x^2 - 16 = 0$
c. $m^2 - 3m - 10 = 0$ **d.** $y^2 - 9y + 8 = 0$
e. $4p^2 + 7p - 15 = 0$ **f.** $6x^2 - 17x - 14 = 0$

12. Group the terms and factor to find the zeros of the polynomial. The first one is done as an example.

$$3xy - 9y + 2x - 6$$
$$(3xy - 9y) + (2x - 6) = 0$$
$$3y(x - 3) + 2(x - 3) = 0$$
$$(3y + 2)(x - 3) = 0$$
$$3y + 2 = 0 \text{ or } x - 3 = 0$$
$$y = -\frac{2}{3} \qquad x = 3$$

a. $2xy - 5y + 4x - 10$ **b.** $x + 2xy - 12y - 6$

13. A computerized machine that manufactures engine parts is profitable to use as long as it produces above a certain number of parts every hour. Profit is calculated using the formula $P = 450 + 7n - n^2$, where n represents the number of parts. What value of n will result in no profit?

14. You have two containers with different quantities of water. Container A has more water than B. From container A pour into B as much water as is already in B. Then from container B pour into A as much water as is already in A. Once again pour as much water into B as is contained in B. Finally, pour 1 L of water from B into A. If there are now 19 L of water in both containers, then how much water was in each at the beginning?

15. Wooden stripping is placed inside a window frame as shown. If the window measures 100 cm by 50 cm and the area of the space left is 864 cm², then find the width of the strip.

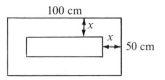

107

4·17 Applications of Polynomials to Problem Solving

Many problems in mathematics can be solved using polynomials.

Example 1

Find an expression for the area of a rectangle whose side lengths are given by the expressions $5x + 6$ and $3x + 4$. All measurements are made in centimetres.

$(3x + 4)$ cm

$(5x + 6)$ cm

$$\begin{aligned}
\text{Area} &= (\text{length})(\text{width}) \\
&= (5x + 6)(3x + 4) \\
&= 15x^2 + 38x + 24
\end{aligned}$$

The area of the rectangle is given by $(15x^2 + 38x + 24)$ cm².

Example 2

A poster has an area of 4000 cm². If the length of the poster is 30 cm longer than the width, then what are the dimensions of the poster?

Let x be the width of the poster.
Then the length is given by the expression $x + 30$.

$$\begin{aligned}
x(x + 30) &= 4000 \\
x^2 + 30x - 4000 &= 0 \\
(x - 50)(x + 80) &= 0 \\
x - 50 = 0 \text{ or } x + 80 &= 0 \\
\text{Either } x = 50 \quad \text{or} \quad x &= -80
\end{aligned}$$

The solution to an equation may not satisfy the conditions given in the original problem. You should look back to the original question to ensure that your answer is possible.
Since dimensions cannot be negative, the only possible solution for x is 50.
Therefore, the width of the poster is 50 cm and the length is 80 cm.

Exercises

1. Find the area of the triangle. All measurements are made in centimetres.

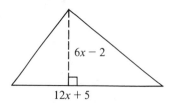

$6x - 2$

$12x + 5$

2. The total cost of a bundle of pens is given by the expression $\$(6x^2 + 11x - 10)$. If you purchase $2x + 5$ pens, then find an expression for the amount that you would pay.

3. The wholesale price of a computer disk is given by $\$(4x - 3)$. If there are $(x^2 - 3x - 2)$ disks in a shipment, then find an expression for the total cost of all the disks.

4. A pilot and a copilot are to be chosen from a group of four people of different ages. If the pilot must always be the older person, then how many different crews can be selected?

5. The dimensions of a parking lot are as shown.
a. Find an expression for the area.
b. Find an expression for the perimeter.
c. If $x = 5$ m and $y = 2$ m, then find the actual area and perimeter.

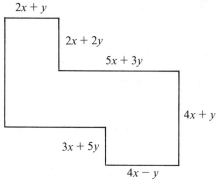

2x + y
2x + 2y
5x + 3y
4x + y
3x + 5y
4x − y

6. Find the volume and the surface area of this closed prism.

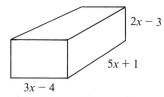

2x − 3
5x + 1
3x − 4

7. A solid sphere inside a cube touches all the sides of the cube. If the radius of the sphere is given by the expression $x + 2$, then find the volume of air contained within the cube but outside the sphere. The formula for the volume of a sphere is $V = \frac{4}{3}\pi r^3$.

8. Two positive numbers that differ by 7 have a product of 858. Find the numbers.

9. The profit in the production of an item is given by the equation $P = 2n^2 + 9n - 45$, where n represents the number of cartons of the item produced. Determine the number of cartons of the item that must be produced to break even.

10. Jenna wishes to purchase a package of licorice for her friends. The regular cylindrical package of licorice is 20 cm in circumference. Since these packages have all been sold out, the store manager says that he would sell her two packages, each 10 cm in circumference and the same height as the regular cylindrical package, for the same price of the larger package. Is this a good buy for Jenna?

11. The mass of a package is given by the expression $3n + 8$. If there are $2n - 1$ of these packages, then find an expression for the total mass of the packages. The mass is measured in grams.

12. Find the area of the trapezoid.
Area $= \frac{1}{2}(a + b)h$.

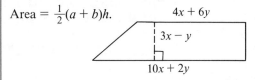

4x + 6y
3x − y
10x + 2y

13. Find the area of the shaded portion of the end of this Quonset hut.

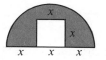

x
x
x   x   x

14. The base of a triangle is 2 cm shorter than the height. If the area of the triangle is 144 cm², find the height of the triangle.

15. If the base of the triangle in Exercise 14 is increased by y cm, then write an expression which represents the increase in the area of the new triangle.

16. In a pen of 132 guinea pigs, 79 have some black fur, 88 have some white fur, and 4 have neither black nor white fur. How many have both black and white fur?

17. The average speed of a car is given by the expression $(4x - 3)$ km/h. If it maintains that rate, then find an expression for the distance it will travel in $(2x + 7)$ h. The distance is measured in kilometres.

4·18 Computer Application — Zeros of a Polynomial

Finding the zeros of a polynomial can be difficult, especially when the polynomial is not easily factored. This program will allow you to guess values to make a polynomial equal to zero. It will tell you whether your guess was too high or too low.

```
10 REM FINDING THE ZEROS OF A POLYNOMIAL
20 PRINT "THE POLYNOMIAL IS X ∧ 2 − 2 * X − 8"
25 PRINT
30 INPUT "WHAT VALUE DO YOU THINK X WILL BE? "; X
40 LET Y = X ∧ 2 − 2 * X − 8
50 PRINT "YOUR GUESS GAVE THE POLYNOMIAL A VALUE OF "; Y
60 IF Y > 0 THEN PRINT "ABSOLUTE VALUE OF YOUR GUESS IS TOO
HIGH"
70 IF Y < 0 THEN PRINT "ABSOLUTE VALUE OF YOUR GUESS IS TOO
LOW"
80 IF Y <> 0 THEN 20
90 PRINT "YOU HAVE FOUND A ZERO OF THE POLYNOMIAL AT "; X
99 END
```

Exercises

1. Explain why the absolute value of the guess is either too high or too low.

2. Which statement defines the polynomial
a. to the user?
b. to the computer?

3. What is the purpose of having the computer return to line 20 if your original guess did not produce a zero?

4. Which line asks for your value of the polynomial?

5. Describe what the computer will print when executing line 50.

6. In line 30, if you guess a value of 1 for X, then what value will the polynomial have?

7. Explain what happens if the value of the polynomial never equals zero.

8. Which line determines when a zero has been identified?

9. Copy and complete this program. It tests possible values for the variable to find the zeros of the polynomial without waiting for the operator to enter a guess.

```
10 REM ■■■■■■■■■■■■■
20 PRINT "THE POLYNOMIAL IS
X ∧ 2 + X − 2"
30 PRINT
40 FOR X = −10 TO 10
50 LET Y = ■■■■■■■■■■
60 IF Y = ■■■ THEN PRINT
"ZERO FOUND AT "; ■■■
70 NEXT ■■■
80 ■■■■■■■■
```

10. What is the function of lines 40 and 70 in the program of Exercise 9?

4·19 Chapter Review

1. Classify each according to the number of terms and the degree of the polynomial, and then arrange in decreasing order of degree in x.
a. $5x + x^2$
b. $-8x^3 - 5 + 12x$
c. $15x^4y$
d. $3y^2 + 8xy - 2x^2$

2. Evaluate each if $a = 4$, $b = -1$, and $c = 3$.
a. $2c + a^2$
b. $4a + 12b - 5c$
c. $3(a + b) + c^2$
d. $a^2 + b^2 - bc$

3. The area of any triangle ABC is given by
$$A = \sqrt{s(s - a)(s - b)(s - c)},$$
where $s = (a + b + c) \div 2$. Find the area of a triangle whose sides are 7 cm, 24 cm, and 25 cm.

4. Find the sum of the two polynomials.
a. $14x - 5y$; $2x + 8y$
b. $6a^2 + a - 8$; $-2a^2 + 5a + 4$
c. $3xy - 9yz + 5xz$; $2xy - 9yz - xz$

5. Subtract the second polynomial from the first polynomial.
a. $6x^2 + 5x - 14$; $8x^2 - x + 3$
b. $2ab + 5bc$; $2bc - 4ac + 9ab$

6. Expand and simplify by collecting like terms.
a. $3a(a^2 - 4a - 2)$
b. $-5x^2(4 - 3x + x^2)$
c. $4(x^2 - 3x - 9) - 5(2x^2 + 1)$
d. $6x(2x + 5) + 3(x^2 + 2)$
e. $x[5 - 3(x + 2)] + 6$

7. Expand and simplify.
a. $(x - 2)(x + 15)$
b. $(x + 3)(x^2 - 2)$
c. $(3x - 1)(x^2 - 5x - 3)$
d. $(x - 3)(x + 2)(x + 5)$
e. $(x - 4)(x + 6) + (2x - 5)(x + 2)$
f. $(5x + 3)(x - 2) - 5(x^2 - 8)$
g. $(x + 3)^2 + (2x + 5)(2x - 5)$

8. Evaluate each if $x = 2$.
a. $8(x - 4) - 2(3x + 5) + x^2$
b. $(x^2 - 4x + 1)(x^2 + 3)$

9. Use variables to represent the statements in algebraic form.
a. The discount is equal to the original price less the sale price. Find an expression for the discount if the original price is given by the expression $12x + 5y - 16z$ and the sale price is given by the expression $-4x + 9y + z$.
b. The electromotive force is equal to the product of the current and the resistance. Find the electromotive force if the current is given by the expression $2x^2 + x - 5$ and the resistance by the expression $4x^2 - 3$.

10. Find the GCF of each pair.
a. $132x^2$, $180x$
b. $-84ab^2c$, $35a^2c^2$

11. Find the two factors of the terms in Column A whose sum appears in Column B.

	Column A	Column B
a.	$12x^2$	$-13x$
b.	$-8x^2$	$2x$
c.	$48x^2$	$-8x$
d.	$-63x^2$	$18x$

12. Factor completely.
a. $2x^2 + 15x - 8$
b. $12x^2 - 7x + 1$
c. $8a^2 + 28a$
d. $36p^2 - 25$
e. $4x^2 + 4x + 1$
f. $4m^3 - 2m^2 - 30m$
g. $12x^3 + 30xy^2 + 6x$
h. $(5x + y)^2 - 9$
i. $4a^2 + 28ab + 49b^2$
j. $75x^2 - 60mx + 12m^2$
k. $4x^4 - 17x^2 - 15$
l. $a^2b^2 - 10ab + 24$
m. $12xy - 5 + 30y - 2x$
n. $10x^6 - x^3y - 2y^2$

13. Simplify the formula by factoring.
a. $A = \pi r^2 + 2\pi rh$
b. $A = 2wl + 2wh + 2hl$
c. $A = p + prt$
d. $A = \pi R^2 - \pi r^2$
e. $A = \frac{1}{2}ah + \frac{1}{2}bh$
f. $a_n = a_1 + nd - d$

14. By grouping those terms which contain a common factor, write the polynomials in nested form and evaluate for $x = 3$.
a. $2x^2 - 5x + 8$
b. $x^2 + 2x - 4$
c. $x^3 - 4x^2 + 5x - 6$
d. $2x^5 - 5x^4 - x^2 - 18$

4·20 Chapter Test

1. What is the numerical coefficient of the third-degree term?
$4x^3y - x^2y + 2xy + 3$

2. What is the degree of this polynomial? Write the polynomial in descending order of degree in b.
$5a^3 - 3ab^2 - a^2b + 16b^4$

3. Evaluate each if $m = -4$, $n = 2$, and $p = 6$.
a. $3m^2 - 5np$ **b.** $2(3m + 8n) - 2p$
c. $(3n + m)(2n + p)$ **d.** $2n(3m + 4p - 5)$

4. Add.
a. $3x^2 - 6xy - 8y^2$ **b.** $7p^2 + 3p + 18$
     $-7x^2 + xy + 10y^2$ $6p^2 \qquad - 33$
     $22x^2 - 15xy + 6y^2$

5. Subtract the second polynomial from the first.
a. $(4x^2 + 16xy + y^2); (x^2 - 9xy + 3y^2)$
b. $(5pq - 9qr - 16pr); (28pq + 5qr - 3pr)$
c. $(m^2 - 4); (5m^2 - 2m + 3)$
d. $18; k^2 + 5$

6. Expand.
a. $(4x^2y)(-xy^2z)(-3xz)$
b. $(14a^3b)(2a - 3b^3)$
c. $(xy - 3)(xy + 8)$
d. $(4m - 3n)(2m - 9n)$
e. $(6x - y)(x^2 + 5xy - 3y^2)$
f. $(a^2 + 3a - 3)(a^2 - a - 5)$

7. Expand and simplify.
a. $3x(4x - 5) + 5(x^2 - 1)$
b. $2[4(3y - 2) + 9]$
c. $(x + 3)(x - 2) - (x - 6)(x - 3)$
d. $4(2x - 3)(x - 3) + 12x$
e. $(2x - 1)(x + 4) + 2(x + 3)(x - 3)$
f. $(3x - 2)^2 + (8x + 5)(8x - 5)$
g. $3(2p + 5)(p - 3) - (p + 2)^2$

8. Find all possible values of p that will make the expression factorable.
a. $x^2 + px + 4$ **b.** $3x^2 + px - 2$
c. $x^2 + px - 5$ **d.** $5x^2 - px + 4$

9. Factor completely.
a. $8a^3 - 12a$ **b.** $x^2 - 5x - 24$
c. $49s^2 - 4t^2$ **d.** $4a^2 + 20ab + 25b^2$
e. $18x^2 - 15x + 2$
f. $2x + 1 + 2y(2x + 1)$
g. $6x^2 - 36x + 54$ **h.** $8x^4 - 50y^2$
i. $2t^2 - 3t - 20$ **j.** $15x^2 - 2x - 8$
k. $6ax - 3ay + 10bx - 5by$

10. Simplify the expression by collecting like terms and then factor completely.
a. $(6x^2 - 2x - 37) + (-4x^2 - 3x + 12)$
b. $(3x^2 + x + 4) - (7x^2 + 5x + 5)$
c. $(2x - 1)(8x - 3) + 2(7x - 6)$
d. $3x(x + 4) - 2[x(x + 5) + 1] - 1$
e. $3x(2x + 5) - 5x(x + 3) - 1$

11. Factor completely.
a. $(2x + y)^2 - 4y^2$ **b.** $9m^2 - (2m - 5)^2$

12. Divide.
a. $\dfrac{42x^4y^2 - 24x^3}{6x^3}$ **b.** $\dfrac{3x^3 - x^2 - 3x - 1}{x + 1}$
c. $\dfrac{4x^4 + 12x^3 + x^2 - 24x - 18}{2x + 3}$

13. Find the zeros of the polynomials.
a. $-15x^2 + 40x$ **b.** $36x^2 - 1$
c. $8x^2 - 2x - 15$ **d.** $x^2 + 10x + 25$

14. In a triangle, the longest side is 5 cm longer than twice the shortest side. The third side is 3 cm longer than the shortest side. Find an expression which represents the perimeter of the triangle.

15. In Exercise 14, if the longest side is doubled, then what is the expression for the new perimeter of the triangle?

16. The formula for the lateral surface area of a right circular cone is $S.A. = \pi r(s + r)$. If $s = 8$ cm and $r = 5$ cm, then find the surface area.

17. Tak has 4 more dimes than quarters. If the total value of the dimes and quarters is $2.85, then how many of each coin does he have?

RATIONAL EXPRESSIONS

Tune Up

1. Simplify by collecting the like terms.
a. $5m^2 - 3n - m - 9n + 2m^2$
b. $14a^2 + 6b^2 - 8ab - a^2 + 12ab$
c. $9p + pq - q^2 + 10p^2 + 4q^2 - 6pq$

2. Find the products.
a. $-3(4c + 17d)$ **b.** $2x^2(5x - 2y)$
c. $(5r - 3s)(r + 6s)$ **d.** $(4u + 3v)^2$
e. $(x + 3y)(4x^2 - 5xy - y^2)$

3. Perform the indicated operations and simplify.
a. $4(2a - b) - (6a + 5b) + 8a$
b. $2 + 3(m + 3n) - 5(6n - m)$
c. $(4x + y)(x - 2y) + 2(3x - y)^2$
d. $4(a - 2b)(a - b) - 3(2a + 3b)(a + b)$

4. Factor completely.
a. $5t^2 - 8t$ **b.** $6m^3n - 3m^2n^2 - 24mn^3$
c. $p^2 + 5pq - 14q^2$ **d.** $36x^2 - 1$
e. $16y^2 + 24y + 9$ **f.** $3a^2 - 2a - 16$
g. $8 - 2x - 3x^2$ **h.** $4n^2 + 18n - 36$

5. Determine the Greatest Common Factor of each.
a. $12a, 18ab$
b. $8p^2, 28pq^2$
c. $2c(c + 3), c(c - 3)$
d. $4(a + 2b), (a + 2b)$
e. $(3x + 2)(3x + 2), (3x + 2)(x - 1)$
f. $m^2 - 4, m^2 + 3m + 2$
g. $k^2 + 2k - 8, 2k^2 + 8k$

6. Determine the Least Common Multiple of each.
a. $6p, 9pq$
b. $3x^2, 15xy^2$
c. $2m(m - 1), 10(m + 2)$
d. $(3p - 5), (p + 2)(3p - 5)$
e. $(2a + b)(a - 3b), (2a + b)(2a - b)$

7. Multiply.
a. $\dfrac{5a}{2} \times \dfrac{3b}{4c}$ **b.** $\dfrac{2mn}{5p} \times \dfrac{8n}{3}$
c. $\dfrac{6x}{4y} \times \dfrac{3xy}{2}$ **d.** $\dfrac{4y^2}{s} \times \dfrac{3s}{8u}$

8. Perform the indicated operations.
a. $\dfrac{5}{6} + \dfrac{3a}{2}$ **b.** $\dfrac{12}{5x} - \dfrac{5}{3} + \dfrac{1}{2}$

9. Solve.
a. $2x + 14 = 12$ **b.** $3x - 9 = 8$
c. $\dfrac{x + 6}{7} = 5$ **d.** $\dfrac{2x - 1}{3} = 9$
e. $\dfrac{3}{2}x - \dfrac{2}{3} = \dfrac{1}{5}$ **f.** $\dfrac{1}{2}x + 12 = -5\dfrac{2}{3}$

10. Which sentences are true and which sentences are false?
a. $3(x + 6) = 3x + 21$
b. $2(x + 7) = 2x + 14$
c. $-3(x - 1) = -3x - 3$

11. In your own words, explain the meaning of the distributive property.

5·1 Simplifying Rational Expressions

Rational numbers are numbers which can be written in the form $\frac{a}{b}$, where a and b are integers, and $b \neq 0$. When a polynomial is divided by a polynomial, the resulting expression is a **rational expression.**

These are examples of rational expressions.

$$\frac{15}{x+4} \qquad \frac{2x-3}{6x+2} \qquad \frac{x^2+3x+8}{x^2-5x-12} \qquad \frac{x^3-4x+2}{x^2-15x-40}$$

> A rational expression is the quotient of two polynomials.

The denominator of a rational expression cannot equal zero because division by zero is undefined. This can result in restrictions being placed on the possible values of variables.

Example 1

State the restrictions on the values of x.

a. $\dfrac{4x-5}{x-6}$

Since $x = 6$ makes the denominator equal zero, the rational expression is defined as long as $x \neq 6$.

b. $\dfrac{3x^2+7x-2}{2x(x+3)}$

If $2x(x+3) = 0$, then the expression is undefined.

$\therefore 2x \neq 0$ and $x+3 \neq 0$

$\therefore x \neq 0$ and $x \neq -3$

A rational expression can be simplified by dividing the numerator and the denominator by a factor common to each.

Example 2

Simplify. $\dfrac{6x+10}{2}$

$$\frac{6x+10}{2} = \frac{2(3x+5)}{2}$$

Divide the numerator and the denominator by 2.

$$= 3x+5$$

Example 3

Determine the restrictions on the values of x and simplify. $\dfrac{x^2-3x}{x^2+4x-21}$

$$\frac{x^2-3x}{x^2+4x-21} = \frac{x(x-3)}{(x+7)(x-3)}$$

Find the restrictions on the variable before simplifying.

$\therefore x \neq -7$ and $x \neq 3$

$$= \frac{x}{x+7}$$

Exercises

1. Determine the restrictions on the values of x.

a. $\dfrac{3y}{2x}$

b. $\dfrac{12}{x-9}$

c. $\dfrac{2}{x^2-4x}$

d. $\dfrac{x+12}{x^2+9x+14}$

e. $\dfrac{5}{x^2-3x+2}$

f. $\dfrac{x^2+3x+15}{3x^2-2x-5}$

2. Simplify using common factors.

a. $\dfrac{36}{20}$

b. $\dfrac{-16}{12}$

c. $\dfrac{5ab^3}{40a^2b}$

d. $\dfrac{63m^2np^2}{27mn^4p}$

e. $\dfrac{16x+4}{2}$

f. $\dfrac{8}{6x-16}$

3. Simplify.

a. $\dfrac{8x+10}{6x-2}$

b. $\dfrac{3x^2-6x}{9x^2+15x}$

c. $\dfrac{6x^2y+16xy^2}{12xy+6xy^2}$

d. $\dfrac{15ab+45ac}{20a^2+20ac}$

e. $\dfrac{6pq^2-10p^2}{6p^2q+12pq^2}$

f. $\dfrac{16m^3n+32mn^2}{72m^2n-48m^3}$

4. Express each in lowest terms.

a. $\dfrac{x^2+x-6}{4-x^2}$

b. $\dfrac{x^2+4x-5}{x^2-2x+1}$

c. $\dfrac{x^2+8x+12}{3x^2+6x}$

d. $\dfrac{x^2+2x-24}{x^2+9x+18}$

e. $\dfrac{a^2-25}{a^2+13a+40}$

f. $\dfrac{y(x+3)-2(x+3)}{x^2+6x+9}$

5. Simplify. Identify the restrictions on the variables.

a. $\dfrac{2x^2-x-15}{x^2+x-12}$

b. $\dfrac{6x^2+5x-6}{2x^2-7x-15}$

c. $\dfrac{8x^2-10x+3}{4x^2+5x-6}$

d. $\dfrac{25x^2-10x+1}{3-14x-5x^2}$

e. $\dfrac{25t^2-16}{10t^2-3t-4}$

f. $\dfrac{8p^2+6p+1}{8p^2-2p-3}$

g. $\dfrac{3c^2+13c-10}{9c^2-4}$

h. $\dfrac{20-7s-6s^2}{3s^2+5s-12}$

6. Express each in lowest terms.

a. $\dfrac{2a^2+5ab-3b^2}{a^2-9b^2}$

b. $\dfrac{12x^2+28xy-5y^2}{6x^2+5xy-y^2}$

c. $\dfrac{3m^2-16mn-12n^2}{6m^2+7mn+2n^2}$

d. $\dfrac{25y^2-16x^2}{4x^2-17xy+15y^2}$

e. $\dfrac{2p^2-3pq-20q^2}{4p^2+16pq+15q^2}$

f. $\dfrac{9a^2+12ab+4b^2}{3a^2-16ab-12b^2}$

7. Determine the restrictions on x and simplify.

a. $\dfrac{5x^2+13x+6}{x^2+5x+6}$

b. $\dfrac{3x^2-x-4}{8x-6x^2}$

c. $\dfrac{x^2-6x+9}{2x^2-9x+9}$

d. $\dfrac{6x^2-29x-5}{x^2-9x+20}$

8. Simplify. Identify the restrictions on the variables.

a. $\dfrac{2x^2-2x-40}{2x^2+16x+32}$

b. $\dfrac{9x^3+12x^2+4x}{15x+10}$

c. $\dfrac{5x^3+20x^2-60x}{3x^3+19x^2+6x}$

d. $\dfrac{2a^2+6ab-36b^2}{10a^2-28ab-6b^2}$

e. $\dfrac{105p^2+18pq-24q^2}{25p^2-4q^2}$

f. $\dfrac{18m^3+27m^2n-5mn^2}{6m^2n-49mn^2+8n^3}$

9. A farmer divides his herd of cattle among his three children. The eldest is given half the herd, the youngest receives one sixth, and the middle child receives 6 more than the youngest. How large was the farmer's herd?

10. Calculate the average speed of a 24 km round trip if half of the trip was covered at 8 km/h and the other half at 12 km/h.

Historical Note

Johann Kepler (1571-1630)

It has been said that almost any problem can be solved if one continuously worries over it and works on it for a sufficiently long time. Thomas Edison once said that inventions are one percent inspiration and ninety-nine percent perspiration. This is demonstrated by Johann Kepler's tenacity in solving problems concerning planetary motion. He was convinced that planets revolved in orbits around a central sun, and he wanted to determine the motion and position of these orbits. Kepler used Tycho Brahe's observations on the motion of planets. The problem was to obtain a pattern of motion that coincides with Brahe's observations. Kepler arrived at a hypothesis and then sifted through a "mountain" of tedious calculations to confirm or reject the hypothesis. After twenty-one years, he succeeded in formulating his first two laws of planetary motion, and ten years later, he formulated his third law. Using the library, research and explain Kepler's three laws.

5·2 Multiplying and Dividing Rational Expressions

When multiplying and dividing rational expressions, follow the same procedure that was used when multiplying and dividing rational numbers.

Example 1

Multiply and simplify. State the restrictions on the values of the variables.

a. $\dfrac{5x^2y}{6y} \times \dfrac{2x}{3x^2}$

$= \dfrac{10x^3y}{18x^2y}$ *Recall how to divide exponents.*

$= \dfrac{5x}{9}$ $x \neq 0,\ y \neq 0$

b. $\dfrac{x^2 - 3x}{x^2 - x - 6} \times \dfrac{x^2 + x - 2}{4x}$

$= \dfrac{x(x - 3)}{(x - 3)(x + 2)} \times \dfrac{(x + 2)(x - 1)}{4x}$ *Always factor if possible.*

$= \dfrac{x(x - 3)(x + 2)(x - 1)}{4(x)(x - 3)(x + 2)}$ *Reduce the common factors.*

$= \dfrac{x - 1}{4}$ $x \neq 3,\ x \neq -2,\ x \neq 0$

Example 2

Divide and simplify. State the restrictions on the values of the variables.

a. $\dfrac{3ab^2}{5b^3} \div \dfrac{9a}{2b}$

$= \dfrac{3ab^2}{5b^3} \times \dfrac{2b}{9a}$ *Neither the numerator nor the denominator of the divisor can equal zero.*

$= \dfrac{6ab^3}{45ab^3}$

$= \dfrac{2}{15}$ $b \neq 0,\ a \neq 0$

b. $\dfrac{2x^2 - 3x - 20}{2x^2 + 11x + 15} \div \dfrac{3x^2 - 13x + 12}{x^2 - 9}$

$= \dfrac{2x^2 - 3x - 20}{2x^2 + 11x + 15} \times \dfrac{x^2 - 9}{3x^2 - 13x + 12}$

$= \dfrac{(2x + 5)(x - 4)}{(2x + 5)(x + 3)} \times \dfrac{(x + 3)(x - 3)}{(3x - 4)(x - 3)}$

$= \dfrac{x - 4}{3x - 4}$ $x \neq -\dfrac{5}{2},\ x \neq -3,\ x \neq \dfrac{4}{3},\ x \neq 3$

Example 3

A triangle has a height of $\dfrac{4x + 6}{x + 1}$ units and an area of $\dfrac{2x^2 + 7x + 6}{x + 2}$ square units. Find the base length of this triangle.

$A = \tfrac{1}{2}bh$

$\therefore b = 2A \div h$

$= 2\left(\dfrac{2x^2 + 7y + 6}{x + 2}\right) \div \dfrac{4x + 6}{x + 1}$

This triangle is possible only if $x \neq -2$, $x \neq -1$, and $x \neq -\dfrac{3}{2}$.

$= 2\left(\dfrac{2x^2 + 7y + 6}{x + 2}\right) \times \dfrac{x + 1}{4x + 6}$

$= 2\left(\dfrac{(2x + 3)(x + 2)}{x + 2}\right) \times \dfrac{x + 1}{2(2x + 3)}$

$= x + 1$

The triangle has a base length of $x + 1$ units.

116

Exercises

1. Multiply and simplify.

a. $\dfrac{6}{25} \times \dfrac{10}{9}$

b. $\dfrac{3}{5} \times \dfrac{20}{35} \times \dfrac{21}{24}$

c. $\dfrac{15a}{6b} \times \dfrac{4ab}{10a}$

d. $\dfrac{2x}{3y} \times \dfrac{-6}{8y} \times \dfrac{4y}{10x}$

e. $\dfrac{24m^2}{15n^2} \times \dfrac{8mn}{12m^3}$

f. $\dfrac{-18a^2b}{10a} \times \dfrac{15b}{20ab^2}$

2. Divide and simplify.

a. $\dfrac{5}{6} \div \dfrac{3}{8}$

b. $\dfrac{-5}{12} \div \dfrac{15}{16}$

c. $\dfrac{8x}{15y^2z} \div \dfrac{12x^2}{25z}$

d. $\dfrac{-3a^2}{16b} \div \dfrac{10a}{12b^2}$

e. $\dfrac{40m^2n}{15n^2} \div \dfrac{24m^4}{9mn^2}$

f. $\dfrac{56a^2}{30ab^5} \div \dfrac{16a^3b}{15ab}$

3. Perform the operations and simplify.

a. $\dfrac{12a}{20b^2} \times \dfrac{15ab}{24} \div \dfrac{30a^3}{36b^3}$

b. $\dfrac{4xz}{9y^2} \div \dfrac{10xy}{xyz} \times \dfrac{15yz}{8x^3}$

c. $6 \times \dfrac{3a}{5b^2} \div \dfrac{18a}{10b}$

d. $\dfrac{4x}{3y} \times \dfrac{30x^2}{12y} \times \dfrac{48xy^3}{54x} \div \dfrac{5x^2}{9}$

4. Multiply and simplify.

a. $\dfrac{x^2 - 25}{2x^2 - 10x} \times \dfrac{8x}{x^2 + 3x - 10}$

b. $\dfrac{x^2 + 3x - 18}{x^2 - 9} \times \dfrac{x^2 - x - 6}{x + 6}$

c. $\dfrac{2x^2 - 32}{x^2 - 16} \times \dfrac{x^2 + 2x - 8}{2x - 4}$

d. $\dfrac{-20x^2}{4x^2 - 36x} \times \dfrac{x^2 - 10x + 9}{x^2 - 4x + 3}$

e. $\dfrac{25x - 5x^2}{x^2 - 25} \times \dfrac{x^2 - x - 30}{x^2 - 2x - 24}$

5. An engineer designed a triangular steel structure with these dimensions.

a. What is its area?

b. If $a = 21$ cm and $b = 8$ cm, then what is its actual area?

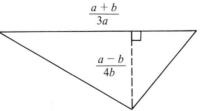

6. Perform the operations and simplify. Determine the restrictions on the variable.

a. $\dfrac{a^2 - 3a - 10}{3a^2 + 7a - 6} \div \dfrac{a - 5}{a + 3}$

b. $\dfrac{48x - 12x^2}{x^2 - 8x + 16} \times \dfrac{x - 4}{3x^2}$

7. Simplify by performing the indicated operations.

a. $\dfrac{6x^2 - 7x - 5}{4x^2 - 8x - 5} \times \dfrac{8x^2 - 18x - 5}{-12x - 3}$

b. $\dfrac{4x + 20}{6x^2 - 6} \div \dfrac{x^2 - 25}{5x^2 + 5x}$

c. $\dfrac{8x - 5}{12x} \times \dfrac{x^2 + 6x + 8}{8x^2 + 11x - 10} \times \dfrac{10x}{x + 2}$

d. $\dfrac{15x^2 + x - 2}{12x^2 + 11x - 5} \times \dfrac{4x^2 + 17x + 15}{10x + 4}$

e. $\dfrac{4x^2 - 12x + 9}{6x^2 - 7x - 3} \div \dfrac{18x - 12x^2}{3x^2 + 16x + 5}$

f. $\dfrac{2x^2y + 18xy^2}{16y^2} \times \dfrac{2x^2 + 7xy - 4y^2}{2x^2 + 17xy - 9y^2}$

g. $\dfrac{2a^2 + ab - 15b^2}{4a^2 - 8ab - 5b^2} \times \dfrac{8a^2 + 4ab}{6ab + 6b^2}$

8. Determine the restrictions and perform the indicated operations to simplify.

a. $\dfrac{6x^2 + 12x}{x^2 - 3x - 10} \times \dfrac{x^2 - 25}{4x}$

b. $\dfrac{6x^2 - 23x - 4}{6x^2 - 17x - 3} \div \dfrac{x + 2}{x - 3}$

c. $\dfrac{x^2 - 4}{2 - x}$

9. A triangle has a height of $\dfrac{2x + 3}{x + 1}$ units and an area of $\dfrac{x^2 + 4x + 3}{2x^2 + 7x + 3}$ square units. Find the base length of the triangle in simplest form.

10. If the total distance travelled from Regina to Saskatoon is given by the expression $\dfrac{3x^2 + x - 4}{2x - 4}$ km and the rate of travel is given by the expression $\dfrac{3x + 4}{x^2 - 4}$ km/h, then find an expression for the total time required to travel the total distance.

Using the Library

Write a short essay on continuing fractions. Through the use of examples, explain how they are related to irrational numbers.

5·3 Addition and Subtraction I

As is the case when adding or subtracting rational numbers, the addition and subtraction of rational expressions requires finding a common denominator.

Example 1

Find the Least Common Multiple (LCM) of each.

a. 12, 28

$LCM = 84$

b. $4x$, $18x^2y$, $6xy$

LCM of 4, 18, and 6 is 36.
LCM of x, x^2, and x is x^2.
LCM of y and y is y.
$\therefore$ LCM of $4x$, $18x^2y$, and $6xy$ is $36x^2y$.

Example 2

Add or subtract.

a. $\dfrac{x}{2} + \dfrac{y}{5}$

$= \dfrac{5x + 2y}{(2)(5)}$

$= \dfrac{5x + 2y}{10}$

b. $\dfrac{9}{2x} + \dfrac{4}{x^3}$

$= \dfrac{9(x^2)}{2x(x^2)} + \dfrac{(2)(4)}{(2)x^3}$

$= \dfrac{9x^2}{2x^3} + \dfrac{8}{2x^3}$

$= \dfrac{9x^2 + 8}{2x^3}$ $\{x \neq 0\}$

c. $\dfrac{2a}{25} - \dfrac{a - 3}{15a}$

$= \dfrac{(2a)(3a)}{25(3a)} - \dfrac{(5)(a - 3)}{(5)(15a)}$

$= \dfrac{(3a)(2a) - 5(a - 3)}{75a}$

$= \dfrac{6a^2 - 5a + 15}{75a}$ $\{a \neq 0\}$

Example 3

Simplify.

a. $\dfrac{x^2 - 5x}{x + 2} + \dfrac{2x - 10}{x + 2}$

b. $\dfrac{2x^2 + 8x + 15}{2x^2 - x - 15} + \dfrac{4x^2 + 17x + 10}{2x^2 - x - 15}$

Since we already have common denominators, simplify by collecting like terms, factor the resulting numerator and denominator, and divide by the polynomial that is common to both the numerator and the denominator.

$= \dfrac{x^2 - 3x - 10}{x + 2}$

$= \dfrac{(x - 5)(x + 2)}{x + 2}$

$= x - 5$ $\{x \neq -2\}$

$= \dfrac{6x^2 + 25x + 25}{2x^2 - x - 15}$

$= \dfrac{(2x + 5)(3x + 5)}{(2x + 5)(x - 3)}$

$= \dfrac{3x + 5}{x - 3}$ $\left\{x \neq \dfrac{-5}{2}, x \neq 3\right\}$

Exercises

1. Find the LCM of each.

a. 16, 24   **b.** $18x$, $30xy$

c. $12a^2$, $20ab^3$ **d.** $9x^2y$, $27x^3y^2$

e. $15x$, $5xy$, $20y$ **f.** $2x^2$, $6xy$, $8xy^2$

g. $6ab$, $3bc$, $12ac$ **h.** $3x^2$, $5y$, $6xy$

2. Write each expression with a denominator of $5xy$.

a. $3x$ **b.** $\dfrac{2x}{y}$

c. $3 + x + y$ **d.** $2x - 8y$

3. Add. Write your answer in lowest terms.

a. $\dfrac{6x}{5} + \dfrac{3y}{2}$ **b.** $\dfrac{3a}{4} + \dfrac{a}{8}$

c. $\dfrac{5x}{12} + \dfrac{7x}{18}$ **d.** $\dfrac{x}{6} + \dfrac{3x}{10}$

4. Subtract. Write your answer in lowest terms.

a. $\dfrac{10a}{3} - \dfrac{5b}{2}$ **b.** $\dfrac{4x}{9} - \dfrac{x}{6}$

c. $\dfrac{2x}{15} - \dfrac{9x}{10}$ **d.** $\dfrac{15x}{8} - \dfrac{3}{2}$

5. Write each as an equivalent rational expression with the denominator indicated.

a. $5x = \dfrac{\blacksquare}{y^2}$ **b.** $3x + 1 = \dfrac{\blacksquare}{x}$

c. $\dfrac{4x}{y} = \dfrac{\blacksquare}{yx^2}$ **d.** $\dfrac{x+1}{y} = \dfrac{\blacksquare}{y(x-1)}$

e. $\dfrac{2y+2}{x} = \dfrac{\blacksquare}{3x(y+1)}$ **f.** $\dfrac{2(x+1)}{3(x-1)} = \dfrac{\blacksquare}{3(x^2-1)}$

6. Perform the indicated operations and write your answer in lowest terms.

a. $\dfrac{5}{2a} + \dfrac{10}{3a^2}$ **b.** $\dfrac{3}{4x^2} - \dfrac{7}{10x}$

c. $\dfrac{2}{9mn^2} - \dfrac{5}{12m^2n}$ **d.** $\dfrac{2c}{ab} + \dfrac{3b}{ac}$

e. $\dfrac{3}{4x} + \dfrac{5}{6y} - \dfrac{9}{8z}$ **f.** $\dfrac{10}{a} - \dfrac{3c}{ab} + \dfrac{2}{c}$

7. Simplify.

a. $\dfrac{2x+5}{3} + \dfrac{x-1}{4}$ **b.** $\dfrac{16a}{5} - \dfrac{a+2}{2}$

c. $\dfrac{5x-6}{12} + \dfrac{x+4}{3}$ **d.** $\dfrac{2x+10}{15} + \dfrac{3x}{20}$

e. $\dfrac{a-3}{5} + \dfrac{a+2}{2} + \dfrac{2a+1}{4}$

8. Simplify. Determine the restrictions.

a. $\dfrac{8}{2x+3} + \dfrac{2x-5}{2x+3}$ **b.** $\dfrac{6x-2}{x+4} - \dfrac{4x+1}{x+4}$

c. $\dfrac{x+6}{x+5} + \dfrac{2x+9}{x+5}$ **d.** $\dfrac{2x^2+1}{2x+1} + \dfrac{13x+1}{2x+1}$

9. Perform the indicated operations and simplify.

a. $\dfrac{2x+3}{6x} + \dfrac{x-4}{8x^2}$ **b.** $\dfrac{4a}{3b} - \dfrac{2a-5}{5a} + 2$

c. $\dfrac{6x+1}{5x} + \dfrac{2x-12}{10}$ **d.** $\dfrac{8a-3b}{4ab} - \dfrac{a-10}{6a^2}$

e. $\dfrac{1}{xy^2} + \dfrac{2y}{3x^2} + \dfrac{5x}{6y}$ **f.** $\dfrac{5}{2p} + \dfrac{3}{5q} - \dfrac{2}{3pq}$

g. $\dfrac{2m}{9n} - \dfrac{m-3}{2m} + \dfrac{5mn+1}{3mn}$

h. $\dfrac{9x-2}{2} - \dfrac{15x}{8} - \dfrac{7x-4}{6}$

10. Add $\dfrac{5x^2-8x-3}{x-3} - \dfrac{3x+12}{x-3}$ to the sum of $\dfrac{x^2+2x-8}{x^2+2x-15} + \dfrac{x^2+7x+3}{x^2+2x-15}$. Write your answer in simplest form.

11. Simplify.

a. $\dfrac{14x-2}{4x-3} - \dfrac{6x+4}{4x-3}$

b. $\dfrac{x^2-6x-10}{2x+7} + \dfrac{x^2+7x-11}{2x+7}$

c. $\dfrac{x^2-12x+3}{x^2-8x-20} + \dfrac{2x^2-17x-13}{x^2-8x-20}$

d. $\dfrac{3x^2+7x}{x^2-3x+2} - \dfrac{2x^2+8}{x^2-3x+2}$

e. $\dfrac{5x^2+3x-4}{2x^2+11x+15} - \dfrac{4x^2+3x+5}{2x^2+11x+15}$

12. Perform the indicated operations and simplify. Determine the restrictions on x.

a. $\dfrac{10x}{x+6} + \dfrac{2x^2-5}{x+6} - \dfrac{x+13}{x+6}$

b. $\dfrac{8}{15x} + \dfrac{4-3x}{6x^2}$

13. A foreman installing a steel pipeline wanted a pipe that is 24 cm in diameter. When he went to the steel plant, he found that there was no 24 cm diameter pipe. However, the plant offered him two steel pipes each with a diameter of 12 cm. The foreman thought that he could combine the two smaller pipes to replace the larger one. Was he correct in his thinking?

5·4 Addition and Subtraction II

Examine the expressions $2x$ and $x + 4$. Although each contains the variable x, in the first case x is a factor; but in the second case, it is a term. The Least Common Multiple (LCM) is found by multiplying the common factor, if any exists, by the other factors. In this case, the LCM of $2x$ and $x + 4$ is the product $2x(x + 4)$.

Example 1

Add.

a. $\dfrac{5}{2x} + \dfrac{3}{x + 4}$

$= \dfrac{5(x + 4) + 3(2x)}{2x(x + 4)}$

$= \dfrac{5x + 20 + 6x}{2x(x + 4)}$ Leave the denominator as the product of two factors.

$= \dfrac{11x + 20}{2x(x + 4)}$ $x \neq 0, x \neq -4$

b. $\dfrac{6a}{a - 1} + \dfrac{a - 3}{a + 2}$

$= \dfrac{6a(a + 2) + (a - 3)(a - 1)}{(a - 1)(a + 2)}$

$= \dfrac{6a^2 + 12a + a^2 - 4a + 3}{(a - 1)(a + 2)}$

$= \dfrac{7a^2 + 8a + 3}{(a - 1)(a + 2)}$ $a \neq 1, a \neq -2$

Particular care must be taken in the subtraction of rational expressions because of the possible removal of brackets preceded by a negative sign.

Example 2

Perform the operations and simplify.

a. $\dfrac{4y}{y + 3} - \dfrac{5y}{2x}$

$= \dfrac{(4y)(2x) - 5y(y + 3)}{2x(y + 3)}$

$= \dfrac{8xy - 5y^2 - 15y}{2x(y + 3)}$ $x \neq 0, y \neq -3$

b. $\dfrac{6x}{2x + 5} - \dfrac{x - 3}{x + 1}$

$= \dfrac{6x(x + 1) - (x - 3)(2x + 5)}{(2x + 5)(x + 1)}$

$= \dfrac{6x^2 + 6x - [2x^2 - x - 15]}{(2x + 5)(x + 1)}$

$= \dfrac{6x^2 + 6x - 2x^2 + x + 15}{(2x + 5)(x + 1)}$

$= \dfrac{4x^2 + 7x + 15}{(2x + 5)(x + 1)}$ $x \neq -1, x \neq \dfrac{-5}{2}$

c. $\dfrac{3}{(2p + 5)(p - 4)} + \dfrac{8}{(2p + 5)(p + 2)}$

$= \dfrac{3(p + 2) + 8(p - 4)}{(2p + 5)(p - 4)(p + 2)}$ The LCD contains the factor $(2p + 5)$ as well as the other factors $(p - 4)$ and $(p + 2)$.

$= \dfrac{3p + 6 + 8p - 32}{(2p + 5)(p - 4)(p + 2)}$

$= \dfrac{11p - 26}{(2p + 5)(p - 4)(p + 2)}$ $p \neq \dfrac{-5}{2}, 4, \text{ or } -2$

120

Exercises

1. Find the Least Common Multiple of each.

a. $2x, 2x - 3$ **b.** $x - 6, x + 4$

c. $3(x - 3), 5(x - 3)$

d. $2x + 1, (2x - 1)(2x + 1)$

e. $(x - 4)(x + 8), (x + 7)(x - 4)$

f. $(x + 2)(x - 3), 4x(x - 3)$

g. $(x - 5)(x + 5), (x + 5)(x + 5)$

h. $3x(3x + 4), (3x + 4)(x - 2)$

i. $2(x - 1)(x + 1), (x + 1)(x - 1)$

2. Find the Least Common Denominator of each.

a. $\dfrac{1}{x + 5} + \dfrac{1}{4x}$ **b.** $\dfrac{2}{x - 3} - \dfrac{5}{x + 2}$

c. $\dfrac{1}{4x} - \dfrac{9}{2(x - 2)}$

d. $\dfrac{8}{(x - 4)(x + 4)} + \dfrac{3}{(x + 1)(x + 4)}$

e. $\dfrac{6}{x + 3} - \dfrac{1}{x + 2} + \dfrac{3}{x - 2}$

f. $\dfrac{5}{6x} + \dfrac{2}{3x + 5} + \dfrac{1}{2x}$

3. Perform the operations in Exercise 2 and state the restrictions on the values of x.

4. Add or subtract.

a. $\dfrac{8}{3x + 2} + \dfrac{14}{x - 4}$ **b.** $\dfrac{2}{x - 2} - \dfrac{5}{x - 6}$

c. $\dfrac{16}{5x + 2} + \dfrac{1}{2x - 7}$ **d.** $\dfrac{9}{4x - 1} - \dfrac{3}{4x + 1}$

e. $\dfrac{12}{5x - 6} + \dfrac{3}{4x + 5}$ **f.** $\dfrac{2}{3 - x} + \dfrac{-4}{3 + x}$

5. Perform the indicated operations. Reduce the expression to lowest terms.

a. $\dfrac{4}{x} + \dfrac{2}{x + 3}$ **b.** $\dfrac{4x - 2}{5x + 1} + \dfrac{3x}{2}$

c. $\dfrac{8x}{3x + 4} - \dfrac{2}{x}$ **d.** $\dfrac{2x + 7}{x^2 + 1} - \dfrac{4}{5x}$

e. $\dfrac{x^2 + 2x - 3}{x + 2} + \dfrac{x - 4}{2}$ **f.** $\dfrac{3x^2 - x - 3}{5x - 1} - \dfrac{2x + 1}{4}$

6. The width and length of a rectangle are given by the expressions $\dfrac{x + 5}{(x - 1)(x - 2)}$ and $\dfrac{2x}{(x - 2)(x + 2)}$ respectively. Find an expression for the perimeter of the rectangle and express it in its simplest form.

7. Simplify.

a. $\dfrac{2x - 1}{x + 3} + \dfrac{5x}{x - 4}$ **b.** $\dfrac{2x}{x + 5} - \dfrac{x - 5}{3x - 1}$

c. $\dfrac{x + 1}{x - 4} + \dfrac{x - 2}{2x + 5}$ **d.** $\dfrac{x + 10}{x - 2} + \dfrac{3x - 2}{8x}$

e. $\dfrac{x + 1}{x + 2} + \dfrac{4 - x}{x - 2}$ **f.** $\dfrac{4x - 3}{2x - 3} - \dfrac{3x - 4}{2x + 1}$

8. Simplify.

a. $2x + \dfrac{x - 6}{x + 3}$ **b.** $\dfrac{4x + 7}{x - 2} - 12$

c. $\dfrac{9x^2 - 8}{2x + 5} - 3x$ **d.** $1 + \dfrac{5 - x}{10x + 3}$

9. Melissa's age is given by the expression $\dfrac{4x + 5}{(x - 4)(x + 2)}$. If her brother is five years older, then find a rational expression which represents his age.

10. Simplify.

a. $\dfrac{9x}{2(x + 3)} + \dfrac{5}{4(x + 3)}$ **b.** $\dfrac{12}{3(x - 4)} + \dfrac{3}{2(x - 4)}$

c. $\dfrac{2x}{3(3x - 4)} - \dfrac{5}{2(3x - 4)}$ **d.** $\dfrac{8x - 6}{6(5x + 6)} + \dfrac{9}{2(2x + 5)}$

11. Simplify. Determine the restrictions on x.

a. $\dfrac{8}{(x - 6)(x + 2)} + \dfrac{3}{(x + 2)(x + 3)}$

b. $\dfrac{x}{(3x - 4)(3x + 4)} + \dfrac{4}{(3x - 4)(x + 2)}$

c. $\dfrac{6}{(2x + 5)(2x - 3)} - \dfrac{6}{2x(2x + 5)}$

d. $\dfrac{12}{(3x + 1)(x - 2)} - \dfrac{5}{(3x + 1)(x + 2)}$

12. The numbers 1 through 16 are placed in sequence in successive rows of a 4 by 4 square. If four numbers are selected so that no two of them are in the same row or the same column, what will be their sum? Show that this sum will be a constant regardless of the four numbers chosen.

13. Simplify.

a. $\dfrac{x + 3}{(4x - 1)(x + 2)} + \dfrac{2x - 1}{(x - 2)(x + 2)}$

b. $\dfrac{4x + 6}{(3x + 1)(3x + 1)} - \dfrac{3}{(3x + 1)(2x - 1)}$

c. $\dfrac{x + 8}{(5x - 2)(x + 2)} - \dfrac{x + 5}{(5x - 2)(x + 1)}$

d. $\dfrac{2x - 5}{(4x + 3)(x + 2)} + \dfrac{x + 3}{(3x - 2)(x + 2)}$

5·5 Addition and Subtraction III

It is often easier to find a common denominator if the original denominator is factored first.

Example 1

Find the Least Common Multiple.

a. $3x + 6, \quad 5x + 10$

$3x + 6 = 3(x + 2)$

$5x + 10 = 5(x + 2)$

$\text{LCM} = 15(x + 2)$

b. $2x^2 + 11x - 6, \quad 2x^2 - 9x + 4$

$2x^2 + 11x - 6 = (2x - 1)(x + 6)$

$2x^2 - 9x + 4 = (2x - 1)(x - 4)$

$\text{LCM} = (2x - 1)(x + 6)(x - 4)$

Example 2

Perform the indicated operations and simplify.

a.
$$\frac{4}{x^2 - x - 6} + \frac{5}{x^2 - 4}$$

$$= \frac{4}{(x + 2)(x - 3)} + \frac{5}{(x + 2)(x - 2)}$$

$$= \frac{4(x - 2) + 5(x - 3)}{(x + 2)(x - 2)(x - 3)}$$

$$= \frac{4x - 8 + 5x - 15}{(x + 2)(x - 2)(x - 3)}$$

$$= \frac{9x - 23}{(x + 2)(x - 2)(x - 3)} \qquad \boxed{x \neq -2, 2, \text{ or } 3}$$

b.
$$\frac{3p}{p^2 + 3p - 18} - \frac{p - 4}{5p^2 + 30p}$$

$$= \frac{3p}{(p + 6)(p - 3)} - \frac{p - 4}{5p(p + 6)}$$

$$= \frac{3p(5p) - (p - 4)(p - 3)}{5p(p + 6)(p - 3)}$$

$$= \frac{15p^2 - (p^2 - 7p + 12)}{5p(p + 6)(p - 3)}$$

$$= \frac{15p^2 - p^2 + 7p - 12}{5p(p + 6)(p - 3)}$$

$$= \frac{14p^2 + 7p - 12}{5p(p + 6)(p - 3)} \qquad \boxed{p \neq 0, -6, \text{ or } 3}$$

Example 3

Add.

$$\frac{4a^2 - 7a - 15}{a^2 - 9} + \frac{2a^2 + a - 6}{12a^2 - 16a - 3}$$

$$= \frac{(4a + 5)(a - 3)}{(a + 3)(a - 3)} + \frac{(2a - 3)(a + 2)}{(6a + 1)(2a - 3)}$$

$$= \frac{4a + 5}{a + 3} + \frac{a + 2}{6a + 1}$$

$$= \frac{(4a + 5)(6a + 1) + (a + 2)(a + 3)}{(a + 3)(6a + 1)}$$

$$= \frac{25a^2 + 39a + 11}{(a + 3)(6a + 1)}$$

$\boxed{\text{The restrictions are } a \neq -3, 3, -\dfrac{1}{6}, \text{ or } \dfrac{3}{2}.}$

Example 4

Perform the indicated operations and simplify.

$$\frac{2}{3m - 1} + \frac{5}{m^2 - 4} - \frac{3}{m - 2}$$

$$= \frac{2}{3m - 1} + \frac{5}{(m - 2)(m + 2)} - \frac{3}{m - 2}$$

$$= \frac{2(m - 2)(m + 2) + 5(3m - 1) - 3(3m - 1)(m + 2)}{(3m - 1)(m - 2)(m + 2)}$$

$$= \frac{2m^2 - 8 + 15m - 5 - 9m^2 - 15m + 6}{(3m - 1)(m - 2)(m + 2)}$$

$$= \frac{-7m^2 - 7}{(3m - 1)(m - 2)(m + 2)}$$

$\boxed{\text{The restrictions are } m \neq \dfrac{1}{3}, -4, \text{ or } 2.}$

122

Exercises

1. Find the LCM of each.

a. $3x - 9, 8x - 24$

b. $2k + 3, 4k^2 - 9$

c. $n^2 - 10n + 16, n^2 - 4n - 32$

d. $2t^2 + 15t + 18, t^2 + 10t + 24$

e. $25x^2 - 1, 10x^2 + 23x - 5$

f. $6b^2 + 30b, 3b^2 + 11b - 20$

2. Write each with a denominator of $(2x - 1)(x + 5)$.

a. $\dfrac{4}{2x - 1}$

b. $\dfrac{2x}{x + 5}$

c. $\dfrac{3}{x}$

d. $\dfrac{-2x^2}{-x - 5}$

3. Perform the indicated operations and simplify. Determine the restrictions on x.

a. $\dfrac{x - 2}{x - 4} + \dfrac{x + 1}{x^2 - 16}$

b. $\dfrac{3 - 8x}{x + 2} + \dfrac{x + 1}{x - 1}$

c. $\dfrac{x^2}{x^2 + 5x - 24} - \dfrac{2}{3}$

d. $15 + \dfrac{3x + 12}{x^2 - 1}$

e. $\dfrac{5x}{2x^2 - 5x - 12} + \dfrac{6}{2x^2 + 11x + 12}$

4. Perform the indicated operations and simplify. Determine the restrictions on x.

a. $\dfrac{x + 1}{x} - \dfrac{5x}{10x^2 - 3x}$

b. $\dfrac{3x + 4}{x^2 + 4x + 4} + \dfrac{5x - 2}{3x^2 + 5x - 2}$

c. $\dfrac{4}{4x^2 + 18x - 36} + \dfrac{5}{3x^2 + 21x + 18}$

d. $\dfrac{10}{4x^3 - 3x^2 - x} - \dfrac{1}{2x^3 - 2x}$

e. $\dfrac{3x + 2}{12x^2 + 11x + 2} - \dfrac{3x - 2}{12x^2 - 5x - 2}$

5. Factor and divide where possible before adding or subtracting.

a. $\dfrac{2x - 12}{2x^2 - 13x + 6} + \dfrac{3x + 5}{3x^2 + 14x + 15}$

b. $\dfrac{12a}{24a^2 + 4a} + \dfrac{a^2 - 4}{a^2 - 7a - 18}$

c. $\dfrac{x + 6}{2x^2 + 7x - 30} - \dfrac{4 - x}{x^2 - x - 12}$

d. $\dfrac{12p^2 - 13p - 4}{8p^2 + 22p + 5} + \dfrac{5p^2 + 15p}{p^2 + 9p + 18}$

6. Add or subtract.

a. $\dfrac{5x^2 + 7x - 6}{5x^2 + 17x - 12} - \dfrac{2x^2 + 7x - 4}{2x^2 + 3x - 2}$

b. $\dfrac{15y - 3x}{x^2 - 10xy + 25y^2} + \dfrac{6}{2x + y}$

c. $\dfrac{y^2 - 10y + 25}{6y^2 - 36y + 30} - \dfrac{2y + 4}{8y^2 + 20y + 8}$

d. $\dfrac{10a^2 - 11ab + 3b^2}{12a - 6b} + \dfrac{a^2 - b^2}{a^2 + 2ab + b^2}$

7. Find the LCM of each.

a. $3, 9, 5$

b. $2x, x - 4, x + 1$

c. $x + 3, x - 3, 2x + 7$

8. A cat is trying to climb a tree but has just been declawed. The cat manages to climb 3 m in the first minute and in the second minute it slides back down 2 m. This continues until the cat has finally reached the top of the tree. If the tree is 30 m tall, how long does it take the cat to climb the tree?

9. Simplify.

a. $\dfrac{5}{x + 4} + \dfrac{3}{2x + 5} + \dfrac{1}{x - 3}$

b. $\dfrac{2x}{3x - 1} - \dfrac{4}{3x + 1} + \dfrac{3}{5x}$

c. $\dfrac{6}{x + 4} + \dfrac{-5}{2x + 1} - \dfrac{8}{x - 3}$

d. $\dfrac{3x + 9}{x^2 - 9} + \dfrac{10}{2x - 5} + \dfrac{2x}{x^2 + 3x}$

e. $\dfrac{10x^2 - 5x}{2x^2 + x - 1} - \dfrac{6}{x - 4} + \dfrac{x + 5}{x^2 + 7x + 10}$

10. Kelly travels $2x + 5$ km from his home at a rate of $x + 3$ km/h. On his return trip over the same distance, he increases his rate by 2 km/h. What is Kelly's total travelling time?

11. If two resistances, r and s, are connected in a parallel circuit, the total resistance R is given by this formula.

$$\frac{1}{R} = \frac{1}{r} + \frac{1}{s}$$

a. Express R in terms of r and s.

b. Express r in terms of R and s.

c. Express s in terms of R and r.

5·6 Equations with Rationals

Solving equations involving rational expressions requires finding a common denominator for all polynomials in the equation.

Example 1

Solve for x. $\dfrac{3x}{4} - 4 = \dfrac{x-2}{3}$

$$12\left(\frac{3x}{4} - 4\right) = 12\left(\frac{x-2}{3}\right)$$
$$9x - 48 = 4x - 8$$
$$5x = 40$$
$$x = 8$$

12 is the Least Common Denominator of the equation.

Check:

L.S.	R.S.
$\dfrac{3(8)}{4} - 4$	$\dfrac{8-2}{3}$
2	2

All solutions must be verified.

∴ It checks.

Example 2

Solve. $\dfrac{x+1}{x+3} + \dfrac{2x+8}{x+3} = 0$

$$\frac{3x+9}{x+3} = 0 \qquad x \neq -3$$
$$(x+3)\left(\frac{3x+9}{x+3}\right) = (x+3)(0)$$
$$3x+9 = 0$$
$$x = -3$$

Since $x \neq -3$, there is no solution to this equation.

Example 3

Solve. $\dfrac{x+2}{2x+3} - \dfrac{3x}{6x+1} = 0$

Since $2x+3 \neq 0$ and $6x+1 \neq 0$, $x \neq -\dfrac{3}{2}$ and $x \neq -\dfrac{1}{6}$.

$$(2x+3)(6x+1)\left(\frac{x+2}{2x+3} - \frac{3x}{6x+1}\right) = 0(2x+3)(6x+1)$$
$$(6x+1)(x+2) - (2x+3)(3x) = 0$$
$$6x^2 + 13x + 2 - 6x^2 - 9x = 0$$
$$4x + 2 = 0$$
$$x = -\frac{1}{2}$$

Since the value for x is not a restricted value, $x = -\dfrac{1}{2}$.

Exercises

1. For Example 2 in the display, give a different proof to show that there is no solution.

2. Find the LCD of each equation.

a. $\dfrac{5x}{3} - \dfrac{x}{2} = 4$

b. $\dfrac{x+8}{4} + \dfrac{2x-5}{6} = 1$

c. $\dfrac{3}{2x} - \dfrac{1}{x-5} = 0$

d. $\dfrac{2}{4x-1} + \dfrac{5}{x+3} = 8$

e. $\dfrac{6}{5x} - \dfrac{2}{x+2} = 3$

3. Solve. Check your answers.

a. $\dfrac{x-6}{3} + \dfrac{x}{2} = 4$

b. $\dfrac{4x-5}{2} + \dfrac{x+3}{6} = 0$

c. $\dfrac{6x}{5} = \dfrac{2x+3}{2}$

d. $3 + \dfrac{4-x}{2} = 5x$

e. $\dfrac{4}{3}(x+1) - \dfrac{2}{5}(5x+2) = 2$

f. $\dfrac{3x-2}{8} + \dfrac{2(x+5)}{3} = 2$

4. Solve. Check your answers.

a. $\dfrac{12}{2x-5} + \dfrac{6}{x+3} = 0$ b. $\dfrac{5}{4x} - \dfrac{3}{x+2} = \dfrac{2}{x}$

c. $\dfrac{4}{5x+2} = \dfrac{1}{3x-1}$ d. $2 + \dfrac{5x}{x-4} = \dfrac{4}{3}$

e. $\dfrac{2}{x} - \dfrac{10}{6x-1} = \dfrac{1}{2x}$ f. $\dfrac{4}{2x+1} + \dfrac{x}{x-3} = 1$

5. Solve.

a. $\dfrac{x-3}{2x+1} = \dfrac{2x-5}{4x+3}$

b. $6 = \dfrac{2x-5}{x} + \dfrac{4x-1}{x+1}$

c. $\dfrac{3x^2+4x-4}{x^2-4} = \dfrac{6x^2+3x}{2x^2+11x+5}$

d. $\dfrac{6x^2-30x}{8} + \dfrac{x^2}{4} = \dfrac{2x^2-9}{2}$

e. $\dfrac{6x+5}{3x-1} - \dfrac{4x+1}{2x} = 0$

f. $0 = \dfrac{2x-3}{x+1} + \dfrac{5-8x}{4x}$

6. Three quarters of a number exceeds half of the number by 8. Find the number. Verify your solution.

7. Find two numbers such that the smaller number is 6 less than the larger and is also two thirds of the larger number. Verify your solution.

8. The team of Jan and Mike drove in a car rally for a total of 6 h. How far did each drive?

	D (km)	r (km/h)	t (h)
Jan	x	92	$\dfrac{x}{92}$
Mike	$x+50$	80	$\dfrac{(x+50)}{80}$

9. Divide 56 into two parts such that the ratio of the larger part to the smaller part is $\dfrac{5}{2}$. Find the two parts. Verify your solution.

10. The Antigonish soccer team has won half of the 16 games it has played. How many additional games must it play and win to increase this ratio to three quarters?

11. A number of students are evenly spaced around a circle. They have been numbered starting with one. Number 8 is opposite number 20. How many students are in the circle?

12. Solve for b.

$\dfrac{2b-3}{b-5} - \dfrac{b}{b+4} = \dfrac{20b-37}{b^2-b-20}$

Braintickler

A man went to a camera shop and selected a camera worth $50. The next day he returned it and selected a camera worth $100 and started to walk out of the store. The manager ran after him and said that the man owed him $50 for the camera. The man replied that he did not owe him anything as he had already given him $50 plus a $50 camera for a total of $100. Where is the flaw in this argument?

125

5·7 Computer Application — Rationals

Any pair of fractions in the form $\frac{a}{b}$ and $\frac{c}{d}$ can be added by the computer. The following program will ask you to input the two fractions and will then add them. This program will not reduce the fraction to its lowest terms.

```
10 REM A PROGRAM TO ADD TWO FRACTIONS
20 INPUT "THE FIRST NUMERATOR "; A
30 INPUT "THE FIRST DENOMINATOR "; B
40 INPUT "THE SECOND NUMERATOR "; C
50 INPUT "THE SECOND DENOMINATOR "; D
60 LET P = A * D + B * C
70 LET Q = B * D
80 PRINT A; "/"; B; " + "; C; "/"; D; " = "; P; "/"; Q
90 END
```

Exercises

1. What is the purpose of line 60 in the program of the display? line 70?

2. Modify the program from the display to find the difference of two fractions.

3. Predict what the computer will output if A = 3, B = 5, C = 1, and D = 4. Run the program. Was your prediction reasonable?

4. Write a program using the INPUT command that will print both the product and quotient of any two fractions in nonreduced form.

5. Write a program that will multiply two mixed numbers. (*Hint:* Consider fractions in the form $A\frac{B}{C}$ and $D\frac{E}{F}$.)

6. The INTEGER (INT) function will change any real number to the next, smaller, integer value. For example, INT(10.8) = 10, or INT(−9.8) = −10. What will the computer output for each of these lines?

a. 10 INT(9.9)   **b.** 20 INT (11 / 6)
c. 30 INT(0.8 * 7)   **d.** 40 INT (11.2 + 2.7)

7. "Grade 10 students should be allowed to use a programmable calculator or a hand-held calculator for all classroom assignments and tests." Write a short essay either defending or denying this statement.

8. The following program will print the least common denominator between any two fractions.

```
10 PRINT "TYPE IN THE
DENOMINATORS OF THE TWO
FRACTIONS FOR WHICH YOU
WISH TO FIND THE LCD. TYPE
THE SMALLER DENOMINATOR
FIRST, THEN A COMMA, AND
THE LARGER."
20 INPUT A, B
30 IF A > B THEN 10
40 FOR X = 1 TO 100
50 LET M = X * A
60 IF INT(M / B) = M / B
THEN 80
70 NEXT X
80 PRINT M; " IS THE LCD
OF "; A; " AND "; B
90 END
```

Predict what the computer will output if A = 6 and B = 4.

5·8 Chapter Review

1. State the restrictions on x.

a. $\dfrac{3x}{8 - x}$ **b.** $\dfrac{2x - 1}{4x^2 + 12x}$

c. $\dfrac{6}{x^2 - 4x - 5}$ **d.** $\dfrac{-5}{4x + 3}$

e. $\dfrac{x + 2}{6x} + \dfrac{4}{3 + x}$ **f.** $\dfrac{10}{2x - 9} - 5x$

2. Find the LCM.

a. 16, 10 **b.** $-3x^2,\ 24xy$

c. $2x,\ 2x - 5$ **d.** $x - 1,\ x^2 - 2x + 1$

e. $6x + 12,\ 4x + 8,\ 2x - 4$

f. $x^2 - 9,\ x^2 + x - 6$

3. Find the LCD.

a. $\dfrac{5x - 3}{6} + \dfrac{9x}{4}$ **b.** $\dfrac{5}{6} + \dfrac{4}{x - 2}$

c. $\dfrac{3}{x^2 - 4} - \dfrac{1}{x^2 - 7x + 10}$

d. $\dfrac{9x}{x + 3} - \dfrac{2}{x - 3} + \dfrac{1}{3x}$

e. $\dfrac{x}{2x - 4} + \dfrac{3}{4x} + \dfrac{5}{x - 2}$

4. Simplify.

a. $\dfrac{28x^2 y}{35xy}$ **b.** $\dfrac{5a + 10}{a + 2}$

c. $\dfrac{2x^2 + 7x + 3}{6x^2 - 7x - 5}$ **d.** $\dfrac{9 - 4x}{4x^2 - 5x - 9}$

e. $\dfrac{30m^2 + 18m}{5m^2 - 17m - 12}$ **f.** $\dfrac{4x^2 - 25}{10x - 4x^2}$

g. $\dfrac{16y^2 - x^2}{2x^2 - 7xy - 4y^2}$ **h.** $\dfrac{3b^2 - ab - 10a^2}{8a^2 - 2ab - b^2}$

5. Simplify.

a. $\dfrac{12p^3 q}{5q^2} \times \dfrac{20pq^2}{3q}$

b. $\dfrac{5x + 15}{10} \times \dfrac{2x^2 + 4x}{x + 3}$

c. $\dfrac{2a}{6a - 12b} \div \dfrac{b}{a - 2b}$

d. $\dfrac{2x^2 + 15x + 7}{4x^2 - 1} \times \dfrac{8x - 4}{x + 4}$

6. Simplify.

a. $\dfrac{y - 4}{6} + \dfrac{2y + 1}{4}$ **b.** $\dfrac{8x + 3}{2} - 5x$

c. $\dfrac{3}{a + 2} + \dfrac{5}{6a - 1}$ **d.** $\dfrac{x}{2x + 7} + \dfrac{2x}{4x - 3}$

7. If half of a number is added to one third of the same number, then the result is 90. Find the number.

8. How many millilitres of concentrate must be added to 150 mL of a 4% solution to increase its concentration to 10%?

9. Express each in simplest terms.

a. $\dfrac{5}{x^2 + 7x - 30} + \dfrac{6}{2x^2 + 19x - 10}$

b. $\dfrac{4x}{9x^2 - 25} - \dfrac{x - 1}{3x^2 + x - 10}$

c. $\dfrac{9y + 3}{3y^2 - 11y - 4} + \dfrac{2 - y}{y^2 - 8y + 12}$

d. $\dfrac{x^2 + x - 20}{x^2 + 2x - 15} + \dfrac{2x + 9}{2x^2 + 3x - 27}$

e. $\dfrac{2x}{5x - 1} + \dfrac{1}{x + 4} - \dfrac{3}{x + 2}$

f. $\dfrac{5x}{2x + 1} - \dfrac{6}{3x} + \dfrac{2x}{x - 5}$

g. $\dfrac{a^2 - 49}{4a^2 + 31a + 21} + \dfrac{8a + 4}{4} - \dfrac{2}{3}$

h. $\dfrac{a^2 + 4b^2}{a^4 - 16b^4} + \dfrac{1}{a^2 + 3ab + 2b^2}$

10. Solve.

a. $\dfrac{3x - 1}{4} + \dfrac{7x - 2}{5} = 2x$

b. $\dfrac{x - 5}{12} = \dfrac{2x + 3}{8} - \dfrac{x}{3}$

c. $\dfrac{3x - 4}{x + 5} = \dfrac{6x - 1}{2x + 11}$

d. $\dfrac{2}{x^2 + 2x - 24} + \dfrac{3}{2x^2 + 7x - 30} = 0$

e. $\dfrac{8x - 12}{2x^2 + 9x - 18} = \dfrac{5x}{3x^2 - x}$

11. A rectangular poster has an area of 3000 cm².
a. Write an expression for its width in terms of its length.
b. Write an expression for the increase in the length when the width is increased by x cm.
c. What is the original width of the poster if the width is increased by 15 cm and the original length is 75 cm?

5·9 Chapter Test

1. Determine the restrictions on x.

a. $\dfrac{2x}{3x^2}$

b. $\dfrac{18}{x+5}$

c. $\dfrac{3x-1}{x^2-7x-8}$

d. $\dfrac{9x^2-1}{6x^2-x-1}$

2. Find the LCM.

a. $-8, 12, 15$

b. $6x, 15xy$

c. $4ab, 10bc, 2ac$

d. $x, x-2$

e. $3x+1, 3x-1$

f. $x^2-y^2, x+y$

g. $a-b, b-a$

h. $5x-10, 3x-6$

3. Find the LCD.

a. $\dfrac{x-4}{8} - \dfrac{5x}{6}$

b. $\dfrac{3}{2x+1} + \dfrac{5}{2x}$

c. $\dfrac{5x+2}{12x} - \dfrac{x-3}{8} + \dfrac{4x+1}{3x}$

d. $\dfrac{1}{x^2+2x} - \dfrac{3}{x+2}$

e. $\dfrac{x+6}{2x^2+9x+10} + \dfrac{4x}{2x^2+5x}$

4. Reduce to lowest terms.

a. $\dfrac{-15a^3b}{20ab^2}$

b. $\dfrac{12x^4}{8x^2y}$

c. $\dfrac{15x-3x^2}{6x}$

d. $\dfrac{4c+8d}{6d+3c}$

e. $\dfrac{x^2-6x+8}{x^2-16}$

f. $\dfrac{6x^2-3x}{2x^2+x-1}$

g. $\dfrac{6-x}{5x-30}$

h. $\dfrac{9-x^2}{2x^2-x-15}$

5. Simplify.

a. $\dfrac{12a^2}{5b} \times \dfrac{20ab^2}{32a}$

b. $\dfrac{-6p^2}{10q} \times \dfrac{8q}{3p^4}$

c. $\dfrac{4b}{3c^2} \div \dfrac{6b}{15ac}$

d. $\dfrac{24}{16b^2} \times \dfrac{2a}{3} \div \dfrac{a^3}{5b}$

e. $\dfrac{6x+12y}{8x} \times \dfrac{2y}{x+2y}$

f. $\dfrac{15mn}{m^2-n^2} \times \dfrac{m^2+3mn-4n^2}{12m^2}$

g. $\dfrac{4x^2-y^2}{8x^2} \div \dfrac{2x^2+7xy-4y^2}{2xy}$

h. $\dfrac{6-x}{x^2-9x+18} \times \dfrac{2x-6}{5x^2+1}$

i. $\dfrac{3p^2+14p+15}{p^2+6p+9} \times \dfrac{12p+4p^2}{9p^2-25}$

6. Simplify.

a. $\dfrac{6}{x} + \dfrac{3}{2x}$

b. $\dfrac{1}{a} - \dfrac{8}{b}$

c. $\dfrac{4}{c} - \dfrac{1}{3c} + \dfrac{6}{5c}$

d. $\dfrac{3x-1}{4} + \dfrac{2x}{3}$

e. $\dfrac{m-6}{4} - \dfrac{2m+5}{9}$

f. $\dfrac{2y+3}{10y} + \dfrac{y-2}{8y}$

7. Find two numbers such that one number is 8 more than the other. The quotient of the smaller divided by the larger number is $\dfrac{2}{3}$.

8. The focal length of a lens is denoted by f and the distance of the object to the lens and the image to the lens is given by d_o and d_i respectively. If the object distance is 2 cm greater than the image distance, then find the expression for the focal length.

$$\dfrac{1}{f} = \dfrac{1}{d_o} + \dfrac{1}{d_i}$$

9. Simplify. State the restrictions on the variable.

a. $\dfrac{8}{2x-3} + \dfrac{4}{3-2x}$

b. $12x - \dfrac{4x-1}{x+3}$

c. $\dfrac{3x}{x-2} + \dfrac{x+2}{x-4}$

d. $\dfrac{15a}{a^2-a} + \dfrac{a+2}{a^2+10a+16}$

e. $\dfrac{6}{y-3} - \dfrac{4}{2y+1} + \dfrac{4}{5y}$

f. $\dfrac{x-4}{2x+1} + \dfrac{3x}{2x-1} + \dfrac{5}{1-2x}$

10. Solve.

a. $\dfrac{3a-4}{2} + \dfrac{a+2}{5} = 1$

b. $\dfrac{x+3}{15} - \dfrac{x-1}{20} = 2$

c. $\dfrac{4}{2x-5} - \dfrac{3}{x+1} = 0$

d. $\dfrac{6x}{3x-5} = \dfrac{2x+1}{x-1}$

11. Find an expression for the area of the shaded part of the diagram in factored form.

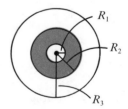

CHAPTER SIX

GEOMETRY

Tune Up

1. Illustrate each with the aid of a diagram. Label and name each part of the diagram.
a. a point　　　　　**b.** a line
c. a ray　　　　　　**d.** a line segment
e. a plane　　　　　**f.** intersecting rays

2. What is the minimum number of points needed to determine each?
a. a line　　　**b.** a plane　　　**c.** space

3. Draw a diagram to illustrate congruent line segments.
a. Label each segment and write a mathematical statement which states their congruence.
b. Define congruent line segments.

4. Draw a diagram to illustrate opposite rays.

5. Draw a diagram to illustrate each.
a. three collinear points
b. three noncollinear points

6. Define these terms.
a. complementary angles
b. supplementary angles

7. Find the complement of each angle.
a. $35°$　　　**b.** $63°$　　　**c.** $57°$　　　**d.** $89°$
e. $12°$　　　**f.** $49°$　　　**g.** $x°$　　　**h.** $(15-2x)°$

8. Find the supplement of each angle.
a. $75°$　　　**b.** $120°$　　　**c.** $3°$　　　**d.** $178°$
e. $89°$　　　**f.** $127°$　　　**g.** $y°$　　　**h.** $(65+4x)°$

9. Write a definition for each type of triangle with reference to angles. Use a diagram to reinforce your definition.
a. an acute triangle
b. a right triangle
c. an obtuse triangle
d. an isosceles triangle

10. Write a definition for each type of triangle with reference to lengths of sides. Use a diagram to reinforce your definition.
a. a scalene triangle
b. an isosceles triangle
c. an equilateral triangle

11. Can the definitions of Exercise 10 be given in terms of angles instead of sides?

6·1 Angles — An Introduction

Before an understanding of geometry is reached, basic terms and definitions must be understood. This section will review the basic terms and definitions used in previous years, as well as introduce some of the new terms that will be needed throughout this chapter.

Recall that an **angle** is formed by two rays having a common endpoint. This endpoint is called the **vertex** of the angle, while the **rays** are the "sides" of the angle. Any angle may be named by a single letter as long as there is no chance of misinterpretation. Otherwise, three letters are used to name the angle.

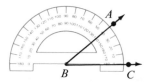

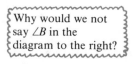
Why would we not say ∠B in the diagram to the right?

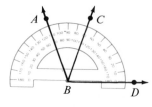

The measure of an angle is the amount one of the rays must be rotated in order to coincide with the other ray. Angles are generally measured in degrees. Recall that one complete revolution is 360°.

There are many different types of angles. They are classified according to their measure.

Name of Angle	Measure of Angle (x)
Acute	$0° < x < 90°$
Right	$x = 90°$
Obtuse	$90° < x < 180°$
Straight	$x = 180°$
Reflex	$180° < x < 360°$

Two rays are said to be **opposite** if they have a common endpoint and point in opposite directions (forming an angle of 180°).
Two angles are **adjacent** if they have one common side.
A **linear pair** of angles has one common side and the second sides form opposite rays.
Vertically opposite angles are the nonadjacent angles formed by two intersecting lines.
Congruent angles are angles that have the same measure.

Example

From the diagram at the right, find an example of these angles or pairs of angles.

a. acute   ∠BFA or ∠DFE
b. obtuse   ∠AFE
c. right   ∠AFC or ∠CFD
d. vertically opposite   ∠BFA and ∠DFE
e. adjacent   ∠CFD and ∠DFE
f. supplementary   ∠AFB and ∠BFD
g. complementary   ∠AFB and ∠BFC
h. linear pair   ∠BFC and ∠CFE
i. congruent angles   ∠AFB and ∠EFD

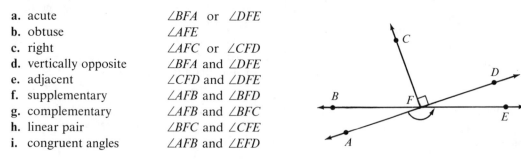

Exercises

1. In your own words, define acute angle, obtuse angle, straight angle, and reflex angle. Use a diagram to reinforce your definitions.

2. Draw an acute angle, an obtuse angle, and a reflex angle. Estimate the size of each angle. Use a protractor to check your estimation. Was your estimation reasonable?

3. Calculate the measure of each pair of complementary angles. (*Hint:* Set up an equation.)

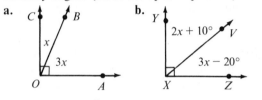

a. **b.**

4. Calculate the measure of each pair of supplementary angles.

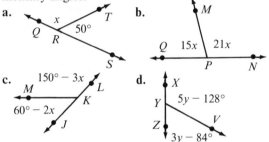

a. **b.**

c. **d.**

5. Using the definition of a linear pair of angles from the display, explain what is implied about the sum of the measures of a linear pair of angles.

6. The two angles shown form a linear pair of angles. Calculate the size of each angle.

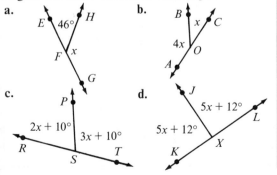

a. **b.**

c. **d.**

7. Using the diagram, find an example of each angle or pair of angles.

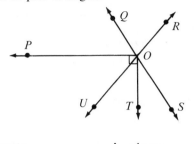

a. acute	**b.** obtuse
c. right	**d.** vertically opposite
e. adjacent	**f.** linear pair
g. supplementary	**h.** complementary

Historical Note

What is geometry?

Originally, geometry was thought of as the branch of mathematics concerned with the properties of space. The ancient Egyptians and Babylonians used geometric principles to determine the area of fields, and volumes of buildings, such as temples and pyramids. The term *geometry* is derived from the Greek words meaning "earth measure".

Modern geometry is thought of as a form of logic, not measurement. If a set of basic assumptions is regarded as a group, then everything can be considered as having properties that remain constant. Whether or not the derivations are true in our own world is not an issue. Using this point of view, Bertrand Russell once remarked that "mathematics may be defined as the subject in which we never know what we are talking about, nor whether what we say is true."

Using the Library

Use the library to investigate how geometry has been defined over the years. Come to a conclusion about what you consider geometry to be. Be prepared to defend your conclusion.

131

6·2 Angles

Besides the basic terms and definitions associated with geometry, there are certain postulates and theorems. A **postulate**, like a definition, is a statement that is accepted as being true without proof. A **theorem** is a statement that must be proved before it is accepted as true.

For example, consider the statement that if two lines intersect at a point, then the vertically opposite angles formed are congruent. If we can prove this statement, then we will have a theorem that can be used whenever the need arises.

One possible approach is to cut out the two vertically opposite angles and superimpose them to determine if they are congruent. Another method is to measure the angles with a protractor. Such methods are **inductive proofs**. But due to the possibility of human error in these methods, they do not prove **beyond all possible doubt** that the two angles are congruent.

A **deductive proof** can be used to prove the theorem beyond all possible doubt. A deductive proof is a series of logically connected statements. The proof begins with definitions, postulates, or other theorems already proved to be true. The proof proceeds by showing that the new theorem follows logically from statements we already know to be true beyond doubt. For each statement in the proof, a reason is given for why we know the statement is true.

There are seven properties that can be useful when proving a statement to be true. These properties are shown in the table.

Property	Statement
Addition Property	If $a = b$, then $a + c = b + c$.
Subtraction Property	If $a = b$, then $a - c = b - c$.
Multiplication Property	If $a = b$, then $ac = bc$.
Division Property	If $a = b$ and $c \neq 0$, then $\dfrac{a}{c} = \dfrac{b}{c}$.
Reflexive Property	If $a = b$, then $b = a$; $a = a$.
Transitive Property	If $a = b$ and $b = c$, then $a = c$.
Substitution Property	If $a = b$, then b can be substituted for a.

Prove this statement deductively. $\angle AOC \cong \angle BOD$

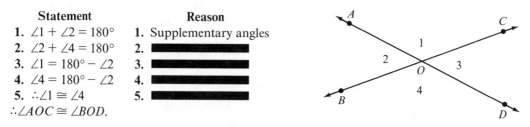

Statement	**Reason**
1. $\angle 1 + \angle 2 = 180°$	1. Supplementary angles
2. $\angle 2 + \angle 4 = 180°$	2. ▬▬▬▬▬
3. $\angle 1 = 180° - \angle 2$	3. ▬▬▬▬▬
4. $\angle 4 = 180° - \angle 2$	4. ▬▬▬▬▬
5. $\therefore \angle 1 \cong \angle 4$	5. ▬▬▬▬▬
$\therefore \angle AOC \cong \angle BOD$.	

Theorem If two straight lines intersect at a point, then the vertically opposite angles are congruent. This is the **opposite angle theorem**.

Exercises

1. Complete the reason for each statement for the proof in the display.

2. In your own words, describe the opposite angle theorem.

3. State the properties needed to arrive at the given conclusions.

a. $\frac{1}{2}x - 5 = 10$
∴$x = 30$

b. If $3a = b$,
and $3a + 7 = 12$
∴$b + 7 = 12$

c. $2x = 3y$
∴$3y = 2x$

d. If $5a = 2b$,
and $2b = 3c$
∴$5a = 3c$

4. State the properties needed to arrive at the given conclusion. The equation of one line is $2x + 5y = 9$ and the equation of a second line is $3x - y = 5$. They intersect at the point $(2, 1)$.

5. Copy and complete to find the measures of $\angle KLM$ and $\angle MLP$.

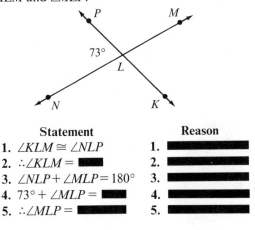

Statement	Reason
1. $\angle KLM \cong \angle NLP$	1. ▮▮▮
2. ∴$\angle KLM =$ ▮▮	2. ▮▮▮
3. $\angle NLP + \angle MLP = 180°$	3. ▮▮▮
4. $73° + \angle MLP =$ ▮▮	4. ▮▮▮
5. ∴$\angle MLP =$ ▮▮▮	5. ▮▮▮

6. Find the measure of all the angles in each.

a.
b.

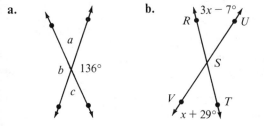

7. Calculate the measure of $\angle POR$.

a.
b.

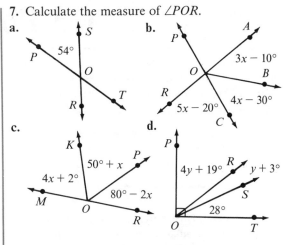

c.
d.

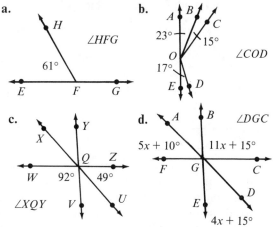

8. Find the time between 03:00 and 04:00 when the hands of a clock are 24° apart.

9. Find the measure of the angle indicated.

a.
$\angle HFG$
b.
$\angle COD$

c.
$\angle XQY$
d.
$\angle DGC$

10. Ayube, Ellen, Joe, and Ali are waiting to have their picture taken. They are to be arranged according to height from the shortest to the tallest. The photographer does not know who each of these people are, but does have the following information.

i) Joe is shorter than Ayube.
ii) There are at least two people shorter than Ayube.
iii) Ali is not the shortest person.
iv) Ellen is taller than Ayube.
In what order should the photographer place the names beneath the photograph?

6·3 Polygons

The study of various shapes is a major component of modern geometry. In this section, we will study the properties of two-dimensional shapes, referred to as **polygons**. A polygon is formed by line segments joining three or more points, no three of which are collinear (they do not lie in the same straight line). The simplest example of a polygon is the triangle.

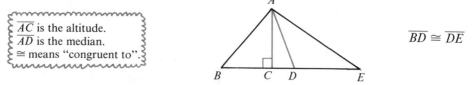

$\overline{AC}$ is the altitude.
$\overline{AD}$ is the median.
$\cong$ means "congruent to".

$\overline{BD} \cong \overline{DE}$

A **quadrilateral** is a polygon formed by joining four points of which no three are collinear.
Consecutive or adjacent angles in a quadrilateral share a common side.
Consecutive or adjacent vertices are at the endpoints of the same side.
Consecutive or adjacent sides have a common endpoint.
Angles, vertices, and sides of a quadrilateral which are not consecutive are called **opposite angles**, **opposite vertices**, and **opposite sides**.
A **diagonal** is a line segment which joins opposite or nonconsecutive vertices.

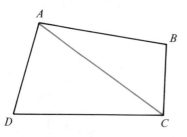

In quadrilateral $ABCD$:
$\angle A$ and $\angle B$ are consecutive angles.
$\angle B$ and $\angle D$ are opposite angles.
B and C are consecutive vertices.
A and C are opposite vertices.
$\overline{AD}$ and $\overline{AB}$ are consecutive sides.
$\overline{AD}$ and $\overline{BC}$ are opposite sides.
$\overline{AC}$ is a diagonal.

There are many different types of quadrilaterals. The following definitions apply to the opposite sides and magnitudes of the angles.
A **trapezoid** is a quadrilateral with exactly one pair of parallel sides.
A **parallelogram** is a quadrilateral with each pair of opposite sides parallel.
A **rectangle** is a parallelogram with four right angles.
A **rhombus** is a parallelogram all of whose sides are congruent.
A **square** is a rectangle all of whose sides are congruent.

Example

Draw a Venn diagram for the above definitions and decide whether these claims are true or false.
a. All squares are rectangles. (true)
b. All rectangles are parallelograms. (true)
c. All rhombuses are rectangles. (false)
d. All squares are rhombuses. (true)

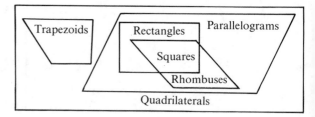

Exercises

1. Modify the definitions for the various quadrilaterals in the display to include angles as well as side lengths.

2. A **regular polygon** is one in which every angle is equal in measure and every side is equal in length.
a. What is a regular polygon of three sides called?
b. What is a regular polygon of four sides called?

3. Polygons are often classified according to the number of sides each contains. Copy and complete this chart listing the most common types of polygons.

Number of Sides	Type of Polygon	Number of Sides	Type of Polygon
3	triangle	8	
4		9	
5		10	
6		12	
7		n	n-gon

4. Draw an acute triangle, a right triangle, and an obtuse triangle. By measuring, find the midpoint of each of the sides. Draw the 3 medians (line from a vertex to the midpoint of the opposite side) of each triangle. You will notice that they meet at one point. This point is called the **centroid**.

5. For each, if the statement is always true, then write true. If the statement is not always true, replace the underlined word with a description to make it true.
a. Consecutive angles of a square are congruent.
b. A parallelogram is a rectangle.
c. A rhombus is a parallelogram.
d. A rectangle is equilateral.
e. Each angle of a square is a right angle.
f. A square is a rhombus.
g. A rhombus is equiangular.
h. The angles of a parallelogram are congruent.
i. A parallelogram with congruent sides and angles is a square.
j. A rectangle has exactly one pair of parallel sides.

6. Make an accurate drawing of a parallelogram, a trapezoid, a rectangle, a square, a rhombus, and a quadrilateral. Make sure your quadrilateral is not one of the other figures you have already drawn. Draw the diagonals in each figure. By measuring, determine an answer for each of the following and write a statement in the form of a rule. The first one is done for you.

In which figure(s) are the diagonals congruent to each other?
The diagonals of the squares and the rectangles are congruent.

a. In which figure(s) do the diagonals bisect each other?
b. In which figure(s) are the diagonals perpendicular?
c. In which figure(s) are consecutive angles congruent?
d. In which figure(s) are opposite angles congruent?
e. In which figure(s) are consecutive angles supplementary?

7. Draw each polygon. Draw the diagonals in as many polygons as necessary to copy and complete the chart.

Polygon	Number of Sides	Number of Diagonals	Difference
Triangle	3	0	
Quadrilateral	4	2	2
Pentagon	5	5	3
Hexagon	6		
Septagon	7		
Octagon	8		
Nonagon	9		
Decagon	10		
n-gon	n		

8. An equilateral triangle is always equiangular. Show by giving a counterexample that an equilateral polygon of more than three sides is not necessarily equiangular.

9. There are nine discs numbered from 1 to 9. How many ways can a sum of 15 be found using only three discs at a time?

6·4 Similar Figures

Similar figures are used extensively to make things more manageable. For example, a road map is a reduced version of the world around us. A photograph of microscopic life can be enlarged and used to study what we cannot see otherwise. Can you find other examples of similar figures that are used in this manner?

> If any two figures are related by a reduction or an enlargement, then the two figures are similar.

In the diagrams to the right, $\triangle ABC$ has been reduced and relabelled as $\triangle XYZ$. By measuring the corresponding angles, you will notice that $\angle A \cong \angle X$, $\angle B \cong \angle Y$, and $\angle C \cong \angle Z$. Because this is a reduction, the length of each side has been reduced by the same amount. Therefore,
$\dfrac{\overline{AB}}{\overline{XY}} = \dfrac{\overline{BC}}{\overline{YZ}} = \dfrac{\overline{CA}}{\overline{ZX}}$, and $\triangle ABC \sim \triangle XYZ$.

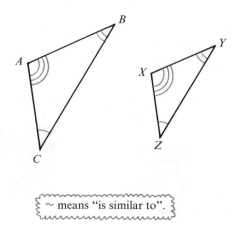

> $\sim$ means "is similar to".

Example

A group of hikers walked from Camp A to Camp B, and then to Camp C where they decided to rest for the night. They wanted to know how long the bridge was. They drew the diagram shown. They knew that $\angle A \cong \angle D$, $\angle B \cong \angle E$, and that the distance to the bridge, $\overline{EC}$, is 900 m. They also knew that they had walked 400 m from Camp A to Camp B, and 300 m from Camp B to Camp C. How long is the bridge?

Since two pairs of corresponding angles are congruent , and since $\angle ACB \cong \angle DCE$ (vertically opposite angles), therefore, $\triangle ABC \sim \triangle DEC$.

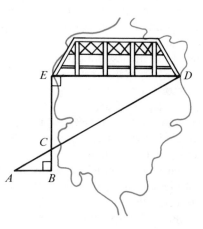

$$\therefore \frac{\overline{AB}}{\overline{DE}} = \frac{\overline{BC}}{\overline{EC}} = \frac{\overline{CA}}{\overline{CD}}$$

$$\frac{400}{\overline{DE}} = \frac{300}{900} = \frac{500}{\overline{CD}}$$

> $\overline{CA}$ is 500 m by the Pythagorean Relation.

$$\frac{400}{\overline{DE}} = \frac{300}{900}$$

$$\overline{DE} = 1200$$

Therefore, the length of the bridge is 1200 m.

Exercises

1. State the corresponding angles and sides in each pair of triangles.

a.

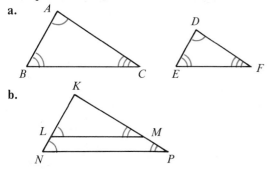

b.

2. Refer to the diagram in the display. Show the steps to prove that $\overline{CD}$ is 1500 m.

3. Calculate the lengths of the sides labelled x in each.

a.   **b.**

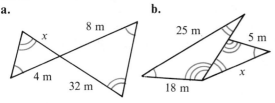

4. Find the lengths of the sides labelled x, y, and z.

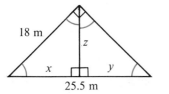

5. A contractor was asked to build this roof on a house. If the materials cost $14/m², then how much should the contractor charge for the materials? (*Hint:* Find the lengths of all three sides and find the area with Heron's Formula.)

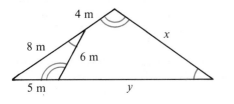

6. Present an argument to support this theorem. (*Hint:* Use the fact that the sum of the angles in a triangle is 180°.)

> **Theorem** If two angles of one triangle are congruent to two corresponding angles of another triangle, then the triangles are similar.

7. To make a planning decision, the mayor of Sarnia had to know the height of the tallest building in the city. This information was not recorded in any of the municipal records. She asked the city planner to find this out for her. The city planner thought of three possible methods to find the height of the building.

i) Drop a steel ball from the top of the building and time how long it takes to hit the ground with a stopwatch. Then use the information in the formula $d = 4.9t^2$.

ii) Tie a ball to a spool of thread and lower the ball until it reaches the ground. Then measure the thread in 10 m sections using a tape measure.

iii) Measure the shadow cast by the Sun of himself and the building at the same time during the day. Because he knows his own height, he can use similar triangle ratios to find the height of the building.

a. Which of these methods do you think will produce the most accurate result? Explain.

b. Write an argument defending the choice of a plan that you did not pick in part **a**.

8. A street on a hill is 250 m long and it rises to a level 45 m above the starting point. To light the street entirely, a light must be placed so that it is at a point on the road 29 m above the starting point. How far up the hill should the light pole be placed?

9. A guy wire from the top of a church steeple barely passes over the top of an antenna 10 m above the ground. The guy wire meets the ground at a point 15 m from the base of the antenna. If the horizontal distance from the point of contact to the base of the steeple is 55 m, then how long is the guy wire?

6·5 Parallel Lines — An Introduction

Two lines drawn in the same plane will either intersect or never intersect. Two lines drawn in the same plane that never intersect are **parallel** lines. Two lines drawn in different planes that never intersect and are not parallel are called **skew** lines.

Example

How many lines can be drawn through a point, P, not on ℓ_1 and parallel to ℓ_1?

Intuition tells us that there is only one such line. Euclid stated this as a postulate about 300 B.C.

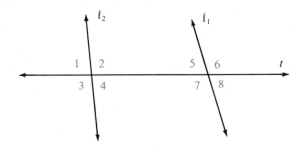

$\ell_1 \| \ell_2$ means that ℓ_2 is parallel to ℓ_1.

> **Postulate** Through any point, P, not on ℓ_1, there is exactly one line parallel to the given line in the same plane.

These are some of the basic definitions that will be necessary for any work with parallel lines.

A **transversal** is a line or line segment that intersects two or more lines in unique points. In the following diagram, line t (a transversal), intersects ℓ_1 and ℓ_2 in two places. Eight angles are formed.

Angles 1, 3, 6, and 8 are **exterior** angles. Angles 2, 4, 5, and 7 are **interior** angles. Some of the pairs of angles have commonly-used names.

Alternate interior angles are any pair of angles which are interior and on opposite sides of the transversal. Examples are $\angle 2$ and $\angle 7$, or $\angle 4$ and $\angle 5$. Alternate angles can be associated with the shape of the letter Z or N.

Corresponding angles are any pair of angles where one is an interior angle and one is an exterior angle and both are on the same side of the transversal. Examples are $\angle 1$ and $\angle 5$, or $\angle 4$ and $\angle 8$. Can you find another example? Corresponding angles can be associated with the shape of the letter F.

There are also **consecutive interior angles**. Recall the definition of consecutive angles from Section 6·3 on polygons. Examples are $\angle 2$ and $\angle 5$, or $\angle 4$ and $\angle 7$. Consecutive interior angles can be associated with the shape of the letter U or C.

138

Exercises

1. In your own words, explain the terms "transversal", "corresponding angles", and "alternate interior angles".

2. Find an example of each from the diagrams.

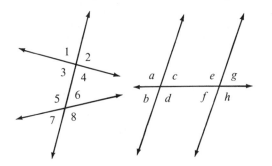

a. an exterior angle
b. an interior angle
c. a pair of corresponding angles
d. a pair of alternate interior angles
e. a pair of consecutive interior angles
f. a pair of vertically opposite angles

3. Draw a parallelogram with a diagonal. Is this diagonal a transversal? Explain.

4. In the display, two parallel lines were defined as any two lines that can be extended indefinitely and never meet. What does this imply about the perpendicular distance between the two lines at any point on the lines? Explain.

5. Using only compasses and a straightedge, construct two parallel lines.
a. Draw a transversal intersecting both lines.
b. Measure all the alternate interior angles formed by the transversal and the parallel lines.
c. Write a conclusion about the alternate interior angles of parallel lines in the form of a postulate.

6. Using the diagram you drew for Exercise 5, measure all the consecutive interior angles.
a. Find the sum of the consecutive interior angles.
b. Write a conclusion about the sum of the consecutive interior angles in the form of a postulate.

7. The postulate shown in the display is a substitute for Euclid's **parallel postulate** as given in his book *Elements*. This postulate was first stated by John Playfair in the eighteenth century. Euclid stated the postulate as follows: "If a straight line intersects two straight lines so as to make the interior angles on one side of it together less than two right angles, these straight lines will intersect, if infinitely produced, on the side on which the angles are together less than two right angles."
a. Describe in your own words, what the postulate means.
b. Draw a diagram to help reinforce your explanation in part **a**.

8. From the photograph, find three examples of vertical parallel lines, three examples of horizontal parallel lines, and three examples of lines that could be transversals.

9. A parallelogram was defined as a quadrilateral with parallel opposite sides. In your own words, explain why the opposite angles of any parallelogram are congruent.

10. Using six toothpicks, create four equilateral triangles with each side equal to the length of one toothpick.

11. Using nine toothpicks, create seven equilateral triangles with each side equal to the length of one toothpick.

139

6·6 Parallel Lines

Euclid's parallel postulate is shown in the first box below. There have been many attempts to prove it without the use of other parallel line theorems, but the attempts have been unsuccessful. As a result, this statement continues to remain a postulate and not a theorem. Remember, a theorem is a statement that can be proved deductively.

> **Postulate** If two lines are cut by a transversal, then the consecutive interior angles are supplementary.

Example

Draw two parallel lines and a transversal, *t*. Prove each of the following statements.
a. If a transversal cuts two parallel lines, then the alternate interior angles are congruent.
b. If a transversal cuts two parallel lines, then the corresponding angles are congruent.

1. Understand the Problem
a. In geometry, it is often a successful problem-solving strategy to draw a diagram. In this case, draw a diagram and mark all the given information on it.
b. We want to show that when a transversal cuts two parallel lines, that the alternate interior angles and the corresponding angles are congruent.

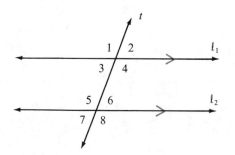

> $>$ on two lines means that they are parallel.

2. Develop a Plan
Once the diagram is drawn, use the above parallel postulate and supplementary angles to prove each statement.

3. Carry Out the Plan

Statement	Reason
1. $\angle 4 + \angle 6 = 180°$	**1.** Parallel postulate
2. $\angle 5 + \angle 6 = 180°$	**2.** Straight line
3. $\angle 4 = 180° - \angle 6$	**3.** Subtraction property
4. $\angle 5 = 180° - \angle 6$	**4.** Subtraction property
5. $\therefore \angle 4 \cong \angle 5$	**5.** Reflexive property

Similarly, $\angle 3 \cong \angle 6$.

4. Look Back
State the proof as a theorem.

> **Theorem** If two parallel lines are cut by a transversal, then the alternate interior angles are congruent.

Exercises

1. Draw two parallel lines and a transversal. Copy and complete to show that the corresponding angles are congruent. Label your diagram in a similar manner to the one in the display.

Statement	Reason
1. $\angle 3 \cong \angle 6$	**1.** ▮▮▮▮▮▮
2. $\angle 6 \cong \angle 7$	**2.** ▮▮▮▮▮▮
3. $\therefore \angle 3 \cong \angle$▮	**3.** Transitive property

State the conclusion as a theorem in the form of an "if ... then" statement.

2. Copy and complete to find the measure of $\angle ABC$.

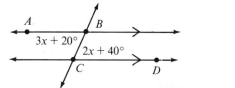

Statement	Reason
1. $\angle ABC \cong \angle BCD$	**1.** ▮▮▮▮▮▮
2. $\therefore 3x + 20 = 2x + 40$	**2.** Substitution property
3. $x = 20$	**3.** ▮▮▮▮▮▮
4. $\angle ABC = 3(■) + 20$	**4.** ▮▮▮▮▮▮
$= ■■°$	

3. Find the magnitude of the indicated angles.

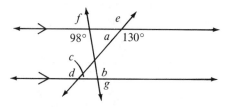

4. Find the measure of $\angle ABC$.
a.

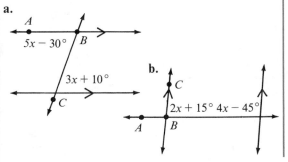

b.

5. Calculate the measure of each indicated angle.
a.

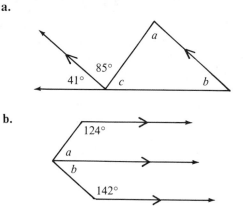

b.

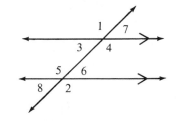

6. Write an argument to prove that $\angle 1 \cong \angle 2$.

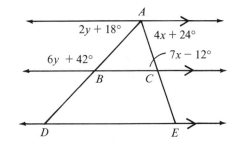

7. Find the measure of each angle in $\triangle ABC$ and trapezoid $BCED$.

8. In the diagram below, $\ell_1 \| \ell_2$. Prove that $\angle 1 + \angle 2 + \angle 3 = \angle 4 + \angle 2 + \angle 5$. Write a statement about the sum of the angles in a triangle from this proof.

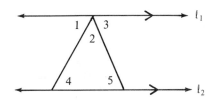

6·7 Constructions

Compasses and a straightedge can be used to perform constructions. From these constructions, certain conclusions (or **hypotheses**) can be reached. This type of reasoning is called **inductive reasoning**. (*Note:* A Mira can be used in place of compasses and a straightedge.)

1. To construct an angle congruent to a given angle.

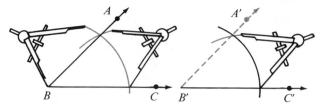

2. To bisect an angle.

3. To construct the perpendicular bisector to a (line) segment.

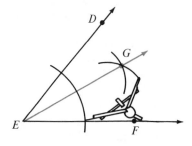

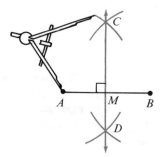

4. To construct a line perpendicular to a given line through a point *P* not on the line.

5. To construct a line perpendicular to a given line through a point *P* on the line.

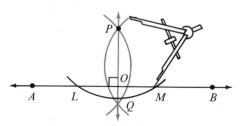

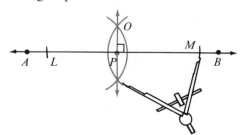

6. To construct a line parallel to a given line through a point *P* not on the line.

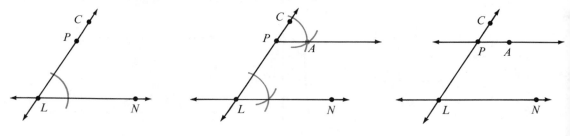

Exercises

1. In inductive reasoning, a sufficient number of examples should be examined before a conclusion is reached. You also should never look at specific cases. For example, when trying to establish facts about all triangles, you should not look at only equilateral triangles. Explain why these two conditions are necessary when using inductive reasoning.

2. In your own words, write a brief description of how to perform the constructions shown in the display.

3. Use a straightedge and compasses, or a Mira, to perform each construction. Check your constructions using a protractor.
a. Draw a line segment AB. Construct the perpendicular bisector of $\overline{AB}$.
b. Draw $\angle ABC$ as an obtuse angle. Construct the bisector of $\angle ABC$.
c. Draw any $\angle ABC$. Construct an angle congruent to $\angle ABC$.
d. Draw a line AB with point P on the line. Construct a perpendicular to $\overleftrightarrow{AB}$ through P.
e. Draw a line AB with point P not on the line. Construct a perpendicular to $\overleftrightarrow{AB}$ through P.
f. Draw a line AB with point P not on the line. Construct a line through P parallel to $\overleftrightarrow{AB}$.

4. Draw an acute triangle, a right triangle, and an obtuse triangle. Using only compasses and a straightedge, or a Mira, perform each construction.
a. In each triangle construct the bisectors of each angle. Write a conclusion in the form of a postulate. The point that you have located is called the **incentre** of the **inscribed circle**. Draw the inscribed circle by using the incentre such that the circle touches the three sides of the triangle.
b. In each triangle construct the perpendicular bisector of each side. Extend the bisectors if necessary so that they intersect. Two or more lines that intersect at the same point are **concurrent**. The point of intersection is called the **circumcentre** of the **circumscribed circle**. Using the circumcentre, draw a circle around the triangle such that the circle passes through each vertex of the triangle.

5. Draw an acute triangle, a right triangle, and an obtuse triangle. In each triangle locate the midpoints of two sides and draw a line through them. Write a hypothesis for the relationship that exists between this line and the third side of the triangle.

6. Draw an isosceles triangle. Construct the bisector of the vertex of the angle formed by the two congruent sides. What relation exists between this line and the base (the side opposite the vertex)? Write your conclusion in the form of a postulate.

7. Draw an acute triangle, a right triangle, and an obtuse triangle. Using a straightedge and a protractor, or a Mira, draw the three altitudes for each triangle. By extending the altitudes as necessary you will notice that they meet at a point. This point is called the **orthocentre**. What is the meaning of "ortho" in the word "orthocentre"?

8. Draw any quadrilateral. Locate the midpoint of each side. Join the midpoints to form another quadrilateral. What conclusion can you formulate about the new quadrilateral? Write your conclusion in the form of a postulate.

9. Draw a large triangle in the middle of a page. Using the constructions in this section locate the circumcentre, C, the centroid (point of intersection of the medians of the triangle), T, and the orthocentre, H. If your constructions are done accurately, then C, T, and H will be **collinear**.
a. The line containing these points is called the **Euler line**. Measure $\overline{CT}$ and $\overline{TH}$ on the Euler line. You should find that $\overline{TH} = 2\,\overline{CT}$.
b. Find the midpoint of $\overline{CH}$. This point is the centre of a circle called a **nine-point circle**. It contains the "feet" of the three altitudes of the triangle, the midpoints of the sides of the triangle, and the midpoints of the altitudes from their vertices to H. Draw the circle.

10. What does the prefix "circum" mean in the term "circumcentre"?

143

6·8 Angles of Triangles

In previous years, you learned that the sum of the angles in a triangle is 180°. This can be shown to be true using inductive reasoning. For example, the measure of the angles of various triangles could be found using a protractor and a hypothesis could be formed that the sum of the angles will always be 180°. Another inductive proof is to cut out the angles, push them together, and hypothesize that they will always form a straight angle. However, due to "human error" that can result in this type of measurement, these methods do not prove **beyond doubt** that the sum of the angles is always 180°. To prove this beyond doubt, a deductive proof is necessary.

Example

Prove that the sum of the angles of any triangle is 180°.

Construct $\triangle ABC$ with a straight line, l_1, parallel to $\overline{BC}$ and passing through A.

Statement	**Reason**
1. $\angle 4 + \angle 3 + \angle 5 = 180°$	1. Straight line
2. $\angle 5 \cong \angle 2$	2. Alternate interior angles
3. $\angle 4 \cong \angle 1$	3. Alternate interior angles
4. $\therefore \angle 1 + \angle 3 + \angle 2 = 180°$	4. Substitution property

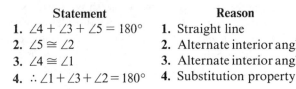

> **Theorem** The sum of the measures of the angles in any triangle is 180°.

Exercises

1. Find the measure of each indicated angle.

a. 27°, 47° x **b.** 87°, 46°, z **c.** 48°, x, x

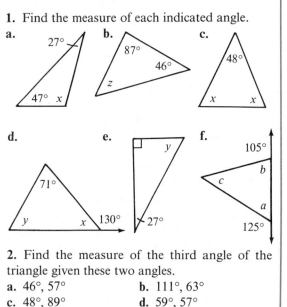

d. 71°, y, x, 130° **e.** y, 27° **f.** 105°, b, c, a, 125°

2. Find the measure of the third angle of the triangle given these two angles.

a. 46°, 57°   **b.** 111°, 63°
c. 48°, 89°   **d.** 59°, 57°
e. $3x°, 5x°$ **f.** $2x - 30°, x + 10°$

3. The measure of one angle of a triangle is 54°. The other two angles have the same measure. Find the measures of the two congruent angles.

4. Calculate the measure of each indicated angle.

a.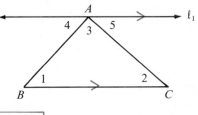

b.

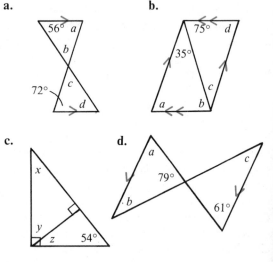

c.

d.

144

5. Calculate the measure of each angle.

a.
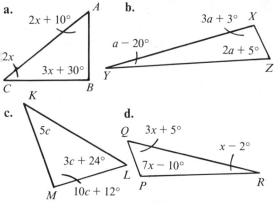
$2x + 10°$ ... A
$2x$
$3x + 30°$
C ... B

b.
$3a + 3°$ ... X
$a - 20°$
$2a + 5°$
Y ... Z

c.
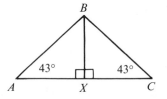
K
$5c$
$3c + 24°$
M ... $10c + 12°$

d.
Q ... $3x + 5°$
$x - 2°$
$7x - 10°$
L
P ... R

6. Calculate the measures of $\angle ABX$ and $\angle CBX$.

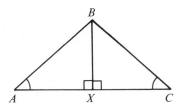
B
$43°$ ... $43°$
A ... X ... C

7. In $\triangle ABC$, $\angle A \cong \angle C$ and $\overline{BX} \perp \overline{AC}$. Provide an argument for $\angle ABX \cong \angle CBX$.

B
A ... X ... C

8. Two angles of a triangle are complements of each other. If the measure of the first is four times the measure of the second, find the measures of all the angles of the triangle.

9. Calculate the measure of each indicated angle.

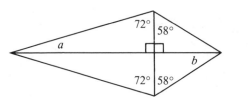
$72°$ $58°$
a
b
$72°$ $58°$

10. To calculate the sum of the measures of the angles of a polygon, two methods can be used.

a. A point can be chosen in the interior of the polygon and all the vertices joined to that point. The sum of the measures of all the triangles formed could be calculated. What would have to be subtracted from the sum to get the sum of the measures of the angles of the polygon? Write a hypothesis for the sum of the angles of a polygon.

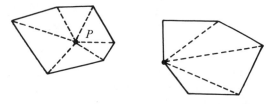
P

b. One of the vertices could be chosen and segments drawn to all the other nonconsecutive vertices. The sum of the measures of all the triangles formed could be calculated. Write a hypothesis for the sum of the angles of a polygon.

c. Using either method, find the sum of the angles of the polygons. Use a calculator if one is available.

Polygon	Sum of the Angles
Triangle	
Quadrilateral	
Pentagon	
Hexagon	
Heptagon	
Octagon	
Nonagon	
Decagon	
Dodecagon	
n-gon	

6·9 Exterior Angles

If one side of a polygon is extended, the angle between the extended side and the side consecutive to the extended side is called an **exterior angle**.

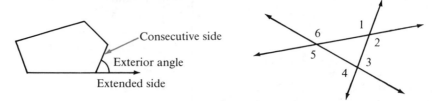

Consecutive side

Exterior angle

Extended side

A triangle has six exterior angles. There are two congruent exterior angles at each vertex. Angles 1, 2, 3, 4, 5, and 6 are all exterior angles. In a triangle, each exterior angle is adjacent and supplementary to an angle of the triangle.

Example

Prove that the exterior angle of any triangle is equal to the sum of the opposite interior angles.

Draw $\triangle ABC$ and extend $\overline{BC}$ to D.

Statement	Reason
1. $\angle 1 + \angle 2 + \angle 3 = 180°$	**1.** ▬▬▬▬▬▬
2. $\angle 3 + \angle 4 = 180°$	**2.** ▬▬▬▬▬▬
3. $\therefore \angle 1 + \angle 2 + \angle 3 = \angle 3 + \angle 4$	**3.** ▬▬▬▬▬▬
4. and $\angle 1 + \angle 2 = \angle 4$	**4.** ▬▬▬▬▬▬

> **Theorem** The exterior angle of any triangle is equal to the sum of the opposite interior angles.

Exercises

1. Name the exterior angle and the opposite interior angles in each diagram.

a.

b.

2. Calculate the measure of the exterior angle in each triangle of Exercise 1.

3. Give the reasons for each statement in the proof in the display.

4. Calculate the measure of each angle in these triangles.

a.

b.

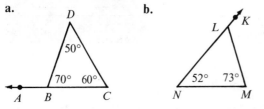

c.

d.

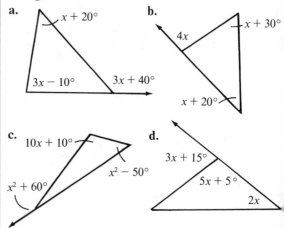

5. Calculate the measure of the indicated angles.

a.

b.

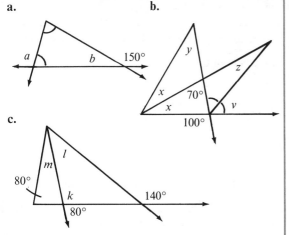

c.

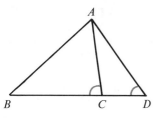

6. In your own words, explain why the markings on the figure indicate an impossible situation.

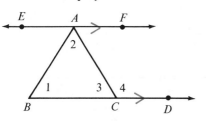

7. Copy and complete this alternate proof for the theorem in the display.

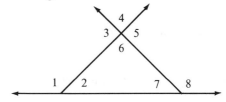

In △*ABC*, extend $\overline{BC}$ to *D* and construct a line, $\overleftrightarrow{EF}$, through *A* parallel to $\overline{BC}$.

Statement	Reason
1. ∠4 + ∠3 = 180°	**1.** ■■■
2. ∠*EAB* ≅ ∠■	**2.** Parallel lines
3. ∠*FAC* ≅ ∠■	**3.** Parallel lines
but	
∠*EAB* + ∠2 + ∠*FAC* = 180°	
4. and $\overleftrightarrow{EF} \parallel \overline{BD}$	**4.** ■■■
5. ∴ ∠*EAB* + ∠2 ≅ ∠4	**5.** ■■■
6. ∴ ■■■	**6.** ■■■

8. Present an argument to support this theorem.

> **Theorem** The exterior angle of a triangle is greater than either of the opposite interior angles.

9. What can be said about each angle in △*RST* if ∠*RTU* is

a. an acute angle? **b.** a right angle?
c. an obtuse angle? **d.** a reflex angle?

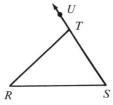

10. In the diagram, find the measure of each indicated angle.

a. ∠6, if ∠2 = 40° and ∠7 = 55°.
b. ∠5, if ∠2 = 55° and ∠7 = 25°.
c. ∠4, if ∠8 = 140° and ∠2 = 60°.
d. ∠1, if ∠4 = 75° and ∠8 = 100°.
e. ∠3, if ∠8 = 85° and ∠1 = 110°.

11. Copy and complete the chart. Use only one exterior angle at each vertex.

Regular Polygon	Measure of Each Exterior Angle	Sum of Exterior Angles
Triangle		
Pentagon		
Hexagon		
Octagon		
Decagon		

12. The radius of a cylindrical can is increased by 10%. To the nearest tenth of a percent, how much must the height be decreased to keep the volume of the cylinder constant?

147

6·10 Congruent Triangles

In this section, we will deal with triangles that are congruent; that is, they have the same size and shape.

Let us look at two triangles that have corresponding parts congruent.

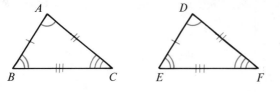

Notice that all six parts are congruent. Hence $\triangle ABC \cong \triangle DEF$.

> If the corresponding angles and the corresponding sides of two triangles are congruent, then the two triangles are congruent.

Shown below are two triangles that are congruent; namely $\triangle PQR$ and $\triangle KLM$. Since the two triangles are congruent, the corresponding angles and the corresponding sides are congruent.

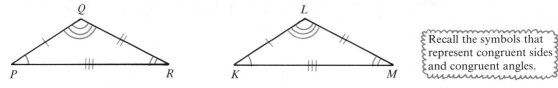

Recall the symbols that represent congruent sides and congruent angles.

The corresponding sides are congruent.

$\overline{PQ} \cong \overline{KL}$
$\overline{QR} \cong \overline{LM}$
$\overline{PR} \cong \overline{KM}$

$\triangle PQR \cong \triangle KLM$

The corresponding angles are congruent.

$\angle P \cong \angle K$
$\angle Q \cong \angle L$
$\angle R \cong \angle M$

Note that the order of the letters is the correspondence of the vertices.

> If two triangles are congruent, then the corresponding parts are congruent.

Exercises

1. State the corresponding sides and angles and then give the congruence between the two triangles.

a.

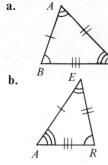

b.

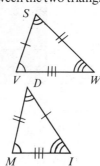

2. Write a statement using symbols to show that the triangles are congruent.

a.

b.

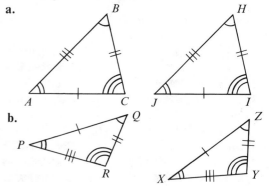

3. Write the congruence statement for each pair of triangles.

a.

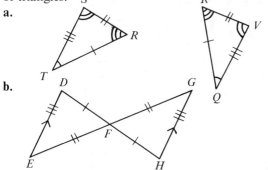

b.

4. If two triangles are congruent, then the corresponding angles and sides are congruent. Draw each pair of congruent triangles and indicate the congruent parts. The first one is partially done for you.

a. $\triangle ABC \cong \triangle KLM$

b. $\triangle RST \cong \triangle PQR$

c. $\triangle EFG \cong \triangle EHG$

5. Sketch and label a diagram for each to calculate the magnitude of the indicated part.

a. $\triangle QRS \cong \triangle MNP$
$\overline{RS} = (3m + 60)$ cm
$\overline{NP} = (5m + 20)$ cm
Calculate $\overline{RS}$.

b. $\triangle HEN \cong \triangle LIK$
$\overline{HN} = (7x - 12)$ m
$\overline{LK} = (28 - 3x)$ m
Calculate $\overline{HN}$.

c. $\triangle EFG \cong \triangle XYZ$
$\angle E = (4x - 18)°$
$\angle X = (2x + 34)°$
Calculate $\angle X$.

d. $\triangle PEN \cong \triangle BIC$
$\angle N = (5x + 15)°$
$\angle C = (2x + 45)°$
Calculate $\angle C$.

6. Each of the following refers to a pair of congruent triangles. State the congruence between the two triangles from the partial information given. Draw and label each diagram.

a. $\overline{BK} \cong \overline{SR}$, $\angle E \cong \angle I$
b. $\overline{IS} \cong \overline{KP}$, $\overline{IR} \cong \overline{KL}$
c. $\angle Q \cong \angle U$, $\angle W \cong \angle O$, $\angle E \cong \angle J$
d. $\overline{CV} \cong \overline{TY}$, $\overline{VX} \cong \overline{YX}$

7. Copy and complete if $\triangle ASD \cong \triangle LKJ$.

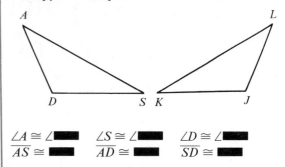

$\angle A \cong \angle$ ▮ $\angle S \cong \angle$ ▮ $\angle D \cong \angle$ ▮
$\overline{AS} \cong$ ▮ $\overline{AD} \cong$ ▮ $\overline{SD} \cong$ ▮

8. Since the definition of congruent triangles is the only means we have at present of proving two triangles congruent, what would you have to know in order to show that any two triangles, *DEF* and *KLM*, are congruent?

9. Given $\triangle WRS$ and $\triangle HGK$, where $\overline{WR} \cong \overline{HG}$, $\overline{WS} \cong \overline{HK}$, $\overline{RS} \cong \overline{GK}$, $\angle W \cong \angle H$, $\angle R \cong \angle G$, and $\angle S \cong \angle K$. Draw a diagram of the two triangles and show the congruent parts. Write an argument for $\triangle WRS \cong \triangle HGK$.

10. If $\triangle ABC \cong \triangle ACB$, then what conclusion can be drawn about $\triangle ABC$? Write an argument to show that your conclusion is correct. (*Hint:* Which are corresponding angles?)

11. If $\triangle ABC \cong \triangle ACB$ and $\triangle ABC \cong \triangle BAC$, then what conclusion can be drawn about $\triangle ABC$? Write an argument to show that your conclusion is correct.

12. A circle is drawn and two points are placed on the circumference.
a. If the two points are connected, then how many regions are formed?
b. If three points are chosen and all possible segments are drawn to connect the points, then how many regions are formed?
c. Find the regions formed for five points, six points, and *n* points.

13. Is it possible for two triangles to be both similar and congruent? Explain.

6·11 Computer Application — Angles of a Polygon

The relationship between the interior angles of a triangle and its exterior angles has been examined in this chapter. In this section, the general relationship between the interior angles of a regular polygon and the exterior angles will be examined. The computer will be used then to evaluate angles of various regular polygons using the relationships that have been discovered. Recall that an interior angle and its corresponding exterior angle are supplementary.

Exercises

1. Consider any regular polygon.

a. If one of the interior angles of a polygon has a measure of 150°, then what is the measure of its corresponding exterior angle?

b. Find the sum of the measures of the interior angles of a regular pentagon.

c. Find the sum of the measures of the exterior angles of a regular hexagon. Remember to include only one exterior angle at each vertex.

d. Describe the steps that you used in parts **b** and **c** in order to arrive at the answer.

2. Below is a program that will calculate the sum of the measures of the interior angles of a pentagon where one vertex was chosen and all possible diagonals were drawn to the other vertices forming a number of triangles.

```
10 REM ████████████
20 LET N = 5
30 LET A = 180 * (N − 2)
40 PRINT "THE SUM OF
   THE MEASURES OF THE
   INTERIOR ANGLES OF A
   PENTAGON IS "; A
50 END
```

a. Draw a regular pentagon and all possible diagonals.

b. Complete the REM statement by giving the purpose of the program.

c. Why is N equal to 5?

d. Why do we multiply N − 2 by 180?

3. This program will calculate the sum of the measures of the exterior angles in a hexagon.

```
10 REM CALCULATE THE SUM OF
   THE EXTERIOR ANGLES
20 LET N = 6
30 LET A = 180 * (N − 2)
40 PRINT "THE SUM OF THE
   INTERIOR ANGLES IS "; A;
   " DEGREES"
50 PRINT "EACH INTERIOR
   ANGLE HAS A MEASURE OF ";
   A / N; " DEGREES"
60 PRINT "EACH INTERIOR
   ANGLE HAS A MEASURE OF ";
   180 − A / N; " DEGREES"
70 PRINT "THE SUM OF THE
   EXTERIOR ANGLES IS ";
   N * (180 − A / N); " DEGREES"
80 END
```

a. Describe the function of each line in this program and predict what the output will be before running the program.

b. Modify this program to print the sum of the measures of the exterior angles of any regular polygon from 3 to 10 sides.

4. Suppose you were assigned to talk to Grade 6 math students as part of a class project. Your discussion topic was the future of mathematics. Before you start, one student claims that from now on, all mathematical problems will be solved by sophisticated electronic machines, and all mathematics today is computer oriented. Explain how you would answer this student.

6·12 Chapter Review

1. Explain the difference between a line and a line segment.

2. If A, B, and C are collinear, name the line that contains the three points in three different ways.

3. These angles are complementary. Find the measure of each angle.

a.

b.

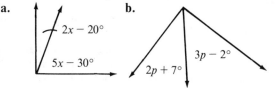

4. These angles are supplementary. Find the measure of each angle.

a.

b.

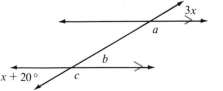

5. Name the quadrilateral(s) which have the properties listed.

a. All the sides are congruent.

b. The sum of the measures of the interior angles is 360°.

c. The sum of the measures of the exterior angles is 360°.

d. Has exactly one pair of parallel sides.

e. All the angles are right angles.

f. Both pairs of opposite sides are parallel.

g. All the sides are congruent and all the angles are congruent.

6. Find the measure of the indicated angles.

a.

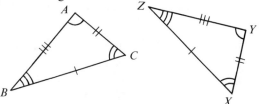

b.

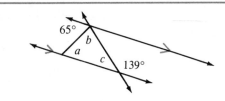

7. Using a straightedge and compasses, or a Mira, draw the perpendicular bisectors of the four sides of a quadrilateral. Are the four bisectors concurrent? Under what conditions could they be concurrent?

8. Calculate the measures of each of the angles in the triangles.

a.

b.

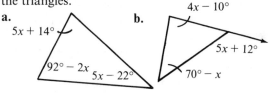

9. Write an argument to support this statement. If two angles of a triangle are congruent to two angles of a second triangle, then the third angles of the triangles are also congruent.

10. If one angle in a triangle is twice a second angle and the third angle is 20° more than the first, calculate the size of each angle in the triangle.

11. In 1910, a chocolate bar cost 10¢, a bottle of pop cost 4¢, while bubble gum was ten for a penny. If a person purchased 100 different items for a dollar, how many chocolate bars, bottles of pop, and pieces of bubble gum were purchased?

12. Write the six congruences in this pair of congruent triangles.

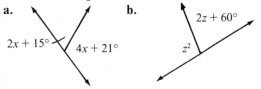

151

6·13 Chapter Test

1. On the number line, which pairs of segments are congruent?

A B C D E F G H I J K L M
−6   0   6

a. $\overline{AC}$ and $\overline{IK}$ **b.** $\overline{DJ}$ and $\overline{GM}$
c. $\overline{AK}$ and $\overline{BM}$ **d.** $\overline{DL}$ and $\overline{JB}$

2. Copy and complete each statement.
a. The complement of 56° is ▬▬.
b. The supplement of 87° is ▬▬.
c. The measure of an exterior angle of a triangle is 78° and one opposite interior angle is 40°. The measure of the other opposite interior angle is ▬▬.
d. If one acute angle in a right triangle is 59°, the other is ▬▬.
e. The complement of $5x°$ is ▬▬.
f. The supplement of $(70 − 2x)°$ is ▬▬.
g. If the measures in degrees of three angles of a triangle are $2x$, $2x + 40$, and $x + 45$, then the three angles are ▬▬, ▬▬, and ▬▬ respectively.

3. If $\overline{AB} \perp \overline{XY}$, find the value of x and y.
a.

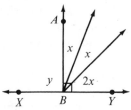

b.

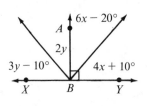

4. If $\triangle ABC \cong \triangle PQR$, which statements are true?
a. $\overline{AB} \cong \overline{QR}$ **b.** $\angle B \cong \angle Q$
c. $\overline{AC} \cong \overline{PR}$ **d.** $\angle BAC \cong \angle QRP$
e. $\overline{RQ} \cong \overline{CB}$ **f.** $\angle CAB \cong \angle RPQ$

5. Find the measure of the interior angles in each figure.

a.

b.

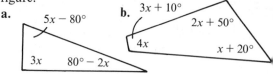

6. In the ancient aboriginal village of Quieta, the people believed that the only way to bring rain to help grow their summer crops was to pray to the gods before a temple built of 14 pillars such that there were seven rows with 4 pillars in each row. Draw a diagram to show the design of the temple.

7. Find the measure of each indicated angle.

a.   **b.**

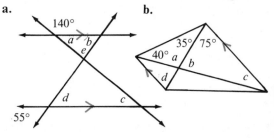

8. Construct an acute triangle. Label the vertices A, B, and C. Find the three medians of the triangle and label them $\overline{AM}$, $\overline{BN}$ and $\overline{CP}$. Label the centroid (point of concurrence of the medians) O. Measure $\overline{AO}$ and $\overline{OM}$, $\overline{BO}$ and $\overline{ON}$, and $\overline{CO}$ and $\overline{OP}$.
a. What relationship exists between each pair?
b. The centre of gravity of a triangle is its centroid. If $\overline{AM}$, $\overline{BN}$, and $\overline{CP}$ are 18 cm, 15 cm, and 12 cm respectively, how far is the centre of gravity from each of the vertices of the triangle?

9. The measure of the supplement of an angle is 40° more than the measure of the angle. Find the measure of each angle.

10. Two supplementary angles have measures such that the first is 5 times the second. Find the measures of each.

Cumulative Review Chapters 4–6

1. State the degree of each polynomial and write in descending order of degree in x.
a. $5x^2 - x^3 + 2$
b. $4x^2 - 3x^2(x^2 - 5)$
c. $(x^2 - 4x - 5)(3 - x^2)$

2. Find the value of each polynomial if $p = -3$, $q = 2$, and $r = 5$.
a. $2pq - 4qr$
b. $2r - p^2q$
c. $\dfrac{8qr + 3p}{q}$
d. $\dfrac{4p + 5q - r}{2p}$

3. Simplify by performing the indicated operations.
a. $8xy - 2yz + 9xz - yz + 5xz - 12xy$
b. $3a^2b + 8a^2b^2 - 2ab^2 - a^2b^2 - 15a^2b$
c. $(6m^2 - 4mn + 7) + (m^2 + 9mn - 12)$
d. $(4u - 3v^2) + (u^2 + 6u) - (8u^2 + 5v^2)$
e. $(2a^2 - 15b^2) - (a^2 + 6ab + b^2) + (3a^2 - 12ab - 8b^2)$

4. Multiply. Simplify by collecting like terms.
a. $3u(6v - 2u) + 4(5u^2 + 8uv)$
b. $8p - 3(p + 7q) + 2(4q - 3p)$
c. $(2x - 5)(3x^2 - 10x + 1)$
d. $(6y - 1)(y + 3) + (4y - 5)(y + 2)$
e. $(3k - 4)(3k + 4) - (2k + 1)^2$
f. $5(x - 3)(x + 2) - 3(2x + 1)(x - 4)$
g. $4(3p + 2)(p + 2) + 2(p - 4)^2$
h. $(m + 2)(3m - 1)(4m + 3)$

5. Factor completely.
a. $10a^2 + 16ab$
b. $2m^2 + m - 15$
c. $3k^2 + 5k - 8$
d. $16x^2 - 8x + 1$
e. $2x^3 - 10x^2 + 12x$
f. $3x^2 - 75y^2$
g. $4p^2 + 13pq - 12q^2$
h. $18r^2 - 50t^2$
i. $8a^2 + 22ab + 5b^2$
j. $-8xy^2 + 12xy - 24x^2y$
k. $4a(2b - 1) - 3(2b - 1)$

6. Divide.
a. $\dfrac{5a^3b + 20ab^2}{5ab}$
b. $\dfrac{2x^2 + 6x}{x + 3}$
c. $\dfrac{2a^3 - 3a^2 + 10a - 15}{2a - 3}$

7. Find the zeros of each polynomial.
a. $6x - 8$
b. $2x(x - 4)$
c. $(m - 3)(4m + 1)$
d. $(2k + 5)(k - 4)$
e. $a^2 - 7a - 8$
f. $2t^2 + 7t + 5$

8. Point A is the midpoint of the base of the rectangle. Find the area of the rectangle.

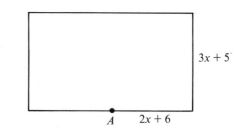

9. Determine the perimeter and area of this rectangle.

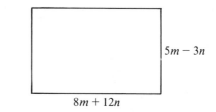

10. Four numbers are defined as $(a - 2b)$, $(4a + b)$, $(3a - 5b)$, and $(2a - 3b)$.
a. Find the sum of the four numbers.
b. Find the sum of the products of the first two numbers and the last two numbers.

11. The area of a triangle is given by the expression $3x^2 - 5xy + 2y^2$ square units. Find the height of the triangle if the base length is $x - y$ units.

12. The distance, s, an object travels is given by the formula $s = \frac{1}{2}at^2$, where a is the acceleration of the object and t is the time of travel. If an object is being accelerated at $6p$ m/s^2 and travels for $2p - 1$ s, then find the distance travelled by the object.

153

Cumulative Review Chapters 4–6

13. Copy and complete the magic square so that the sum of each row and column is defined by the expression $5a^2 - 2ab - 8b^2$.

$2a^2 + 3ab$		$4ab - b^2$
	$5a^2 + b^2$	
		$7a^2 - ab - 3b^2$

14. William Speak shot six arrows at the target shown and scored 111 points. Where did the six arrows land?

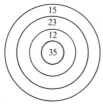

15
23
12
35

15. The volume of a cone is given by the formula $V = \frac{1}{3}\pi r^2 h$. Find the volume of a cone with a radius of $2a + b$ units and a height of $\dfrac{12a}{\pi}$ units.

16. Give the restrictions for the variables.

a. $\dfrac{-8}{3x}$ **b.** $\dfrac{5n}{n-2}$ **c.** $\dfrac{2x+6}{x+3}$

d. $\dfrac{4}{a^2-9}$ **e.** $\dfrac{y^2+3}{y^2+2y-3}$

17. Simplify by dividing by the common factors.

a. $\dfrac{15m^3n}{40mn^4}$ **b.** $\dfrac{18a^2-15ab}{24ac+6ab}$

c. $\dfrac{x^2-4x-32}{x^2+2x-8}$ **d.** $\dfrac{3m^2-14m+8}{6m^2-m-2}$

e. $\dfrac{12p^2+20pq+3q^2}{36p^2-q^2}$ **f.** $\dfrac{25k^2+60kt+36t^2}{15k^2+18kt}$

18. Perform the indicated operations and write in simplest form.

a. $\dfrac{12p}{5pq^2} \times \dfrac{20p^3q}{9q}$ **b.** $\dfrac{4x^3y}{5xy^2} \div \dfrac{12xz}{15y^3z}$

c. $\dfrac{3a^2+6a}{-a^2-a+2} \times \dfrac{a^2-3a+2}{a^2-2a}$

d. $\dfrac{4m^2-11mn-3n^2}{16m^2-n^2} \times \dfrac{20m^2-5mn}{m^2-3mn}$

19. Determine the LCM of each.

a. $12a, 15ab^2$ **b.** $p-2q, 2q$

c. $2x+6, x+3$ **d.** x^2-1, x^2-x-2

20. Perform the operations and simplify the expressions.

a. $\dfrac{9}{6a} + \dfrac{3}{4b}$ **b.** $\dfrac{2}{p} - \dfrac{5}{3q} + \dfrac{3}{pr}$

c. $\dfrac{m+3}{12} + \dfrac{4m-1}{8}$ **d.** $\dfrac{6b}{5a} - \dfrac{3}{10ab}$

21. Simplify by performing the indicated operations.

a. $\dfrac{5}{4m} - \dfrac{3}{m^2+2m}$

b. $\dfrac{4}{x^2+2x-8} + \dfrac{2}{x^2-16}$

c. $\dfrac{2k^2+k-3}{k^2-1} + \dfrac{6k^2}{3k^2-12k}$

d. $\dfrac{8s^2+18st-5t^2}{16s^2-t^2} - \dfrac{3s^2+8st-3t^2}{s^2+5st+6t^2}$

22. If $x = \dfrac{1}{a-4}$ and $y = \dfrac{2}{3a+1}$, then write $3x - 2y$ in terms of a.

23. Solve for x.

a. $\dfrac{x+4}{3} + \dfrac{2x-5}{6} = 2$

b. $\dfrac{x+2}{2} + 3 = \dfrac{4x-3}{5}$

c. $\dfrac{4}{5}(x-2) - \dfrac{1}{3}(2x+9) = 0$

d. $\dfrac{3}{x} = \dfrac{5}{x+2}$

e. $\dfrac{5}{8} + \dfrac{4}{2x+3} = 2$

f. $\dfrac{5}{3x+2} + \dfrac{x}{x-2} = 1$

Cumulative Review Chapters 4–6

24. A triangle has an area of 80 cm².
a. Write an expression for the base of the triangle if the altitude is h cm.
b. If the area is kept constant but the height is decreased n cm, then find the expression for the base.

25. In a car rally, Jenna must travel 15 km in the city and 80 km on the open highway.
a. If she averages 45 km/h in the city and 90 km/h on the highway, how long will it take for Jenna to complete the course?
b. If Jenna averages m km/h in the city and increases her average speed by n km/h on the highway, how long does it take to complete the course?

26. Which number does not belong to the sequence? Explain.
1, 3, 6, 9, 12

27. Three playing cards are placed in a row.
The three is to the left of the queen.
The diamond is to the right of the club.
The queen is to the right of the ten.
The club is to the left of the spade.
The ten is next to the queen.
The spade is to the right of the diamond.
What are the three cards and what order are they placed in the row?

28. Define each term.
a. acute angle   **b.** supplementary angles
c. obtuse angle   **d.** complementary angles

29. Two angles are supplementary. One angle is defined by the expression $150 - 3x$. The other angle is defined by the expression $60 - 2x$. Find the measures of the two angles.

30. If two straight lines intersect at a point, then the vertically opposite angles are congruent.
a. What is the name given to this theorem?
b. Prove this theorem.

31. Calculate the measure of $\angle POR$.

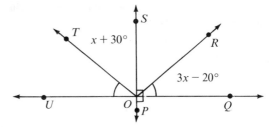

32. All squares are rectangles but not all rectangles are squares. Explain.

33. Define the term "regular polygon".
a. What is a regular polygon of three sides called?
b. What is a regular polygon of four sides called?

34. Calculate the lengths of the sides labelled x and y.

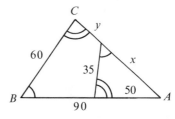

35. How many lines can be drawn through the point P parallel to ℓ_1? Explain.

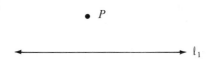

36. Find an example of each using the lines and the transversal shown.
a. alternate interior angles
b. congruent angles
c. exterior angles

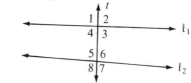

155

Cumulative Review Chapters 4 – 6

37. Find pairs of congruent angles and supplementary angles using these parallel lines and the transversal.

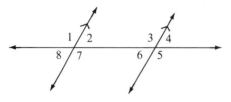

38. Find the magnitude of the indicated angles.

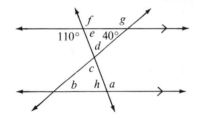

39. Find the measure of ∠ABC.

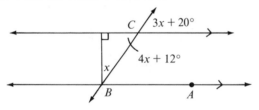

40. Construct a line, parallel to a given line, through a point not on that line.

41. Construct the perpendicular bisector of both parallel lines in the last exercise.

42. A dinner requires cooking in the microwave for 8 min. However, the timer on the microwave is broken and you have only two sand timers that can measure 2 min and 5 min respectively. How could you be sure that your dinner remains in the microwave for exactly 8 min?

43. Prove that the angles of a triangle form a sum of 180°.

44. Calculate the measure of each angle in this triangle.

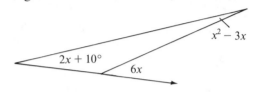

45. What is necessary in order to show that two triangles are congruent?

46. Are these two triangles congruent? Explain.

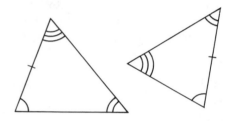

47. A contractor was hired to build a roof on a house. The diagram of the roof is shown. If the materials cost $17.50/m², then how much should the contractor charge for materials?

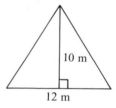

48. Describe how four equilateral triangles can be made from six identical toothpicks.

49. Is it possible to have a triangle that has two parallel sides? Explain.

50. Give a definition of each in terms of angles and side lengths.
a. scalene triangle
b. equilateral triangle
c. isosceles triangle

COORDINATE GEOMETRY

Tune Up

1. Use a Cartesian coordinate system.
a. Plot the points $(1, 1)$, $(1, -1)$, $(-1, 1)$, and $(-1, -1)$.
b. Join the points.
c. Measure the lengths of each line segment.
d. Measure the angles formed by the line segments.
e. What type of polygon is formed by these points?
f. What ordered pair describes the intersection of the two axes on the grid?
g. In what quadrant does each point lie?

2. Explain each term.
a. parallel   **b.** perpendicular
c. slope   **d.** polygon

3. Two airplanes are flying towards Rolfton. One leaves Burlington and flies 150 km east and then 185 km north to arrive at the airport. The other plane leaves Kitchener and flies 95 km north and 240 km east to arrive at the airport.
a. Which airplane has the farthest to fly?
b. Which airplane is closer to Rolfton before they actually leave the ground?
c. If they were both to leave at the same time, how much faster would one plane have to fly than the other to arrive at Rolfton at the same time?

4. A special type of rhombus is a square. Review the definition of a rhombus to explain why this is true.

5. Write the negative reciprocal of each.
a. $\frac{4}{3}$ **b.** -1 **c.** 0 **d.** 0.6

6. Copy and complete.
$x^2 + y^2 = \sqrt{\rule{2cm}{0.3cm}}$

7. April is standing 5 km away from Joey and Rebecca is standing 17 km away from Joey but Joey is not between April and Rebecca. How far does Joey have to jog in order to be directly between April and Rebecca?

8. Perform the indicated operations.
a. $-2 + (-5) - (-9)$ **b.** $3 \times (-5) + (-8) \div 2$
c. $\{3(9 - 16) - (-14)\} \div (-5)$

9. A farmer has a parcel of land in the shape of a trapezoid as shown. She sells half of the land to a local builder. When it came time to divide the land, the farmer said, "By drawing a diagonal I cut the land in half. Then you will have half and I will have half." Should the builder accept this deal? Explain.

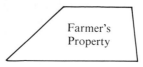
Farmer's Property

7·1 The Coordinate Grid

Ordered pairs can be graphed using a system of intersecting lines called the **Cartesian coordinate system**. The two coordinate axes are perpendicular to each other and are called the **x-axis** and the **y-axis**. The point of intersection of the x- and y-axes is the **origin** (0, 0).

The two coordinate axes divide the plane into four **quadrants**. Each ordered pair plotted on this system is composed of two parts; the x-coordinate or the **abscissa**, and the y-coordinate or the **ordinate**.

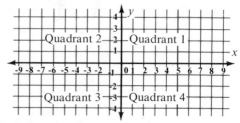

The system is perfectly symmetric with respect to the x-axis, the y-axis, and the origin. All horizontal lines are parallel, all vertical lines are parallel, and their intersections form right angles. However, there are other coordinate grids in mathematics.

Example 1

Describe the ordered pair shown on this grid.

Although this is not an easy system to use, it does provide a way of identifying a point on the plane. This type of grid is especially useful when drawing distortions. The point P is at $(5, -2)$.

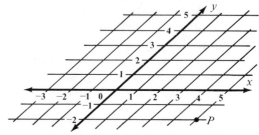

Example 2

Describe the ordered pair shown on this grid.

This is another type of grid that is not common. It is used mainly for artistic applications and in the study of **topology**. Topology is the study of properties of geometric figures that remain unchanged when figures are distorted. The point M is at $(-2, 1)$.

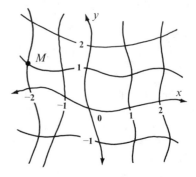

Example 3

Describe the ordered pairs shown on this grid.

This type of grid is called a **polar coordinate** grid. The abscissa is measured as the distance along the ray from the origin, while the ordinate is the angle that is formed by the ray and the positive horizontal axis. This type of grid is useful when comparing a distance measure and an angle measure. The points C and D are at $(3, 50)$ and $(4, 210)$.

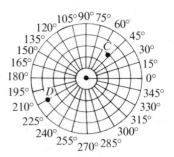

158

Exercises

1. Find an ordered pair that is symmetric with the point $(4, -1)$ under each of the following conditions.

a. symmetric about the x-axis

b. symmetric about the y-axis

c. symmetric about the origin

2. Identify the coordinates of each point of the letter W.

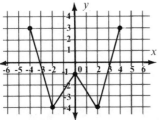

3. Identify the coordinates of the three points A, B, and C.

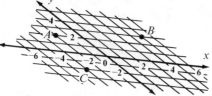

4. List the ordered pairs of the seven vertices.

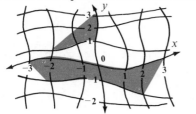

5. Construct a distorted grid. Copy this figure onto the new grid.

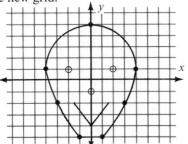

6. State the ordered pairs for the points on this grid.

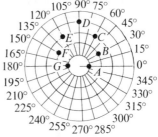

7. A **unicursal curve** is a curve or an object that can be drawn without lifting your pencil from the page and without crossing or retracing any lines. Construct a unicursal curve on a coordinate grid and challenge a classmate to draw your unicursal curve by giving the ordered pairs that describe your curve. One possible unicursal curve is given.

Historical Note

Rene Descartes (1596-1650)
Descartes is described as the founder of analytical geometry. His invention of a coordinate system to give a graphic picture of number relations brought about a dramatic change in both mathematics and physics. It provided science with an analytical diagram to plot varying relations.

One story states that the initial idea for analytical geometry came to him while watching a fly crawling about the ceiling near a corner of his room. It occurred to him that the path of the fly could be described if he knew the relation connecting the fly's distances from the two connecting walls.

Another mathematician living about the same time was Pierre de Fermat. Although they never worked together, they had many of the same ideas. Use your library to research Pierre de Fermat and compare their ideas on the coordinate system.

7·2 Slope On the Coordinate Grid

When an architect designs a stairway, a stadium, or the roof of a house, the steepness or **slope** of each must be considered. In each case, the slope is a ratio of the vertical height (the rise) to the horizontal length (the run). On a Cartesian coordinate grid, this ratio can be found if two points on a straight line segment are known.

$$\text{Slope} = \frac{\text{rise}}{\text{run}}$$
$$= \frac{y_2 - y_1}{x_2 - x_1}$$

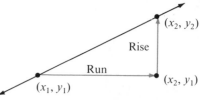

Example 1

Identify the slope of this line and find another point on the line.

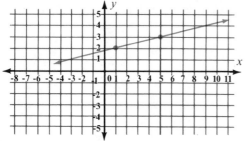

Two points on this line can be identified as (1, 2) and (5, 3).

Therefore, slope $= \frac{3 - 2}{5 - 1}$
$$= \frac{1}{4}$$

By starting at the point (5, 3), or any point on the line, another point on the line can be identified by moving across 4 units and up 1 unit. This new point is (9, 4).

> Points that lie on the same straight line are **collinear** points.

Example 2

Find the slope of a vertical line.

Construct any vertical line. In this case, we drew the line through the points (1, 1) and (1, 4).

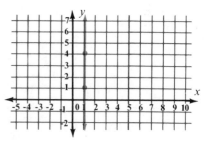

$$\text{Slope} = \frac{\text{rise}}{\text{run}}$$
$$= \frac{3}{0}$$

Since division by zero is undefined, the slope of a vertical line is **undefined**.

160

Exercises

1. Determine the slope of each of these line segments by counting the blocks.

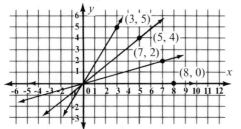

a.   b.   c.

2. On a single grid, draw six line segments, passing through the origin, and having these slopes.
$\frac{1}{2}$, 1, 2, 4, 8, and 16

3. Determine the slopes of these lines.

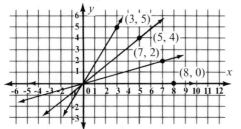

4. Draw lines passing through the origin and having these slopes.
-1, $\frac{-1}{2}$, $\frac{-1}{4}$, $\frac{-1}{8}$, and $\frac{-1}{16}$

5. Determine the slopes of these lines.

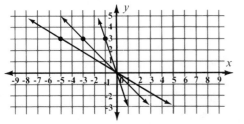

6. Draw three line segments passing through the point $(-2, 1)$ with slopes of 0, $\frac{3}{4}$, and $\frac{-3}{4}$.

7. Determine the coordinates of one other point on the line passing through each of these points.
a. $(2, 1)$ and $(6, 9)$
b. $(-3, 2)$ and $(5, 0)$
c. $(-4, -9)$ and $(6, -1)$

8. Are the points in each set collinear? Explain.
a. $(1, 1), (4, 4), (5, 5)$
b. $(-1, -2), (0, -3), (3, -5)$

9. Find two other collinear points.
a. $(-7, 0)$ and $(15, 0)$ **b.** $(-3, 5)$ and $(5, -3)$

10. Each pair of numbers gives the slopes of two lines and their point of intersection. Draw each pair of lines on graph paper.
a. $1, -1, (0, 0)$ **b.** $2, -2, (1, 0)$
c. $3, \frac{1}{3}, (0, 1)$ **d.** $\frac{2}{3}, \frac{3}{2}, (0, -2)$
e. $-6, \frac{1}{6}, (-3, 2)$ **f.** $\frac{2}{3}, \frac{-3}{2}, (1, 4)$

11. Select several stairways at home, or at school.
a. Measure the rise and run for several steps on each stairway.
b. Calculate the slope of the stairway.
c. Draw the stairway to scale on a grid.
d. Compare your findings with those of others to determine whether stairways always have the same slope.

12. A straight expressway ramp meets an elevated road that is 14 m above ground.
a. If the ramp begins 84 m from the elevated road, then what is the slope?
b. What are the heights of three support pillars spaced evenly between the ground and the elevated road?
c. If the ramp began 105 m from the elevated road, then what would be the slope?

13. Consider the slope of a line joining the points (p, q) and $(2p, 2q)$.
a. Determine the slope of the line passing through these two points.
b. Find two other points collinear with the given points.
c. Explain how to determine whether $(0, 0)$ is collinear with the two given points.

14. Find a value of v such that the line between the two given points will have the slope indicated.
a. $(2, v), (7, 1)$, slope of 2
b. $(v, -3), (-1, 0)$, slope of -1
c. $(-4, v), (v, 3)$, slope of 0

7·3 Slope Relationships

There are two specific slope relationships that are useful in the study of coordinate geometry.

Example 1

Calculate and compare the slopes of these two parallel lines.

Slope of $\ell_1 = \dfrac{-1 - 3}{4 - (-4)}$

$= \dfrac{-1}{2}$

Slope of $\ell_2 = \dfrac{0 - 2}{-2 - (-6)}$

$= \dfrac{-1}{2}$

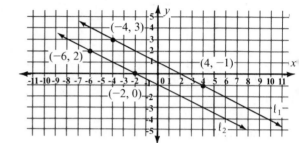

> Parallel lines have equal slopes.

Example 2

Calculate and compare the slopes of these two perpendicular lines.

For ℓ_1, slope $= \dfrac{-1 - 5}{6 - (-3)}$

$= \dfrac{-2}{3}$

For ℓ_2, slope $= \dfrac{7 - (-2)}{6 - 0}$

$= \dfrac{3}{2}$

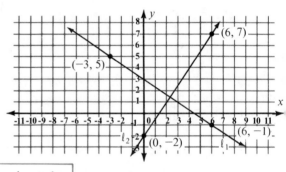

> Perpendicular lines have slopes that are negative reciprocals.

Three points, A, B, and C, are collinear if and only if the slopes of $\overline{AB}$, $\overline{BC}$, and $\overline{AC}$ are equal. We can use this information to solve slope-related problems by setting up these proportions.

$$\frac{y_1 - y}{x_1 - x} = \frac{y_2 - y_1}{x_2 - x_1} = \frac{y_2 - y}{x_2 - x}$$

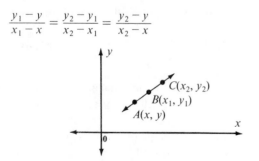

Example 3

Given $A(2, 3)$ and $B(7, 5)$, find a point $C(10, y)$ that is collinear to points A and B.

Slope of $\overline{AB} \cong$ Slope of $\overline{BC}$.

$\therefore \dfrac{5 - 3}{7 - 2} = \dfrac{y - 5}{10 - 7}$

$y = 6.2$

Therefore, the point is $C(10, 6.2)$.

Exercises

1. Identify five pairs of parallel or perpendicular lines from this list.

a. Line 1 through (0, 0) and (5, −4).
b. Line 2 through (−2, 3) and (2, 8).
c. Line 3 through (−6, −1) and (6, −1).
d. Line 4 through (0, 3) and (3, 0).
e. Line 5 through (−7, 2) and (−2, 7).
f. Line 6 through (−3, 1) and (5, 3).
g. Line 7 through (−8, −5) and (4, −2).
h. Line 8 through (1, 8) and (7, 3.2).
i. Line 9 through (2, −1) and (2, 7).
j. Line 10 through (−9, 6) and (−2.8, −0.2).
k. Line 11 through (0, −4) and (6, 1.4).

2. Show that two sides of this trapezoid are parallel.

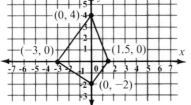

3. Determine if this is a right triangle.

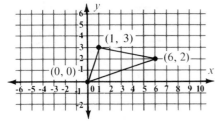

4. Use your results from Exercise 1 to identify point(s) that satisfy these conditions.

a. Two points on a line parallel to Line 3.
b. The point at which Line 5 crosses the y-axis.
c. A third point on Line 6 with an x-value of 4.
d. Two points on a line perpendicular to Line 7.
e. Two points on a line parallel to Line 9.
f. The point on Line 10 that intersects the y-axis.
g. Any point above Line 2.
h. The point, B, on the line passing through (0, 0) and B(5, y), parallel to Line 4.
i. The point, A(x, −3), on the line passing through (1, 2) and perpendicular to Line 2.

5. Identify two points that meet these conditions for a line.

a. Parallel to the x-axis and crossing the y-axis at (0, 2).
b. Passing through the origin with a slope of −2.
c. Perpendicular to the y-axis and passing through the point (3, −5).
d. Passing through the point (−3, −1) with a slope of $\frac{5}{3}$.

6. If a line passing through the point (x_1, y_1) has a slope of $\frac{a}{b}$, then find the slope of a perpendicular line passing through the same point.

7. Use the slope relationships between parallel and perpendicular lines to name four points that are vertices of a rectangle whose sides are not parallel to either the x-axis or y-axis.

8. Find the point C so that A, B, and C are collinear.

a. A(−7, 0), B(15, 4), C(3, y)
b. A(8, −3), B(2, 5), C(x, 7)
c. A(−3, 2), B(3, 4), C is on the y-axis
d. A(3, −3), B(−1, 5), C is on the x-axis

9. Find point D so that the altitude, $\overline{AD}$, meets $\overline{BC}$.

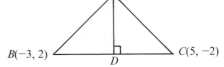

10. Into how many different pieces can the interior of a circle be cut by drawing only four straight lines across the circle?

11. Shade eight individual squares in this grid so that no two shaded squares lie in the same horizontal, vertical, or diagonal line.

7·4 Distance Between Points

A major use of coordinate systems is in determining the distance between points. For example, in a geography text, many of the maps have grids. Astronomers use grids to identify the positions of stars. The advantage of using these grid systems is that the distance between any two points can be calculated.

The distance between any two points on a Cartesian grid is found by using the Pythagorean Relation. Recall that the rise and the run represent distances that are perpendicular to each other.

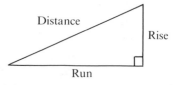

Example 1

Find the distance between the points $A(1, 5)$ and $B(7, 13)$.

In Section 7·2, rise is $y_2 - y_1$ and run is $x_2 - x_1$.

$$\overline{AB}^2 = (y_2 - y_1)^2 + (x_2 - x_1)^2$$
$$\overline{AB} = \sqrt{(y_2 - y_1)^2 + (x_2 - x_1)^2}$$
$$= \sqrt{(13 - 5)^2 + (7 - 1)^2}$$
$$= \sqrt{64 + 36}$$
$$= \sqrt{100}$$
$$= 10$$

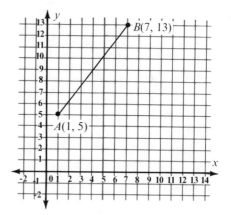

The distance between the points $A(1, 5)$ and $B(7, 13)$ is 10 units.

$$\boxed{\overline{AB} = \sqrt{(y_2 - y_1)^2 + (x_2 - x_1)^2}}$$

Example 2

Find the distance between $A(-6, 1)$ and $B(5, -4)$.

$$\overline{AB} = \sqrt{(-4 - 1)^2 + (5 - [-6])^2}$$
$$= \sqrt{(-5)^2 + (11)^2}$$
$$= \sqrt{25 + 121}$$
$$= \sqrt{146}$$
$$\doteq 12.08$$

The distance between points A and B is approximately 12.08 units.

Exercises

1. Calculate the distance between each pair of points correct to two decimal places.

a. $(3, 1)$ and $(7, 4)$ **b.** $(1, 3)$ and $(5, 0)$

c. $(-3, 2)$ and $(5, 2)$ **d.** $(-5, 6)$ and $(2, -1)$

e. $(-3.4, -5)$ and $(0, 7)$ **f.** $(-4, -1)$ and $(21, 2)$

g. $(0, 1)$ and $(0, -3.5)$ **h.** $(-6, 0)$ and $(3.21, 0)$

2. Use a 1 cm grid to produce a drawing of the letters V and Y. Have each necessary slope be 2 and the width of each part of the letter be 2 cm.

3. A grid may be used to construct letters for advertising. The scale on this grid is 1 cm = 0.5 m.

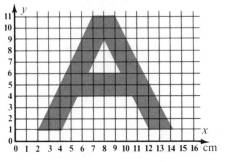

a. What is the slope of the left side of the letter? of the right side?

b. Find the outside perimeter of the letter.

c. Is the interior triangle isosceles or equilateral?

4. Find the distance between each pair of points.

a. (a, b) and (c, d) **b.** $(2s, s)$ and $(-2s, s)$

c. $(t, 3t)$ and $(-t, -3t)$

d. $(2a + 1, a - 3)$ and $(0, 0)$

5. Verify that $\triangle PQR$ is isosceles.

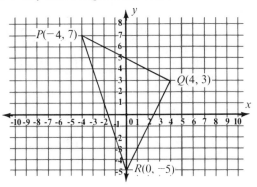

6. Use the vertices of *PQRS*.

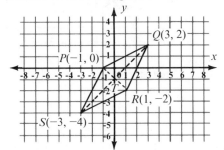

a. Verify that the quadrilateral is a rhombus by calculating the length of each side.

b. Determine the length of each of the diagonals.

c. Verify that the diagonals bisect each other at the point $T(0, -1)$.

7. A city planner is visiting sites located on a grid at the points $(0, 0)$, $(2, 4)$, $(3, -3)$, and $(5, 3)$. The scale is 1 unit represents 300 m. Find the shortest possible distance covered in moving from the origin to each of the other points in any order.

Using the Library

Refer to *Mathematics, Life Science Library*, Bergamin, David; Time Incorporated, pages 80-88. How do map makers locate points on Earth? Who established the principle of curved lines for longitude and latitude? What does "logito, ergo, sum" mean?

Historical Note

Amalie Emmy Noether (1882-1935)

Emmy Noether, generally regarded as one of the great mathematicians, was born in Germany in 1882. She became a professor at Byrn College in Pennsylvania in 1933 and was also a member of the Institute for Advanced Study at Princeton. Her studies in the field of abstract algebra, and in particular abstract rings, have been particularly important in the field of modern algebra.

7·5 Midpoint of a Line Segment

The **midpoint** of a line segment is an important location in many problems involving coordinate geometry; in particular, those that involve symmetry. We have an intuitive sense of where the midpoint is. However, mathematically the midpoint can be calculated. It is the point on a segment that is equidistant from both endpoints. For example, the midpoint of a segment that is 3 cm long is the point 1.5 cm from each endpoint.

In numerical calculations, the midpoint between two numbers is found by adding the numbers and dividing by two. For example, in the case of the numbers 12 and 32,

$$\frac{12 + 32}{2} = \frac{44}{2}$$
$$= 22$$

Therefore, 22 is the number midway between 12 and 32.

Example

Find the midpoint of the line segment joining the points $A(1, 6)$ and $B(9, 2)$.

The midpoint is found by separate calculations of the average x-coordinate and the average y-coordinate.

Average x-coordinate $= \dfrac{1 + 9}{2}$
$= 5$

Average y-coordinate $= \dfrac{6 + 2}{2}$
$= 4$

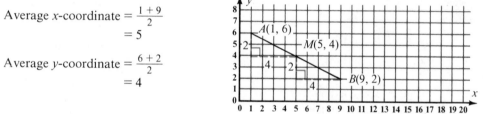

Therefore, $(5, 4)$ is the midpoint of the line segment AB.

> The midpoint of the line segment joining the ordered pairs $A(x_1, y_1)$ and $B(x_2, y_2)$ is determined by calculating the average of the abscissas and average of the ordinates.
>
> $$\text{Midpoint} = \left(\frac{x_1 + x_2}{2}, \frac{y_1 + y_2}{2}\right)$$

Exercises

1. Indicate whether these statements are true or false by calculating lengths.
a. $(2, 6)$ is the midpoint of the segment joining $(0, 0)$ and $(4, 12)$.
b. $(-3, 5)$ is the midpoint of the segment between $(1, 7)$ and $(-7, -3)$.
c. $(4.2, 8)$ is equidistant from $(0, 3)$ and $(8.4, 3)$.
d. $(0, 6.25)$ is equidistant from $(-5, 1.2)$ and $(1, -0.75)$.

2. Calculate the midpoint between each of these pairs of points.
a. $(3, 9)$ and $(7, 12)$ **b.** $(-2, 1)$ and $(5, 13)$
c. $(0, 6)$ and $(6, 0)$ **d.** $(-5, -2)$ and $(0, 0)$
e. $(-3, -7)$ and $(4, -1)$ **f.** $(-3.2, 0)$ and $(0, 5.1)$

3. An isosceles triangle is formed by the points $A(1, 2)$, $B(5, 5)$, and $C(1, 8)$. Find the area of this triangle.

4. Construct a straight line spiral by following these steps.

Start at the origin and move 1 unit to the right. From this new point move up 2 units. After this point has been found, move 3 units to the left. From this point, move down 4 units. Continue this process until the point (5, 6) is reached.

a. List the ordered pair of each vertex in the pattern.

b. Draw a second spiral beginning at (0, 0) and moving to each successive midpoint of the original spiralling segments. List the coordinates of each of these points.

5. Find an expression for the midpoint between $(a, 3a - 2)$ and $(-a, -3a + 2)$.

6. Find the points that will divide the line segment identified by the two endpoints into four equal parts.

a. (18, 30), (3, 5)   **b.** (2, 36), (−8, −10)
c. (−12, 33), (−2, −8)   **d.** (−5, −30.7), (−12, −8.1)
e. (0, −39.4), (4.8, 0)   **f.** $(a, b), (c, d)$

7. A right triangle has vertices at $(-1, -1), (-1, 3)$, and $(2, -1)$.

a. Draw the triangle on a coordinate grid and find the midpoint of the hypotenuse.

b. Show that the midpoint is equidistant from each vertex.

8. The line segment joining $(3, 2\sqrt{3})$ and $(0, -6\sqrt{3})$ is the diameter of a circle.

a. Find the centre of the circle.

b. Calculate the radius of the circle.

9. Verify by calculating lengths that T is the midpoint of the diagonals of quadrilateral $MNOP$.

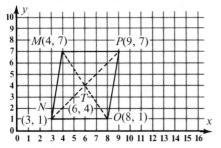

10. Calculate the length of $\overline{PQ}$ if P and Q are midpoints of two sides of $\triangle ABC$.

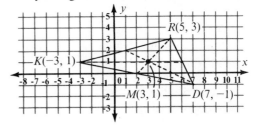

11. The three medians of $\triangle KRD$ meet at (3, 1). Verify that this point of intersection is two thirds of the way along each of the medians.

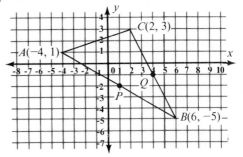

12. Using the triangle from Exercise 4, find the **centroid** of the triangle. The centroid is the intersection point of the line segments drawn from the vertex to the midpoint of the opposite side. These line segments are the **medians** of the triangle.

13. Copy this shape into your notebook. Draw two straight lines that divide this shape into three congruent parts.

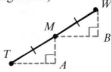

14. M is the midpoint of $\overline{TW}, \overline{MA} \perp \overline{TA}, \overline{WB} \perp \overline{MB}$, and $\overline{TA} \parallel \overline{MB}$. Show that $\triangle TMA \cong \triangle MWB$. (*Hint:* What are the requirements to show that two triangles are congruent?)

7·6 Proofs in Coordinate Geometry

Through coordinate geometry, the properties of polygons can be investigated and verified. We will use the four-step problem-solving method to assist in the investigation.

Example

Show that the quadrilateral with vertices at $A(-3, 2)$, $B(-1, 3)$, $C(0, 1)$, and $D(-2, 0)$ is a rhombus.

Understand the Problem
1. What information is given?
The coordinates of the vertices.

2. What question is to be answered?
Show that the figure is a rhombus; that is, we must show that all sides are equal in length.

Develop a Plan
To show that the line segments are the same length, use the formula $d = \sqrt{(y_2 - y_1)^2 + (x_2 - x_1)^2}$.

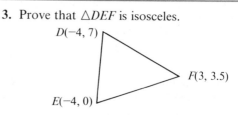

Carry Out the Plan
Using the formula, $\overline{AB} = \sqrt{5}$ units, $\overline{BC} = \sqrt{5}$ units, $\overline{CD} = \sqrt{5}$ units, and $\overline{AD} = \sqrt{5}$ units.

Look Back
Since all sides are congruent, the figure is a rhombus.

Exercises

1. Refer to the example in the display.
a. Show how the length of $\overline{AD}$ was found.
b. All rhombuses have opposite sides parallel as well as equal. Show that the opposite sides are parallel. (*Hint:* Use the four-step problem-solving model.)

2. Prove that ℓ_1 is a perpendicular bisector of $\overline{BC}$.
a.   **b.**

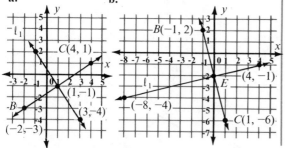

3. Prove that $\triangle DEF$ is isosceles.

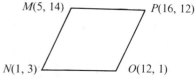

4. Prove that quadrilateral $MNOP$ is a parallelogram.

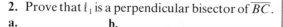

5. Prove that quadrilateral $JKLM$ is a parallelogram.

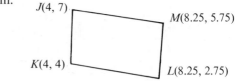

6. Using coordinate geometry, verify each property.
a. A point on the perpendicular bisector of $\overline{ST}$ is equidistant from S and T. (*Hint:* Select a specific point and use this as a guide for the general case.)

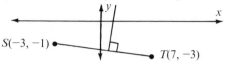

b. One altitude of this isosceles triangle is also a median of the triangle.

7. A quadrilateral is formed with vertices at $(5, 4)$, $(-5, 5)$, $(-5, -4)$, and $(5, -5)$.
a. Use coordinate geometry to determine what type of quadrilateral this is.
b. Which vertex is farther from the origin?
c. Use slopes to determine the four points at which the sides of this figure intersect the x-axis and y-axis.
d. Join the points from part **c** to form a second quadrilateral. Determine what type of figure these new segments produce.

8. Find a set of points that will describe each polygon. Pick each point from a different quadrant.
a. a rectangle   **b.** a right triangle
c. an equilateral triangle   **d.** a parallelogram
e. a rhombus   **f.** a trapezoid

9. A security robot is being designed to patrol a new shopping mall. It will begin at location 1 and must check each of the eight other locations every 30 min. The diagram indicates the distances between locations in metres. Find the shortest possible distance covered in checking each location and returning to the starting point.

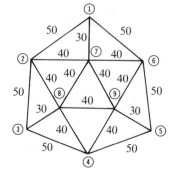

10. Prove that the slopes of any two perpendicular lines are negative reciprocals. Use these steps as a guide.

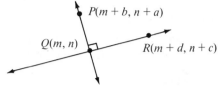

a. Let the slopes of the two lines be represented by $\frac{a}{b}$ and $\frac{c}{d}$ respectively, and let the point of intersection of the lines be $Q(m, n)$.
b. Select two points, $P(m + b, n + a)$ on one line, and $R(m + d, n + c)$ on the other.
c. Use the distance formula to determine an algebraic expression for the distance $\overline{PQ}$.
d. Repeat use of the distance formula to determine expressions for the lengths of $\overline{QR}$ and $\overline{PR}$.
e. Expand and simplify the expression for the length of $\overline{PR}$.
f. Since the given lines are perpendicular, $|\overline{PQ}|^2 + |\overline{QR}|^2 = |\overline{PR}|^2$ because of the Pythagorean Relation. Substitute the expressions from parts **c** and **e** into the relation.
g. Simplify the equation to complete the proof that the slopes $\frac{a}{b}$ and $\frac{c}{d}$ are negative reciprocals.

11. A kite is in the shape of a quadrilateral having two pairs of adjacent sides equal in length. Consider a quadrilateral with vertices at $(p, 0), (-p, 0)$, $(0, q)$, and $(0, r)$. A shape is a kite if the diagonals are perpendicular. Show that this shape is a kite.

12. Triangles ABC and LMN are shown.
a. Show that each side of $\triangle LMN$ is twice that of the corresponding side of $\triangle ABC$.
b. Show that the area of $\triangle LMN$ is four times the area of $\triangle ABC$.

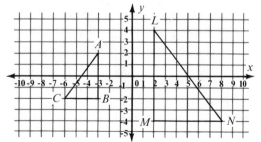

169

7·7 Computer Application — Slopes

Checking for the collinearity of points can entail some routine and repetitive calculations. A computer is often useful in making these routine checks.

```
10 REM THIS PROGRAM CHECKS THREE POINTS FOR COLLINEARITY
20 INPUT "WHAT ARE THE COORDINATES OF THE FIRST POINT?"; X, Y
30 INPUT "WHAT ARE THE COORDINATES OF THE SECOND POINT?"; X1, Y1
40 INPUT "WHAT ARE THE COORDINATES OF THE THIRD POINT?"; X2, Y2
50 LET S1 = (Y1 - Y) / (X1 - X)
60 LET S2 = (Y2 - Y1) / (X2 - X1)
70 LET S3 = (Y2 - Y) / (X2 - X)
80 IF S1 = S2 = S3 THEN 95
85 PRINT "SLOPES ARE NOT EQUAL, THEREFORE THE POINTS ARE NOT
COLLINEAR."
90 GOTO 99
95 PRINT "SLOPES ARE EQUAL, THEREFORE THE THREE POINTS ARE
COLLINEAR."
99 END
```

Exercises

1. Define the term "collinear".

2. Describe how the program in the display checks for the collinearity of points.

3. Modify the program to deal with the possibility that the three points are in a vertical line.

4. Write a program that will input two points and calculate the distance between them.

5. Modify the program of Exercise 3 to determine the midpoint between the two given points.

6. In many hospitals, vital signs are monitored by computer. Discuss the advantages and disadvantages of a computer monitoring vital signs as opposed to physically monitoring vital signs.

7. Copy and complete this program that will find the area of any triangle given the vertices of the triangle. This program will use Heron's Formula for the area of the triangle.

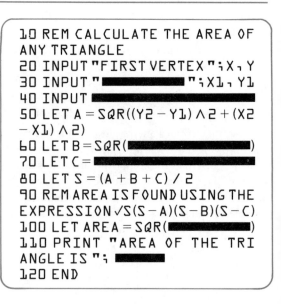

```
10 REM CALCULATE THE AREA OF
ANY TRIANGLE
20 INPUT "FIRST VERTEX "; X, Y
30 INPUT "              "; X1, Y1
40 INPUT
50 LET A = SQR((Y2 - Y1) ∧ 2 + (X2
- X1) ∧ 2)
60 LET B = SQR(              )
70 LET C =
80 LET S = (A + B + C) / 2
90 REM AREA IS FOUND USING THE
EXPRESSION √S(S - A)(S - B)(S - C)
100 LET AREA = SQR(          )
110 PRINT "AREA OF THE TRI
ANGLE IS ";
120 END
```

a. Describe what lines 50, 60, and 70 do.

b. What is the purpose of line 80?

c. Why is there a REM statement in line 90?

d. If line 100 was input as
LET AREA = SQR(S(S − A)(S − B)(S − C)),
an error would result. Why?

7·8 Chapter Review

1. Find three points equidistant from $(0, 0)$.

2. Name a point symmetric with $(-5, 1.4)$
   a. about the y-axis   **b.** about the origin.

3. Calculate the slope of a line passing through each pair of points.
   a. $(1, 3)$ and $(7, 5)$ **b.** $(-3, 0)$ and $(5, 2)$
   c. $(-4, -1)$ and $(5, 0)$ **d.** $(-5, -1)$ and $(6, -2)$
   e. $(1, 82)$ and $(-9, 82)$ **f.** $(-2, 3)$ and $(-2, 0)$
   g. $(-5.2, 1)$ and $(0.6, 2.4)$
   h. $(-7, 1.5)$ and $(12, 1.5)$

4. Locate one other point collinear with each pair of points.
   a. $(2, 4)$ and $(-3, 0)$ **b.** $(0, 0)$ and $(-9, 5)$
   c. $(\frac{5}{2}, -3)$ and $(\frac{9}{4}, 1)$ **d.** $(0, 12)$ and $(12, 0)$

5. Identify one point on a line that passes through the origin and has a slope equal to 150.

6. Identify one point on a line that passes through the point $(0, 2)$ and has a slope of less than 0.01.

7. Identify a point on the line through $(-2, 5)$ with a slope of $-\frac{1}{2}$.

8. Calculate the missing value so that point C is collinear with points A and B.
   a. $A(7, -5)$, $B(6, -3)$, $C(x, 4)$
   b. $A(-11, -4)$, $B(-8, 4)$, $C(8, y)$

9. Describe the coordinates of any point on a vertical line passing through the point (a, b).

10. Show, without graphing, that the points $(-5, 1)$, $(0, 3)$, and $(4.5, 4.75)$ are not collinear.

11. Use a calculator to find, correct to two decimal places, the distance between each pair of points.
    a. $(-5, 8)$ and $(1, 0)$ **b.** $(-2, -10)$ and $(4, -8)$
    c. $(-3.75, 0)$ and $(5, 8.50)$ **d.** $(\sqrt{5}, 0)$ and $(0, \sqrt{5})$

12. Determine the midpoint of the line segment joining each pair of points.
    a. $(1, 9)$ and $(9, 1)$
    b. $(0, 12)$ and $(12, 0)$
    c. $(-9, 0)$ and $(9, 0)$
    d. $(-3.2, 2)$ and $(6.5, -4.3)$

13. Identify which of the lines passing through these pairs of points are parallel.
    a. $(0, 5)$ and $(-5, 0)$
    b. $(0, 0)$ and $(0, 15)$
    c. $(-3, 6)$ and $(2, 11)$
    d. $(-4, 1)$ and $(-4, 3.8)$
    e. $(-10, -10)$ and $(0.2, 0.2)$
    f. $(6, 1)$ and $(18, 1)$

14. List four points such that the lines passing through each pair of points are perpendicular.

15. Determine the coordinates of any point on a line that passes through $(5, 1)$ and
    a. is parallel to the x-axis.
    b. is parallel to a line passing through the points $(0, 1)$ and $(1, 0)$.
    c. is perpendicular to the x-axis.
    d. is perpendicular to the line passing through the points $(4, 23)$ and $(9, 1)$.

16. Use coordinate geometry to confirm that the diagonals of this square are perpendicular.

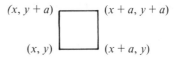

17. Show that one of the medians in this isosceles triangle is also an altitude.

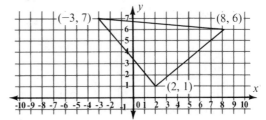

7·9 Chapter Test

1. Plot the points $M(0, 5)$, $N(-6, -2)$, and $P(5.4, -3.2)$ on a coordinate grid.

a. Join the points to form a triangle and calculate the slopes of each of the three sides.

b. Determine whether $\triangle MNP$ is a right triangle.

c. Identify the triangle as scalene, isosceles, or equilateral. Explain.

d. Determine the midpoint of each of the sides of $\triangle MNP$.

e. Calculate the slopes of each of the three line segments joining the midpoints of $\overline{MN}$, $\overline{NP}$, and $\overline{MP}$.

f. Calculate the lengths of these same three line segments.

g. What is the relationship between the line segment joining the midpoints of two sides of the triangle and the third side?

h. Identify any two points R and V such that $\overline{RV}$ is parallel to line segment $\overline{MN}$.

i. At what point does the median from N meet side $\overline{MP}$?

j. Identify a point, T, such that quadrilateral $MNPT$ is a parallelogram.

k. Identify any one point, S, such that $\overline{ST}$ is perpendicular to $\overline{NP}$.

2. Draw lines through the origin with these slopes.

$\frac{1}{2}, 1, \frac{3}{4}, 4$

3. Draw lines through the point $(-3, 2)$ with these slopes.

$\frac{-3}{5}, -1, -8, \frac{5}{3}$

4. Find the slope
a. of a horizontal line.
b. of a vertical line.

5. Identify two points in quadrant 4 that are collinear with $(-3, 5)$ and $(1, 1)$.

6. List the coordinates of three points 5 units away from the point $(-1, -3)$.

7. Calculate the area of a triangle whose vertices are at $(1, 4)$, $(5, 2)$, and $(4, 5)$.

8. The points $P(2, 1)$, $Q(8, 1)$, and $R(6, 7)$ are the vertices of an isosceles triangle. Show that the median from R is the perpendicular bisector of $\overline{PQ}$.

9. Use coordinate geometry to confirm these geometric properties.

a. A point on the perpendicular bisector of the line segment joining $(-2, 5)$ and $(4, 3.75)$ is equidistant from the ends of the segment.

$(-2, 5)$

$(4, 3.75)$

b. The line segment joining the centre of the circle to the midpoint of the chord is perpendicular to the chord.

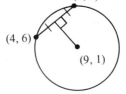

$(8, 8)$

$(4, 6)$

$(9, 1)$

c. The diagonals of this rectangle are perpendicular.

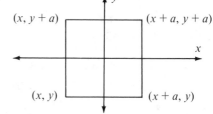

$(x, y + a)$ $(x + a, y + a)$

(x, y) $(x + a, y)$

10. Select any four points on a coordinate grid and join them to form a quadrilateral.

a. Calculate the midpoint of each side of the figure.

b. Join the four midpoints to form a second quadrilateral, then use coordinate geometry to prove that this new figure is a parallelogram.

RELATIONS AND VARIATIONS

Tune Up

1. Find the next three ordered pairs in each.
a. $(1, 3), (2, 6), (3, 9), \ldots$
b. $(1, 1), (2, 4), (3, 9), \ldots$
c. $(1, 1), (2, 3), (3, 5), \ldots$

2. Copy and complete each table of values.

a.

n	$-n$
1	
2	
3	
4	
5	
6	

b.

p	$4p - 1$
-3	-13
-2	
-1	
0	
1	
2	

c.

x	$3x^2 - 5$
-4	43
-2	
0	
2	
4	
6	

3. Copy and complete to find the missing abscissa or the missing ordinate.
a. $(1, 15), (2, 14), (3, \blacksquare), \ldots, (7, 9), \ldots, (12, \blacksquare), \ldots,$
$(15, \blacksquare)$
b. $(-3, -3), (-2, -1), (-1, 1), (0, 3), (1, \blacksquare), (2, 7),$
$\ldots, (\blacksquare, 13), \ldots, (8, \blacksquare)$
c. $(1, 31), (2, 28), (3, 25), (4, 22), (5, \blacksquare), (6, \blacksquare), \ldots,$
$(\blacksquare, 13), \ldots, (\blacksquare, 10)$

4. Graph the ordered pairs from Exercise 3.
a. What will be the y-value in Exercise 3, part **b**, if the x-value is $\frac{1}{2}$? the x-value is $-\frac{1}{2}$?
b. What will be the y-value in Exercise 3, part **b**, if the x-value is -8? the x-value is 10?

5. Give a definition for the slope of a line.

6. Set up a table displaying the real numbers 3, 5.7, 11, 13.5, and their squares and cubes. Use a calculator if one is available.

7. Describe the density property as it refers to the set of real numbers.

8. A square is inscribed in a semicircle as shown below. Find x in terms of r.

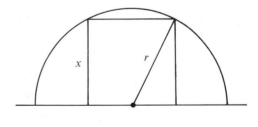

9. Cheryl, Jacob, and Ayube rented a van to help them move. The van cost them $60 each. How much would the van cost each person if Ali and Dee also shared the cost?

8·1 Relations

Over the years, mathematicians have provided us with an organized method for handling relationships between various quantities. When two quantities or sets are related, the set of all possible pairings within those two sets is called a **relation**.

A relation connects items in one set with items in another set.

A relation can be expressed in a number of different ways. Four such ways are shown below. For example, if one ticket costs $10.50, then the relation can be displayed as follows.

1. In words

1 ticket costs $10.50
2 tickets cost $21.00
3 tickets cost $31.50
n tickets cost $10.50 \times n$

2. By a mapping

$1 \longrightarrow 10.50$
$2 \longrightarrow 21.00$
$3 \longrightarrow 31.50$
$n \longrightarrow 10.50n$

3. By a table of values

Number	Cost
1	10.50
2	21.00
3	31.50
n	10.50n

4. By ordered pairs

(1, 10.50)
(2, 21.00)
(3, 31.50)
(n, 10.50n)

Exercises

1. Describe, in your own words, the mathematical meaning of the term "relation".

2. The relations given below are in words. Express the same relations using the other three methods outlined in the display.
a. the number of nickels in a pile and the value of the pile
b. the number of metres in any length and the corresponding number of centimetres
c. the number of consecutive natural numbers, beginning with 1, and the sum of those numbers

3. Refer to the display. List the ordered pair that describes the total cost of each.
a. 9 tickets **b.** one dozen tickets **c.** 35 tickets

4. Using a 24 h clock, consider a relation that pairs the time of day with the total number of minutes elapsed. For example, (09:20, 560) is one pair in this relation. Show six such pairs in a table of values.

5. A taxi charges $2.00 for the first 0.3 km and $0.35 for each tenth of a kilometre thereafter. How much does it cost to travel these distances?
a. 1.3 km   **b.** 2.8 km   **c.** 4.9 km

6. Pick any page in this text to find values for these ordered pairs.
a. (number of lines of print on the page, number of occurrences of the word "the" on the page)
b. (length of a word, number of vowels in that word)
c. (number of words in any sentence, number of punctuation marks in that sentence)

7. This formula for finding prime numbers has been proposed.
$n^2 - 3n + 43, n \in W$
a. List six numbers and the prime numbers generated by the formula.
b. Show that this formula does not always yield prime numbers by finding a value of n that produces a composite number.

8. In some relations, the first element maps onto 2 or more second elements. For example, $y = \pm\sqrt{x}$. This is called a **one-to-many** mapping. Explain and give examples of a **many-to-one** mapping and a **one-to-one** mapping.

9. Define a function. What type(s) of relations in Exercise 8 will produce functions?

174

8·2 Relations and Their Graphs

A set of ordered pairs can be plotted on the Cartesian coordinate grid to give us a picture or graphic representation of a relation. This picture is often useful in understanding and using a relation.

Example 1

Using a table of values, find four ordered pairs in the relation between the length of one side of a square and its perimeter. Graph the relation.

Side Length (cm)	Perimeter (cm)
1	4
2	8
3	12
4	16

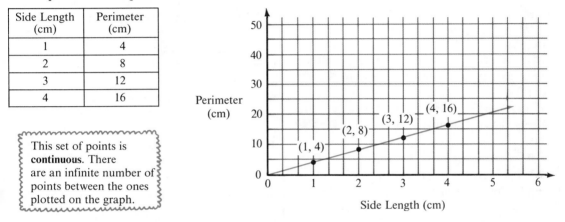

This set of points is **continuous**. There are an infinite number of points between the ones plotted on the graph.

The graph of all such pairs is a straight line. Any relation that forms a straight line is a **linear** relation.

> If a constant increase (decrease) in one variable results in a constant increase (decrease) in the other variable, then the relation is linear.

Example 2

Using a table of values, find five ordered pairs for the relation that defines the set of real numbers and their cubes.

Number	Cube
−2	−8
−1	−1
0	0
1	1
2	8

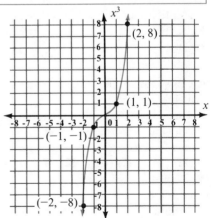

The graph of all such pairs does not form a straight line. Any relation that does not form a straight line is a **non-linear** relation.

> If a constant increase (decrease) in one variable does not result in a constant increase (decrease) in the other variable, then the relation is non-linear.

Exercises

1. Copy and complete.
a. A set of ordered pairs of numbers is called a ███████.
b. Points in a ████████ relation will lie in a straight line.
c. A straight line pattern indicates that the growth between the two variables is ███████.
d. ████-████████ relations will not have straight-line graphs.

2. Copy and complete.
a. If the first value in each pair is a natural number, then the graph will show a set of ███████ points.
b. If the values in the pairs include all real numbers, then the graph will show a set of ███████ points.

3. Why is the origin included in the graph of Example 1 in the display?

4. Copy and complete by referring to Example 1 of the display. Use a calculator if one is available.
a. What are the missing values in the pairs (3.5, ■), (■, 21.16), and (■, 302.76)?
b. Is (3.1, 12.61) a point on the graph? Explain.
c. Identify one other point on the graph between the first two points listed in the table of the display.

5. Copy and complete. Use a calculator if one is available.
a. This relation describes the number of litres of gasoline purchased at $0.559/L and the total cost of the purchase.
(20, ■), (30.26, ■), (42.89, ■), (■, 15.00), (■, 20.00), (■, 32.50)
b. Graph this relation.
c. Is this a linear relation or a non-linear relation?

6. Select 10 people of different ages.
a. Set up a table of values to record each of their ages and heights.
b. Graph these ordered pairs.

c. Compare your results with those of your classmates. Draw conclusions about the ages of people and their heights based on these results.

7. Consider a vehicle whose wheels are 38 cm in diameter.
a. How far will this vehicle move after one full revolution of the wheel?
b. Set up a table of values showing the number of revolutions and the distance, *m*, it moves in 100, 300, 740, 1000, and 1250 revolutions. Use a calculator if one is available to arrive at answers that are correct to the nearest metre.
c. Plot these five points on a graph to the best of your ability.
d. Draw a smooth line or curve through the five points to illustrate the pattern in this relation.

8. Find four pairs of numbers whose sum is equal to its product.
a. Describe this relation in words.
b. Graph this relation.

9. Using six different circles, find the ordered pairs that relate the radius of the circle to its area correct to one decimal place. Use a calculator if one is available.
a. Plot these ordered pairs.
b. Draw a smooth line or curve through these points. Is the relation continuous? Explain.
c. Is the relation linear? Explain.

10. Conduct a study to examine the relationship between the length of the human finger and the width of its fingernail.
a. Measure the fingers on a number of people, from the base to the tip, on the palm side of the hand. Then measure each nail at its widest point and record the results as ordered pairs.
b. Graph the ordered pairs.
c. Is there a pattern in the relationship? Note that in graphing the results of measurements, the graphical patterns may not be exact. Mathematicians usually draw a line or curve that best fits the points, even though it is not an exact fit. Such graphs are referred to as **linear regression models** or the **curve of best fit**.

11. Conduct an original study to investigate the relationship between any two varying quantities that are measurable.
a. Gather the data.
b. List and graph the ordered pairs.
c. Draw the curve of best fit and comment on the relationship in terms of constant change and continuous points. If there is no curve of best fit, the points are said to be **isolated**.

12. The data presented in this table of values shows the change in a city's population over a period of years.

Years	Population
10	23 650
20	25 430
30	28 930
40	36 170
50	50 050
60	78 280
70	134 530
80	247 270

a. Graph the data on a coordinate grid and draw the curve of best fit.
b. What does the graph indicate about the population growth over the eighty years?

13. The following pairs are members of a common relation in trigonometry. This relation pairs the measure of an angle with a ratio of lengths associated with those angles.
(0, 0), (30, 0.5), (45, 0.7), (60, 0.9), (90, 1), (120, 0.9), (135, 0.7), (150, 0.5), (180, 0)
a. Graph these points.
b. Draw the curve of best fit for these points.
c. Is the relation linear or non-linear? Explain.
d. List one unique feature of this relation that has not been evident in previous relations in this section.

14. For a donut, the area of the hole is equal to the area of the donut itself. Describe in words the relationship between the diameter of the hole and the diameter of the donut.

15. Describe in words the relation for any horizontal line on the Cartesian plane.

16. Describe in words the relation for any vertical line on the Cartesian plane.

17. Seoui and Joey went for a ride on a roller coaster. This graph shows how high they were above the ground.

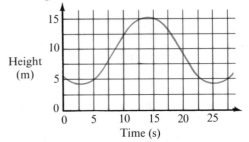

This non-linear up-and-down motion graph shows **simple harmonic motion**.
a. What is the maximum height of the coaster?
b. What is the minimum height of the coaster?

8·3 Variations

In every relation there is a **variation** between the two variables. The type of variation can be determined by the type of graph each relation produces.

Example 1

Mai-Lee rode in a bike-a-thon. She had pledges of $2.50/km. Construct a table of values and graph this relation.

Distance (km)	1	2	3	4
Pledges ($)	2.50	5.00	7.50	10.00

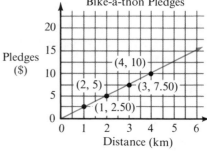

This **linear** graph starts at the origin and shows a constant growth between the variables. The amount pledged increases regularly as the distance ridden increases. This is a **direct variation**. The amount pledged **varies directly** with the distance ridden.

Example 2

A sales representative receives $150/week plus a $20 commission for each unit sold. Graph this relation.

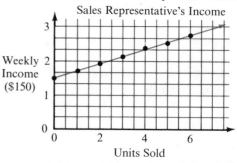

This **linear** graph does not begin at the origin. The salary consists of two parts; a **fixed part**, which is an income of $150/week, and a **variable part**, which is $20 for each unit sold. The commission varies directly with the number of units sold. This is a **partial variation**.

Example 3

Graph the relation that describes the time taken to run 10 km and the average speed.

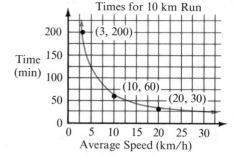

This **non-linear** graph shows the time decreasing as the speed increases. However, the decrease is not constant. The faster the speed, the lower the time. The time varies inversely as the speed. This is an **inverse variation**. For each ordered pair, the product of the abscissa and ordinate is constant.

Not all variations fit into these three categories. The variables in linear relations always vary directly or partially, however, variables in non-linear relations do not necessarily vary inversely.

Exercises

1. Which of these graphs represent a direct variation?

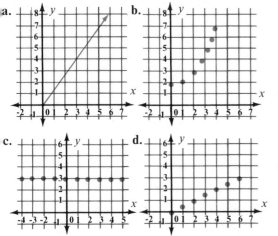

2. Use the relations given to construct the table of values for Example 2 of the display. Does the graph match the table of values?

3. Copy and complete for a direct variation.
a. The graph is ■■■■■.
b. The growth is ■■■■■.
c. The point (■, ■) is common to all direct variations.

4. Which of the following graphs represent a partial variation?

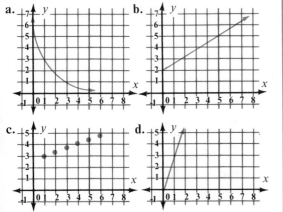

5. Copy and complete for a partial variation.
a. The graph is ■■■■■.
b. The origin is not a part of this relation because ■■■■■■■■■■■■■■■■■■■■.

6. Which of these graphs represent an inverse variation?

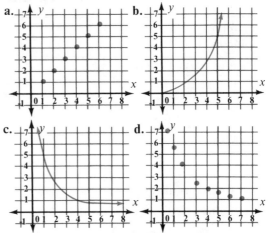

7. Copy and complete for an inverse variation.
a. The graph is non-■■■■■.
b. One variable ■■■■■ as the other variable increases.
c. The product of the values in each pair is ■■■■■.

8. Graph the relation described in each of these tables of values and identify, with reasons, the type of variation described.

a.

Number	2	3	5	8	10	12
Cost	3.8	5.7	9.5	15.2	19	22.8

b.

Voltage	8	32	64	76	88	100
Current	2	8	16	19	22	25

c.

Area	4.8	8.0	13.28	16.16	24
Width	3	5	8.3	10.1	15

9. Two angles of a triangle are labelled x and y. The third angle always stays the same. What type of variation would best describe the relation between x and y? Explain.

10. The volume of a cube varies directly as the cube of the length of its side.
a. Construct a table of values for this relation.
b. Plot the points.
c. Is this a linear relation?

179

8·4 Direct Variation

An aircraft is flying at a constant speed of 620 km/h. The table of values and the graph show the relationship between distance and time.

Time (h)	Distance (km)
1	620
2	1240
3	1860
4	2480

As time is doubled, distance is doubled. As time is tripled, distance is tripled ...

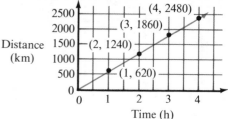

The variation is direct. When one variable is increased by a factor of k, the other variable is also increased by a factor of k. We say that distance varies directly as time and is written as $d = kt$, or $k = \dfrac{d}{t}$, where k is called the **constant of proportionality**. In this case, the constant of proportionality is 620.

For any two quantities a and b in direct variation, $a \propto b$ and $a = kb$, where k is the constant of proportionality.

α means "proportional to".

Example 1

Observers of a space launch were stationed at various distances from the launch pad. The time taken for sound to reach them is shown in the table of values. Is this a direct variation?

Distance (km)	Time (s)
1	3.01
2	6.02
3	9.03

For a direct variation, there must exist a constant of proportionality. In this case, $k = \dfrac{3.01}{1} = \dfrac{6.02}{2} = \dfrac{9.03}{3} \dots$.

Therefore, a constant of proportionality exists, and this is a direct variation.

Example 2

The amount of money a contestant can collect in a skate-a-thon varies directly as the number of laps skated. For the full 80 laps, a contestant can earn $100.

a. Find an equation relating the number of laps skated to the total amount collected.
b. What amount would be collected if a contestant skated 45 laps?
c. How many laps would have to be completed in order to collect $66.25?

a. Let L represent the number of laps completed.
Let A represent the amount of money collected.
$A = kL$
$\quad = 1.25L$

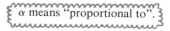

$k = \dfrac{100}{80} = 1.25$

b. Substitute 45 for L in the equation of part **a.**
$A = 1.25 \times 45$
$\quad = 56.25$
The contestant would collect $56.25.

c. Substitute 66.25 for A in the above equation.
$66.25 = 1.25 \times L$
$\dfrac{66.25}{1.25} = L$
$\quad 53 = L$ The contestant would have to skate 53 laps.

180

Exercises

1. Copy and complete.
a. If the ratio of the elements in each ordered pair is a constant, then the variation is ███████.
b. The constant is called the ███████ ████.
███████.

2. Find the constant of proportionality for the relation involving side length and perimeter of an equilateral triangle.

3. Refer to the aircraft moving at 620 km/h, as described in the display. Use the constant of proportionality to determine each. Use a calculator if one is available.
a. the distance travelled in 3.75 h
b. the time to travel 4030 km
c. the distance travelled in 4 d
d. how far it travels in a year
e. how far it travels in 1 month

4. The side length and perimeter of a square vary directly. Use the constant of proportionality to copy and complete these ordered pairs. Use a calculator if one is available.
a. (7, ■) **b.** (8.3, ■) **c.** (■, 87.6) **d.** (■, 192)

5. A student saves $4.75 each week.
a. Copy and complete the table of values that involves the number of weeks, w, and the total amount saved, s.

w	s
1	4.75
2	9.50
	33.25
20	

b. Find how much this student will have saved after nine weeks, four months, one year, and two and one half years.
c. Graph the relation.
d. Check the ratio of savings to number of weeks in order to verify that the variation is direct. Is this value the same as the constant of proportionality?

6. Which of the following relations are examples of direct variations? Explain the reasons for your selections.
a. (3, 9), (4, 12), (5, 15), (14, 42)
b. (age, mass) for any member of your class
c. (day of month, temperature)
d. (−3, 6), (−2, 4), (−1, 2), (1, −2)
e. (5.2, 20), (6.2, 30), (7.2, 40)

7. Find three ordered pairs for each direct variation and find the constant of proportionality.
a. **b.**

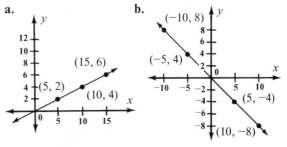

8. The force of a punch varies directly with the acceleration of the punch. If the force is 8 N when the acceleration is 732 cm/s², then find the force when the acceleration is 1098 cm/s².

9. Determine a set of ordered pairs that lists the diameter and circumference of four different coins: a penny, a nickel, a dime, and a quarter. Is the variation between diameter and circumference direct? Explain. Use a calculator if one is available.

10. Use a newspaper to determine the current price for gold bullion in Canadian dollars.
a. List six ordered pairs describing different amounts of bullion and the value of the gold.
b. Is this an example of direct variation? Explain.
c. Express the variation as a mathematical equation.

11. If the area of a circle varies directly as the square of the radius, then use the variables A and r to identify the constant ratio.

12. If the volume of a sphere varies directly with the cube of the radius, then express the constant ratio using variables.

8·5 Partial Variation

A motorbike was rented for $19/d plus $0.13/km. The table of values and the graph show this relationship.

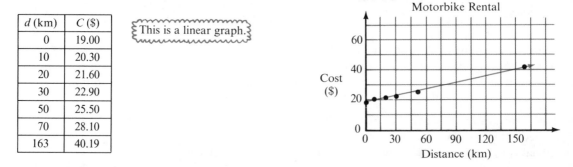

d (km)	C ($)
0	19.00
10	20.30
20	21.60
30	22.90
50	25.50
70	28.10
163	40.19

This is a linear graph.

Motorbike Rental

Cost ($)

Distance (km)

Although this graph is a straight line, it does not represent a direct variation. If one variable is doubled, then the other variable is not doubled. This type of variation is called a **partial variation** because part of the rental fee includes a **fixed part** that does not vary with the distance driven and a **variable part** that varies directly as the distance driven. This relation can be described mathematically as

$$C = 19 + 0.13d.$$

Fixed Cost

Direct Variation

If two quantities a and b are in partial variation, then $a = f + kb$ where f is the fixed part and kb is the variable part.

Example

An appliance repair service charges $32 plus $17.50/h for labour. Set up a table of values for the relation, graph it, and find the mathematical equation that represents this variation.

Let L represent the total cost of the repair.
$L = 32 + 17.5t$

t (h)	L ($)
1	49.50
2	67.00
3	84.50

This is a partial variation. There is a fixed part and a variable part. This graph does not pass through the origin.

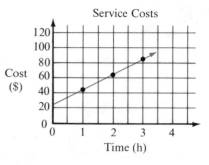

Service Costs

Cost ($)

Time (h)

Exercises

1. Copy and complete.
a. In a partial variation there is always a ▬▬▬▬ part and a variable part.
b. The variable part changes at a ▬▬▬▬ rate.
c. In your own words, explain a partial variation.

2. In a mountain range the temperature at ground level is 20°C and it decreases 4°C for every 800 m above that level.
a. At what altitude is the temperature 0°C?
b. Is this an example of partial variation? Explain.

3. A telephone company uses partial variation when it calculates long-distance rates. It charges a fixed rate of $3.25 for the first three minutes, and an additional $0.65/min thereafter.
a. Copy and complete this table of values.

Length of Call (min)	Total Charge ($)
1	3.25
3	3.25
4	3.90
6	
10	
	11.05

b. Use two ratios from the table to show that the variation is not direct.
c. What is the fixed part of this variation?

4. A student has a small business printing decks of personalized playing cards. There is a fixed charge of $8 per deck, and an additional charge of $0.10 per letter for the buyer's name.
a. Set up a table of values with five entries to show the cost per deck.
b. Is this an example of partial variation? Explain.
c. Graph this relation.
d. Explain why this graph is a linear relation.

5. A shoe salesperson earns $350/week and receives 6% commission on the total sales for the week.
a. List four ordered pairs in the relation that pairs total sales with weekly earnings.
b. Express the partial variation in equation form using the variables s and w.

6. A 60 L tank filled with gas is leaking at a rate of 3 mL each month.
a. Draw a graph that illustrates the decreasing amounts of gas in the tank over a period of 1 a.
b. Identify the type of variation from the graph.
c. Write the equation that describes this variation.

7. A school banquet has fixed costs of $370 to cover printing, decorations, and a gift for the guest speaker. In addition it will cost $8.50 to feed each person in attendance.
a. Draw a graph showing this partial variation between the number of people attending and the total cost.
b. Calculate the price per ticket that must be charged to enable the school to break even on the banquet if there are 10, 20, 50, 80, or 100 people in attendance.

8. Four car-rental companies are having promotions to attract business. They advertise in the following manner.
Trans-Canada — $16/d plus $0.055/km
Cole Rentals — $30/d plus $0.02/km
Emerson — $0.08/km
K & C Rentals — $35/d with no cost for distance travelled
a. On the same set of axes, draw a graph of each of the variations described in the four options. Show the total cost for a range of distances travelled from 0 km to 500 km.
b. Identify the type of variation for each offer.
c. Comment on the best deal using your graph as a reference.

Braintickler

Dana was brilliant with numbers, but often made mistakes in spelling. Her friend Hector teased her when she wrote "to" instead of "two" and would always correct her. "You're a square Dana; all you can do is math problems. You can't even spell."

Dana responded angrily, "If AGE, TWO, NOT, and TO are perfect squares, then you're a TWO + TO + TOO."

What was Dana calling Hector?

183

8·6 Inverse Variation

It is often more economical for a group of people to share the cost of an item than it is for one person. For example, if a van is needed for a trip that costs $64, then the rental cost is $64 whether one person rents the van or ten people share in the cost.

Example 1

Judy, a store owner, wants to raise $500 in capital through the sale of shares in her store. The table of values and the graph show the relationship between the number of shares sold and the value of each share.

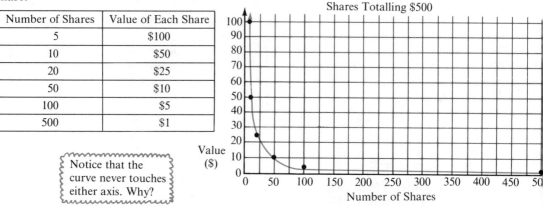

Number of Shares	Value of Each Share
5	$100
10	$50
20	$25
50	$10
100	$5
500	$1

Notice that the curve never touches either axis. Why?

The table shows that when one variable is multiplied by 2, the other variable is divided by 2; when one variable is multiplied by 5, the other variable is divided by 5; and so on. If the product of the variables is constant, then the relation is an **inverse variation**.

> For two quantities a and b which vary inversely, $ab = k$ or $a = \dfrac{k}{b}$.

Example 2

The number of hours needed to paint a house varies inversely as the number of people painting. If a house can be painted in 8 h by 3 people, then how many people are needed to paint the same house in 3 h?

Let n represent the number of people painting the house.
Let t represent the time required for the people to paint the house.

Since n varies inversely as t, the product nt is a constant.
Substituting 8 for t and 3 for n, a constant of 24 is found.

$$\therefore nt = 24$$
when $t = 3$,
$$3n = 24$$
$$n = 8$$

Therefore, 8 people are needed to paint a house in 3 h.

Exercises

1. Copy and complete.
a. In an inverse variation, one quantity ███████ as the other decreases.
b. In an inverse variation, the ████████ of the abscissa and the ordinate is constant.
c. In your own words, explain what is meant by an inverse variation.

2. In drilling a hole in a certain metal, the speed of the drill (s r.p.m.) varies as the diameter (d cm) of the drill.

s	575	1150	2300	4600
d	2	1	0.5	0.25

Explain how to show that this is an example of an inverse variation.

3. Over a 360 km distance, four different drivers recorded the following times and average speeds under various weather conditions.

Time (h)	⟶	Average Speed (km/h)
3.6	⟶	100
4.0	⟶	90
4.5	⟶	80
6.0	⟶	60

a. Check the product of each pair of values.
b. If the product is constant, then the average speed varies ████████ as the time.

4. At a community cleanup each Saturday, the time taken to clean up the local park varies inversely with the number of volunteers.
a. Set up a table showing six possible ordered pairs.
b. Verify that this is an inverse variation by determining the product of each pair.
c. Express the relation mathematically using the variables t and v.

5. A certain vehicle depreciates (loses value) each year. Its value varies inversely with its age. If the value of the vehicle after one year is $23 000, and the initial purchase price is $46 000, then find each.
a. What is its value after two years?

b. What is its value after five years?
c. Use the variables v and a to express this relation mathematically.
d. Is the car ever worth $0? Explain.

6. There are sets of ordered pairs of real numbers whose product is 100.
a. List six of these pairs.
b. Demonstrate that these numbers vary inversely.
c. Plot each pair of numbers on a graph.
d. Is the result a linear graph or a non-linear graph?

7. Rent-a-Balloon offers groups an opportunity to ride in a hot-air balloon. The cost per person varies inversely as the number of people.
a. If the maximum number of people allowed is 12 at a cost of $6.50/person, then what is the cost per person if only 5 people go for a ride?
b. Determine four more pairs in this relation.
c. Graph this relation.

8. Which of these relations is an inverse variation?

a.

Age	1	3	5	7	9	11	13	15
Mass	9	27	34	45	63	68	73	76

b.

10 ⟶	75
20 ⟶	37.5
30 ⟶	25
40 ⟶	18.75
50 ⟶	15

c. (1, 98), (2, 49), (5, 40), (10, 20), (11, 9)

9. One angle of a triangle is 80°. The other two angles vary inversely. Find an equation that relates the other two angles.

10. The exposure time for photographing an object varies inversely as the square of the diameter of the lens. The exposure time is 0.0025 s when the lens diameter is 2 cm.
a. Write an equation describing the relation of time and diameter.
b. Find the diameter of a lens when the exposure time is 0.04 s.

185

8·7 Variation Problems

There are a number of strategies that we can use to solve problems. Two of the many strategies used in this chapter are using graphs and solving equations for the relations described.

Example

Variation Publisher received bids from three companies to print their newest math book. Company A offered to publish the book for $0.05/page, Company B offered to publish it for $15 plus $0.01/page, and Company C offered a flat rate of $23. When is Company A the most economical company to publish the book? Company B? Company C?

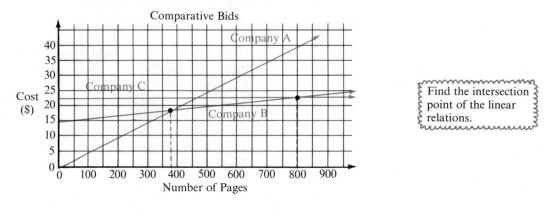

Find the intersection point of the linear relations.

Exercises

1. From the example in the display, when is each company the most economical?

2. The air resistance on a plane varies directly as the speed of the plane. If the air resistance is 5400 units at a speed of 675 km/h, then what is the air resistance at a speed of 900 km/h?

3. A spring is stretched by a 10 kg mass. If the distance stretched varies directly with the mass, then write an equation describing this variation.

4. The cost of operating a car includes fixed amounts such as insurance and a vehicle permit, and a varying amount based on the distance driven.
a. Write an equation describing this partial variation if the fixed costs are $735 and the variable cost is $0.26/km.
b. Graph this relation.

5. The distance a train travels at a uniform speed varies directly as the time it takes to travel that distance. If the train travels 200 km in 1.6 h, then write an equation that describes the variation. How far does the train travel in 3.9 h?

6. Comment on the way the two variables change in each equation.
a. $w = Rh$, where w represents a weekly wage, h is a number of hours worked, and R is a constant
b. $as = 6.3$, where a is the atomic weight of an element and s is its specific heat capacity
c. $fw = p$, where f is the frequency of a radio wave, w is the wavelength, and p is a given constant
d. $m = kr^2$, where m is the mass of a disc, r is its radius, and k is a given constant

7. The fundamental frequency of a string varies inversely as its length. If the fundamental frequency of a 50 cm string is 250 cycles/s, then find the fundamental frequency for a 25 cm string.

8·8 Interpolation and Extrapolation

Sometimes only a portion of a graph or a portion of a table of values is given, and data is required that is not included in the table or shown on the graph. This will require us to estimate the values that are required either between two values that are known or beyond the range of the known data.

Example

This graph shows the relation between the distance and time for a moving object. How far does the object move in 3.5 s? in 6.5 s?

t (s)	d (m)
1	7.5
2	15.0
3	22.5
4	30.0
5	37.5

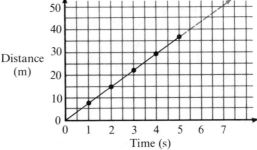

From the graph, the object moved approximately 26 m in 3.5 s, and approximately 48 m in 6.5 s. Since the graph only went to (5, 37.5), it was extended to include (6.5, 48.75).

> Estimating a value between known values is **interpolation**, and estimating values beyond known values is **extrapolation**.

Exercises

1. Copy and complete.
a. Interpolation involves estimating values ▬▬▬▬ known values.
b. Extrapolation involves extending the graph to estimate ▬▬▬▬ known values.

2. The data in this table was gathered from an experiment with a rolling ball.

t (s)	d (m)
2	2.4
4	5.0
6	7.5
8	10.0
10	12.0

a. Plot the points on a graph and draw the curve of best fit.
b. Use interpolation to estimate the distance rolled after 9 s.
c. Use extrapolation to estimate the distance rolled in 12 s.

3. Determine the value of each. Redraw the graphs and interpolate or extrapolate as necessary.
a. p when $q = 3.5$
q when $p = 7$
b. w when $u = 67$
u when $w = 6.5$

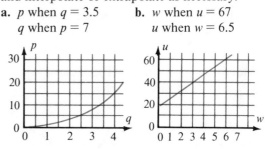

Using the Library

1. Write a report on how Eratosthenes calculated the circumference of the Earth.
2. Use the *Wonderful World of Mathematics*, Lancelot Hogben, page 51. Explain how the early Hindu and Muslim mathematicians may have solved the algebraic equation $\frac{3n}{5} = 60$.

8·9 Computer Application — Values in Variation

The surface area of a spherical balloon increases as the balloon increases in size. This will print a table of values for this variation.

```
10 REM TABLE OF VALUES FOR RADIUS AND SURFACE AREA OF SPHERE
20 REM R REPRESENTS THE RADIUS; S REPRESENTS THE SURFACE AREA
30 PRINT "RADIUS", "SURFACE AREA"
40 LET PI = 3.14159
50 FOR R = 0 TO 20 STEP 0.5
60 LET S = 4 * PI * R ∧ 2
70 PRINT R, S
80 NEXT R
90 END
```

Exercises

1. State the formula for the surface area of a sphere.

2. What is the purpose of line 80 in the program in the display?

3. Predict the first four pairs of numbers that the program will print.

4. Modify the program from the display to check whether this is an inverse relation.

5. Modify the program from the display to add a column that will list the values of R^2.

6. Modify the program from the display to find the ratio of S to R^2.

7. What conclusion can be arrived at for the ratio of S to R^2?

8. Write a program to print a table of values for the radius and the volume of a sphere. ($V = \frac{4}{3}\pi r^3$)

9. The "pirating" of software packages has become a controversial point in recent years. With the help of three of your classmates, write an argument defending the position of each person below. Each of you could play one "role" to help in the discussion.

a. Ali, a high school student, has a copy of the new computer game "McWidget". His friend Tamara wants to copy it. She has often given him copies of her games and he wants to be a good friend and reciprocate.

b. Tamara is a student in the same class as Ali. He has the new computer game and she wants a copy to play on her computer at home. Since she has given Ali copies of her games in the past, she feels it is only right that Ali give her a copy.

c. Shannon knows that Ali has a copy of "McWidget". Tamara is her best friend. She informed them that her mother wrote the game, and that her mother's income is generated through royalties earned as the game is sold. Shannon feels that it is unethical for Ali to copy the game.

d. Phillippe's father is a lawyer. He has suggested to Phillippe that he tell his friends that it is illegal to copy the games. The teacher will not allow the computers to be used for copying software and that there must be other ways found to allow Tamara to use the game.

8·10 Chapter Review

1. Copy and complete.

a. If a relation is linear, then its graph is a ▆▆▆▆▆ line.

b. In a direct variation, the two values vary at a ▆▆▆▆▆ rate.

c. Points that do not lie in a straight line are called ▆▆▆▆▆.

d. A continuous relation has an ▆▆▆▆▆ number of ordered pairs.

e. Two parts, fixed and variable, characterize a ▆▆▆▆▆ variation.

f. If two quantities vary ▆▆▆▆▆, the graph of the relation is non-linear.

g. A graph of a partial variation will not include the point (▆, ▆).

h. Interpolation is used to estimate values ▆▆▆▆▆ known values.

2. Custom Pizza advertises the "best-priced pizza in town". It will make any size and charges $0.18/cm for each centimetre of diameter requested, and $0.35/item of topping. Another company, Pizza Only, advertises 20, 46, and 60 cm pizzas, with four items, for $6.25, $7.80, and $9.00 respectively.

a. Graph the two relations to compare size and cost on the same axes.

b. Refer to the graph to comment on which of these two companies offers the "best deal".

3. Determine the constant of proportionality in these relations. Use a calculator if one is available.

a. (3, 21), (5, 35), (6.2, 43.4), (7.8, 54.6)

b. (0.0517, 1.6544), (0.3725, 11.92), (0.9514, 30.4448)

4. The pairs of numbers in these relations vary inversely with one another. Determine the missing values.

a. (3, 2064), (4, ▆), (6, 1032), (▆, 774)

b. (−3, 2.04), (6, ▆), (12, ▆), (0.3, ▆)

5. What type of variation is illustrated by this graph? Explain.

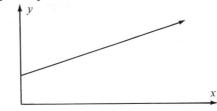

6. These ordered pairs show the relationship between the height of each step from the ground and the distance from the first step.
(25, 35), (45, 63), (65, 91), (85, 119)

a. Plot these points on a graph.

b. Is this a linear relation or a non-linear relation?

c. Is the graph of all the steps in this stairway a set of isolated points or of continuous points?

d. Is the origin a possible pair in this relation? Explain.

e. Does the graph increase at a constant rate? Explain.

f. Identify the variation in this relation. Explain.

g. Determine the constant of proportionality, if one exists.

h. Express this variation in mathematical form using the variables d and h.

7. The following table compares Canadian and British currencies.

Canadian Dollar	British Pound
1	
2.20	
	5
	12
	20

a. Use a newspaper to find the current currency exchange rate to complete the table.

b. Draw an accurate graph of the relation.

c. Determine the value in pounds of 32 Canadian dollars.

d. Determine the Canadian dollar value of 50 pounds.

8·11 Chapter Test

1. Copy and complete.
a. If two variables change at a constant rate, then the graph of the relation is a ▮▮▮▮▮ line.
b. In a direct variation the ratio of the two quantities is ▮▮▮▮.
c. In an inverse variation the ▮▮▮▮ of the two quantities is constant.
d. Extrapolation is used to estimate values ▮▮▮▮ known values.

2. Identify the variation in each of these relations as either direct, partial, inverse, or other.
a. (5, 4.8), (6, 4), (8, 3), (10, 2.4)
b. (−2, 9), (−3, 8), (−4, 6), (−5, 3)
c. (0, 12), (1, 15), (2, 18), (3, 21), (4, 24)
d. (1.25, 6.25), (1.40, 7.00), (0.75, 3.75), (2.82, 14.10)

3. Copy and complete these sets of ordered pairs in which the variation is indicated.
a. (2, 9), (4.5, ▮), (6, ▮)   Inverse variation
b. (0.3, ▮), (▮, 16.1), (1.0, 23)   Direct variation

4. Listed below are some ordered pairs in the relation describing the length of the side of a cube and the volume of that cube.
(1, 1), (2, 8), (3.2, 32.768), (4, 64), (5, 125)
a. Is this a relation of isolated points or continuous points?
b. Explain how to recognize that the variation is not direct, partial, or inverse.
c. Explain why this is not an example of partial variation.
d. Explain why this is not an inverse variation.

5. For the relation that pairs natural numbers and their squares,
a. list six of the pairs;
b. explain why the relation is not an example of either a direct, partial, or inverse variation.

6. Determine the constant of proportionality for this relation.
20 ⟶ 105   30 ⟶ 157.5
25 ⟶ 131.25   35 ⟶ 183.75

7. Acceleration varies directly as the force applied. Write an equation that describes the variation if a force of 209 N produces an acceleration of 47.5 m/s².

8. The cost for household water in some areas is determined by a fixed charge of $4.83 for the meter and an additional charge of $4.086 for each ten thousand litres used.
a. List five pairings of litres and cost.
b. Graph the relation.
c. Explain in words how to recognize the type of variation from the pairings and from the graph.
d. Express the variation mathematically using the variables L (in ten thousands) for the litres of water used, and c for the cost.

9. The following water temperatures were recorded at the depths indicated as ordered pairs.
(10, 18), (15, 12), (20, 9), (30, 6)
a. Identify the type of variation.
b. Graph the relation.

10. The volume of a gas at constant temperature varies inversely with the pressure. The volume is 4.63 L when the pressure is 752 mm Hg. What is the volume at 1380 mm Hg?

11. An experiment on fuel consumption produced the following data.

Speed (km/h)	Consumption (L/100 km)
10	19.1
30	15.1
50	13.2
70	14.9
90	15.7
100	17.3
110	18.0

a. Draw a smooth curve that best fits this relation.
b. Interpolate from the graph to determine the fuel consumption at 80 km/h.
c. Explain why an extrapolation to determine fuel consumption at 140 km/h may not be accurate.

EQUATIONS & GRAPHING

Tune Up

1. Solve for x.

a. $3x - 12 = 15$ **b.** $7x - 2(x - 3) = 4(5x - 1)$

c. $16 - \frac{2}{3}x = 24$ **d.** $\frac{a}{4} - \frac{3}{5} = 2$

e. $\frac{1}{3}(2x + 7) - \frac{3}{4} = \frac{2}{3}(x + 1)$

f. $\frac{4c - 1}{2} + \frac{c - 6}{3} = \frac{c}{4}$

2. Find two ordered pairs that satisfy each equation.

a. $y = 3x - 8$ **b.** $y = -\frac{5}{2}x + 20$

3. Write each as a mathematical equation.

a. Three times a number increased by two is the same as the number increased by four.

b. Three quarters of an amount is six more than the amount decreased by ten.

c. Six years from now Ahmad's age will be twice what it was five years ago.

4. Calculate the slope of a line passing through these points.

a. $(4, 1), (6, 3)$ **b.** $(-2, 4), (5, -2)$

c. $(-3, -1), (5, 1)$ **d.** $(0.5, -12), (10.75, 7)$

5. Graph these inequalities on an integer line.

a. $x > 3$ **b.** $x \le 7$ and $x > -2$

c. $x < -3$ or $x \ge 1$

6. Find each.

a. the y-value when $x = 0$.

b. the x-value when $y = 0$.

  i) $x + y = 7$ ii) $y = 4x - 8$

  iii) $0.5x - 7.5y = 11.25$ iv) $9x - 5y - 12 = 0$

7. Express each equation in terms of the indicated variable.

a. $2a + 2b = P; a$

b. $5x - 4y = 12; y$

c. $5m + 2n - 10 = 0; n$

8. Write an expression that satisfies each statement.

a. p varies directly as q.

b. v varies inversely as s.

9. A five-year-old child lives on the twenty-third floor of an apartment building. Every morning, he rides the elevator down to the lobby and walks out the front door on his way to school. Every evening, he rides the elevator up to the sixteenth floor and then walks up the remaining stairs to get back to his apartment. Explain why this boy uses this rather unique method of going to and from his apartment.

10. Graph these two straight lines to find the point of intersection.

$x + y = 3; x - y = 1$

9·1 Translating English and Mathematics

Many relations can be described by an **equation** defining the relationship between two or more quantities. Determining the equation that relates any number of quantities in a relation is an important process in problem solving.

Example 1

Dodie's present age is twice Heather's age two years ago. Express Dodie's present age in terms of Heather's age.

The problem-solving model can be used to help us find the equation.

Understand the Problem
a. The equation that we must find relates Dodie's age to Heather's age. The equation involves present age and past age.
b. We must find an algebraic equation relating the variables concerning Dodie's present age and Heather's age two years ago.

Develop a Plan
Since the equation must relate the ages of two different girls, select appropriate variables to represent the ages of the two girls. Express these quantities in terms of each other.

Carry Out the Plan
Let d represent Dodie's age.
Let h represent Heather's age.
$d = 2(h - 2)$

Look Back
Therefore, $d = 2(h - 2)$.
Is this answer reasonable? To help us answer this question, we could pick an age for Heather and check Dodie's age. Dodie is older than Heather.
If Heather is twelve years old, then Dodie is twenty years old.

The Look Back section of this example brings us to the next step with equations. That is, we must be able to use the equation that is presented. Solving for a particular variable in terms of the other, or substituting for variables to find the value of another variable are also important processes in mathematics.

Example 2

Find Heather's age if Dodie is eighteen years old.

Using the equation from Example 1, we must solve for h.
$$d = 2(h - 2)$$
$$\frac{d}{2} = h - 2$$
$$\frac{d}{2} + 2 = h$$

Since Dodie is eighteen years old, Heather is $\frac{18}{2} + 2$ or eleven years old.

Exercises

1. Translate each into an equation.

a. The perimeter, p, of a square is four times the length of one side, s.

b. The cost, c, in dollars of printing a book is equal to $3.25 plus $0.015/page, p.

c. The total mass, m, of a carton filled with cans is 85 kg and an additional 1.5 kg per can, c.

d. The total number, y, of pieces of fruit yielded by an orchard is 230 times the number of trees, n.

e. The total number of days, d, a person has lived is 365.25 for every year that person has been alive.

f. The total time, t, required to install a muffler is $2\frac{3}{4}$ h and an additional 6 min for each clamp required, c.

2. Match each of these three equations with one of the four word statements.

   i) $R = 6 + 0.25p$ ii) $C = \pi d$

   iii) $E = 6.00 + 0.02a$

a. The exchange fee for a certain currency is $6.00 plus 2% of the amount being exchanged.

b. The circumference of a circle is equal to π times the diameter of the circle.

c. The energy cost to run an appliance is 6 times the age of the appliance.

d. A recipe requires 6 dollops of sugar and an additional $\frac{1}{4}$ dollop for each person served over five.

3. This relation involves partial variation. The total labour cost, L, is determined by taking a $25 flat charge for a home visit and an additional $18/h for the labour.

Which equation(s) describes the total labour cost?

a. $L = 25h$ **b.** $L + 25 = 18h$

c. $L = 25 + 18h$ **d.** $h = L + 25$

4. A restaurant owner decides on the quantity of lemonade to make each day during the summer by applying the following rule:

Make 60 glasses plus 5 additional glasses for each degree Celsius given in the forecast.

a. Write an equation that expresses the total number of glasses made, g, in terms of the temperature, t.

b. List three ordered pairs that show the production of lemonade.

5. Write an equation for each relation.

a. the relation between the long-distance charge, c, for a telephone call and the length of the call, m, in minutes when there is a minimum charge of $3.60 and an additional charge of $0.96/min

b. the relation between the education tax, t, paid by a homeowner, and the assessed-property value, v, if the tax is calculated by multiplying the assessed value by a standard rate of 128.64

c. the relation in which the pressure, p, varies inversely with the volume of a gas, v

d. the relation between the number of sides, n, of a polygon and the sum of its interior angles, s, if the sum is always determined by multiplying 180° by two less than the number of sides in the polygon

e. the relation between the money saved, m, and the regular cost, C, of buying an item that is reduced by 20%

6. Write equations to describe these relations.

a. the perimeter, p, and the width, w, of any rectangle whose length is 5 more than twice its width

b. the selling price, S, and the cost price, C, of items that are marked up 35%

c. the height, h, and the area, A, of any triangle whose base is three times its height

d. the total value, v, and the number of quarters, q, in a jar

e. the interest earned, I, in a savings account, s, when the annual rate of interest is 9.25%

f. the weekly income, I, on the total sales, s, if the salesperson earns $300.00 + 6% of the total sales

g. the total cost of a personalized T-shirt at $14.95 for the shirt and $0.27/letter

7. Translate each into a mathematical equation.

a. The total cost of a number of books at $6.95 each is reduced by $0.05 for each book purchased.

b. The total cost of purchasing sheets of paper at 2.2¢ per sheet decreases by 0.01¢ per sheet for every sheet over 1000 sheets.

8. Write each equation in words.

a. $A = \frac{h}{2}(a + b)$

b. $S = \sqrt{h^2 + \left(\frac{d}{2}\right)^2}$

c. $D = \sqrt{l^2 + w^2 + h^2}$

9·2 Information from Equations

Understanding how the variables in an equation relate to each other is an important part of problem solving. Even solving a simple problem can require the relating of two or more variables.

Example 1

In 1603, a lookout tower was built 30 m from the shoreline. The shoreline has been eroding at a rate of 1.5 cm/a. In what year will the shoreline reach the tower?

The problem-solving model can be used to help solve this problem.

Understand the Problem
a. The rate of erosion of the shoreline is 1.5 cm/a. The tower was built 30 m from the shoreline in 1603.
b. We are asked to find the year that the shoreline will reach the tower.

Develop a Plan
Because we are concerned with the relationship between two variables — the amount of erosion and the number of years that erosion has been taking place — an equation can be written to relate the two variables and then solved for the unknown variable.

Carry Out the Plan
Let e represent the amount of erosion measured in centimetres.
Let a represent the number of years the shoreline has been eroding.
$\therefore e = 1.5a$
The original distance from the shoreline must be measured in centimetres to keep the distances consistent.
$3000 = 1.5a$
$a = 2000$

Look Back
It will take 2000 a for the shoreline to reach the tower and that will happen in the year 3603. Notice that the equation provides all the necessary information in a condensed form.

Example 2

In the equation $A = 10d + 25q$, d represents the number of dimes and q represents the number of quarters. What does A represent?

Since d represents the number of dimes, then $10d$ could represent the value of the dimes in cents. Similarly, since q represents the number of quarters, $25q$ could represent the value of the quarters in cents. Therefore, A will represent the total value in cents of the dimes and the quarters.

Exercises

1. Translate these equations into English sentences.

a. $P = 4s$

b. $V = \pi r^2 h$

c. $V = \frac{4}{3}\pi r^3$

2. In a hockey game, a player is awarded 1 point for every goal and 1 point for every assist. Find an equation that can represent this relationship if the player scored 37 points over the course of the season.

3. Using your equation from Exercise 2, if the player scored 20 goals, then how many assists were scored? Explain.

4. Translate the equation $A = \pi r^2$ into English.

a. Find A when r is 3.

b. Find r when A is 10.

c. Find r when A is π^3.

d. Is it possible to have a negative value for r? Explain.

5. "The distance an object moves varies directly as the product of its velocity and its time of movement."

a. In your own words, explain what this quotation means.

b. Find an equation that satisfies this relation.

c. Express your equation from part **b** in terms of the time the object is moving.

6. Explain the meaning of the variables in this formula: $A = 600(1 + i)$, where $0 < i < 1$. Justify your answers.

7. Translate these equations into word statements involving age.

a. $(a + 6) = 4a$

b. $a + 12 = 5(a - 8)$

c. $a - 5 = \frac{1}{2}a$

8. Why is it necessary to understand how to relate variables in an expression?

9. Copy and complete the table.

English Expression	Algebraic Expression in One Variable	Algebraic Expression in Two Variables
The sum of two numbers is 24.	$x, 24 - x$	x, y where $x + y = 24$
One number is larger than another by 3.	$y, y + 3$	$x = y + 3$
The sum of two consecutive integers is 33.		
The length of a rectangle is twice the width.		
One number is twice another.		
The cost of two items is in the ratio 3:2.		

Using the Library

Pierre de Fermat, the French lawyer and "amateur" mathematician, once stated that there do not exist positive integers, x, y, z, and n such that $x^n + y^n = z^n$ where $n > 2$. This famous conjecture is known as Fermat's Last Theorem. The only hint that this conjecture can be proven was given by Fermat himself. In the margin of one of his many books, he wrote, "To divide a given cube into two cubes, or a number to the fourth power into two numbers to the fourth power, or in general any power whatever into two powers of the same denomination is impossible and I have assuredly found an admirable proof to this, but the margin is too narrow to contain this."

Using the library, write a short essay on Fermat's Last Theorem stating what book the quote was found in, why this theorem has the distinction of having the greatest number of incorrect proofs, some of the famous mathematicians who have tried and failed to prove this theorem, and what connection the mathematician Paul Wolfskehl has with this proof.

9·3 Graphing Equations

A problem can sometimes be solved by drawing a graph of a relation that satisfies that problem. This requires the plotting of points for the relation. Construct a table of values, draw a line or curve through the points, and analyse the graph to find all the patterns that exist within that graph.

Example 1

Construct a table of values and plot the graph of the relation defined by $y = 5$.

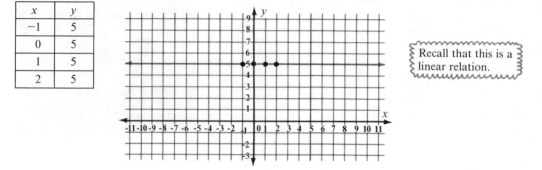

x	y
-1	5
0	5
1	5
2	5

Recall that this is a linear relation.

A pattern emerges as soon as we start plotting the points on the graph. It does not matter what value we choose for x, the value for y will be 5. All lines and curves continuing forever are indicated with arrows on each end. This relation can also be shown using set-builder notation as $\{(x, y) \mid y = 5, x, y \in R\}$.

Example 2

Construct a table of values and draw a graph for the relation defined by the equation $y = 4 - 0.3x^2$.

x	y
-3	1.3
-2	2.8
-1	3.7
0	4.0
1	3.7
2	2.8
3	1.3

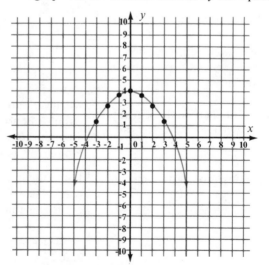

This graph shows that the greatest value for y occurs at the point where $x = 0$. The y-values then decrease regardless of whether the x-value is positive or negative. Such graphs are called **parabolas**.

Exercises

1. List and plot five ordered pairs for each relation.
a. $x + 4y = 12$, $x, y \in N$
b. $y = 2x + 3$, $x, y \in Q$
c. $3x - y = 15$, $x, y \in R$

2. Set up a table of values and graph each relation.
a. $\{(x, y) \mid y = 2x + 3\}$ **b.** $\{(x, y) \mid y = 5x - 1\}$
c. $\{(x, y) \mid y = x^2 + 7\}$ **d.** $\{(x, y) \mid y = -6x + 2\}$
e. $\{(x, y) \mid y = -x - 4\}$ **f.** $\{(x, y) \mid y = 0.25x - 1\}$
g. $\{(x, y) \mid y = 7.5x - 0.45\}$
h. $\{(x, y) \mid xy = 12\}$

3. Identify the non-linear relations in Exercise 2.

4. Set up a table of values for each relation and graph the relation.
a. $y = 3$ **b.** $7.3 = y$ **c.** $x = -2$ **d.** $y = 0$
e. Why is a table of values helpful in graphing a relation?

5. Graph each. $x, y \in R$
a. $x = y$ **b.** $y = 7$
c. $x + y = 0$ **d.** $x - y + 5 = 0$
e. $6x + y - 10 = 0$ **f.** $0.24x - 1.30y + 7.50 = 0$

6. Write an equation that satisfies each condition. Graph your equation.
a. a linear equation
b. an equation that is a direct variation
c. a non-linear equation

7. In your own words, describe the way the y-value changes as the x-value increases.

a. **b.**

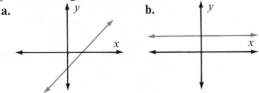

8. Select ordered pairs to show that an equal increase in the x-value of a linear equation will result in an equal increase in the y-value of the same linear equation. (*Hint:* Use any linear equation.)

9. The equations $y = x$ and $y = \dfrac{1}{x}$ are reciprocal relations.
a. On the same coordinate grid, graph the two relations described by these equations.
b. List the differences in these two graphs.
c. What point is common to both relations?
d. What is the x-intercept for each graph?

10. The **domain** of a relation is the set of all possible x-values for the relation. Find the domain in each of these relations.

a. **b.**

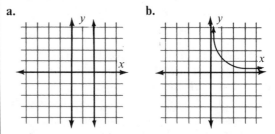

11. The **range** of a relation is the set of all possible y-values for the relation. Find the range for each of these relations.

a. **b.**

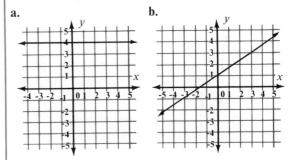

12. This smooth curve in the form of a wave is a common relation in the study of trigonometry.

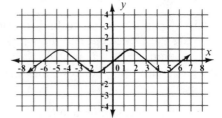

a. Find the range of this relation.
b. In your own words, describe the way the y-value changes as the x-value increases.

9·4 Graphing Linear Equations I

A **linear equation** is characterized by the fact that no term in the equation has a degree greater than one. For example, $3x - 5y = 7$ is a linear equation because x is of degree one and y is of degree one. Equations such as $4x + y^2 = 2$ or $xy = 6$ are non-linear equations because y^2 has a degree of two and xy also has a degree of two. Identifying whether an equation is linear or non-linear is an important process in mathematics.

Example 1

The points (4, 3), (8, 1), and (10, 0) are shown on the coordinate grid. Show that these points are collinear, i.e. that they lie on the same straight line.

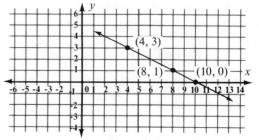

Join the three points. It appears that the points form a straight line. However, we must prove that these points lie in the same straight line. This can be done using the slope of a line. For points to be collinear, they must lie on the same straight line. Therefore, the slope between any two points must be the same.

For the points (4, 3) and (8, 1):

$$m = \frac{1 - 3}{8 - 4}$$
$$= -\frac{1}{2}$$

For the points (8, 1) and (10, 0):

$$m = \frac{0 - 1}{10 - 8}$$
$$= -\frac{1}{2}$$

Therefore, the points lie on the same straight line and are collinear.

From this result, any linear equation can be plotted by finding just two points satisfying the relation and drawing a straight line through those two points.

Example 2

Draw the graph of this relation.
$\{(x, y) \mid x + 3y = 6, x, y \in R\}$

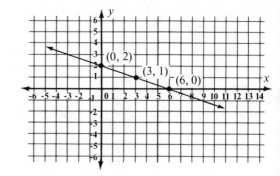

Generally, the easiest points to find in a linear equation are the x-intercept and the y-intercept. For the equation $x + 3y = 6$: if $x = 0$, then $y = 2$; and if $y = 0$, then $x = 6$. Therefore, the intercepts are the ordered pairs (0, 2) and (6, 0).

As a check of the calculations, a third point can be plotted on the grid to show that the line joining the intercepts also passes through the new point. One possibility is the point (3, 1).

198

Exercises

1. Define the term "collinear". Show that these points are collinear.
a. (1, 1), (2, 2), (3, 3), …
b. (0, 2), (3, 2), (4, 2), …
c. (−3, 4), (0, 2), (3, 0), …

2. Identify a third point on the line passing through the ordered pairs (−3, 1) and (5, 0).

3. Find each.
 i) the x-intercept
 ii) the y-intercept
 iii) a third ordered pair on the line
a. $y = 6x − 12$ **b.** $4x − y = 8$
c. $2x − 6y = 12$ **d.** $6x + 4y = 20$

4. Identify the linear equations in this set of equations. Justify your answer.
a. $y = 2x − 5$ **b.** $x − 3y = 7$
c. $6x^2 − y = 2$ **d.** $x = 3$
e. $xy + 3 = 9$ **f.** $4x − 5y + 1 = 0$

5. Graph these equations.
a. $y = x + 4$ **b.** $x + 3y = 15$
c. $2x − y = 8$ **d.** $4x − 3y = 16$

6. Graph each equation.
 i) Before attempting to plot the graph, identify each as linear or non-linear.
 ii) Explain whether or not the decimal and fractional coefficient determine linearity.
a. $0.5x − 3.1y = 15.25$
b. $\frac{4}{3}x + \frac{1}{2}y = 13\frac{1}{4}$

7. Find the x-intercept and the y-intercept of each relation. Use a calculator if one is available.
a. $\{(x, y) \mid 1.65x − 37.05y = 14.20\}$
b. $\{(x, y) \mid 0.07x + 1.3y − 42 = 0\}$
c. Can the x- and y-intercepts be used to plot a relation?

8. Identify one other point on each line.

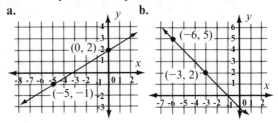

9. The equation $m = 6 + 0.2n$ describes the total mass, m, in kilograms of a crate containing n oranges.
a. Graph the relation defined by the equation.
b. Is this a set of continuous points?
c. What is the mass of the crate when it is empty?

Historical Note

Ada Byron Lovelace (1815-1852)
Augusta Ada Byron Lovelace was born on December 10, 1815. Her mother, Annabella, had a strong interest in and an aptitude for mathematics, and many of her friends recognized this ability in young Ada. In fact, Ada's understanding of mathematics was so great that she was invited to see Charles Babbage's Difference Engine, the first calculator, when it was first demonstrated. Sophia DeMorgan, the wife of mathematician Augustus DeMorgan, described the demonstration in this manner: "While the rest of the party gaped at this beautiful instrument with the same sort of expressions and feeling that savages are said to have shown on first seeing the looking glass, Miss Byron, as young as she was (18 at the time), understood its workings and saw the great beauty of the invention."

By the mid-twentieth century, Charles Babbage would be recognized as a founder of modern computers, and Ada Byron Lovelace as the first person to detail the process known as computer programming.

Ada Byron Lovelace described a math game called **Solitaire**. Describe how this game is played by researching the life of Ada Byron Lovelace in your library.

9·5 Graphing Linear Equations II

In the previous section, it was shown that the slope between any two ordered pairs on a straight line is constant. This suggests that a linear relation can be defined by its slope and one ordered pair on the graph.

Example 1

Graph the linear relation defined by the equation $y = 2x + 4$. Find the slope of this line and describe any unique relationships that exist.

This is a linear relation because the terms do not have a degree greater than one. Therefore, the x-intercept and the y-intercept can be used to plot the graph. In this case, the intercepts are given by the ordered pairs $(-2, 0)$ and $(0, 4)$.

$$m = \frac{4 - 0}{0 + 2}$$
$$= 2$$

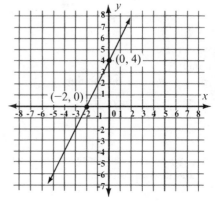

This graph has a slope of 2, which is the numeric coefficient of the variable x; and a y-intercept of 4, which is the constant term.

> A linear relation is defined by the equation $y = mx + b$, where m is the slope of the line and b is the y-intercept.

Example 2

Using the y-intercept and the slope, graph the equation $y = -2x + 3$.

From the equation, the slope is equal to -2 and the y-intercept is 3.

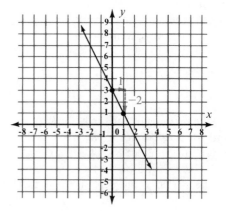

Exercises

1. Identify the slope and one point on each line.

a.   **b.**

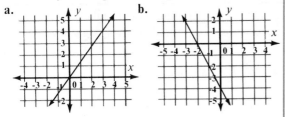

2. Draw the graph of the lines having the given slope and passing through the given point.

a. slope = 3; point (4, 1)

b. slope = 1; point (−2, −3)

c. slope = −2; point (2, 0)

d. slope = $-\frac{3}{2}$; point (0, −1)

e. slope = 0; point (4, 3)

3. Find the y-intercept of each line. Explain how you arrived at your answer.

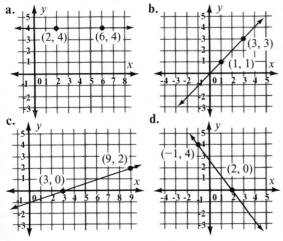

4. Identify the slope and the y-intercept of each line. Graph each line.

a. $y = 3x + 2$ **b.** $y = -4x + 6$ **c.** $y = \frac{3}{5}x - 2.5$

d. $y = 5x$ **e.** $y = -2$ **f.** $x = 7$

5. Graph each equation. Verify that the slope is the numeric coefficient of x and that the y-intercept is the constant.

a. $y = 5x - 2$ **b.** $y = \frac{3}{2}x + 5$ **c.** $y = 0.6x - 5.2$

6. Identify each of the lines in this diagram by a point and a slope.

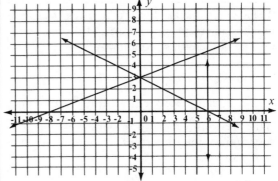

7. The population of Pembroke is presently 25 000. It will increase each year by 500 people.

a. Graph the relation that pairs the total population, p, and the number of years, y.

b. Find the slope of this line.

8. Nadia started a savings account with $50 and she plans to add $15 to it each week.

a. Graph the linear relation that pairs the number of weeks, w, with the total amount saved, s.

b. What is the slope of this graph?

9. A reducing clinic promised that Pat, whose mass is 154 kg, would lose 2.5 kg/month.

a. Graph the linear relation that pairs the total mass of Pat, t, with the number of months, m.

b. Calculate the slope of the line and explain how the slope relates to the situation.

10. A linear relation has a slope of $\frac{1}{2}$ and passes through the point (2, 3). Construct the graph of this relation. In your own words, describe the process that you used.

Braintickler

Brian and Trevor both ran up a moving escalator. Brian took 3 steps at a time and Trevor took 2 steps at a time. Trevor took 24 steps to reach the top; Brian took 30. If each of them moved at a constant rate, then how many steps are visible when the escalator is stopped?

9·6 Writing Linear Equations

We have seen that any linear relation can be graphed using either two points from the relation, the slope and the y-intercept, or the slope and any one point. The equation of the line also can be determined from any one of these three conditions.

Example 1

Find an equation for the straight line with a slope of -3 and a y-intercept of 5.

In the previous section, the general equation of a straight line was given by $y = mx + b$, where m is the slope and b is the y-intercept. Therefore, the equation of the line can be found by substituting values.
$\therefore y = -3x + 5$

Example 2

A botanist treated a plant with a special type of fertilizer. She recorded the height of the plant in centimetres after 2 d, 4 d, and 6 d. Find an equation for the growth rate of the plant if the treatment was continued indefinitely.

x	y
2	3
4	6
6	9

In order to find an equation of the line, it must be linear. Therefore, the slope of the line must be constant throughout. By finding the slope between the ordered pairs, we can verify that the slope of the line will be $\frac{3}{2}$.

The equation of a line relates the two variables at one point in time. Therefore, it must take into account all possibilities.
Let (x, y) represent any point on the line.
Since the slope of the line is constant, the slope from any point to (x, y) must also be constant.

Therefore, $\dfrac{3}{2} = \dfrac{y - 3}{x - 2}$

> The point (2, 3) was used for slope in this case. Any of the other points could have been used.

$$3(x - 2) = 2(y - 3)$$

> Cross multiply.

$$3x - 6 = 2y - 6$$
$$3x = 2y$$
$$y = \frac{3}{2}x$$

What does this equation imply about the x-intercept and the y-intercept?

Example 3

Find an equation for the line passing through the point $(2, -4)$ which has a slope of $-\frac{3}{4}$.

Let (x, y) represent any point on the line.
$$\therefore \frac{-3}{4} = \frac{y + 4}{x - 2}$$
$$-3(x - 2) = 4(y + 4)$$
$$-3x - 10 = 4y$$
$$-\frac{3}{4}x - \frac{5}{2} = y$$

Exercises

1. Let (x, y) represent any point on the line. Find the equation of the line passing through the given point which has the indicated slope.

a. $(4, 1)$; 2 **b.** $(-1, 6)$; -7

c. $(-3, 1)$; $\frac{1}{2}$ **d.** $(5, -2)$; $-\frac{3}{4}$

2. Find an equation of a line passing through these points.

a. $(0, 0)$ and $(6, 5)$ **b.** $(5, 1)$ and $(7, 3)$
c. $(-4, 2)$ and $(5, 1)$ **d.** $(-7, -3)$ and $(3, 0)$
e. $(-6, -5)$ and $(1, -1)$ **f.** $(-5, -5)$ and $(-3, 4)$
g. $(-3, -12)$ and $(-1, -5)$ **h.** $(4, -1)$ and $(4, 7)$
i. $(2, 0)$ and $(8, 0)$ **j.** $(0, -3)$ and $(0, 6)$
k. $(-4.7, 3)$ and $(2.1, 3)$

l. $\left(\frac{1}{2}, \frac{2}{3}\right)$ and $\left(\frac{3}{4}, \frac{4}{5}\right)$

3. Find an equation for each line. Express your equation in the form $y = mx + b$.

a. slope $= 1$; passing through $(0, 5)$
b. slope $= -3$; passing through $(-3, 2)$
c. slope $= 0$; passing through $(1, -4)$
d. slope $= -\frac{1}{2}$; passing through $(-3, -2)$
e. slope $= 3$; y-intercept is -3
f. passing through the ordered pairs $(0, 0)$ and $(1, 2)$
g. parallel to the x-axis and passing through the ordered pair $(4, 3.5)$

4. Find an equation for each of these straight lines.

a. passing through the ordered pairs $(-3, 1.7)$ and $(8, 6.2)$
b. has an x-intercept of 9 and passing through the ordered pair $(-2, 5)$
c. passing through the point $(3, -4)$ and is parallel to the line $y = x$
d. the line that passes through the points (x, y) and (x_1, y_1) and has a slope of m. This is another general form for the equation of a straight line.

5. Find an equation for each line.

a. the x-axis   **b.** the y-axis

6. The table shows a linear relationship between an increase in pollution measured in parts per million from water samples, p, and the length of time the increase took measured in months, m. Write an equation for this relation.

p	2	5.4	8.8
m	2	4	6

7. Selkirk High School makes a cold punch for the Open House. The amount made is determined by a formula involving the temperature on the given day. Last year the temperature was 20°C and they made 480 cups. The year before it was 24°C and they made 556 cups. The formula is a linear equation involving the number of cups, c, and the temperature in degrees Celsius, t.

a. Use the data from the last two years to write an equation relating c and t.
b. How many cups should be prepared this year if the temperature is predicted to be 16°C?

8. The annual cost of operating a car is determined by a linear equation describing the partial variation between the cost, c, and the number of kilometres driven, k, in thousands. The cost of operating a car for 18 000 km is $3235; and the cost of operating a car for 23 000 km is $3885.

a. Find a linear equation that defines this relationship.
b. How many kilometres must be driven for the annual cost to be $3469?

9. The cost of taking a team of 17 players to a tournament is $507.50. For 22 players the cost is $620.00. The relation between the cost and the number of players is linear.

a. Write an equation to describe this relation.
b. Find the cost of taking 19 players.

10. Find an equation for the line containing the median of this triangle and passing through the vertex at $(1, 2)$.

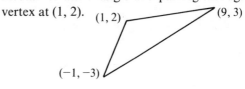

$(1, 2)$ $(9, 3)$

$(-1, -3)$

9·7 Families of Lines

A set of linear equations having either one point or a slope in common is called a **family of lines**.

Example 1

The set of lines shown in the graph all cross the y-axis at one point. Describe this family of lines with a general equation.

There are many other lines that pass through the point $(0, 5)$ other than the ones shown here. All the lines in this family have a different slope. Since the slope varies, but the y-intercept is constant at 5, the family of lines can be characterized by this equation: $y = mx + 5$, $m \in R$.

In this instance, the variable m is used as a **parameter**. A parameter is assigned any value to identify one particular member of the family.

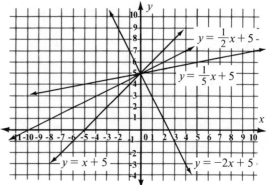

Example 2

Find an equation for the family of lines that share the point $(4, 3)$.

Let (x, y) represent any point on all members of this family of lines.
$$\therefore m = \frac{y - 3}{x - 4}$$
$$m(x - 4) = y - 3$$
$$y = m(x - 4) + 3$$

In this case, m is used as the parameter.

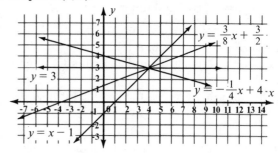

Example 3

Graph three members of the family of lines described by the equation $y = 2x + b$.

This equation describes the infinite family of lines having a common slope of 2, and each member having a different y-intercept. In this case, the y-intercept, b, is the parameter.

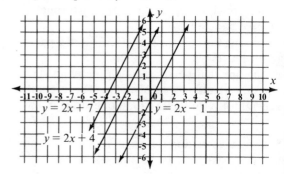

Exercises

1. Graph three examples of members from each family of lines. Describe the parameter in each case.

a. $y = mx$ **b.** $y = mx + 2$

c. $y = mx - 3$ **d.** $y = 4x + b$

e. $y = -\frac{1}{2}x + b$ **f.** $y = b$

2. Write an equation for the family of lines having these characteristics.

a. a slope of 2 **b.** a slope of $-\frac{5}{3}$

c. a slope of 0 **d.** a slope that is undefined

e. a y-intercept of -4 **f.** a y-intercept of 0

3. Write an equation for the family of lines sharing the common point.

a. $(2, 1)$ **b.** $(-3, 1)$ **c.** $(0, 3)$

d. $(4, 0)$ **e.** $(2\frac{3}{4}, \frac{1}{2})$ **f.** $(-1, -1)$

4. Write an equation for the family of lines parallel to the x-axis.

5. Write an equation for the family of vertical lines.

6. Identify the parameter in each equation.

a. $y = mx - 2$ **b.** $y - 5 = m(x + 3)$

c. $y = 4x + b$ **d.** $x = a$

7. Write an equation for any one particular member of the family of lines in each.

a. Exercise 2, part **b** **b.** Exercise 3, part **a**

c. Exercise 6, part **c** **d.** Exercise 4

e. Exercise 5 **f.** Exercise 8, part **b**

8. In your own words, describe how each family of lines would appear when they are graphed.

a. $y = kx$ **b.** $x + y = c$

c. $4x + 2y = k$ **d.** $px - 7y = 13$

e. $y = a$ **f.** $y = m(x + 6) - 8$

g. $y - 5 = m(x - 1)$ **h.** $y = m(x - 7)$

9. Write an equation to identify the family of lines shown in each graph.

a.
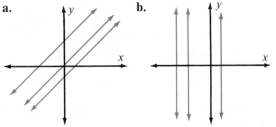

b.

10. Write an equation describing each family of lines.

a.
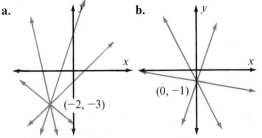

b.

$(-2, -3)$

$(0, -1)$

11. Write an equation for the family of parallel lines that are perpendicular to the line $6x - 5y - 1 = 0$.

12. Write an equation for the family of lines so that they can all be a diameter of this circle.

$\bullet\ (4, 3)$

13. List five possible points of intersection of the family of lines described by the equation $x = a$ with any five members of the family of lines described by the equation $y = 3x + b$.

Braintickler

A missile travelling at 0.8 the speed of light leaves Earth for Pluto. Four minutes later a missile from Pluto leaves for Earth travelling at 0.7 the speed of light. Which of the two planets are the missiles closer to when they meet if the two planets are at a maximum separation distance?

9·8 The General Linear Equation: $Ax + By + C = 0$

Mathematics can be described as a language. It is a method for communicating ideas precisely and accurately. Once the symbols are understood, you can communicate with anyone around the world.

Throughout this chapter, we have been finding the equation of a straight line in the form $y = mx + b$. This form of the equation is extremely useful when information about the slope and the y-intercept is either given or required. However, when the slope and the y-intercept are not a major concern, a linear equation can be expressed in the form $Ax + By + C = 0$.

Example 1

Convert the equation $y = 6x - 5$ from the $y = mx + b$ form to the form $Ax + By + C = 0$ and identify the values for A, B, and C.

$y = 6x - 5$
$0 = 6x - 5 - y$ Subtract y from both sides.
$0 = 6x - y - 5$
$\therefore A = 6$, $B = -1$, and $C = -5$.

Notice the signs on the values for A, B, and C.

Example 2

Graph the equation $2x + 3y + 12 = 0$.

This is a linear equation since none of the terms have a degree higher than one. Therefore, the graph of this equation can be found by plotting two points and drawing a straight line through those two points. This case is not different from the equations of the form $y = mx + b$. Therefore, the x-intercept and the y-intercept can be used.

Let $x = 0$.
$\therefore 3y + 12 = 0$
$\quad y = -4$

Let $y = 0$.
$\therefore 2x + 12 = 0$
$\quad x = -6$

Therefore, two points on this graph are $(0, -4)$ and $(-6, 0)$.

A third point on the graph could be found as a check for your graph. That point also would have to be on the line. This can be found by substituting a value for one variable into the equation and solving the equation to find the value for the other variable.

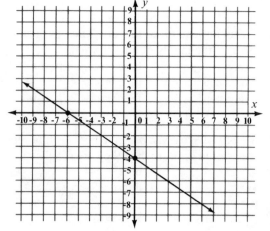

206

Exercises

1. Identify the values for A, B, and C in each equation.

a. $5x - 2y + 9 = 0$ **b.** $2x + y - 3 = 0$
c. $7x - 3y = 0$ **d.** $x - y + 1 = 0$
e. $2x - 5 = 0$ **f.** $3y = 17$

2. Find three ordered pairs that satisfy each equation in Exercise 1. Give two ways in which you can tell that each equation is linear.

3. Express each equation in the form $Ax + By + C = 0$. Identify the values for $A, B,$ and C in each.

a. $y = 3x - 7$ **b.** $y = -x - 7$
c. $3y - 2 = -5x$ **d.** $x - y = 13$
e. $2x - 12 = 0$ **f.** $4y = 20$
g. $y = \frac{3}{4}x + \frac{9}{4}$ **h.** $y = \frac{-2}{3}x - \frac{4}{5}$

4. Graph each equation on the same coordinate grid. In your own words, describe the family of lines generated by these three equations.

a. $2x + 9y = 0$
b. $6x - 4y = 0$
c. $0.6x - 2.1y = 0$

5. Graph each equation on the same coordinate grid. In your own words, describe the family of lines generated by these three equations.

a. $5x + 2 = 0$
b. $-7x - 10 = 0$
c. $0.2x - 13.5 = 0$

6. Graph each equation on the same coordinate grid. In your own words, describe the family of lines generated by these three equations.

a. $5y + 2 = 0$
b. $-12y - 40 = 0$
c. $5.6y - 70.65 = 0$

7. Describe the family of lines generated by the graphs of linear equations in the form $Ax + By + C = 0$ when both A and C are 0.

8. Determine the slope of each line.

a. $5x + 2y + 9 = 0$
b. $-3x + y - 12 = 0$
c. $7x - 3y - 1 = 0$

9. Given the equation $Ax + By + C = 0$, find an equation for the slope of a line. (*Hint:* Rewrite this equation in the form $y = mx + b$.)

10. Find the y-intercept of each line.

a. $9x + 3y + 15 = 0$
b. $6x - 2y + 8 = 0$
c. $-5x - 6y - 10 = 0$

11. Given the equation $Ax + By + C = 0$, find an equation for the y-intercept of the line. (*Hint:* Let $x = 0$ and isolate the variable y.)

12. Find the x-intercept of each line.

a. $5x + 2y + 18 = 0$
b. $11x - 3y + 55 = 0$
c. $-x - 3y + 16 = 0$

13. Given the equation $Ax + By + C = 0$, find an equation for the x-intercept of the line. (*Hint:* Let $y = 0$ and isolate the variable x.)

14. A spiral spring with a 10 kg mass attached to the end stretches 22 cm. With a 20 kg mass, the same spring stretches 28 cm. Use this data to write a linear equation in the form $Ax + By + C = 0$ describing the relation between the mass and the length the spring stretches.

15. Use the information given in the graphs to find an equation in the form $Ax + By + C = 0$ for each line.

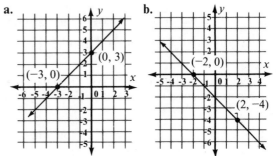

207

9·9 Parallel and Perpendicular Lines

Recall that parallel lines belong to the family of lines that have equal slopes; while perpendicular lines belong to the family of lines whose slopes are negative reciprocals.

Example 1

Find an equation of the line passing through $(5, -2)$ and parallel to the line $3x - 5y + 1 = 0$. Since the two lines are parallel, they both have the same slopes. Therefore, the slope of the required line is $\frac{3}{5}$. Can you verify this?

Let (x, y) represent any point on the required line.

$$\frac{3}{5} = \frac{y + 2}{x - 5}$$

Equation for the slope of a line.

$$3(x - 5) = 5(y + 2)$$
$$3x - 15 = 5y + 10$$
$$3x - 5y - 25 = 0$$

Notice that the only difference between the two equations is found in the "C" term. This is a result of the lines being parallel.

Example 2

Find an equation of the line passing through the point $(5, -1)$ and perpendicular to the line $x - 3y - 8 = 0$.

Since these two lines are perpendicular, the slopes are negative reciprocals.
Therefore, the slope of the required line is -3.
Let (x, y) represent any point on the required line.

$$-3 = \frac{y + 1}{x - 5}$$
$$-3(x - 5) = y + 1$$
$$0 = 3x + y - 14$$

Exercises

1. Verify that the line passing through $(2, 7)$ and $(8, -2)$ is perpendicular to the line passing through the points $(-5, -4)$ and $(5, 2)$.

2. Find an equation of a line passing through $(1, 1)$ and parallel to the line with a slope of $-\frac{2}{5}$.

3. Find an equation of a line passing through $(0, 4)$ and perpendicular to the line $5x - 7y + 2 = 0$.

4. Use a graph to find equations for four lines that will intersect to form a rhombus.

5. Find the equations for the two lines containing the diameters of this circle.

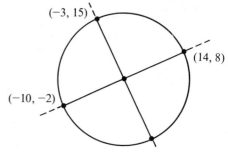

6. Determine whether the altitude AD passes through the point $(-1, 6)$ in the interior of $\triangle ABC$ where $A(6, -2)$, $B(-6, 3)$, and $C(2, 10)$.

9·10 Systems of Linear Equations

A **system of equations** is a set of two (or more) equations. Solving a system of equations involves finding the value of the variables that satisfy both equations. One way of solving a system of equations is graphically. Drawing the graphs of the equations on the same grid will yield a point of intersection. This point will be a solution to the system of equations.

Example

Spacequest is travelling on a course defined by the equation $x + 2y - 10 = 0$ for a rendezvous with Outermath. Outermath is travelling on a course defined by the equation $2x + y - 11 = 0$. At what point will the two spacecrafts rendezvous?

These two equations are shown on the grid. They intersect at the point (4, 3). Therefore, the two spacecrafts will intersect at the point (4, 3).

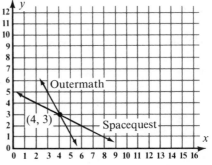

Exercises

1. Determine the point of intersection of these pairs of linear equations by graphing.

a. $x = 5$; $y = x$ **b.** $x = -3$; $y = 4$
c. $x = 2$; $y = 5x - 1$ **d.** $y = x$; $y = -2x - 6$
e. $y = 7x - 4$; $y = -7x - 4$

f. $y = 2.75x + 12$; $y = \frac{1}{4}x + 2$

g. $x + 2y - 8 = 0$; $3x - y - 3 = 0$
h. $x - y - 3 = 0$; $x + y - 5 = 0$
i. $3x + 4y = 16$; $x - 2y = 2$
j. $2x + y - 7 = 0$; $x - 2y - 1 = 0$

2. Without graphing, select from this list a pair of lines that will not intersect. Explain the reason for your choice.

a. $x = 7$ **b.** $y = x$
c. $y = -5$ **d.** $y = -2x + 3$
e. $y = 5x + 1$ **f.** $2x + y - 1 = 0$
g. $x - y + 4 = 0$ **h.** $x - y - 1 = 0$

3. Find an equation of a line that will intersect the line $y = 4x - 2$ on the y-axis. Explain how you arrived at your answer.

4. Find an equation of a line that will intersect the line $7x - 3y = 0$ at the origin. Explain how you arrived at your answer.

5. Find a system of two linear equations that will intersect at these points.
a. $(0, -2)$ **b.** $(3, 0)$ **c.** $(1, 4)$ **d.** $(-3, 5)$

6. The system of $y = 3$ and $y = x^2 - 1$ includes a linear equation and a non-linear equation. Use a graph to determine the two solutions to this system.

7. Graph this system of two non-linear equations to determine the number of solutions. Identify the solutions from the graph.
$y = x^2$ and $x^2 + y = 2$

9·11 Solution by Substitution

When graphing a system of equations does not produce a clear or obvious solution, another process must be used to solve the problem. The solution to a system of equations also can be found using **substitution**. The expression for one of the variables obtained from one of the equations is substituted into the other equation.

Example 1

Solve this system of equations. $\quad 4x - 3y = 6$
$$2x - y = 4$$

Understand the Problem
We must find the values for x and y that satisfy each equation.

Develop a Plan
Use the process of substitution to solve for both variables in each equation.

Carry Out the Plan
$4x - 3y = 6$ ① The equations are numbered
$\quad 2x - y = 4$ ② for reference.
From ②, $y = 2x - 4$. ③
Substitute this expression for y in equation ①.
$4x - 3(2x - 4) = 6$
$\quad 4x - 6x + 12 = 6$
$\qquad -2x = -6$
$\qquad\quad x = 3$
Substitute $x = 3$ into equation ③.
$y = 2(3) - 4$
$\quad = 2$

Look Back
The solution to the system is the point (3, 2). This can be verified graphically.

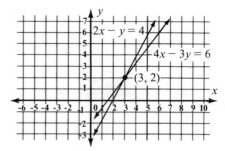

Example 2

A popular math book is to be translated from French into English. The cost for the translation is given by the equation $C = F + Wn$, where F is the fixed cost, W is the translation cost per word, and n is the number of words to be translated. If the cost for translation is $200 for 600 words and $300 for 1400 words, then find the cost of translating a 5000-word chapter.

$200 = F + 600W$ ①
$300 = F + 1400W$ ②
From ①, $F = 200 - 600W$. ③
Substitute the expression for F from ③ into equation ②.
$\quad 300 = 200 - 600W + 1400W$
$\quad 100 = 800W$
$0.125 = W$
Substitute $W = 0.125$ into ①.
$200 = F + 600(0.125)$
$125 = F$

The fixed cost is $125 and the cost of translating each word is $0.125. Therefore, $C = 125 + 0.125n$. To find the cost of translating 5000 words, substitute 5000 for n.
$C = 125 + 0.125(5000)$
$\quad = 750$

The translation cost is $750.

210

Exercises

1. When solving a pair of linear equations, what are you trying to find?

2. In your own words, explain how the method of substitution works when solving a system of two equations and two unknowns.

3. In the Look Back section of the problem-solving model, the solution to the system can be verified by another method other than graphically. The values for the variables can be substituted into both of the equations to see if the left side of the equation equals the right side of the equation in each case. Verify, other than graphically, that the point $(3, 2)$ is a solution to the pair of equations solved in Example 1.

4. In Exercise 3, explain what is wrong if your values for the variables satisfy the first equation but not the second equation.

5. Solve and verify your solution for the variables.

a. $7x - y = 3$
$y = 18$

b. $4x - y = -5$
$3x - y = 7$

c. $x + y = 3$
$x - y = 5$

d. $x + 2y = 6$
$-2x + y = 8$

e. $2x - y = 1$
$x + y = 5$

f. $6x + y = 1$
$2x + y = -3$

6. Find an equation for each of the lines in the graph. Find the point of intersection and verify that the result is reasonable by first estimating the point of intersection using the graph.

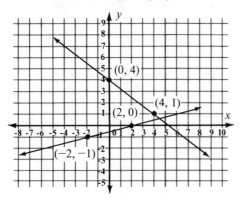

7. Which pair of linear equations has a solution of $(1, 3)$?

a. $x + 2y = 7$
$2x + 3y = 11$

b. $3x + 4y = 15$
$2x - y = -2$

c. $x - y = -2$
$5x - 5y = -10$

d. $4x - 5y = -9$
$x + y = 4$

8. Solve. Verify your answer either graphically or by substitution.

a. $3x + 6y = 4$
$x - 2y = 48$

b. $3x + 2y = -1$
$x - 3y = 7$

c. $x + 2y = 0$
$3x + 4y = 6$

d. $2x + 3y = 7$
$3x - y = 5$

e. $2x + 3y = -22$
$3x - 2y = 6$

f. $2x + 3y = 4$
$4x + 5y = 3$

9. Solve. Verify your answer.

a. $4x + 3y - 10 = 0$
$5x - 7y + 52 = 0$

b. $6x - 5y - 2 = 0$
$4x + 3y - 14 = 0$

10. Find the solution for each.

a. $\{(x, y) \mid 2x + 5y = 4 \text{ and } 4x - y = 8, x, y \in R\}$

b. $\{(x, y) \mid 7x - 9y = 0 \text{ and } x - y = 2, x, y \in R\}$

11. A desk clerk is paid every week according to the equation $P = F + Rn$, where P is the amount the desk clerk is paid, F is the fixed rate of income for the first 35 h, R is the rate of pay for each hour of overtime worked, and n is the number of hours of overtime that the desk clerk works. During the last two weeks, the desk clerk worked 45 h and 52 h and received \$375 and \$417 respectively.

a. Find the fixed wage for the first 35 h and the overtime rate per hour.

b. Find how much pay will be received for 57 h of work.

c. Find how many hours must be worked in order to receive \$549.

12. Solve for the variables. Verify each answer.

a. $\dfrac{x}{2} + \dfrac{y}{2} = 7$
$\dfrac{2x}{3} + \dfrac{3y}{4} = 10$

b. $\dfrac{2x}{3} - \dfrac{4y}{5} = -2$
$3x - 2y = -4$

211

9·12 Solution by Elimination

A system of equations can be solved using **elimination**.

Example 1

Solve. Verify the solution. $3x + y = 9$
$$2x + y = 7$$

Understand the Problem
We must solve for x and y so that they satisfy both equations simultaneously.

Carry Out the Plan
$3x + y = 9$ ①
$2x + y = 7$ ②
Since the numerical coefficients of the y-terms are the same in both equations, subtract equation ② from equation ① to eliminate the variable y and solve for x.

$$\begin{array}{r} 3x + y = 9 \text{ ①} \\ \text{Subtract.} \quad 2x + y = 7 \text{ ②} \\ \hline 1x + 0y = 2 \text{ ③} \end{array}$$

$\therefore x = 2$
Substitute $x = 2$ into equation ②. $2(2) + y = 7$
$$y = 3$$

Develop a Plan
We will subtract one equation from the other to eliminate the y-variable.

Look Back
The solution to these two equations is the ordered pair (2, 3).
Verify.
$3(2) + 3 = 9$
$2(2) + 3 = 7$
Since these two equations are both true, the solution checks.

Example 2

Solve. $3x - 4y = -6$
$$2x + 3y = 13$$

Understand the Problem
We must solve the two equations to find the values for x and y that satisfy both equations.

Carry Out the Plan
$3x - 4y = -6$ ①
$2x + 3y = 13$ ②
Since neither the numerical coefficients of the variable x nor the variable y are the same, subtracting the equations will not yield one equation and one unknown.

$$\begin{array}{rl} \text{① } \times 2 & 6x - 8y = -12 \text{ ③} \\ \text{② } \times 3 & 6x + 9y = 39 \text{ ④} \\ \hline \text{Subtract.} & 0x - 17y = -51 \end{array}$$

Multiply so the literal coefficients are the same.

$\therefore y = 3$
Substitute $y = 3$ into equation ②. $2x + 3(3) = 13$
$$x = 2$$

Develop a Plan
Write equivalent numerical coefficients so the x-coefficients are the same and eliminate them.

Look Back
The solution to these two equations is the ordered pair (2, 3).
$3(2) - 4(3) = -6$
$2(2) + 3(3) = 13$

Since these two equations are both true, the solution checks.

Exercises

1. Which of these pairs of equations have a solution of $(-2, -1)$?

a. $x + 2y = 5$
$3x - y = 1$

b. $-2x + y = 3$
$5x - 3y = -7$

c. $4x - y = -7$
$3x - y = -5$

d. $x + y = -3$
$x - y = -1$

2. Solve. Use the method of elimination. Explain which variable you are solving for first and why.

a. $3x + 2y = 5$
$2x + 2y = 4$

b. $x + 5y = 11$
$2x + 5y = 12$

c. $3x - 4y = 8$
$5x - 4y = 8$

d. $2x - 3y = -6$
$2x - 5y = -26$

3. Write an equivalent equation with an x-coefficient of 8.

a. $x + 3y = 9$
b. $2x + 8y = 1$
c. $16x - 24y = 32$

4. Solve. Use the method of elimination. (*Hint:* Look for opposite integers.)

a. $2x - y = 9$
$5x + y = 26$

b. $-3x - 2y = 13$
$3x + 5y = -19$

c. $7x - 5y = -27$
$-3x + 5y = 23$

d. $\frac{1}{2}x - y = 4$
$-\frac{1}{2}x - 3y = 4$

5. Explain two ways of verifying your answers to Exercises 1 and 2. Use both methods to verify your solution to Exercise 1, part **d**.

6. Solve. Use the method of elimination and verify your solutions. Explain which variable you are eliminating and why.

a. $7x + 6y = -22$
$x + 8y = -4$

b. $4x - 2y = 14$
$2x + 4y = 22$

c. $2x - 3y = 10$
$3x - y = 1$

d. $5x - 4y = -22$
$3x + 8y = 18$

7. Solve.

a. $5x + 3y = 31$
$3x - 5y = -29$

b. $7x + 5y = 3$
$3x - 2y = -11$

c. $3x - 2y = 4$
$2x + 3y = 7$

d. $4x + 3y = 3$
$3x - 2y = -19$

8. A car depreciates in value as it gets older according to the equation $V = I - Dn$, where V is the present value of the car, I is the initial value of the car, D is the depreciation per year, and n is the age of the car measured in years. If a car is worth $6200 after 2 a, and $1800 after 7 a, then find each.
a. How much money was spent to purchase the car.
b. How much the car could reasonably be sold for after 5 a.

9. These three lines intersect to form a triangle.
a. Find the vertices of the triangle.
b. Show that this is a right triangle.

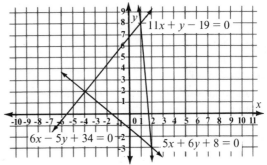

10. Find the point of intersection of the diagonals of this trapezoid.

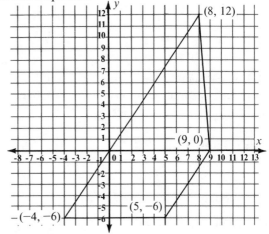

11. A cyclist in a 3 d race begins the last day 18 km behind the leader. Reports indicate that the leader is holding a 36 km/h pace. If the cyclist plans to average 40 km/h, how long will it take to catch the leader?

213

9·13 Solution by Comparison

Two methods for solving pairs of linear equations have been introduced so far. A third method involves the elimination of a variable by comparing two identical equations obtained from the original equations.

Example 1

Solve. $3x + y = 1$
$\qquad 4x - 2y = 8$

Understand the Problem
We must solve the two equations for the variables x and y.

Develop a Plan
Both equations can be rewritten in the form $y = mx + b$. Using the transitive property, these two equations can then be compared to solve for x.

Carry Out the Plan
$3x + y = 1$ ①
$4x - 2y = 8$ ②
From equation ①, $y = -3x + 1$. ③
From equation ②, $y = 2x - 4$.   ④
From equations ③ and ④,
$-3x + 1 = 2x - 4$
$\qquad -5x = -5$
$\qquad\quad x = 1$
Substitute into equation ② to obtain $y = -2$.

Look Back
The solution to these equations is the ordered pair $(1, -2)$.
Verify.
$3(1) + (-2) = 1$
$4(1) - 2(-2) = 8$

Since these two equations are both true, the ordered pair $(1, -2)$ is the solution to the system of equations.

Example 2

Solve. $2x + 3y = 9$
$\qquad 3x - 2y = 7$

Understand the Problem
Solve the system of equations for the variables x and y.

Develop a Plan
Use the method of comparison to express one of the variables in terms of the other, and then compare the two equations.

Carry Out the Plan
$2x + 3y = 9$ ①
$3x - 2y = 7$ ②
From equation ①, $x = \dfrac{9 - 3y}{2}$. ③

From equation ②, $x = \dfrac{7 + 2y}{3}$. ④

$\dfrac{9 - 3y}{2} = \dfrac{7 + 2y}{3}$

$3(9 - 3y) = 2(7 + 2y)$ ⟨Cross multiply.⟩
$27 - 9y = 14 + 4y$
$\qquad\quad y = 1$
Substitute into equation ③ to obtain $x = 3$.

Look Back
The solution to the system is the ordered pair $(3, 1)$.
Verify:
$2(3) + 3(1) = 9$
$3(3) - 2(1) = 7$

Since these two equations are both true, the ordered pair $(3, 1)$ is the solution to the system of equations.

214

Exercises

1. In your own words, outline the process of solution by comparison for two linear equations.

2. When solving two linear equations by the process of comparison, does it matter whether x is expressed in terms of y or that y is expressed in terms of x? Explain.

3. Consider the equations $x + y = 3$ and $2x + 2y = 8$. Using the process of comparison to solve the two equations, show that there is no possible solution to the pair of equations. Refer to the graphs of each equation and explain why there is no point of intersection.

4. Explain how you would recognize that a pair of linear equations has no solution.

5. Solve using the method of comparison. Verify your answers.

a. $x + 2y = 3$
   $2x + 6y = 8$

b. $3x - y = 9$
   $2x - 2y = 2$

c. $4x + y = 0$
   $6x - 5y = -13$

d. $3x - 6y = 4$
   $5x + 4y = 2$

6. Solve using the method of comparison. Verify your answers.

a. $x + y = 4$
   $2x + y = 8$

b. $3x - 2y = 8$
   $x + 3y = -1$

c. $7x + 4y = -17$
   $4x + 3y = -9$

d. $-2x - 4y = 18$
   $4x - y = -9$

7. Slapstick Manufacturing will make hockey sticks to order. They charge the purchaser according to the equation $C = F + Hn$, where C is the cost in dollars to the purchaser, F is the fixed manufacturing cost, H is the cost per hockey stick, and n is the number of sticks ordered. Two players on a team order 30 sticks and 42 sticks and were charged $378 and $435 respectively. If a player has $415 to spend on hockey sticks, then how many sticks can be purchased?

8. Find the ordered pair described by each set.
a. $\{(x, y) \mid 2x - y = 5 \text{ and } 3x + 2y = 11, x, y \in R\}$
b. $\{(x, y) \mid -x - y = 3 \text{ and } -2x - 4y = 14, x, y \in R\}$

9. A special type of transmission for a racing car cost $350 000 to develop and an additional $15 000 to manufacture each engine. Once completed, each transmission sells for $40 000.
a. Graphically find how many transmissions must be sold for the manufacturer to break even.
b. Find the equations of the two lines in your solution to part **a**.
c. Verify that the point of intersection is correct by solving the two equations using the process of comparison.

10. Determine the equation of each line.
a. parallel to the line $y = 3x - 2$ and passing through the point of intersection of the two lines $2x + 3y = 5$ and $3x - y = 2$
b. perpendicular to the line $3x - y = 5$ and passing through the point of intersection of the lines $x - 2y = -4$ and $5x + 2y = 16$

11. A triangle has vertices at the points $(3, 1)$, $(2, 4)$, and $(-3, 1)$. The line $2x - 3y = -2$ passes through this triangle at two points.
a. Plot the vertices on a coordinate grid and join them to form a triangle.
b. On the same coordinate grid, draw the line defined by $2x - 3y = -2$.
c. From the graph, estimate the points of intersection of the line and the triangle.
d. Verify your estimation by finding the equations of the two necessary lines and solve for the points of intersection using the process of comparison.

Use any of the three methods of solution studied so far to solve Exercise 12.

12. A triangle is formed by the lines $2x - 5y = -11$, $3x + 2y = 12$, and $x - y = 5$.
a. Graph the three lines on the same coordinate grid to form a triangle.
b. Find the vertices of the triangle.
c. What type of triangle is this?

13. What is the largest number than can be written using two digits?

14. What is the smallest number than can be written using two digits?

9·14 Translating into Mathematics

Equations are used to solve problems. However, the equations can only be written after the facts of a problem have been translated from English into mathematics.

Example 1

Find two numbers that have a sum of 15 and a difference of 7.

Understand the Problem

The facts of the problem; namely, that two numbers have a sum of 15 and have a difference of 7, must be translated into mathematics.

Develop a Plan

Since we have to find the value of two variables, two equations can be set up and solved.

Carry Out the Plan

Let x represent the larger number.
Let y represent the smaller number.
$x + y = 15$ ①
$x - y = 7$ ②
Once the two equations have been set up, we can solve for x and y using any of the three methods. In this case, the method of elimination is used.
① + ② $2x = 22$
     $x = 11$
Substitute into equation ① to solve for y.
     $y = 4$

Look Back

The two numbers are 11 and 4.
Recall that problems of this type also can be solved using equations in one variable. This is a good check for the work done in two variables.
Let x represent the larger number.
∴$15 - x$ is the smaller number.
$x - (15 - x) = 7$
$x - 15 + x = 7$
     $2x = 22$
     $x = 11$
∴One number is 11 and the other number is $15 - 11$ or 4.

Example 2

A golf club charges an initiation fee and a monthly fee. At the end of three months, a member had paid $480. At the end of the year, the member had paid $750. Find the initiation fee and the monthly fee.

Understand the Problem

The facts of the problem must be translated into equations.

Develop a Plan

Since we are trying to find two values — the initiation fee and the monthly fee — two equations can be set up and solved.

Carry Out the Plan

Let x represent the initiation fee.
Let y represent the monthly fee.
 $x + 3y = 480$ ①
$x + 12y = 750$ ②
The process of elimination can be used to solve for the two variables.
② − ① $9y = 270$
     $y = 30$
Substitute into equation ① and solve for x.
$x + 3(30) = 480$
     $x = 390$

Look Back

The initiation fee for the golf club is $390 and the monthly fee is $30. Can you verify this solution?

Exercises

For Exercises 1 to 3, find the second equation that would be necessary to complete the solution.

1. The sum of two numbers is 32. The larger exceeds the smaller by 8. Find the numbers.
$x + y = 32$

2. Doran has a mass that is 10 kg less than Tessa's. Together they have a mass of 109 kg. Find their masses.
$x - y = 10$

3. Divide 12 into two parts so that when one number is doubled and the other number is tripled, the sum is 29.
$2x + 3y = 29$

4. Solve the equations in Exercises 1 to 3. Explain why you used the method you did.

5. Ming has $3.70 in nickels and quarters. He has four more nickels than quarters.
Let x represent the number of quarters.
Let y represent the number of nickels.
$$x - y = 4 \quad \text{①}$$
$$25x + 5y = 370 \quad \text{②}$$
a. Explain how equation ② was found.
b. Complete the solution to find how many nickels and quarters Ming has.

For Exercises 6 to 9, find and solve two equations relating the variables.

6. A number of dimes and quarters have a value of $17.25. If there are fifteen fewer quarters than dimes, then how many of each coin are there?

7. To see a play, 4 adults and 11 children paid $13.75. Two nights later, 7 adults and 13 children paid a total of $22.25 to see the play. How much would one child and one adult have to pay to see the play?

8. The sum of the digits in a two-digit number is 10 and the difference of the digits is 4. Find the two-digit number.

9. A vending machine contains twice as many nickels as dimes. If the total amount of money in the vending machine is $15, then find how many nickels and how many dimes there are?

10. A father is 4 times as old as his daughter. Five years ago, he was 7 times as old as his daughter.
Let x represent the father's present age.
Let y represent the daughter's present age.
$$x = 4y \quad \text{①}$$
$$x - 5 = 7(y - 5) \quad \text{②}$$
a. Explain how these two equations were found.
b. Find the present ages of the father and the daughter.

11. Vanilla ice cream sells for $3.00/kg and chocolate ice cream sells for $4.00/kg. What quantities of each should be used to make up a 50 kg barrel selling for $3.75/kg?
a. Study the table shown below.

Ice Cream	Mass (kg)	Price ($/kg)	Value ($)
Vanilla	x	3.00	3.00x
Chocolate	y	4.00	4.00y
Mixture	50	3.75	187.5

b. From the table, one equation is $3x + 4y = 187.5$. Find the other equation.
c. Solve these two equations for x and y.
d. State how much vanilla and how much chocolate ice cream will be needed for the 50 kg barrel.

12. Cashew nuts are sold at $8.00/kg and shelled nuts are sold at $5.00/kg. What quantities of each would a store owner put into a 100 kg barrel so that it could be sold for $6.80/kg? (*Hint:* Set up a table similar to the one in Exercise 11, part **a.**)

13. Last year, Niki's age was half of her mother's age. Next year the sum of their ages will be 79. Find their present ages.

14. The cost of 4 kg of tea and 5 kg of coffee is $58. The cost of 7 kg of tea and 2 kg of coffee is $71. Find the cost per kilogram of the tea and the coffee.

217

9·15 Linear Systems: 3 Cases

A system of linear equations is either **independent, inconsistent,** or **dependent**. An **independent** system has exactly one point of intersection or **one solution**. An **inconsistent** system has no intersection points or **no solution** because the two lines are parallel. A **dependent** system has an infinite number of intersection points or **infinitely many solutions** because the two lines are coincident. The term "dependent" is used because the value of x is dependent on the value of y and the value of y is dependent on the value of x.

Example 1

Is this system dependent, inconsistent, or independent?
$$3x - y = 4$$
$$2x + 3y = -1$$

To discover which a system is, try to solve for the variables using one of the three solution methods presented earlier. If there is a solution, then the system is independent. If the solution does not make sense (for example $1 = 0$), then the solution is inconsistent. If the solution is $0 = 0$, then the system is dependent.

$3x - y = 4$ ①
$2x + 3y = -1$ ②
From equation ①, $y = 3x - 4$. ③
Substitute into equation ②.
$2x + 3(3x - 4) = -1$
$$x = 1$$
Substituting this value into equation ③ will give $y = -1$.

Since the two equations have a unique solution, they are an independent set of equations.

Example 2

Show that this system of equations is inconsistent.
$$4x - 2y = 3$$
$$4x - 2y = -1$$

To show that this system is inconsistent, try to solve for the variables.
$4x - 2y = 3$ ①
$4x - 2y = -1$ ②
① − ② $\quad 0 = 4$ ③

Since $0 = 4$ is impossible, this is an inconsistent system.

Example 3

Solve this system. $\{(s, t) \mid 4s - t + 8 = 0 \text{ and } 6s - 1.5t + 12 = 0, s, t \in R\}$
$4s - t = -8$ ①
$6s - 1.5t = -12$ ②
From equation ①, $t = 4s + 8$. ③
Substitute equation ③ into equation ②.
$6s - 1.5(4s + 8) = -12$
$$0 = 0$$

This result indicates that the value of s depends on the value of t, and vice versa.

Exercises

1. Without solving these systems of linear equations, identify each as being either independent, inconsistent, or dependent. (*Hint:* Check the slopes).

a. $8x + 3y + 12 = 0$ and $24x + 9y + 12 = 0$

b. $a - 2b = -7$ and $5a - 10b + 35 = 0$

c. $s = 1.5t - 4$ and $3s - t + 1 = 0$

d. $\frac{2}{3}x - 3y + \frac{7}{3} = 0$ and $2x - 9y + 7 = 0$

e. Compare the left side and right side of an inconsistent system and a dependent system. What do you find?

2. In your own words, describe the terms "independent", "inconsistent", and "dependent". Draw a graph to enhance your definitions.

3. Solve each system of equations. Describe the type of system each represents.

a. $3x - 5y = -7$
   $5x + 9y = -16$

b. $2a - 5b = -1$
   $a - 4b = -2$

c. $y = -\frac{3}{2}x + 1$
   $3x + 2y - 2 = 0$

d. $4x - 12y = 18$
   $\frac{1}{3}x - y + \frac{3}{2} = 0$

4. Solve for v and w. Identify each system as dependent, inconsistent, or independent.

a. $\frac{5}{2}v - \frac{23}{5}w = 33$
   $\frac{7}{2}v + \frac{4}{5}w - 10 = 0$

b. $\frac{2}{5}v - \frac{4}{3}w + \frac{7}{10} = 0$
   $12v - 40w + 14 = 0$

5. Which of these pairs of lines intersect at the point $(-2, 4)$?

a. $x - 2y - 7 = 0$ and $y = -2x - 6$

b. $3x - y + 10 = 0$ and $7x - 2y - 1 = 0$

c. $y = 2x + 4$ and $y = -\frac{1}{2}x + 8$

d. $y = 3x + 10$ and $3x + 2y - 2 = 0$

6. Given the equation $x - 2y = 6$, write a second equation so that the two equations produce

a. an inconsistent system.

b. a dependent system.

7. Graph each equation and the equation that is the sum of these two equations.
$x + y = 3$
$x - y = 5$
Explain how this illustrates that "any ordered pair that is the solution to the two equations simultaneously is also a solution to the sum of the two equations."

8. Two rental companies use different formulas to find the charge for renting their equipment. The first company uses the formula $r = 20h + 18$ and the second company uses the formula $r = 22h + 16$, where r is the total rental cost and h is the cost per hour of rental time.

a. Graph the two equations on the same coordinate grid and use the graph to comment on which company offers the better deal. (*Hint:* Estimate the point of intersection.)

b. Solve the system algebraically to determine when their rental fees are the same.

9. A mail-order gift company sends 12 000 catalogues to customers in and out of the country. The cost of distribution inside the country is $0.30 per catalogue and $0.35 per catalogue mailed outside the country. They have a budget of $3800 for the distribution. How many should be sent inside and how many outside the country to distribute the maximum number of catalogues?

10. A contractor has hired a landscaper and a student helper. One day they were paid $77.56 between them when the landscaper worked 4 h and the student 2 h. The next day they were paid $117.20 and they worked 5 h each. Find their individual hourly wages.

11. Two insurance companies determine their premiums using different formulas. One uses the formula $p = 2a + 23$ and the other uses the formula $p = 2.3a + 11$, where p is the annual premium and a is the purchaser's age.

a. At what age do the companies charge the same premium?

b. When does one company offer the better deal? Explain.

9·16 Graphing Inequalities

A plane is divided into three distinct sets of points by any line. These are the points on the line, the points below the line, and the points above the line.

Example 1

Graph the inequality. $2x + 3y \leq 12$

The graph of the equation $2x + 3y = 12$ is drawn and the three regions are defined by S_1, S_2, and S_3 respectively. Notice that S_2 is the region defined by the equation. Which of the three regions are included in the inequality? Since the equation $2x + 3y = 12$ is part of the inequality, S_2 is part of the region. Also, because $(0, 0)$ is a solution to $2x + 3y \leq 12$, the region S_1 is part of the solution. Therefore, the graph of the solution is the regions S_1 and S_2.

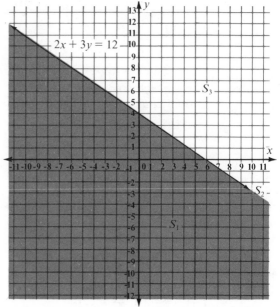

Example 2

Graph the solution set. $\{(x, y) \mid 3x - y \geq 6 \text{ and } x + 2y > 6, \ x, \ y \ \epsilon \ R\}$

The graphs of $3x - y = 6$ and $x + 2y = 6$ are shown on the coordinate grid. Notice the dotted line for $x + 2y = 6$. This indicates that the region defined by $x + 2y = 6$ is **not** part of the solution set. The graph of the solution set is the region where the graphs of the two inequalities overlap and its boundaries.

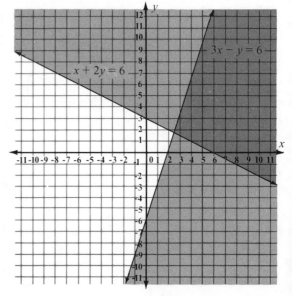

Exercises

1. Graph each inequality.

a. $y < x$ **b.** $y < x + 2$
c. $y \geq -x + 2$ **d.** $y \leq 4x - 3$
e. $y > -7x + 5$ **f.** $y > 3x - 1$

2. For each part of Exercise 1, use the graph to identify two ordered pairs that satisfy the inequality.

3. Graph the relations defined by each.
a. $y > x$ **b.** $y \geq 0$ **c.** $y \leq 0$

4. Convert to the form $y = mx + b$ and graph.
a. $3x + y \leq 6$ **b.** $x + 2y - 3 \geq 0$
c. $-6x - 5y - 10 > 0$ **d.** $9x - 6y + 22 > 0$

5. Is the point $(-3, 7)$ in the region above or below the line $y = x - 4$? Use an inequality to explain your answer.

6. List any three points that lie in the region described by each inequality.
a. $2.5x + 3.27y - 4.0 < 0$

b. $\frac{3}{4}x - \frac{2}{3}y + 17 \geq 0$

7. Graph the set of points satisfying these conditions.

a. $y < -x + 2$ and $y > \frac{1}{4}x$
b. $y \geq 0$ and $y < 3x - 2$
c. $x \leq 7$ and $y \leq 1$
d. $y > -4x - 1$ and $y < -4x + 1$
e. $x + y \geq 0$ and $3x - 5y < 4$

8. For each pair of inequalities in Exercise 7, identify one ordered pair that satisfies both inequalities.

9. Write an inequality to describe each of the graphs.

a. **b.**

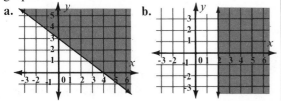

10. Write an inequality or pair of inequalities to describe the shaded region in each graph.

a. **b.**

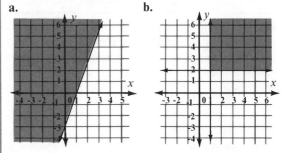

11. List the three inequalities whose intersection describes this region.

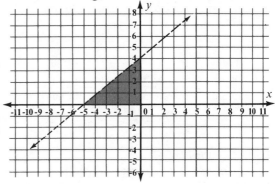

12. An 85 ha farm is to be planted with beans and cucumbers for which no more than $10 000 is available. Beans cost $250/ha to plant and cucumbers cost $90/ha to plant. Draw a graph to show the number of hectares of each crop that can be planted.

13. List five inequalities that combine to describe this region.

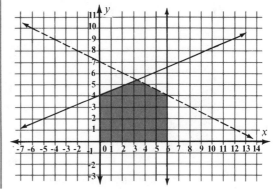

9·17 Linear Programming

In all businesses, the owner wants to maximize profits, and this usually means minimizing the costs of producing a product. Decisions made that will help maximize the profits to a business, while minimizing the costs of production, often result from a process in mathematics called **linear programming**.

Example

Mathracquet manufactures two types of racquets — tennis racquets, which show a profit of $15 each, and squash racquets, which show a profit of $10 each. It takes 15 min to mold the frame of each tennis racquet and 5 min to string the racquet; while a squash racquet requires 10 min to mold and 15 min to string. How many of each should be made to maximize the profit for each 7 h manufacturing shift?

Understand the Problem

A chart often helps to summarize the given information.

Type of Racquet	Time to Mold	Time to String
Tennis	15 min	5 min
Squash	10 min	15 min

Develop a Plan

Identify two variables that will represent the number of tennis racquets and the number of squash racquets manufactured each shift. Identify an expression for profit using these variables, and find the restrictions on the variables.

Let x represent the number of tennis racquets and y represent the number of squash racquets manufactured per shift.

Carry Out the Plan

The quantity to be maximized is profit.
$P = 10x + 15y$
Since the number of racquets produced cannot be negative, the restrictions on the variables are $x \geq 0$ and $y \geq 0$.
The time spent molding and stringing the racquets cannot exceed 7 h or 420 min.
$15x + 10y \leq 420$ and $5x + 15y \leq 420$
or $3x + 2y \leq 84$ and $x + 3y \leq 84$

Graph the inequalities to show the profit region.

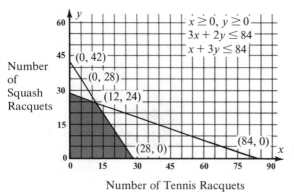

Number of Squash Racquets

Number of Tennis Racquets

Look Back

Set up a chart to show the profit at each vertex.

Vertex	Profit: $P = 10x + 15y$
(0, 0)	$10(0) + 15(0) = 0$
(0, 28)	$10(0) + 15(28) = 420$
(12, 24)	$10(12) + 15(24) = 480$
(28, 0)	$10(28) + 15(0) = 280$

Therefore, in order to maximize the profits, Mathracquet should produce 12 tennis racquets and 24 squash racquets every 7 h shift.

The maximum profit will occur at one of the vertices of this region. Evaluate the profit expression for each vertex to find the maximum profit.

Exercises

1. For the region shown on this graph, test the vertices to find the maximum income given the equation for income, I, is $I = 5x - 2y$. Also check any two points inside the region.

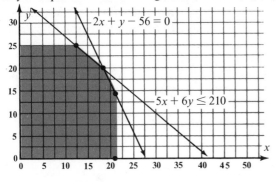

2. Use the constraints on (n, s) described in these three inequalities: $s \geq 6$, $3n + 5s \geq 60$, and $21n + 5s - 150 \geq 0$.
a. Graph the region and identify each vertex.
b. Check the values at each vertex to find the minimum pollution, P, if $P = 3.5n + 1.5s$.
c. Why would we not check values inside the shaded region?

3. An auto-parts plant paints door guards and window trim. The employees can hang up to 6000 door guards and 4000 window trims on the paint line each day. The automatic sprayers can only handle 9000 pieces within specifications. If the cost to paint one door guard is 6¢ and the cost per window trim is 4.5¢, how many of each item should be painted to keep the daily cost to a minimum?

4. A chemical firm produces fertilizers with different compositions of nitrate and phosphate. There must be at least 3 kg of nitrogen and 3 kg of phosphorous in a mix. Their combined amount cannot exceed 30 kg for cost reasons, and all mixes must stay within the formula: three times the amount of nitrate and five times the amount of phosphate is less than 96 kg. The product is priced so the profit is $1.15/kg of nitrate and $1.30/kg of phosphate. Which mixture produces maximum profit?

5. A small company produces two cereals of dried fruit and grain; one is a discount product and the other is a gourmet product. The discount cereal contains 10% dried fruit and the gourmet cereal has 20% dried fruit. The company's profit on the discount product is 13¢ and it is 18¢ on the gourmet product. They have 300 kg of grain and 40 kg of dried fruit in stock. The cereal is sold in 200 g boxes.
Use the linear programming model to determine the number of packages of each product they should make from their stock to earn a maximum profit.

6. A chemical company produces fertilizers with different percentage compositions of nitrate and phosphate. The amount of nitrogen ranges from 3% to 25% of the product, and the phosphorous from 3% to 12%. Their combined maximum cannot exceed 32% of the product. The profit on the fertilizer is $2.55/kg of nitrate and $3.80/kg of phosphate. Their product is only acceptable if the percentage nitrate is at least double the percentage phosphate. What mixture produces maximum profit for the company?

7. A pen manufacturer produces two models of ball-point pens, the *scribe* and the *stylus*. They can produce up to 2000 of the *scribe* cartridges a day and up to 1300 of the *stylus* cartridges. They are only able to obtain 2500 outer casings per day. The casing is the same for both models. The profit on each *scribe* is $1.30, and on each *stylus* it is $1.50. Because of the demand they must produce at least twice as many of the *scribe* as the *stylus*. In order to make a maximum profit, how many of each model should they produce in a day?

8. A cookie manufacturer sells two chocolate-chip cookie mixes, a "Regular" and a "Super Chip". The regular has 10% chocolate chips and the super has 15%. The company sells 100 g bags of the mix and makes 22¢/bag on each regular mix and 34¢/bag on each super mix. The stock is 400 kg of dry mix and 50 kg of chocolate chips. How many bags of each type of mix should be made from this stock to get a maximum profit?

9·18 Computer Application — Solving Pairs of Equations

A computer can be used to solve pairs of linear equations. The program shown is especially useful when solving pairs of equations when the coefficients are not integers. The equations solved by this program are of the form $Ax + By = C$ and $Dx + Ey = F$.

```
10 REM A PROGRAM TO SOLVE PAIRS OF LINEAR EQUATIONS
20 INPUT "THE COEFFICIENTS OF THE FIRST EQUATION ARE ";
   A, B, C
30 INPUT "THE COEFFICIENTS OF THE SECOND EQUATION ARE ";
   D, E, F
40 PRINT
50 PRINT "EQUATION 1 — "; A; "X + "; B; "Y = "; C
60 PRINT "EQUATION 2 — "; D; "X + "; E; "Y = "; F
70 LET CHECK = D * B — E * A
80 IF CHECK = 0 THEN 150
90 LET S1 = (F * B — C * E) / CHECK
100 LET S2 = (D * C — A * F) / CHECK
110 PRINT
120 PRINT "THE SOLUTION FOR X IS "; S1
130 PRINT "THE SOLUTION FOR Y IS "; S2
140 GOTO 160
150 PRINT "NO SOLUTION"
160 END
```

Exercises

1. State the purpose of lines 20 and 30 of the program in the display.

2. Why is it necessary to have lines 70 and 80 in the program?

3. Show how S1 and S2 were arrived at by solving these equations for x and y. (*Hint:* Use the process of elimination.)
$Ax + By = C$
$Dx + Ey = F$

4. Input the program into a computer and run the program to solve these equations.
$3x + 4y = 12$
$1x + 2y = 6$
Is the computer output reasonable?

5. Predict what the computer output will be for these equations.
$5x - 7y = 8$
$5x - 7y = 9$
a. Explain your prediction.
b. Run the program using these equations to verify your prediction.
c. What would the output be if lines 70 and 80 were deleted? Explain.
d. Delete lines 70 and 80 and run the program for the equations to verify your prediction.

6. A teacher decided not to allow students to do their homework on a computer because computer disks are too easy to copy. Also, if the computer breaks down, the student has no way to study for their upcoming exam. Write a short essay either rejecting or defending this position.

9·19 Chapter Review

1. Write an equation, in two variables, to define each.

a. A total weekly wage, w, if an employee is earning $22.50 per week, plus $6.35 per hour, h.

b. The sale price, s, of an item whose regular price, r, is reduced by 15%.

2. For each of the following equations construct a table of values that includes five pairs.

a. $y = 2x - 1$ **b.** $3y = 6x + 2$ **c.** $x - y = 12$

d. $x = 3$ **e.** $4x - 3y + 2 = 0$ **f.** $y = 12$

3. Determine the value of A when $i = 0.08$.

a. $A = 3700 + 3700i$ **b.** $A = 62\ 370(1 + i)$

4. Determine the value of y when $x = -3, 0,$ and 2.5.

a. $y = 4x - 7$ **b.** $x - 5y = 20$

c. $3x + 8y = 76$ **d.** $12.25x - 8.75y = 420$

e. $16x - y - 1350 = 0$ **f.** $\frac{2}{3}x + \frac{3}{5}y - 27 = 0$

5. Graph each relation.

a. $y = x + 3$ **b.** $y = -4x + 4$ **c.** $y = 2.8$

6. Identify the slope and y-intercept in each linear equation.

a. $y = 2x + 7$ **b.** $y = -4x + 2$

c. $y = 0.07x + 1.5$ **d.** $y = 7$

e. $3x - 7y = 35$ **f.** $3x = 5y - 1$

7. Write an equation of a line that has the slope and y-intercept listed.

a. $4, 15$ **b.** $-3, 3$ **c.** $-2, -1.5$

d. $0, 42$ **e.** $-1, 1$ **f.** $\frac{3}{5}, 0$

8. Write an equation for a line with the following characteristics.

a. passes through the origin and the point $(1, 1)$

b. is parallel to the x-axis and has a y-intercept of 5

c. is parallel to the y-axis with an x-intercept of -2

d. passes through the points $(3, 6)$ and $(5, 10)$

e. has a slope of 1 and crosses the y-axis at 0.75

9. Rewrite these equations in the form $Ax + By + C = 0$.

a. $y = 3x + 2$ **b.** $y = 0.5x - 7$

c. $6x = 3$ **d.** $12x + y = 8$

e. $\frac{1}{10}x - \frac{3}{5}y = 6$ **f.** $\frac{1}{2}x = 4y - 8$

10. Describe the appearance of each of these families of lines.

a. $y = mx$ **b.** $y = 3x + b$ **c.** $y = c$

d. $x = k$ **e.** $y = -6x + t$ **f.** $y = m(x - 1) + 2$

11. Write an equation for a family of lines with these characteristics.

a. have a common y-intercept of -2

b. have a slope of $\frac{4}{3}$

c. are parallel to the x-axis

d. pass through the point $(9, -1)$, with a slope of $\frac{2}{3}$

12. Graph each of these inequalities.

a. $y < x + 1$ **b.** $y \geq -x + 1$

c. $y > -2$ **d.** $x + 7y > 0$

e. $6x + 3y + 15 \leq 0$ **f.** $6x - 3y + 15 < 0$

13. Which of the regions described here will contain the point $(5, 3)$?

a. $y < 7x + 1$ **b.** $y > 4$

c. $x < 10$ **d.** $y > -2x + 13$

e. $x + y + 11 > 0$ **f.** $x - y < 4$

14. Use a graph to identify the point of intersection, if there is one, of the two lines.

a. $y = 4$ and $x = 1$

b. $y = 7x$ and $y = -2x$

c. $y = 3x - 1$ and $x - y - 1 = 0$

d. $y = -5x + 2$ and $y = -5x - 1$

15. Solve these systems of equations algebraically.

a. $y = x + 8$ and $y = 3x + 20$

b. $y = 5x - 2$ and $10x - 5y = -3$

c. $x + 7y = 21$ and $x - 4y = 66$

d. $2x + 9y = -3$ and $3x - y = 0$

e. $0.42x - 1.10y = 26.80$ and $x - y = 12$

f. $8.60x + 5.45y = 1268.50$ and $y = x - 10$

9·20 Chapter Test

1. The volume, v, of a gas varies directly with the temperature, t, of the gas. Express this relationship as an equation.

2. List six ordered pairs that satisfy the relation defined by $2x - y + 6 = 0$.

3. Calculate the value of y when $x = -2$ in the equation $4x - 8y - 5 = 0$.

4. Determine the x-intercept and the y-intercept for the linear equation $6x - 3y - 15 = 0$.

5. Graph the relation defined by $y = -3x + 2$.

6. Find the slope and the y-intercept in the equation $y = -x + 10$.

7. Find the slope and the y-intercept of the line represented by the linear equation $0.3x + 2.5y - 12 = 0$.

8. Find an equation of a line with slope $\frac{2}{5}$ and y-intercept $\frac{4}{5}$.

9. Express $y = -5x + 14$ in the form $Ax + By + C = 0$.

10. For the general linear equation $Ax + By + C = 0$, express the slope and the y-intercept in terms of A, B, and C.

11. Graph the family of lines represented by $y = 2x + b$.

12. Describe the graph of the family of lines represented by the equation $y = mx + 7$.

13. Determine an equation for each family of lines.
a. passing through the origin
b. parallel to the x-axis
c. through the point $(0, 1)$
d. through the point $(2, -3)$

14. Use a graph to determine the point of intersection of the two lines.
$y = 4x - 2$ and $7x - 3y - 1 = 0$

15. Solve the system of equations.
a. $x + 5y = 4$ and $y = -2x + 8$
b. $0.75x - 0.40y = 13.50$ and $3x - 2y = 0$

16. In planning for a party, Hilda bought 21 bottles of soft drinks and fruit juice. The bill was $26.41. If the soft drinks cost $0.85 per bottle, and the juice $1.92 per bottle, then how many of each did she buy?

17. A runner plans to jog a 79 km distance in 6 h, mixing a fast speed of 19 km/h and a slower speed of 12 km/h. Find the number of hours that should be run at the fast speed and the number at the slower speed in order to complete the distance in 6 h.

18. Identify two points in the region described by $y > -4x - 2$.

19. Describe in words the region defined by $6x - 3y + 12 \geq 0$.

20. Graph the inequality $y < 3x + 1$.

21. Graph the set of points that satisfy these two conditions: $y > x - 1$ and $3x + 2y - 14 \leq 0$.

22. A student is working to keep the conservation area clean. She agrees to be paid by the number of pieces of garbage she picks up; 3¢ per paper, bottle, can, etc. and 5¢ per food item. She must pick up at least four times as much of the first type as the food items and she must collect at least 750 pieces each day to keep the job. On a given day there is no more than 1000 pieces of garbage in the area. What combination of pieces collected will give her a maximum payment for the day?

226

Cumulative Review Chapters 7–9

1. List an ordered pair that is symmetric with the point $(-3, 1)$ about each.
a. the x-axis
b. the y-axis
c. the origin

2. Find the slope of a line passing through each pair of points.
a. $(3, 4), (6, 8)$ b. $(-4, 3), (4, -3)$
c. $(0, 2), (-5, 0)$ d. $(-7, -6), (3, -6)$
e. $(4, 8), (4, -1)$ f. $(x_1, y_1), (x_2, y_2)$

3. Identify a third point on the line passing through the ordered pairs $(-2, -5)$ and $(5, -1)$.

4. How can you determine whether a set of points is collinear or noncollinear? Use this method to determine whether the ordered pairs $(-4, 5), (0, 3)$, and $(4, 0)$ lie in the same straight line.

5. For what value of a will the line passing through the ordered pairs $(a, 1)$ and $(4, 5)$ have a slope of $\frac{2}{3}$?

6. For what value of b will the line passing through the ordered pairs $(-6, 1)$ and $(b, 4)$ be parallel to the line passing through the points $(7, -2)$ and $(5, 3)$?

7. For what value of c is the line passing through the points $(-8, 1)$ and $(2, c)$ perpendicular to the line passing through the points $(-3, 7)$ and $(0, 5)$?

8. Quadrilateral $ABCD$ has vertices at $A(0, 3)$, $B(-4, -5), C(5, -2)$, and $D(6, 0)$.
a. Define a trapezoid.
b. Prove that quadrilateral $ABCD$ is a trapezoid.

9. Quadrilateral $PQRS$ has vertices at $P(4, 4)$, $Q(-1, -1), R(-2, 6)$, and $S(3, 11)$. Verify that this quadrilateral is a rhombus.

10. Triangle DEF has vertices at $D(-1, 9)$, $E(-4, -2)$, and $F(5, 1)$. Verify that a line segment joining the midpoint of any two sides of the triangle is parallel to the third side and one half of the length of the third side.

11. Calculate the area of a triangle with vertices at the points $(1, 4), (5, 2)$, and $(4, 5)$.

12. A relation is defined by this set of ordered pairs. $\{(0, 0), (1, 1), (2, 3), (3, 6), (4, 10)\}$
a. Is there a pattern in this set of ordered pairs? Explain.
b. Find the next four ordered pairs in the relation.
c. Graph the complete set of ordered pairs.
d. Is this a linear relation? Explain.
e. Draw a smooth curve or line through the ordered pairs that you have plotted.
f. What is the value of y if $x = 1.5$? $x = 12.5$?

13. Copy and complete.
a. Estimating a value between known values is called ▆▆▆▆▆.
b. Estimating a value beyond known values is called ▆▆▆▆▆.
c. In an ordered pair, the x-coordinate is called the ▆▆▆▆▆ while the y-coordinate is called the ▆▆▆▆▆.

14. Consider a relation that describes the number of hours elapsed and the distance travelled by a vehicle with a speed of 135 km/h.
a. Graph the relation.
b. Is this a direct variation, a partial variation, or an inverse variation? Explain.

15. Consider a relation that describes a natural number paired with its reciprocal.
a. Graph this relation.
b. Is this a linear relation or a non-linear relation?
c. Is this a continuous graph? Explain.
d. Is this an increasing relation? Explain.
e. Is there any non-negative value that will never appear in the graph? If so, what is it?

Cumulative Review Chapters 7–9

16. A rugby team organized an eleven aside scrimmage game. The diagram outlines the positions that can be assigned to a player on a rugby team. How old is each player? (*Hint:* Player *A* being either older or younger than player *B* means that if *A* is 21 a, then *B* is not 21 a.)

Forwards

			Hook			
Left	Left	Left		Right	Right	Right
Flanker	Prop	Lock		Lock	Prop	Flanker

Eighth
Left Wing   Man   Right Wing

Fullback

One of the wingers is three years older than the other.
The hook is twenty years old.
The right wing is three years younger than the right prop.
The eighth man is older than the hook.
The youngest member of the squad is eighteen years old.
The oldest member of the team is thirty years old.
The left lock is twenty-four years old.
The left flanker is younger than the hook.
Two of the forwards are a year apart in age.
One of the right forwards is the same age as the player on his left.
One of the right forwards is twenty-seven years old.
The hook is younger than the right flanker and left winger but older than the fullback.
The left lock is older than the left prop and the same age as the right winger.
The left winger is the same age as the right flanker.

17. Describe the similarities and differences between a partial variation, a direct variation, and an inverse variation. You may wish to use graphs to reinforce your explanations.

18. Explain a constant of proportionality.

19. Find the constant of proportionality in a relation that pairs the number of hours elapsed with the corresponding number of minutes elapsed.

20. A student's pay for a part-time job varies directly as the number of hours worked. If the pay for an 8 h shift is $42, then what will the student get paid for a 10 h shift?

21. A hypothesis once stated that a person's adult height varied inversely as the number of soda pops drunk before the age of eighteen. The supporting data showed that a person, 152 cm tall, drank 430 soda pops.
a. If the hypothesis is correct, then what would be the predicted height of someone who drank 817 soda pops?
b. How many soda pops would a person have to drink in order to be 133 cm tall?
c. Is it possible for a person to be 0 cm tall according to the data? Explain.

22. Consider this graph relating the number of kilometres driven in a rental car to the cost of renting the car for one day.

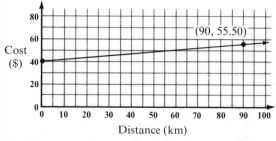

a. What is the fixed cost for renting the car for one day?
b. What does the linear pattern indicate?
c. What is the charge per kilometre for driving the car?
d. Write an equation that can describe this graph.

23. Write an equation for the line passing through the diameter of a circle described by the points $(-3, -1)$ and $(9, 4)$.

Cumulative Review Chapters 7–9

24. Translate each sentence into a mathematical equation.

a. The number of cows in a herd is three times the number of calves.

b. A person's salary is calculated at $5.35/h with a $12 bonus for not being sick.

25. Express this equation as an English sentence. $T = 10d + 25q$

26. The equation $s = 55t$ describes the corresponding values of distance and time at a fixed rate of speed. Without graphing, prove that this relation is linear.

27. Draw a graph of a linear relation with a slope of $-\frac{2}{3}$ and an x-intercept of 1. Find an equation for this line.

28. What is the equation of a horizontal line passing through the x-axis?

29. Write a linear and a non-linear equation for a relation that has no y-intercept.

30. Find the x-intercept and the y-intercept for each equation.

a. $y = \frac{4}{3}x + 1$ **b.** $6x - y + 2 = 0$ **c.** $y = x$

31. Find an equation of the line given by each.
a. passes through the point (4, 1) and has a y-intercept of -3

b. has a slope of $\frac{2}{3}$ and a y-intercept of -3
c. is a horizontal line and passes through the point $(-1, 2)$
d. passes through the ordered pairs $(0, 0)$ and $(1, 2)$
e. passes through the ordered pairs $(-5, 3)$ and $(1, -1)$
f. perpendicular to the line $x + 3y = 0$ and intersects the line $x + 3y = 0$ at the origin
g. passes through the point $(6, -5)$ and is perpendicular to the line passing through the points $(-4, -2)$ and $(8, 3)$

32. Define the terms "domain" and "range".

33. Graph each set using the real numbers, and identify the domain and the range of each set.
a. $\{(x, y) \mid y = -4x + 1\}$
b. $\{(x, y) \mid 8x - 2y = 5\}$
c. $\{(x, y) \mid y = x^2 - 3\}$

34. Find the point of intersection of each pair of lines.

a. $5x - y = -1$
$3x + y = 3$
b. $2x - y = -11$
$6x - 5y = -1$
c. $23x + 15y = 2$
$y = -x - 2$
d. $5x - y = 4$
$x - 6y = 3$
e. $6x - 2y = 7$
$5x + 3y = -1$
f. $3x + 7y = 16$
$x - 4y = -2$
g. $2x - 5y = 13$
$y = 3x$
h. $4x - 3y = 2$
$5x + 4y = -13$

35. Two boats are to rendezvous at a point on a navigational grid. The Mathship is heading on a course described by the equation $5x + 9y = 157$ and Linearboat is on a bearing described by the equation $7x + 3y = 143$. At what point will the two ships rendezvous?

36. The cost of fixing the transmission in a car is calculated using the equation $C = F + Rn$, where C is the cost in dollars, F is a fixed cost for buying the parts, R is the rate per hour for the mechanic, and n is the number of hours that the mechanic works on the car. If a 3 h repair on the transmission costs $250, and a 5 h repair cost $370, then find the fixed cost and the rate charged per hour for fixing any car.
a. Find the cost for a 7.5 h repair on a transmission.
b. Find the number of hours that a mechanic worked on a transmission if the cost was $800 for the work done.

37. For any system of linear equations, what is meant by the terms "independent", "inconsistent", and "dependent"?

Cumulative Review Chapters 7–9

38. For each of the following pairs of equations, define each system as either independent, inconsistent, or dependent. If the system is independent, solve it for the point of intersection.

a. $3x + 2y = 15$
$\quad 6x + 4y = 44$

b. $\quad x - y = 8$
$\quad 2x - 2y = 16$

39. Triangle ABC is defined by the points $A(0, 6)$, $B(-8, 10)$, and $C(4, 0)$. Verify that the medians of this triangle are coincident.

40. Find the coordinates of the point at which the altitude of this triangle meets the base.

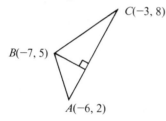

$C(-3, 8)$
$B(-7, 5)$
$A(-6, 2)$

41. Solve for x and y.

a. $\frac{3}{2}x - \frac{2}{3}y = \frac{19}{8}$
$\quad \frac{2}{5}x - \frac{1}{3}y = \frac{16}{15}$

b. $\frac{3}{4}x - \frac{1}{5}y = \frac{101}{20}$
$\quad \frac{7}{3}x + \frac{8}{5}y = \frac{269}{15}$

42. Describe the shaded plane in the coordinate grid using inequalities.

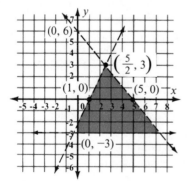

43. Graph each.
a. $\{(x, y) \mid x + y \le 15,\ x, y \in R\}$
b. $\{(x, y) \mid 2x - y > 14,\ x, y \in R\}$

44. Graph each.
a. $\{(x, y) \mid 2x + 3y < 12$ and $3x - y \le 9,\ x, y \in R\}$
b. $\{(x, y) \mid 2x - y > -4$ and $3x + 4y < 24,\ x, y \in R\}$
c. $\{(x, y) \mid -x - y \le 14$ and $-x + y > 8,\ x, y \in R\}$

45. A manufacturer produces grubbles in standard and deluxe models. A standard grubble takes 4 h of labour time to produce, while a deluxe grubble takes 8 h of labour time to produce. The manufacturer has the facilities to employ 20 people, and have the plant open for one 8 h shift every day, five days a week. The manufacturer is on a strict budget and can spend no more than $15 000 per week for materials, and each model costs $100 to produce. The manufacturer must have orders that require a maximum of 50 standard and 40 deluxe grubbles to be produced every week. How many of each should the manufacturer produce in order to realize the maximum profit?

46. Mathfood is experimenting with a new type of food that is high in protein and low in fat. It is to be made from a mixture of two new ingredients: Allmath and Beaumath. There must be at least 8 g of protein and no more than 14 g of fat per 100 g of the mixture. The quantities of protein and fat per 50 g of Allmath and Beaumath are given in the table.

	Protein	Fat
Allmath	4	10
Beaumath	5	5

It is also found that the flavour will not sell on the market if there is three times as much of the ingredient Beaumath as Allmath. If Allmath sells for $0.43/kg and Beaumath sells for $0.86/kg, then what is the minimum cost of the mixture?

47. A two-digit number is three more than one half of the number formed by reversing the digits. If the second digit is 2 more than the first, then what is the original number?

230

DEDUCTIVE GEOMETRY THROUGH PROBLEM SOLVING

Tune Up

1. Each pair of angles is related by a postulate or theorem. Use the diagram and name the postulate or theorem.

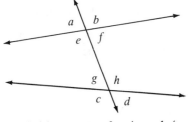

a. ∠g and ∠d
b. ∠a and ∠g
c. ∠f and ∠g
d. ∠f and ∠h
e. ∠g and ∠h
f. ∠b and ∠c

2. Using only a ruler, compasses, and a protractor, construct each triangle.
a. $\overline{AB}$ = 4 cm, $\overline{AC}$ = 4.5 cm, $\overline{BC}$ = 3 cm
b. $\overline{MN}$ = 5 cm, $\overline{NP}$ = 3 cm, ∠N = 55°
c. $\overline{RS}$ = 6 cm, ∠R = 51°, ∠S = 71°
d. $\overline{KL}$ = 2 cm, ∠K = 75°, ∠M = 45°
e. $\overline{XY}$ = 6.2 cm, $\overline{XZ}$ = 3.1 cm, $\overline{YZ}$ = 2.9 cm

3. Find the size of each angle in the triangles.

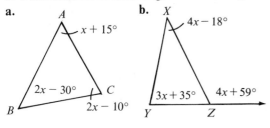

4. State the six congruences between each pair of congruent triangles.
a.

△ABC ≅ △DEF

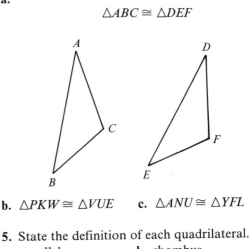

b. △PKW ≅ △VUE   **c.** △ANU ≅ △YFL

5. State the definition of each quadrilateral.
a. parallelogram   **b.** rhombus
c. square   **d.** trapezoid

6. Find the size of angles x, y, and z in each.

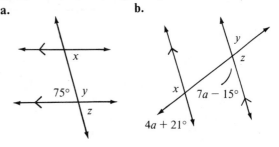

231

10·1 Deductive Reasoning

A series of statements in which the concluding statement follows from the preceding statements is a **deduction**. There are two reasoning processes which will yield a deduction. These processes are **deductive reasoning** and **inductive reasoning**. When using deductive reasoning, subsequent statements are logically developed from a series of preliminary statements. When using inductive reasoning, subsequent statements or conclusions are drawn based on a pattern within the preceding statements.

Example 1

Draw a conclusion using deductive reasoning.

Don is five years older than Doran.
Doran is two years younger than Dean.
Don is twenty-four years old.
Therefore, Dean is twenty-one years old.

Example 2

Draw a conclusion using inductive reasoning.

Silver maples shed their leaves.
Sugar maples shed their leaves.
Red maples shed their leaves.
Therefore, all maples shed their leaves.

In using deductive reasoning, certain "ground rules" must be accepted. In Example 1, it was that the first three statements were true. In geometry, these ground rules are postulates and definitions that lead to theorems. If the definitions or the postulates change, then the theorems must also change.

In an inductive argument, as in Example 2, all the preliminary statements may be true; but if there is another type of maple that does not shed its leaves, the conclusion would be false.

Example 3

What conclusion can be drawn about Jean from these two statements?

All swimmers ride windsurfers.
Jean is a swimmer.
Therefore, Jean rides a windsurfer.

> This is a **deductive argument**.

The conclusion of Example 3 can be written in the form of an "**if ... then**" statement. If Jean is a swimmer, then Jean is a windsurfer. In an "if ... then" statement, the "if" phrase is the **hypothesis** and the "then" phrase is the **conclusion**.

> A **deductive argument** is one in which a statement that applies to all members of a set is applied to a particular member of the set. An **inductive argument** is one in which a statement that applies to several members of a set is applied to all members of the set.

Example 4

What two conclusions can be drawn from these three statements?

If the outside temperature is above 25°C, then the water is warm.
If the water is warm, then Grant will go swimming.
The outside temperature is 32°C.
Therefore, the water is warm and Grant will go swimming.

Exercises

1. Refer to the examples in the display.

a. Explain why Example 1 uses deductive reasoning as opposed to inductive reasoning.

b. Explain why Example 2 is an example of inductive reasoning.

c. Is the conclusion in Example 3 true? Must it be true **if** the first two statements are true?

d. Explain how the two conclusions of Example 4 were drawn. Are these examples of inductive or deductive reasoning?

2. Express each in an "if ... then" statement.

a. A parrot that flies is a bird.

b. A person who is a grade ten student is a brilliant mathematician.

c. The sum of the measures of the interior angles of an object is 180° if the object is a triangle.

d. A person who drives in Saskatchewan always wears a seat belt.

e. Two parallel lines in the same plane never intersect.

f. A person who lives in Toronto lives in Ontario.

3. For each set of statements,

i) write a logical conclusion where possible, and

ii) state whether the conclusion was found by inductive or deductive reasoning.

The first one is done as an example.

Bill, Tom, and Mike are all boys.

Therefore, anyone named Bill, Tom, or Mike is a boy.

This is an example of inductive reasoning as there is a pattern in the statement.

a. If the grass is green, then it has rained. The grass is green.

b. All rectangles are quadrilaterals. Janelle's backyard is a rectangle.

c. If you enter the Death Star, then you are in Darth Vader's territory. If you are in Darth Vader's territory, then you will be disintegrated. You enter the Death Star.

d. If your school has tall students, then it will have a winning basketball team. Your school has tall students.

4. If the sum of the measures of the interior angles of a figure is 180°, then the figure is a triangle. Figure *ABC* has interior angles whose sum is 180°.

a. Write the hypothesis.

b. Write the conclusion.

c. Comment on the truth of the conclusion.

5. For any trapezoid, the sum of the measures of the interior angles is 360°.

a. Write this statement as an "if ... then" statement.

b. Write the conclusion.

c. Comment on the truth of the statement.

6. The Edmonton Oilers have neither the tenacity nor the pugnacity to win another Stanley Cup. On what would two hockey fans have to agree before they could decide if this is a true or a false statement?

7. If two angles are complementary, then their sum is 90°. On what would two people have to agree in order to decide if this is a true or a false statement?

8. "But I don't want to go among mad people," Alice remarked.

"Oh you can't help that," said the Cat; "We're all mad here. I'm mad. You're mad."

"How do you know I'm mad?" said Alice.

"You must be," said the Cat, "or you wouldn't have come here."

Lewis Carroll, *Alice in Wonderland*

What "if ... then" sentence could the Cat use to prove that Alice is mad?

9. It has been stated that the expression $x^2 - x + 41$ always yields a prime number when $x \in W$. This is an example of inductive reasoning that can lead to an incorrect conclusion. Find a value for x that does not yield a prime number.

10. In Chapter 6, the term "**hypothesis**" was used to mean an unproved theory or proposition; a tentative conclusion. In this chapter, we use the term quite differently. How is the term used in this chapter?

233

10·2 Converses

The way in which a statement is written is very important. A reversal of a statement's hypothesis and conclusion can result in a new meaning for the sentence. When the subject and object of a sentence are reversed, a **converse** statement is produced.

Example 1

Write the converse of each statement and decide if it is true or false.

Statement	Converse Statement
1. If you have a boat, then you can waterski.	1. If you can waterski, then you have a boat.
2. If $x = 4$, then $x^2 - 16 = 0$.	2. If $x^2 - 16 = 0$, then $x = 4$.
3. If a line intersects two or more lines at unique points, then it is a transversal.	3. If a line is a transversal, then it intersects two or more lines at unique points.
4. All snakes are reptiles.	4. All reptiles are snakes.
5. All right angles measure 90°.	5. All 90° angles are right angles.

> Interchange the clauses after the words **if** and **then** in the "if ... then" statement.

Converses 1 and 2 are not necessarily true. (In sentence 2, x could also be −4.)
Converses of 3 and 5 are true.
Converse 4 is false.

When a statement and its converse are both true, the two statements can be combined to form one **"if and only if"** statement. For example, sentence 3 above can be written as: a line is a transversal if and only if it intersects two or more lines at unique points.

Example 2

Write the converse of each statement. If the statement and its converse are both true, then combine them to form one "if and only if" statement.

Statement	Converse Statement
1. If you are younger than your sister, then your sister is older than you.	1. If your sister is older than you, then you are younger than your sister.
2. If a triangle has exactly one 90° angle, then it is a right triangle.	2. If a triangle is a right triangle, then it has exactly one 90° angle.
3. If two angles are vertically opposite, then they are congruent.	3. If two angles are congruent, then they are vertically opposite.

Since both the statement and its converse are true for statements 1 and 2, each statement and its converse can be combined to give one true statement.

1. You are younger than your sister if and only if she is older than you.

2. A triangle is a right triangle if and only if it has exactly one 90° angle.

Statement 3 and its converse cannot be combined in an "if and only if" statement because the converse is not necessarily true.

Exercises

1. Write the converse of each statement. Comment on the truth of both the statement and its converse.
a. If it is the Moon, then it shines at night.
b. If it has snowed, then you can make a snowman.
c. If $x > y$, then $y < x$.
d. If flowers grow, then you have planted flower seeds.
e. If people like candy, then they will like ice cream.
f. If you do well in mathematics, then you will do well in physics.
g. If two line segments have the same length, then they are congruent.
h. If two lines are parallel, then the consecutive interior angles are supplementary.

2. Write each as an "if ... then" statement.
a. A spider is an eight-legged animal.
b. A teenager is between the ages of thirteen and nineteen inclusive.
c. A chemist studies molecules.
d. Children under six believe in the Easter Bunny.
e. An equilateral triangle has three congruent sides.
f. A polygon has three or more sides.
g. In driving from Winnipeg to Red Deer you drive through Saskatchewan.
h. The way up is the way down.

3. Write the converse of each statement. Comment on the truth of both the statement and its converse.
a. All right triangles are the sum of one ninety and two forty-five degree angles.
b. Every square is a rectangle.
c. Steam is vaporized water.
d. Lines that intersect at right angles are perpendicular to each other.
e. A helium filled balloon will float in the air.
f. Victoria is located on Vancouver Island.

4. Write a converse statement for each statement in Exercise 2.

5. In Exercises 3 and 4, if both the statement and its converse are true, then write them as "if and only if" statements.

6. Ming was asked to give the converse of the statement, "If you drive over the speed limit, then you run the risk of getting a speeding ticket." Ming answered, "You run the risk of getting a speeding ticket if you drive over the speed limit." Did Ming give the converse correctly? Explain.

7. Write each statement as two "if ... then" statements.
a. Two angles are supplementary if and only if their sum is 180°.
b. Trish is my friend if and only if she lends me her scarf.
c. A triangle is scalene if and only if the lengths of all the sides are different.
d. The expression $x + 3$ is an odd number if and only if x is an even number.

8. Consider this conversation at the Mad Hatter's tea party.

"Then you say what you mean," the March Hare went on.
"I do," Alice hastily replied; "at least — at least, I mean what I say — that's the same thing, you know."
"Not the same thing a bit!" said the Hatter. "Why, you might just as well say, 'I see what I eat' is the same thing as 'I eat what I see'!"
"You might just as well say," added the March Hare, "that 'I like what I get' is the same as 'I get what I like'!"
"You might just as well say," added the Dormouse, who seemed to be talking in his sleep, "that 'I breathe when I sleep' is the same as 'I sleep when I breath'!"
"It *is* the same thing with you," said the Hatter..."
Lewis Carroll, Alice in Wonderland

Write as an "if and only if" statement, the comments made at the tea party by each.
a. The Hatter
b. The March Hare
c. The Dormouse

10·3 Deductive Proofs

Writing a deductive proof is another form of problem solving, and as such, it involves following the four basic steps that you would use in solving any problem.

1. Understand the Problem   **3.** Carry Out the Plan
2. Develop a Plan   **4.** Look Back

To **understand the problem**, it is important that you know the meaning or definition of all the terms in the question. If the question is given in the form of an "if ... then" statement which must be proved, then recall that the "**if**" phrase is the given statement, or hypothesis; and the "**then**" phrase is what you are required to prove, or the conclusion. Drawing diagrams and labelling them, or using an existing diagram, can often help in understanding the problem. Some other strategies that may help are:
a. check for key words;
b. restate the problem in your own words;
c. identify extraneous information;
d. identify the given information and what is required to be proven or found.
These will aid in your understanding of the proof that you are required to write.

When **developing a plan**, it will be necessary to use the geometrical *tools* that are available to you. These include postulates, definitions, algebraic and geometric properties of shapes, and the various theorems of geometry which have been studied up to this point. These tools provide the reasons for any statements that you make in your proof. Problem-solving strategies that may be useful in this chapter include:
a. guessing a solution and checking it;
b. working backwards towards a solution;
c. dealing with similar or simpler situations.

Carrying out the plan involves the writing of the proof in a series of logical statements and deductions, and giving a reason for each statement that you make. Your proof should end with a concluding statement that answers the question.

Finally, **look back** to ensure that you have used deductive reasoning and that your conclusion is the answer to the problem. Also check to see if there is an alternate method that could have been used, or if there are any new facts that could be used in solutions to later problems.

Example

Prove that the opposite angles of a parallelogram are congruent.

1. To better understand this or any problem, ensure that you know the definition of each term, as well as how it is used in the problem. In this case, recall that opposite angles are across from each other, that congruent angles have the same measure, and that a parallelogram is a quadrilateral in which opposite sides are parallel.

To list the information in a deductive proof, it is often best to draw a diagram and label it with all the information that is given. In this case, name each of the vertices in the parallelogram, and label the parallel sides. State what is given and what you are required to prove.

236

GIVEN: *ABCD* is a parallelogram.

REQUIRED: To prove that $\angle A \cong \angle C$ and $\angle B \cong \angle D$.

2. To develop a plan it is necessary to use the tools of geometry. If necessary, review the properties of equations in Section 6·1.

You should ask yourself a variety of questions. Here are a number of questions that could be asked.

a. What do you know about parallel lines? Alternate angles and corresponding angles are congruent and consecutive interior angles are supplementary.

b. We know that $\angle A + \angle B = 180°$ because they are consecutive interior angles. What other pairs are also supplementary? $\angle B$ and $\angle C$, $\angle C$ and $\angle D$, and $\angle A$ and $\angle D$.

c. Are there any alternate angles or corresponding angles? Not with the present diagram.

d. Should we add any other parts to the diagram, such as a diagonal? This can be answered in the Look Back part of the process.

e. If $\angle A$ and $\angle B$ are supplementary and $\angle B$ and $\angle C$ are supplementary, does this tell us anything about $\angle A$ and $\angle C$? They should be the same size. Why? The subtraction property allows us to subtract $\angle B$ from both sides of an equation.

3. After asking and answering these questions, you should have a plan in mind for proving the opposite angles congruent. Carry out the plan by writing it as a formal proof in a two-column format. Use one column for the statements and a second column giving the reasons for making the statements. Start with the given information, and through the process of deductive reasoning, arrive at various conclusions that will lead you to the required conclusions.

Statement	Reason
1. *ABCD* is a parallelogram.	**1.** Given
2. $\overline{AD} \parallel \overline{BC}$	**2.** Definition of a parallelogram
3. $\angle A + \angle B = 180°$	**3.** Consecutive interior angles
4. $\overline{AB} \parallel \overline{DC}$	**4.** Definition of a parallelogram
5. $\angle B + \angle C = 180°$	**5.** Consecutive interior angles
6. $\angle A + \angle B = \angle B + \angle C$	**6.** Transitive property
7. $\angle A \cong \angle C$	**7.** Subtraction property
$\therefore \angle A \cong \angle C$	

Notice that each statement is a logical consequence of the preceding statement or statements. Now, write a proof, using the same format, that will allow you to prove that $\angle B \cong \angle D$.

4. Look back at the proof.

a. Are the statements in logical order? Have we given a correct reason for each statement? At this point, these two questions should both be answered yes.

b. Have you discovered any new facts which could be used later?

c. Could the same proof be used if the figure was a rectangle?

d. Could we use an alternative solution?

These questions, and many others, are the types that you should ask yourself when a proof has been completed and you are checking your work.

Exercises

1. Refer to the diagram and proof shown below. In the diagram, $\angle B \cong \angle C$ and $\overline{AD} \perp \overline{BC}$. Prove that $\angle BAD \cong \angle CAD$.

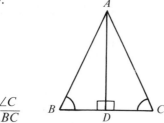

GIVEN: $\angle B \cong \angle C$
$\overline{AD} \perp \overline{BC}$

REQUIRED: To prove that $\angle BAD \cong \angle CAD$.
PROOF:

Statement	Reason
In $\triangle ADB$ and $\triangle ADC$,	
1. $\angle B \cong \angle C$	1. Given
2. $\overline{AD} \perp \overline{BC}$	2. Given
3. $\angle ADB \cong \angle ADC$	3. Definition of a perpendicular
4. $\angle B + \angle ADB + \angle BAD = 180°$	4. Angles of a triangle
5. $\angle C + \angle ADC + \angle CAD = 180°$	5. Angles of a triangle
6. $\angle B + \angle ADB + \angle BAD = \angle C + \angle ADC + \angle CAD$	6. Transitive property
7. $\angle BAD \cong \angle CAD$ $\therefore \angle BAD \cong \angle CAD$	7. Subtraction property

a. What definition(s) must be known in order to understand this proof?
b. What two parts of the proof give what is known and what must be proved?
c. In order to develop a plan, what ideas would be used?
d. State the transitive property.
e. What angles were subtracted from both sides of the equation in step 7?

2. Using $\triangle ABC$ and the perpendicular as shown in Exercise 1, complete a proof for these given and required statements.
GIVEN: $\angle BAD \cong \angle DAC$
$\overline{AD} \perp \overline{BC}$

REQUIRED: To prove that $\angle B \cong \angle C$.
PROOF:

Statement	Reason
In $\triangle ADB$ and $\triangle ADC$,	

3. In the Look Back section of the proof in the display, the question of whether there is an alternate solution to the problem was asked. Copy and complete this alternate proof.
GIVEN: $ABCD$ is a parallelogram.
REQUIRED: To prove that $\angle A \cong \angle C$ and that $\angle B \cong \angle D$.
PROOF:

Statement	Reason
1. Draw the diagonal AC.	1. Parallel lines
2. $\overline{AB} \parallel \overline{DC}$	2. ▆▆▆▆▆▆
3. $\angle BAC \cong \angle DCA$	3. Alternate angles
4. $\overline{AD} \parallel \overline{BC}$	4. ▆▆▆▆▆
5. $\angle DAC \cong \angle BCA$	5. ▆▆▆▆▆
6. $\angle DAB \cong \angle BCD$	6. Addition property
$\therefore \angle DAB \cong \angle BCD$	

Similarly, using diagonal BD, $\angle B \cong \angle D$.

a. In developing this plan, what ideas would be used?
b. What angles were added in step 6?
c. Could this proof serve as a pattern for proving that opposite angles of a quadrilateral are congruent? Explain.

Using the Library

Euclid's *Elements* has made a great impression on the generations of people that have followed this great work. This book has become a model for rigorous mathematical demonstration. A relatively modern outcome has been the creation of a field of study called **axiomatics**, which is devoted to examining the general properties of sets of postulates and of logical thinking.

Using the library, give a more general description of axiomatics, define an axiom and a postulate, and give three major distinctions between an axiom and a postulate. One source that you may wish to use is Howard Eves', *An Introduction to the History of Mathematics*, Saunders College Publishing, 1983.

10·4 Congruent Triangles — S.S.S.

If two triangles are congruent, then the corresponding sides and corresponding angles are congruent. However, it is not necessary to show that all six congruencies hold before two triangles can be proved congruent. The minimum requirements for congruency are stated in the **congruence postulates**.

Congruence postulate — S.S.S. If three sides of one triangle are congruent to three sides of a second triangle, then the two triangles are congruent.

Recall that a postulate is a statement that can be accepted as true without proof. However, we can demonstrate this postulate using inductive reasoning.

Using compasses and a straightedge, construct a triangle with $\overline{AB} = 6$ cm, $\overline{AC} = 5$ cm, and $\overline{BC} = 3$ cm. Cut out your triangle and compare it with two of your classmates' and with the triangle to the right. Are all the triangles congruent?

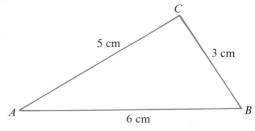

Example

Prove each statement using deductive reasoning.
a. $\triangle RAT \cong \triangle RBP$ **b.** $\triangle RAP \cong \triangle RBT$

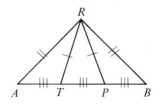

> Recall how lines are shown to be congruent.

GIVEN: $\overline{RT} \cong \overline{RP}$
$\qquad \overline{RA} \cong \overline{RB}$
$\qquad \overline{AT} \cong \overline{TP} \cong \overline{PB}$
REQUIRED: To prove that
a. $\triangle RAT \cong \triangle RBP$.
b. $\triangle RAP \cong \triangle RBT$.
PROOF:

In $\triangle RAT$ and $\triangle RBP$,

Statement	Reason
1. $\overline{RT} \cong \overline{RP}$	**1.** Given
2. $\overline{RA} \cong \overline{RB}$	**2.** Given
3. $\overline{AT} \cong \overline{PB}$	**3.** Given
4. $\triangle RAT \cong \triangle RBP$	**4.** S.S.S.
$\therefore \triangle RAT \cong \triangle RBP$	

In $\triangle RAP$ and $\triangle RBT$,

Statement	Reason
1. $\overline{RP} \cong \overline{RT}$	**1.** Given
2. $\overline{RA} \cong \overline{RB}$	**2.** Given
3. $\overline{AT} \cong \overline{PB}$	**3.** Given
4. $\overline{TP} \cong \overline{PT}$	**4.** Reflexive property
5. $\overline{AP} \cong \overline{BT}$	**5.** Addition property
6. $\triangle RAP \cong \triangle RBT$	**6.** S.S.S.
$\therefore \triangle RAP \cong \triangle RBT$	

Exercises

1. Refer to the example in the display.
a. What information was given before the proof was started?
b. What is required to be proved in part **a**?
c. What is required to be proved in part **b**?
d. How many congruent sides in each triangle are required in order to use the S.S.S. postulate?
e. In the proof of part **b**, what segment was added to both $\overline{AT}$ and $\overline{PB}$?

2. From the information given in the diagrams, which pairs of triangles can be stated as congruent by the S.S.S. postulate?
a.

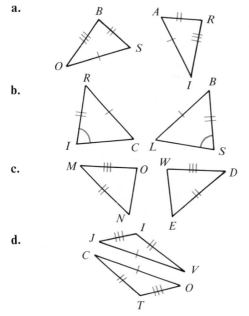

b.

c.

d.

3. Use the given information to produce a formal proof for the congruence of the two triangles.
GIVEN: $\overline{RM} \cong \overline{ST}$
$\overline{NM} \cong \overline{PT}$
$\overline{RN} \cong \overline{SP}$

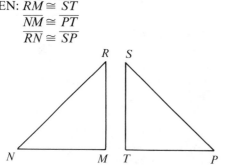

4. Prove that $\triangle GKH \cong \triangle JKH$.

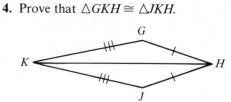

5. Given that D is the midpoint of $\overline{AB}$, and that $\overline{CB} \cong \overline{CA}$, prove that $\triangle ACD \cong \triangle BCD$.

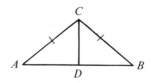

6. Use the diagram to prove that $\triangle RZT \cong \triangle VWS$. (*Hint:* Prove that $\overline{RT} \cong \overline{VS}$.)

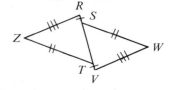

7. State the minimum amount of information which would have to be given in order to prove that each pair of triangles is congruent.
a. $\triangle GJI$ and $\triangle IHG$

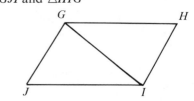

b. $\triangle KLM$ and $\triangle NML$

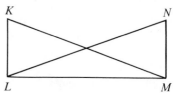

8. A **pentomino** is formed by five congruent squares that share a common side. Sketch the 12 different pentomino patterns. (*Hint:* You may want to use squares of paper or interlocking cubes to help with this problem.) Recall that a reflection image is not different from its object.

240

10·5 Congruent Triangles — S.A.S.

The S.S.S. congruence postulate is not the only postulate that allows us to prove that two triangles are congruent to each other.

Congruence postulate — S.A.S. If two sides and an included angle of one triangle are congruent to two sides and an included angle of another triangle, then the two triangles are congruent.

Example

Given quadrilateral *ABCD* with diagonals that bisect each other, prove that each statement is true. Use the four-step model as a guide to your solution.
a. $\triangle AOB \cong \triangle DOC$ **b.** $\triangle ABD \cong \triangle CDB$

a. Check whether you understand the problem. List what is known and what is to be found. Draw and label a diagram.

GIVEN: Quadrilateral *ABCD*.
       $\overline{AO} \cong \overline{CO}$
       $\overline{BO} \cong \overline{DO}$
REQUIRED: To prove that $\triangle AOB \cong \triangle DOC$.

In order to develop and carry out a plan, decide whether the S.S.S. or the S.A.S. congruence postulate is better suited for this situation.

Statement	Reason
In $\triangle AOB$ and $\triangle DOC$,	
1. $\overline{AO} \cong \overline{CO}$	**1.** Given
2. $\overline{BO} \cong \overline{DO}$	**2.** Given
3. $\angle AOB \cong \angle DOC$	**3.** Vertically opposite angles
4. $\triangle AOB \cong \triangle DOC$	**4.** S.A.S.
$\therefore \triangle AOB \cong \triangle DOC$	

> The S.A.S. postulate is better suited for this situation. Why?

Look back to ensure that the required conclusion has been reached. Explain what is meant by the included angle.

b. Review the definition of congruent plane figures. Two plane figures are congruent **if and only if** the measures of all the corresponding angles and lengths are congruent. This implies that:
1. if the corresponding angles and sides are congruent, then the figures are congruent, and
2. if the figures are congruent, then the corresponding angles and sides are congruent.

This means that once two triangles have been proved congruent, any of the corresponding sides or angles in the triangles are congruent. This is abbreviated as C.P.C.T. (corresponding part in congruent triangles). In $\triangle AOB$ and $\triangle DOC$, in addition to the sides and angles stated in the proof, the following congruences are also true by C.P.C.T. The formal proof will be done in Exercise 3.

     $\overline{AB} \cong \overline{CD}$ $\angle OAB \cong \angle OCD$ $\angle ABO \cong \angle CDO$

Exercises

1. Using compasses and a protractor, construct a triangle with $\overline{AB}$ = 5 cm, $\overline{AC}$ = 4 cm, and $\angle A = 35°$. Compare your triangle with two of your classmates. Are they the same?

2. Name the corresponding sides that would have to be congruent in order to use the S.A.S. congruence postulate.

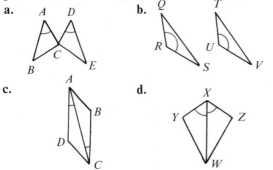

a.

b.

c.

d.

3. Copy and complete to prove that $\triangle ABD \cong \triangle CDB$ from the example in the display.
GIVEN: Quadrilateral $ABCD$.

███████████
███████████

REQUIRED: To prove that $\triangle ABD \cong$ ███████
PROOF:

Statement	Reason
In $\triangle ABD$ and $\triangle CDB$,	
1. $\overline{AB} \cong \overline{CD}$	**1.** ███████████
2. $\angle ABD \cong \angle CDB$	**2.** ███████████
3. $\overline{BD} \cong \overline{DB}$	**3.** ███████████
4. $\triangle ABD \cong \triangle CDB$	**4.** ███████████
∴ ███████████	

4. Prove the indicated triangles congruent by using the S.A.S. congruence postulate.
a. $\triangle RSV \cong \triangle TSV$

b. $\triangle KLM \cong \triangle NOM$

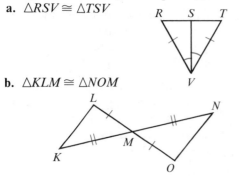

5. It is given that $\overline{AB}$ is the perpendicular bisector of $\overline{MN}$. Write two statements that you know about angles and lengths of segments.

6. In $\triangle PQR$, $\overline{QS}$ is the perpendicular bisector of $\overline{PR}$. Prove that $\triangle PQS \cong \triangle RQS$ and that $\angle P \cong \angle R$.

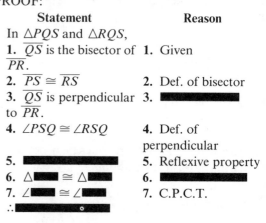

GIVEN: $\overline{QS}$ is the perpendicular bisector of $\overline{PR}$.
REQUIRED: To prove that $\triangle PQS \cong \triangle RQS$ and that $\angle P \cong \angle R$.
PROOF:

Statement	Reason
In $\triangle PQS$ and $\triangle RQS$,	
1. $\overline{QS}$ is the bisector of $\overline{PR}$.	**1.** Given
2. $\overline{PS} \cong \overline{RS}$	**2.** Def. of bisector
3. $\overline{QS}$ is perpendicular to $\overline{PR}$.	**3.** ███████████
4. $\angle PSQ \cong \angle RSQ$	**4.** Def. of perpendicular
5. ███████████	**5.** Reflexive property
6. $\triangle$███ $\cong \triangle$███	**6.** ███████████
7. $\angle$███ $\cong \angle$███	**7.** C.P.C.T.
∴ ███████████ ∘	

7. In the diagram, $\overline{MT} \cong \overline{MB}$ and $\overline{AM} \cong \overline{OM}$.

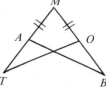

a. What additional information would be required to prove that $\triangle MTO \cong \triangle MBA$ using the S.A.S. congruence postulate?
b. What additional information would be required to prove that $\triangle MTO \cong \triangle MBA$ using the S.S.S. congruence postulate?
c. What two pairs of triangles could be proved congruent if there was sufficient information in order to prove $\angle T \cong \angle B$ by C.P.C.T.?
d. Prove that $\triangle MTO \cong \triangle MBA$.

8. Given △*ABE* with congruent parts as shown on the diagram. Copy and complete parts **a** and **b**, and write a formal proof for part **c**.

a. △*ABC* ≅ △*AED* **b.** △*ADB* ≅ △*ACE*

c. ∠*ADC* ≅ ∠*ACD*

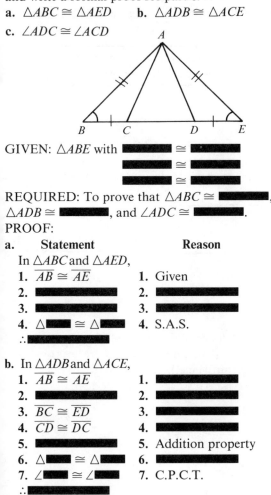

GIVEN: △*ABE* with ▭▭▭ ≅ ▭▭

▭▭ ≅ ▭▭

▭▭ ≅ ▭▭

REQUIRED: To prove that △*ABC* ≅ ▭▭, △*ADB* ≅ ▭▭, and ∠*ADC* ≅ ▭▭.

PROOF:

a.

Statement	Reason
In △*ABC* and △*AED*,	
1. $\overline{AB} \cong \overline{AE}$	1. Given
2. ▭▭▭	2. ▭▭▭
3. ▭▭▭	3. ▭▭▭
4. △▭ ≅ △▭	4. S.A.S.
∴ ▭▭▭	

b.

In △*ADB* and △*ACE*,	
1. $\overline{AB} \cong \overline{AE}$	1. ▭▭▭
2. ▭▭▭	2. ▭▭▭
3. $\overline{BC} \cong \overline{ED}$	3. ▭▭▭
4. $\overline{CD} \cong \overline{DC}$	4. ▭▭▭
5. ▭▭▭	5. Addition property
6. △▭ ≅ △▭	6. ▭▭▭
7. ∠▭ ≅ ∠▭	7. C.P.C.T.
∴ ▭▭▭	

9. Use quadrilateral *YXWZ*, and the information shown in the diagram to answer each of the following.

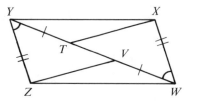

a. What segment will have to be added to both $\overline{YT}$ and $\overline{WV}$ in order to prove that $\overline{YV} \cong \overline{WT}$?

b. What congruence postulate is needed to prove that △*XTW* ≅ △*ZVY*?

c. Prove that △*XTW* ≅ △*ZVY*.

d. What other three congruences will be true if △*XTW* ≅ △*ZVY*?

e. Prove that △*XYW* ≅ △*ZWY*.

f. After you have completed the proof in part **e**, how do you know that $\overline{YX} \cong \overline{WZ}$?

g. Prove that △*WVZ* ≅ △*YTX* using the S.S.S. congruence postulate.

10. In the diagram, $\overline{AD} \parallel \overline{CB}$, $\overline{DE} \cong \overline{BE}$, and $\overline{AD} \cong \overline{CB}$. Prove each.

a. △*ADE* ≅ △*CBE* **b.** $\overline{AE} \cong \overline{CE}$

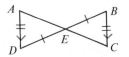

11. A given quadrilateral has diagonals that bisect each other. If this is true, then the quadrilateral should be a parallelogram.

a. Write the above statements as an "if ... then" statement.

b. State the hypothesis and the conclusion of your "if ... then" statement.

12. When you wish to prove an "if ... then" statement, the hypothesis forms the given part of the statement, while the conclusion is what is to be proved. Complete these four steps to prove that if the diagonals of a quadrilateral bisect each other, then the opposite sides of the quadrilateral are congruent.

a. Draw a diagram of a quadrilateral in which the diagonals bisect each other.

b. State the given part in terms of the diagram.

c. State the part to be proved in terms of the diagram.

d. Prove the "if ... then" statement.

Braintickler

Locate seven points, no three of which are collinear, so that every set of three distinct points is the set of the vertices of an isosceles triangle. (*Hint:* Change your point of view.)

10·6 Congruent Triangles — A.S.A.

A third congruence postulate that allows us to prove that two triangles are congruent is stated in terms of a pair of corresponding angles and a contained side.

> **Congruence postulate — A.S.A.** If two angles and a contained side of one triangle are congruent to two angles and a contained side of another triangle, then the two triangles are congruent.

Example

Prove that the opposite sides of a parallelogram are congruent.

1. Understand the Problem
Recall that a parallelogram is a quadrilateral with each pair of opposite sides parallel. Any part of this definition can be used in the proof.

GIVEN: Quadrilateral $ABCD$ is a parallelogram.

$$\overline{AB} \, \| \, \overline{DC}$$
$$\overline{AD} \, \| \, \overline{BC}$$

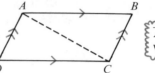

$\overline{AC}$ is a transversal as well as a diagonal. Why?

REQUIRED: To prove that $\overline{AB} \cong \overline{DC}$ and $\overline{AD} \cong \overline{BC}$.

2. Develop a Plan
When there are no triangles present in the diagram, it is often necessary to "create" two triangles in order to prove congruence. This will require the addition or construction of one or more lines onto the existing diagram. In this case, constructing the diagonal (the transversal), AC, creates two triangles that can be proved congruent.

3. Carry Out the Plan
PROOF: Construct transversal AC.

Statement	Reason
In $\triangle ABC$ and $\triangle CDA$,	
1. $\overline{AB} \, \| \, \overline{DC}$	1. Given
2. $\angle BAC \cong \angle DCA$	2. Alternate interior angles
3. $\overline{AD} \, \| \, \overline{BC}$	3. Given
4. $\angle DAC \cong \angle BCA$	4. Alternate interior angles
5. $\overline{AC} \cong \overline{CA}$	5. Reflexive property
6. $\triangle ABC \cong \triangle CDA$	6. A.S.A.
7. $\overline{AB} \cong \overline{DC}$ and $\overline{AD} \cong \overline{BC}$	7. C.P.C.T.
$\therefore \overline{AB} \cong \overline{DC}$ and $\overline{AD} \cong \overline{BC}$	

4. Look Back
Therefore, if a quadrilateral is a parallelogram, then both pairs of opposite sides are congruent. What is meant by the contained side in the A.S.A. congruence postulate?

> **Theorem** The opposite sides of a parallelogram are congruent.

Exercises

1. Using compasses, a protractor, and a straight-edge, construct a triangle with $\overline{AB}$ = 4 cm, $\angle A = 30°$, and $\angle B = 45°$. Compare your triangle with two of your classmates'. Are they the same?

2. Each pair of triangles has one pair of congruent sides. Give the pairs of angles which would have to be congruent in order to use the A.S.A. congruence postulate.

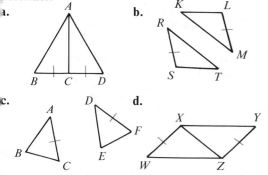

a. **b.**

c. **d.**

3. State which congruence postulate could be used to prove each pair of triangles congruent. If more than one postulate applies, give them both. If no postulate applies, indicate this.

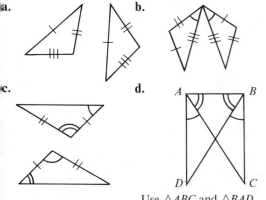

a. **b.**

c. **d.**

Use $\triangle ABC$ and $\triangle BAD$.

4. In $\triangle ABC$, $\overline{AD}$ is the perpendicular bisector of $\overline{BC}$.

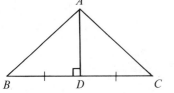

a. What two given statements may be written from the statement "$\overline{AD}$ is the perpendicular bisector of $\overline{BC}$"?

b. Which side is included in both $\triangle ABD$ and $\triangle ACD$?

c. Prove that $\triangle ABD \cong \triangle ACD$.

d. List the three other pairs of sides and angles which are congruent by C.P.C.T.

5. Two hunters, in determining the width of a river, constructed the triangles shown with $\overline{KL} \| \overline{MN}$, $\overline{KP} \cong \overline{NP}$, and $\overline{LP}$ = 85 m.

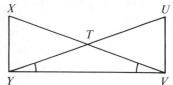

a. Copy the diagram.

b. If $\overline{ML}$ is the transversal, then state the pair of alternate interior angles which are congruent.

c. If $\overline{KN}$ is the transversal, then state the pair of alternate interior angles which are congruent.

d. State the third pair of angles which are congruent and give the reason for the congruence.

e. Are three pairs of congruent angles sufficient for proving the two triangles congruent? Explain.

f. Which pair of angles is not needed to use the A.S.A. postulate?

g. Prove $\triangle KLP \cong \triangle NMP$.

h. Why does $\overline{MP}$ = 85 m?

6. In the figure shown below, $\overline{XY} \perp \overline{YV}$, $\overline{UV} \perp \overline{YV}$, and $\angle TYV \cong \angle TVY$. (*Hint:* When two figures overlap, it is sometimes easier to draw them in separate diagrams.)

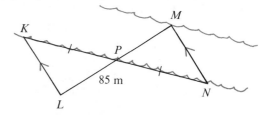

a. Copy the diagram and mark the given information on the diagram.

b. Which side is common to both triangles?

c. Prove $\triangle XYV \cong \triangle UVY$.

7. Three hikers determined the distance across a lake by constructing two triangles as shown. They made $\overline{BC} \cong \overline{CD}$ and $\overline{DE} = 180$ m. Prove that $\overline{BA} = 180$ m.

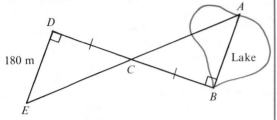

8. In $\triangle ADE$, $\angle 1 \cong \angle 4$ and $\angle 2 \cong \angle 3$.

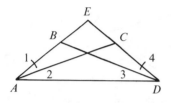

a. What two angles make up $\angle BAD$?
b. What two angles make up $\angle CDA$?
c. Is $\angle BAD \cong \angle CDA$? Why?
d. Prove that $\triangle BAD \cong \triangle CDA$.
e. Prove $\overline{BD} \cong \overline{CA}$.

9. In $\triangle ABE$, $\angle BAC \cong \angle EAD$, $\overline{AB} \cong \overline{AE}$, and $\angle B \cong \angle E$.

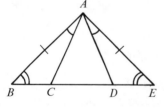

a. State the three congruent parts of each triangle that would be required to prove that $\triangle ABC \cong \triangle AED$.
b. Prove that $\overline{BC} \cong \overline{ED}$.
c. If we wish to prove that $\overline{BD} \cong \overline{EC}$, then what congruent segment(s) should be added to both $\overline{BC}$ and $\overline{ED}$?
d. The final step in a deductive proof is to look back to see if there are alternative methods that could be used in the proof. By using $\triangle ABD$ and $\triangle AEC$, prove that $\overline{BD} \cong \overline{EC}$ in a different way.

For Exercises 10 and 11,
a. ensure that you are familiar with the definitions of all terms in the theorem.
b. write each statement as an "if ... then" statement.
c. draw a suitable diagram and label it.
d. write the given and required information for each theorem.
e. develop a plan for proving the theorem and write the proof of each theorem.
f. look back at your proof and be prepared to use the results in any succeeding theorems.

10. Prove that the diagonals of a parallelogram bisect each other.

11. The following diagrams have two angles and a noncontained side congruent.
a. Prove that $\triangle MNP \cong \triangle RST$.
b. Write an "if ... then" statement for this deduction. Call it the **S.A.A. congruence postulate**. What does S.A.A. stand for?
c. How does this differ from the A.S.A. congruence postulate?

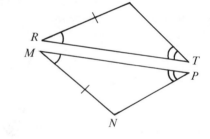

Braintickler

The figure shown below is that of a trapezoid with two angles measuring $90°$. Using only four straight lines, divide the figure into four congruent parts, each of equal size and shape, and each having the same shape as the original figure.

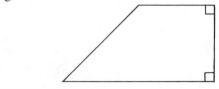

246

10·7 Isosceles Triangles

In Chapter 6, the definition of an isosceles triangle was given as a triangle with two congruent sides. In this section, we will prove certain properties of isosceles triangles.

> **Theorem** In an isosceles triangle, the angles opposite the congruent sides are congruent.

In order to prove this theorem, first draw an isosceles triangle ABC and the bisector of $\angle A$ to intersect $\overline{BC}$ at D. This theorem can also be written as: if a triangle is isosceles, then the angles opposite the congruent sides are congruent.

GIVEN: $\triangle ABC$ where $\overline{AB} \cong \overline{AC}$.
REQUIRED: To prove that $\angle B \cong \angle C$.
PROOF:

Statement	Reason
1. $\overline{AB} \cong \overline{AC}$	1. Given
2. $\angle BAD \cong \angle CAD$	2. Construction
3. $\overline{AD} \cong \overline{AD}$	3. Reflexive property
4. $\triangle BAD \cong \triangle CAD$	4. S.A.S.
5. $\angle B \cong \angle C$	5. C.P.C.T.
$\therefore \angle B \cong \angle C$	

Exercises

1. State, and prove, the converse of the theorem given in the display.

2. In the Look Back step for the proof in the display, prove the theorem in another way. (*Hint:* Draw the median from side $\overline{BC}$ to the vertex A.)

3. Given $\triangle ABC$, with $\overline{AB} \cong \overline{AC}$ and $\angle BAD \cong \angle CAD$. Prove that $\overline{BD} \cong \overline{CD}$ using two different congruence postulates.

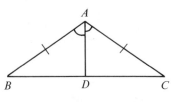

4. Prove that in an isosceles triangle, the bisector of the vertex angle is the bisector of the base.

5. In $\triangle MQR$, $\overline{NP} \parallel \overline{QR}$ and $\overline{MN} \cong \overline{MP}$. Prove that $\overline{MQ} \cong \overline{MR}$.

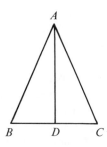

6. Prove that the median from the vertex of an isosceles triangle is perpendicular to the third side. Remember: a median joins the vertex and the midpoint of the opposite side in a triangle.

7. Prove that in an isosceles triangle, the altitude to the base bisects the vertex angle.

8. In $\triangle ACD$, $\overline{AC} \cong \overline{AD}$. Prove that $\angle ACB \cong \angle ADE$.

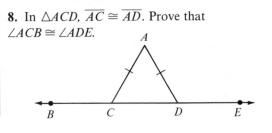

247

10·8 Indirect Reasoning

Sometimes it is not possible to prove directly that something is true. As a result, an attempt is made to prove that it cannot be false. This is called **indirect reasoning**. For example, two lines can be proved parallel by proving that they do not intersect.

There are three steps to follow when using indirect reasoning.

1. State all the possibilities. In this section, we deal with cases where there are only two possibilities: either the statement is true or it is false.
2. Using direct reasoning, prove one alternate possibility leads to a contradiction of at least one known fact.
3. State that since the remaining possibility can't be false, it is the only possible solution.

Consider this reasoning.
Bill is accused of assaulting a store owner during a robbery on October 5. The prosecuting attorney tells the court that during the robbery attempt, the store owner was bitten on the hand leaving a full set of deep teeth marks. Bill's lawyer presents his case saying, "If my client is guilty, then he must have had teeth on October 5. But I have a statement from Bill's dentist which states that his front teeth were removed on October 2 and a new bridge was not installed until October 10. Therefore, Bill could not have been the man who assaulted the store owner on October 5, and he is not guilty of the charge."

Notice that the lawyer followed the three steps of indirect reasoning.

Example

Prove that if two lines are cut by a transversal such that the alternate angles are congruent, then the two lines are parallel.

GIVEN: l_1 and l_2 with a transversal, t, such that $\angle 1 \cong \angle 2$.
REQUIRED: To prove that $l_1 \parallel l_2$.
PROOF:

Statement	Reason
1. Assume that l_1 and l_2 are not parallel and will intersect at P.	**1.** To attempt to prove the contradiction
2. $\triangle RSP$ has an exterior angle, $\angle 1$.	**2.** Definition of an exterior angle
3. $\angle 1 > \angle 2$	**3.** An exterior angle of a triangle is greater than any interior opposite angle.
4. But $\angle 1 \cong \angle 2$.	**4.** Given
5. Steps 3 and 4 are contradictory.	
6. Therefore, the assumption is false.	
7. Therefore, $l_1 \parallel l_2$.	**7.** Indirect reasoning

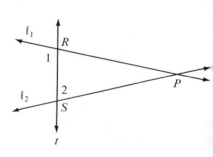

248

<table>
<tr><td colspan="2">

Theorem If two lines are cut by a transversal, such that the **a**lternate **a**ngles are congruent, then the lines are **p**arallel — A.A.P.

</td></tr>
</table>

Exercises

1. Use indirect reasoning to prove each statement below. State the initial assumption that you would make. Remember that the statement and the assumption must cover all cases.

a. All crows are black.

b. In $\triangle XYZ$, $\angle X \not\cong \angle Y$. ($\not\cong$ means "not congruent to".)

c. In $\triangle HIG$, $\angle G$ is a right angle.

d. Variables a and b are not equal.

e. $\ell_3 \parallel \ell_4$.

f. $\triangle RST$ is equilateral.

g. Quadrilateral $ABCD$ is a square.

h. In $\triangle ABC$, $\angle 3$ is not an exterior angle.

2. In $\triangle PQR$, $\angle Q = 55°$ and $\angle R = 75°$. Copy and complete the indirect reasoning proof to show that $\angle P \neq 60°$. Supply your own given and required information, and the reason why each statement is made.

Statement	Reason
1. Either $\angle P = 60°$ or $\angle P \neq 60°$.	**1.** 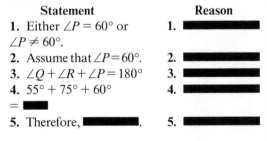
2. Assume that $\angle P = 60°$.	**2.**
3. $\angle Q + \angle R + \angle P = 180°$	**3.**
4. $55° + 75° + 60°$ =	**4.**
5. Therefore,	**5.**

3. In $\triangle ABC$, $\angle A$ is an obtuse angle. Prove that neither $\angle B$ nor $\angle C$ can be obtuse. (*Hint:* Prove $\angle B$ is not obtuse, then prove that $\angle C$ is not obtuse.)

4. If n is a natural number which is prime, then copy and complete this indirect reasoning proof to show that $2n$ is not prime. Supply your own given and required information, and the reasons why each statement is made.

Statement	Reason
1. Either $2n$ is prime or it isn't.	**1.**
2. Assume that $2n$ is prime.	**2.**
3. n is a natural number which is prime. ($n \geq 2$)	**3.**
4. Then, $2n$ is an even number. ($2n \geq 4$)	**4.**
5. Every even natural number greater than 2 is not prime.	**5.**
6. ∴	**6.**

5. If n is an integer such that n^2 is odd, then prove that n is odd.

Historical Note

Seeing is believing, at least we have been led to believe so. Escher is a Dutch artist. The spatial paradoxes which he draws have fascinated people for years. This is a picture reproduced from the book, *The Graphic Work of M.C. Escher*. Notice that the water seems to flow endlessly as it makes four right-angled turns and passes over the waterfall to turn the waterwheel and return to the original channel. What is the trick that Escher used in drawing this picture? Try to find Escher's book in your school library. It contains other examples of his artistic paradoxes. Draw a paradox such as this.

10·9 Parallel Lines

In the previous section, it was shown that two lines are parallel if the alternate interior angles formed by a transversal are congruent. In this section, two additional theorems concerning parallel lines will be introduced and proven.

> **Theorem** When a transversal intersects two lines forming congruent corresponding angles, then the two lines are **parallel** — C.A.P.

GIVEN: ℓ_1 and ℓ_2 with a transversal, t.
  $\angle 3 \cong \angle 7$
REQUIRED: To prove that $\ell_1 \parallel \ell_2$.
PROOF:

Statement	Reason
1. $\angle 3 \cong \angle 7$	1. Given
2. $\angle 7 \cong \angle 6$	2. Vertically opposite angles
3. $\angle 3 \cong \angle 6$	3. Transitive property
4. $\ell_1 \parallel \ell_2$	4. A.A.P.
$\therefore \ell_1 \parallel \ell_2$	

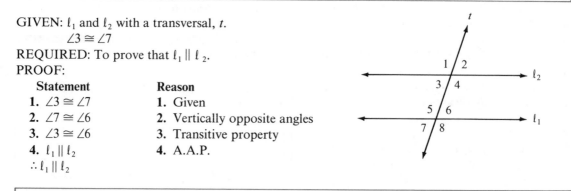

> **Theorem** If a transversal intersects two lines such that two consecutive interior angles are supplementary, then the two lines are **parallel** — C.I.A.P.

The proof of this theorem is left as an exercise.

Exercises

1. Give an example of each using both diagrams.
a. alternate interior angles
b. corresponding angles
c. consecutive interior angles

2. If $\angle 1 \cong \angle 2$, then find the measure of $\angle 3$ and $\angle 4$.

3. Why are C.A.P. and C.I.A.P. used for the two theorems in the display?

4. In which of the figures is $\ell_1 \parallel \ell_2$?

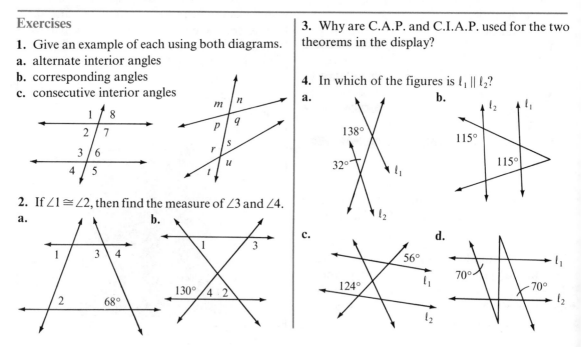

5. Which lines are parallel?

a.

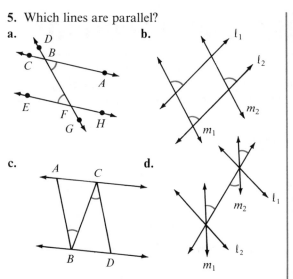

b.

c.

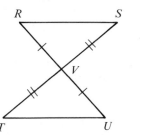

d.

6. Analyze the proof in the display. Describe the plan that was carried out to prove the lines parallel.

7. Prove the C.I.A.P. Theorem stated in the display. State the given and required information and follow a plan similar to the example in the display.

8. In polygon $RSTU$, $\overline{RV} \cong \overline{UV}$ and $\overline{SV} \cong \overline{TV}$.

a. One plan for a deductive proof is to work backwards. If we wish to prove that $\overline{RS} \parallel \overline{TU}$, then name a pair of angles that would have to be congruent.
b. Name the two triangles which would have to be congruent if the angles in part **a** are to be congruent.
c. Is there sufficient information to prove that these two triangles are congruent?
d. By reversing the process, that is working from part **c** to part **a**, prove that $\overline{RS} \parallel \overline{TU}$.

9. In $\triangle ABC$, $\overrightarrow{CE}$ bisects $\angle BCD$.
a. If $\angle A \cong \angle 2$, then prove $\overrightarrow{AB} \parallel \overrightarrow{CE}$.
b. If $\angle B \cong \angle 3$, then prove $\overrightarrow{AB} \parallel \overrightarrow{CE}$.

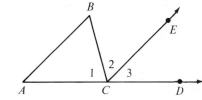

10. Refer to the postulate and second theorem given in the display of Section 6·6. How do they compare to the two theorems in this lesson?

11. In quadrilateral $MNPQ$, $\overline{MN} \parallel \overline{QP}$ and $\angle 1 \cong \angle 2$. Prove that $\overline{MQ} \parallel \overline{NP}$. (*Hint:* Draw a diagonal.)

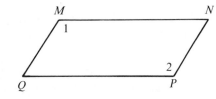

For Exercises 12 and 13, prove the theorem given.

12. If one side of a quadrilateral is both congruent and parallel to the side opposite it, then the quadrilateral is a parallelogram.

13. The diagonals of a rectangle are congruent.

14. Using six congruent squares, how many nets are there that can be folded to form a cube? One is shown for you.

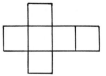

15. Take the 12 pentominos found in Exercise 8 of Section 10·4 and draw them on graph paper. Cut out the 12 shapes and put them together to form a rectangle with these dimensions.
a. 5 by 12   **b.** 4 by 15   **c.** 6 by 10

10·10 The Pythagorean Theorem

The Pythagorean Theorem is one of the more powerful theorems of mathematics. There have been many proofs developed over the years. This section will examine some of these proofs and suggest how you can develop your own proof. This proof was done by James A. Garfield many years before he became President of the United States.

GIVEN: A right triangle NMP with $\angle N$ as the right angle.
REQUIRED: To prove that $c^2 = a^2 + b^2$.
PROOF: Construct $\triangle MKL$ congruent to $\triangle NMP$ so that K, M, and N are collinear.
$\triangle LMP$ is a right triangle since K, M, and N are collinear and $\angle KML + \angle NMP = 90°$. Explain.
$KLPN$ is a trapezoid since $\overline{KL} \parallel \overline{NP}$. Explain.

The area of a trapezoid equals the sum of the areas of the three triangles. Recall that the formula for the area of a trapezoid is given by $A = \frac{1}{2}h(a+b)$, where a and b are the two lengths, and h is the height of the trapezoid.

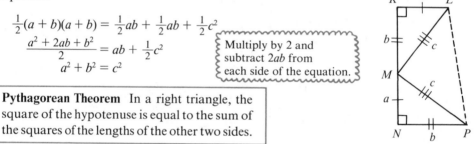

$$\frac{1}{2}(a + b)(a + b) = \frac{1}{2}ab + \frac{1}{2}ab + \frac{1}{2}c^2$$
$$\frac{a^2 + 2ab + b^2}{2} = ab + \frac{1}{2}c^2$$
$$a^2 + b^2 = c^2$$

Multiply by 2 and subtract $2ab$ from each side of the equation.

Pythagorean Theorem In a right triangle, the square of the hypotenuse is equal to the sum of the squares of the lengths of the other two sides.

Exercises

1. State the converse of the Pythagorean Theorem. We shall accept the converse as true without proof.

2. Quadrilateral $MNPQ$ is a square with sides of length $(a + b)$ units. Inside this square there are 4 right triangles whose sides are lengths of a units and b units as shown in the diagram. There is also a quadrilateral with sides of length c units.

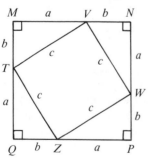

a. How do we know that the four right triangles are all congruent? (Understand the Problem.)
b. How can you establish that $TVWZ$ is a square? (Develop a Plan.)
c. By finding the area of the large square in two different ways, prove the Pythagorean Theorem. (Carry Out the Plan.)

3. In $\triangle PQR$, $\angle R = 90°$ and $\overline{RM}$ is the altitude to $\overline{QP}$.

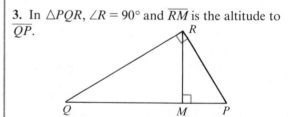

a. If $\overline{QR} = 24$ cm and $\overline{PR} = 18$ cm, then find the length of $\overline{QP}$ and $\overline{RM}$. Use similar triangles to find the length of $\overline{RM}$.
b. If $\overline{RP} = 12$ cm and $\overline{QP} = 20$ cm, then find the length of $\overline{QR}$ and $\overline{RM}$.

10·11 Proofs for Constructions

In Chapter 6, constructions were done using only a straightedge and compasses. In this section, those constructions will be proven deductively. Some extra line segments may be required before starting the proof.

Example

Draw any angle *ABC*. Bisect the angle using compasses and a straightedge. Prove that the construction bisects ∠*B*.

GIVEN: Any angle *ABC*.
REQUIRED: To prove that ∠*B* is bisected after the required construction.
PLAN: To prove that △*ABD* ≅ △*CBD* and hence that ∠*ABD* ≅ ∠*CBD*.
PROOF: Join *A* to *D* and *C* to *D*.

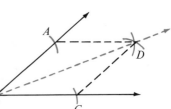

Statement	**Reason**
In △*ABD* and △*CBD*,	
1. $\overline{AB} \cong \overline{CB}$	1. Construction of congruent arcs
2. $\overline{AD} \cong \overline{CD}$	2. Construction of congruent arcs
3. $\overline{BD} \cong \overline{BD}$	3. Reflexive property
4. △*ABD* ≅ △*CBD*	4. S.S.S.
5. ∠*ABD* ≅ ∠*CBD*	5. C.P.C.T.
∴∠*B* is bisected.	

Exercises

For each of the constructions in this section, use only a straightedge and compasses.

1. Draw any ∠*ABC*. Construct a second angle congruent to ∠*ABC*. Prove that the two angles are congruent.

2. Draw $\overleftrightarrow{AB}$ with point *P* on the line. Construct a perpendicular to $\overleftrightarrow{AB}$ through *P*. Label the perpendicular $\overrightarrow{PQ}$. Prove that ∠*APQ* and ∠*BPQ* are right angles.

3. Draw $\overline{AB}$. Construct the perpendicular bisector of $\overline{AB}$. Label the perpendicular bisector $\overleftrightarrow{PQ}$. Prove that $\overleftrightarrow{PQ}$ is the perpendicular bisector of $\overline{AB}$. Remember that you must prove that $\overleftrightarrow{PQ}$ is both perpendicular to, and the bisector of, $\overline{AB}$.

4. Draw $\overleftrightarrow{AB}$ and point *P* not on the line. Construct a line through *P* parallel to $\overleftrightarrow{AB}$. Label a point on the new line, *C*. Prove that $\overleftrightarrow{CP} \parallel \overleftrightarrow{AB}$.

5. Construct an isosceles triangle with congruent sides $\overline{AB}$ and $\overline{AC}$. Construct the bisector of ∠*A* and let it meet $\overline{BC}$ at *D*. Prove that $\overline{AD}$ is an altitude of the triangle.

6. Draw any isosceles triangle with congruent sides $\overline{AB}$ and $\overline{AC}$. Find the midpoint of $\overline{BC}$ and label it *M*. Join *A* to *M*. Prove that
a. $\overline{AM}$ bisects ∠*A*.
b. $\overline{AM}$ is perpendicular to $\overline{BC}$.

7. Draw any triangle *ABC*. Find the midpoint of $\overline{AC}$ and $\overline{BC}$. Label the points *R* and *S* respectively. Prove that $\overline{RS} \parallel \overline{AB}$. (*Hint:* Extend $\overline{RS}$ to *T* such that $\overline{RS} \cong \overline{ST}$. Join *T* to *B*. Prove that △*CRS* ≅ △*BTS*.)

8. Draw any quadrilateral *ABCD*. Locate the midpoint of each side. Join the midpoints to form another quadrilateral. Prove that the new quadrilateral is a parallelogram. (*Hint:* Use the results of Exercise 7.)

10·12 The Circle

The circle is one of the more interesting geometric figures. In this section, the parts of a circle will be reviewed and some of the properties relating to the circle will be introduced.

A circle is a set of points (locus) that are equidistant from a fixed point. This fixed point is the centre of the circle. Study the diagrams to review the parts of a circle.

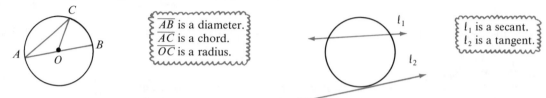

$\overline{AB}$ is a diameter.
$\overline{AC}$ is a chord.
$\overline{OC}$ is a radius.

l_1 is a secant.
l_2 is a tangent.

The four-step problem-solving model, used in deductive proofs with triangles, is also used for deductive proofs with the circle.

Example 1

Prove that if a line is the perpendicular bisector of a chord, then it passes through the centre of the circle.

GIVEN: Circle with centre at O and $\overleftrightarrow{CD}$ as the perpendicular bisector of the chord AB.
REQUIRED: To prove that $\overleftrightarrow{CD}$ passes through centre O.
PROOF:

Statement	Reason
1. $\overline{AC} \cong \overline{BC}$	1. Perpendicular bisector is equidistant from the end-points of a chord.
2. $\overline{AO} \cong \overline{BO}$	2. Radius of a circle
3. O lies on $\overleftrightarrow{CD}$.	3. $\overleftrightarrow{CD}$ is the set of all points equidistant from A and B.
∴O lies on $\overleftrightarrow{CD}$.	

> **Theorem** If a line is the perpendicular bisector of a chord, then it passes through the centre of the circle.

This theorem leads to two interesting corollaries. A **corollary** is a logical inference based on known facts or theorems.

> **Corollaries**
> 1. If a radius is perpendicular to a chord, then it bisects the chord.
> 2. If a radius bisects a chord, then it is perpendicular to the chord.

Example 2

Draw a circle with a radius of 2 cm. Draw a tangent $\overleftrightarrow{AB}$ to the circle at point C. Measure $\angle OCB$ and $\angle OCA$.
$\angle OCB \cong \angle OCA = 90°$.

> **Theorem** If a line is tangent to a circle, then it is perpendicular to the radius at the point of contact.

Exercises

1. Prove that the corollaries in the display are true.

2. Find the measure of ∠OKQ using a protractor. If $\overleftrightarrow{QT}$ is a tangent, then what is the measure of ∠OKT?

3. In the diagram, $\overline{OM} = 5$ cm and $\overline{ON} = 11$ cm. Find the length of $\overline{MN}$. (*Hint:* $\overline{MN}$ is a tangent to the circle.)

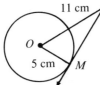

4. This circle has a radius of 5 cm. Find the length of chord $\overline{EG}$ if $\overline{OF} = 3$ cm. (*Hint:* $\overline{OF}$ is the perpendicular bisector of $\overline{EG}$.)

5. The chord of a circle with a radius of 8 cm is 10 cm long. The radius and the chord of the circle intersect at the point P.
a. Draw a diagram and place the given information on the diagram.
b. Calculate the length from the centre of the circle to the point P.

6. State which triangles are congruent and the congruence postulate that proves them congruent.

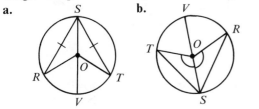

7. How could compasses and a protractor be used to find the centre of a circle?

8. Radius OR is perpendicular to a chord WZ and intersects chord WZ at point P. If $\overline{WP} = 5x - 6$ units and $\overline{PZ} = 3x + 4$ units, then find the length of $\overline{WZ}$.

9. Calculate the measure of ∠ORT.

a.   **b.**

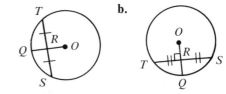

10. In the diagram, $\overline{LN}$ is a diameter and $\overline{LN}$ is perpendicular to $\overline{KM}$. Prove that $\overline{LK} \cong \overline{LM}$.

11. In the diagram, $\overline{AC}$ and $\overline{BD}$ are diameters.
a. Prove that $\overline{AD} \cong \overline{BC}$.
b. Prove that $ABCD$ is a rectangle.

12. Line segments BA and CA are tangents to the circle with centre at O.

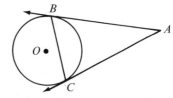

a. Prove that $\overline{AB} \cong \overline{AC}$. (*Hint:* Use a congruence theorem.)
b. This is the **tangent theorem**. State the theorem in the form of an "if ... then" statement.
c. Calculate the measure of ∠A if ∠B = 6h + 20 and ∠C = 12h − 25.

10·13 Angles, Arcs, and Chords

A circle, with centre O, is drawn with chords AC and BC. Line segments AO and BO are radii of the circle. Measure $\angle AOB$ and $\angle ACB$. What relationship do you find between the two angles?

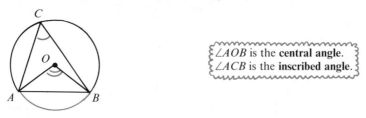

$\angle AOB$ is the **central angle**.
$\angle ACB$ is the **inscribed angle**.

The central angle, and the inscribed angle, are **subtended** by the same arc. In this case, it is arc AB.

Theorem The measure of the central angle is twice the measure of the inscribed angle if they subtend the same arc.

Another circle with inscribed angles QPN and QMN is shown. Using a protractor, find the measure of $\angle QPN$ and $\angle QMN$. What relationship do you find between the two angles?

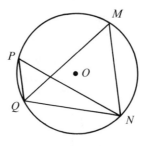

Theorem The measures of two inscribed angles subtended by the same arc are equal.

Exercises

1. In your own words, define the terms "central angle", "inscribed angle", and "subtend".

2. Name the inscribed angles which are subtended by the arc LMN.

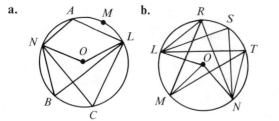

a. **b.**

3. Calculate the measures of $\angle a$, $\angle b$, $\angle c$, and $\angle d$.

a.

b.

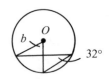

c.

d.

4. Calculate the measures of $\angle m$ and $\angle n$.

a.

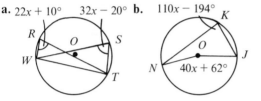

b.

54°

n

$\bullet O$

5. Calculate the measures of $\angle R$ and $\angle K$.

a. $22x + 10°$ $32x - 20°$ **b.** $110x - 194°$

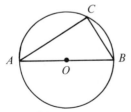

6. Draw a circle with a radius of 3 cm. On this circle, construct the central angle and the inscribed angle subtended by arc AB when the inscribed angles have these measures. What is the measure of the central angle?

a. 62°   **b.** 54°   **c.** 90°   **d.** 105°

7. Write each theorem in the form of an "if ... then" statement.

a. The measure of a central angle is twice that of an inscribed angle subtended by the same arc.

b. The measures of two inscribed angles subtended by the same arc are equal.

8. Consider the inscribed angle subtended by a semicircle. Find the measure of the angle.

Copy and complete to find the measure of $\angle ACB$.
GIVEN: The measure of central angle AOB is 180°.
REQUIRED: To prove that the inscribed angle of a semicircle is 90°.

PROOF:

Statement	Reason
1. $\angle AOB = $ 	**1.** Diameter of the circle
2. $\angle C = \frac{1}{2}(\angle$ ████)	**2.** ████████
3. $\angle C = $ ████████	**3.** ████████

9. Copy and complete the theorem which describes the proof from Exercise 8.

> **Theorem** An inscribed ██████████ in a semicircle is a ████████ angle.

10. Consider the opposite angles of a quadrilateral inscribed in a circle.

a. Measure them to find a possible relationship.

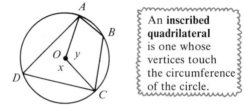

> An **inscribed quadrilateral** is one whose vertices touch the circumference of the circle.

b. Copy and complete to establish the relationship between the opposite angles of an inscribed quadrilateral.
GIVEN: A circle with an inscribed quadrilateral.
REQUIRED: To find a relationship between the opposite angles of the quadrilateral.
PROOF:

Statement	Reason
Consider $\angle D$ and $\angle B$.	
1. $\angle x + \angle y = $ ███°	**1.** Degrees in a circle
2. $2(\angle B) \cong \angle x$	**2.** Inscribed angle
3. $2(\angle D) \cong$ ████	**3.** ████████
4. $\angle x + \angle y \cong 2(\angle B + \angle D)$	
5. but, $\angle x + \angle y = 360°$	
6. $\therefore$ ████ $= 360°$	
7. $\therefore \angle B + \angle D = $ ████	

c. Write a proof, similar to part **b**, to prove that $\angle DCB \cong \angle DAB$.

d. Copy and complete this theorem that summarizes what has been discovered in this exercise.

> **Theorem** Opposite ████ in an inscribed quadrilateral are ████████.

257

10·14 Ratio and the Product of Lengths

There are many relationships that exist between the chords, secants, and tangents of a circle. Some of the relationships are developed in this section.

Theorem If two chords of a circle intersect, then the product of the lengths of the segments of one equals the product of the lengths of the segments of the second.

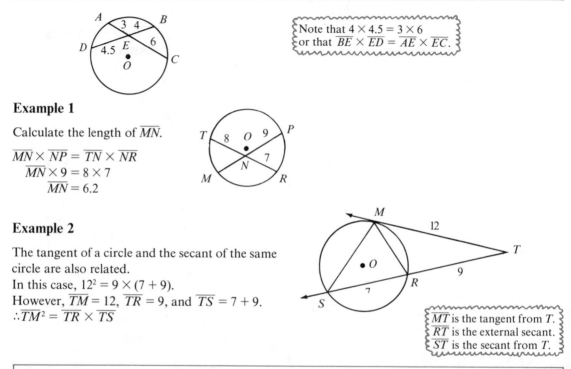

Note that $4 \times 4.5 = 3 \times 6$
or that $\overline{BE} \times \overline{ED} = \overline{AE} \times \overline{EC}$.

Example 1

Calculate the length of $\overline{MN}$.

$$\overline{MN} \times \overline{NP} = \overline{TN} \times \overline{NR}$$
$$\overline{MN} \times 9 = 8 \times 7$$
$$\overline{MN} = 6.2$$

Example 2

The tangent of a circle and the secant of the same circle are also related.
In this case, $12^2 = 9 \times (7 + 9)$.
However, $\overline{TM} = 12$, $\overline{TR} = 9$, and $\overline{TS} = 7 + 9$.
$\therefore \overline{TM}^2 = \overline{TR} \times \overline{TS}$

$\overline{MT}$ is the tangent from T.
$\overline{RT}$ is the external secant.
$\overline{ST}$ is the secant from T.

Theorem If a tangent and a secant intersect outside a circle at a point, T, then the square of the length of the tangent from T equals the product of the lengths of the secant from T and its external secant.

Example 3

How are two secants of a circle related?
In the diagram,
$$3 \times (5 + 3) = 4 \times (4 + 2)$$
$$24 = 24$$
Therefore, $\overline{FH} \times \overline{FG} = \overline{FK} \times \overline{FJ}$.

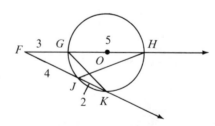

Theorem If two secants intersect outside a circle at a point, F, then the product of the length of one secant and its external secant is the same as the product of the length of the other secant and its external secant.

Exercises

1. Draw a large circle with two chords AC and DB intersecting at E. Measure each segment. After allowing for a possible error in measurement, would you conclude that $\overline{AE} \times \overline{EC} = \overline{DE} \times \overline{EB}$?

2. Calculate the lengths of $\overline{PR}$ and $\overline{TZ}$.

a. **b.**

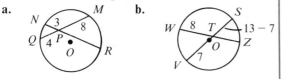

3. Use the diagram and the information given to find the length of the indicated segment.

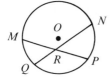

a. If $\overline{MR} = 9.5$, $\overline{RP} = 6.3$, and $\overline{NR} = 4.2$, then find $\overline{QR}$.

b. If $\overline{QR} = 3.7$, $\overline{RN} = 8.1$, and $\overline{RP} = 9.4$, then find $\overline{MR}$.

c. If $\overline{RP} = 5.4$, $\overline{MP} = 13$, and $\overline{RN} = 7.5$, then find $\overline{QN}$.

4. Copy this circle with a tangent and a secant intersecting outside the circle at T. Measure the length of the tangent from T, the secant from T, and the external secant. After allowing for possible error in measurement, would you conclude that $\overline{MT}^2 = \overline{ST} \times \overline{RT}$?

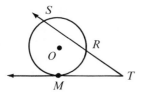

5. Calculate the length of $\overline{DC}$.

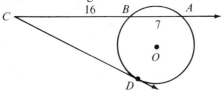

6. Find the length of the indicated line segment.

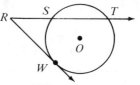

a. If $\overline{RS} = 6.3$ and $\overline{ST} = 5.4$, then find $\overline{RW}$.

b. If $\overline{RW} = 10$ and $\overline{RS} = 8$, then find $\overline{RT}$.

c. If $\overline{RT} = 16$ and $\overline{RW} = 6$, then find $\overline{RS}$.

7. Use the diagram in Exercise 6 to find the length of $\overline{RS}$ and $\overline{RT}$ if $\overline{ST} = 15$ and $\overline{RW} = 10$.

8. Draw a large circle with two secants intersecting outside the circle at F. Label the diagram as shown in the display. Measure each secant from F and each external secant. After allowing for possible error in measurement, would you conclude that $\overline{FH} \times \overline{FG} = \overline{FK} \times \overline{FJ}$?

9. Calculate the length of $\overline{QA}$ and $\overline{TR}$.

a. **b.**

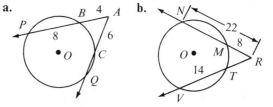

10. Write a proof for the first theorem presented in the display. (*Hint:* Compare $\triangle ADE$ and $\triangle CBE$.) Explain how you Developed a Plan.

11. Write a proof for the second theorem presented in the display. Explain how you Developed a Plan. (*Hint:* Show $\triangle STM \sim \triangle MTR$.)

12. Write a proof for the third theorem presented in the display. Explain how you Developed a Plan.

13. Two concentric pulleys have radii of 24 cm and 26 cm. What is the length of the chord of the larger pulley which is tangent to the smaller pulley?

14. A cross section of a circular storm sewer has a diameter of 1.8 m. When the water is 0.5 m deep, what is the width of the water surface?

10·15 Computer Application — Pythagorean Theorem

Pythagoras had no idea how powerful and useful his theorem was going to be when he first discovered it. Because of the simple nature of the theorem, it can be evaluated on the computer. In the following exercises, a general program for the Pythagorean Theorem will be developed, along with questions that will test your understanding of both the computer and the Pythagorean Theorem.

Exercises

1. Anwar ran out of gas while driving his car on a country road. He walked 4 km north and 5 km east before coming to a service station. In returning to his car, he cut across country.
a. If he walked directly to his car, then how far did he walk on his return trip?
b. How many kilometres did he save on his return trip?
c. Describe, either with an equation or in words, how the return distance was calculated.
d. Describe how you would calculate the distance he saved on the return trip.

2. When Anwar returned home, he wrote a program to calculate both distances in Exercise 1. Copy and complete the program to find Anwar's total return-trip distance.

```
05 REM TO FIND THE DISTANCE
10 REM OF THE RETURN TRIP
20 LET A = 4
30 LET B = 5
40 LET C = ■■■■■■■
50 PRINT "THE RETURN
DISTANCE IS EQUAL TO "; C;
" KM"
99 END
```

Before running the program, predict what the output will be.

3. Anwar then added two more lines to his program.

```
45 S = A + B - C
55 PRINT "S = "; S; " KM"
```

a. What is the purpose of lines 45 and 55?
b. Enter the program including lines 45 and 55 into your computer. Predict the output of the computer before running the program.
c. Run the program. Was your prediction reasonable?

4. Modify the program in Exercise 2, including lines 45 and 55, with an INPUT statement and revise line 55 to describe what S is finding. Use your program to find the return distance and distance saved by a plane which has flown a distance of 300 km from Calgary due north to Edmonton and then 500 km due east to Prince Albert. On the return trip the plane flies straight to Calgary from Prince Albert.

5. Another method of finding Pythagorean triplets is to use the values $a^2 + 2ab$, $2b^2 + 2ab$, and $a^2 + 2b^2 + 2ab$. Use these three expressions to generate five Pythagorean triplets. Write a program which will find all the Pythagorean triplets from $a = 1$ to 5 and $b = 1$ to 5.

6. Computers have become common place in many airports around the world.
a. Explain how computers have made air travel safer.
b. Can you suggest any ways that computers can make road travel safer?

10·16 Chapter Review

1. Write each as an "if ... then" statement.
a. All dogs are animals.
b. A person who travels to Germany travels to Europe.
c. The sum of the measures of the angles of a quadrilateral is 360°.

2. Write each statement as two "if ... then" statements.
a. You will see sharks and poisonous spiders if and only if you are in Australia.
b. Today is Canada Day if and only if it is July 1.

3. State the postulate or theorem which would be used to prove that $\triangle ABC \cong \triangle ABD$ in each.
a.   **b.**

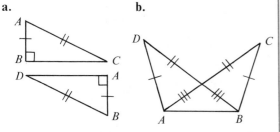

4. In the figure below, $\overline{HO} \perp \overline{OB}$, $\overline{DB} \perp \overline{OB}$, $\overline{OP} \cong \overline{BE}$, and $\overline{HO} \cong \overline{DB}$. Prove each.
a. $\triangle HOE \cong \triangle DBP$ **b.** $\triangle FPE$ is isosceles.

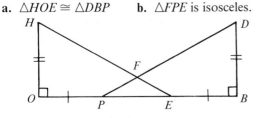

5. Prove by indirect reasoning that a quadrilateral cannot have four obtuse angles.

6. If $\overline{AB} \parallel \overline{CD}$, and $\overline{RT} \cong \overline{ST}$, then prove that $\triangle ABT \cong \triangle DCT$.

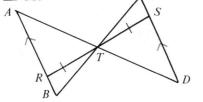

7. Use $\triangle ABE$ to answer each.

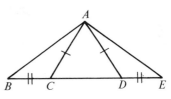

a. If we wished to prove that $\angle BAD \cong \angle EAC$, then which pair of triangles contain these two angles?
b. Which congruence postulate would you use to prove that $\triangle BAD \cong \triangle EAC$?
c. Is it necessary to use the addition property for segments in proving that $\triangle BAD \cong \triangle EAC$?
d. Is it possible to prove that $\angle ACB \cong \angle ADE$?
e. Could you prove that $\triangle ACB \cong \triangle ADE$? If so, which congruence postulate would you use?
f. If $\triangle ACB \cong \triangle ADE$, then is $\angle BAC \cong \angle EAD$?
g. If $\angle BAC \cong \angle EAD$, then by which property is $\angle BAD \cong \angle EAC$?

8. Using parallelogram $ABCD$, prove that $\overline{BF} \cong \overline{DE}$.

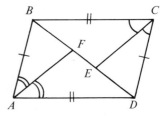

9. If P is a point inside rectangle $ABCD$, then prove that $\overline{PA}^2 + \overline{PC}^2 = \overline{PB}^2 + \overline{PD}^2$.

10. Calculate the measure of each indicated angle.
a.   **b.**

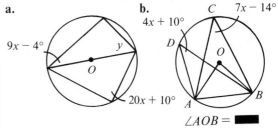

$\angle AOB = $ ▬

261

10·17 Chapter Test

1. Give an example of each.

a. A statement which is true but its converse is false.

b. A statement which is false but its converse is true.

c. A statement and its converse which are both true.

d. A statement and its converse which are both false.

2. Give a reason why each pair of lines is parallel.

a.   **b.**

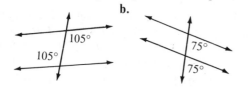

3. Find the pairs of congruent triangles and give the postulate or theorem which proves they are congruent.

a.   **b.**   **c.**

d.   **e.**   **f.**

g.   **h.**

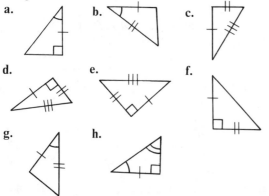

4. Using a straightedge and a protractor, construct an isosceles triangle ABC with $\angle B \cong \angle C$. Extend $\overline{BA}$ to E. Construct the bisector of $\angle EAC$ and label it $\overline{AD}$. Prove that $\overline{AD} \parallel \overline{BC}$.

5. If $\angle ROS \cong \angle TOS$, then prove that $\overline{RS} \cong \overline{TS}$.

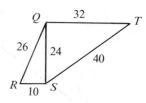

6. Using isosceles triangle QRS, prove each.

a. $\triangle QRT \cong \triangle SRT$

b. $\overline{RT}$ is the perpendicular bisector of $\overline{QS}$.

7. Quadrilateral $MNPQ$ is formed by joining four right triangles. By showing that $MNPQ$ is a square, prove that $c^2 = a^2 + b^2$.

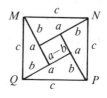

8. Prove that $\overline{RS} \parallel \overline{QT}$.

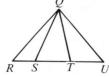

9. In $\triangle QRU$, $\overline{QS} \cong \overline{QT}$ and $\angle RQS$ is not congruent to $\angle UQT$. Prove that $\overline{RS}$ is not congruent to $\overline{UT}$.

10. Calculate the length of each indicated segment.

a.   **b.**

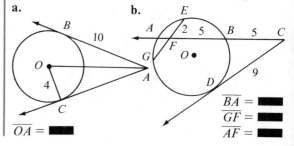

$\overline{OA} = $ ▬▬

$\overline{BA} = $ ▬▬
$\overline{GF} = $ ▬▬
$\overline{AF} = $ ▬▬

TRANSFORMATIONS

Tune Up

1. The points at $A(-5, 1)$, $B(2, 8)$, $C(3, -2)$, and $D(-1, -4)$ are the vertices of a quadrilateral. Find each.
a. the slopes of $\overline{AB}$, $\overline{AC}$, and $\overline{BD}$
b. the lengths of $\overline{BC}$, $\overline{CD}$, and $\overline{AD}$

2. Determine the slopes of the lines defined by each.
a. $3x + y = 1$ **b.** $x - 4y = 0$
c. $2x + 5y = 12$ **d.** $x + 6y = 2$

3. Determine the slopes of the lines perpendicular to these lines.
a. $8x - y = 5$ **b.** $3x + 2y = 5$

4. Using graph paper, draw a figure which satisfies the following conditions.
a. a rectangle with an area of 20 cm²
b. a triangle with a base of 4 cm and an area of 6 cm²

5. Find the point of intersection of these lines.
$3x + 2y = 12$
$x + 5y = 17$

6. A biologist discovered that a certain lily pad doubled in size every day. She further calculated that after 30 d, the pond would be completely covered by the lily pad. How long will it take before $\frac{1}{2}$ of the pond is covered?

7. Copy the diagram.

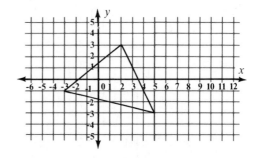

a. Draw the image after a translation under the mapping $(x, y) \rightarrow (x + 1, y + 3)$.
b. Determine the coordinates of the vertices of $\triangle A'B'C'$ under the translation in part **a**.

8. Copy the quadrilateral and draw the image of the quadrilateral under each transformation.
a. a reflection in the x-axis
b. a rotation of 90° about the origin

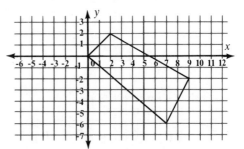

263

11·1 Transformations

The stage of a live theatre is the location of many different transformations or changes. Some pieces of furniture may be moved to other positions to be used in another scene, or other props may be rotated to give the audience a new view of the same object. Between scenes the stagehands quickly slide or rotate heavy objects to make the changes.

In mathematics, geometric figures undergo transformations. Some of these transformations change the figure's position or size. The characteristics which do not change under a transformation are said to be **invariant**. A transformation can be described by a sentence or an algebraic statement.

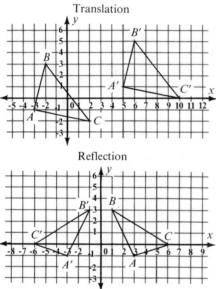

Translation

Reflection

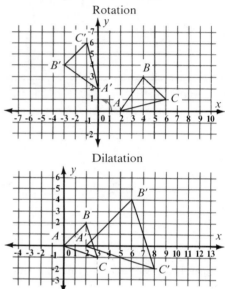

Rotation

Dilatation

Each type of transformation will be described geometrically as a mapping.
A maps onto A' or $A \rightarrow A'$. A' is the image of A.
B maps onto B' or $B \rightarrow B'$. B' is the image of B.
C maps onto C' or $C \rightarrow C'$. C' is the image of C.

Exercises

1. In your own words, describe the transformation which is illustrated.

a.

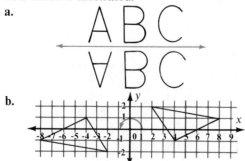

b.

2. Copy the figure shown and draw the images after reflections in the x-axis and the y-axis. Use a Mira if one is available.

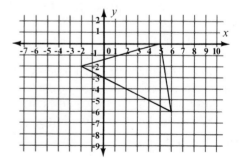

11·2 Translations

Patterned wallpaper is often designed by repeating one basic pattern many times. The whole pattern is made by translating, or sliding, the basic design in various directions until the paper is full. This type of transformation in which the object is slid into a new position is called a **translation**.

> A translation is a transformation in which an object is moved without turns or flips.

Example 1

Express this translation as a mapping: increase x by 5 and increase y by 8.

The mapping would be $(x, y) \rightarrow (x + 5, y + 8)$. All mappings describe the transformation of one set of points onto another set of points.

Properties which do not change in a transformation are **invariant**. If the image of a triangle is found using a translation, then what properties of the triangle are invariant? What happens to the lengths of the corresponding sides? Is there a change in the slopes of the corresponding sides? Are the angles of the two triangles congruent?

Example 2

Examine $\triangle ABC$, with vertices at $A(2, 1)$, $B(4, -4)$, and $C(0, -2)$, and its image under the translation $(x, y) \rightarrow (x + 3, y + 4)$. Find the lengths of the corresponding sides, the slopes of the corresponding sides, and the measures of the corresponding angles.

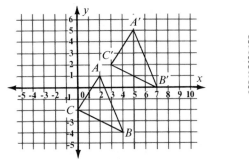

$$\triangle ABC \rightarrow \triangle A'B'C'$$
$$A(2, 1) \rightarrow A'(5, 5)$$
$$B(4, -4) \rightarrow B'(7, 0)$$
$$C(0, -2) \rightarrow C'(3, 2)$$

The length of $\overline{AB} = \sqrt{(x_2 - x_1)^2 + (y_2 - y_1)^2}$
$$= \sqrt{29}$$
Similarly, the length of $\overline{A'B'}$ is $\sqrt{29}$ units; the length of $\overline{BC}$ and $\overline{B'C'}$ is $2\sqrt{5}$ units; and the length of $\overline{AC}$ and $\overline{A'C'}$ is $\sqrt{13}$ units.

The slope of a line is found using the ratio $\dfrac{y_2 - y_1}{x_2 - x_1}$. Using this ratio, the slope of $\overline{AB}$ and $\overline{A'B'}$ is $-\dfrac{5}{2}$; the slope of $\overline{BC}$ and $\overline{B'C'}$ is $-\dfrac{1}{2}$; and the slope of $\overline{AC}$ and $\overline{A'C'}$ is $\dfrac{3}{2}$.

The measure of the corresponding angles can be found using a protractor. The measure of angles C and C' is 85°; A and A' is 58°, and B and B' is 37°.

These results show that the corresponding sides of the triangles are congruent, the corresponding angles of the triangles are congruent, and the corresponding sides have equal slopes. What does it mean when the slopes of lines are equal?

A transformation which preserves length and angle measure is an **isometry**.

Example 3

Explain this statement.

If length is preserved in a transformation, then angle measure is preserved under the same transformation.

This statement can be explained using the congruence postulates for congruent triangles. If the three sides of the object triangle are congruent to three sides of the image triangle, then the two triangles are congruent. When two triangles are congruent, the corresponding angles are congruent. Therefore, when length is preserved under a transformation, angle measure is also preserved.

Example 4

Translate $\triangle PQR$, with vertices at $P(-4, -1)$, $Q(-3, 3)$, and $R(-1, 0)$, under the mapping $(x, y) \longrightarrow (x + 6, y + 1)$. Show that the line segments joining the corresponding vertices of $\triangle PQR$ and $\triangle P'Q'R'$ are congruent and parallel.

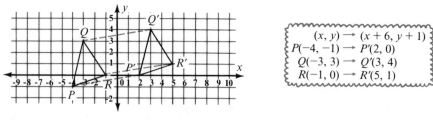

$$(x, y) \longrightarrow (x + 6, y + 1)$$
$$P(-4, -1) \longrightarrow P'(2, 0)$$
$$Q(-3, 3) \longrightarrow Q'(3, 4)$$
$$R(-1, 0) \longrightarrow R'(5, 1)$$

Line Segment	$\overline{PP'}$	$\overline{QQ'}$	$\overline{RR'}$
Slope	$\frac{1}{6}$	$\frac{1}{6}$	$\frac{1}{6}$
Length	$\sqrt{37}$	$\sqrt{37}$	$\sqrt{37}$

Since the slopes of the lines joining the corresponding vertices are equal, the lines are parallel.

Example 5

List the conclusions that can be made regarding the lengths, slopes, and angle measures of an object and its image under a translation. Also list the conclusions that can be made regarding the length and slope of the line segments joining the corresponding vertices in a translation.

The properties of a translation are listed in this chart.

Properties of Translations
a. Lengths, slopes, and angle measures are invariant.
b. The line segments joining the corresponding points of a figure and its image are parallel and congruent.

Exercises

1. Copy the figure shown and draw the image under this translation.

$(x, y) \rightarrow (x - 3, y + 1)$

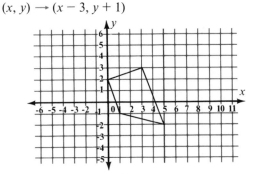

2. Find the coordinates of the image of the point under each translation.

a. $P(-3, 8)$; $(x, y) \rightarrow (x + 5, y - 5)$
b. $Q(2, 1)$; $(x, y) \rightarrow (x - 4, y)$
c. $R(-6, -2)$; $(x, y) \rightarrow (x + 6, y + 3)$

3. Write each translation as a mapping.

a. increase x by 5, increase y by 2
b. increase x by 1, decrease y by 9
c. decrease x by 3, decrease y by 8

4. Graph $\triangle ABC$ with vertices at $A(1, -1), B(3, 3)$, and $C(6, -2)$. Graph the image triangle $A'B'C'$ under this translation.

$(x, y) \rightarrow (x + 5, y - 2)$

5. Find the general mapping rule which translates the points to their images.

a. $J(5, -2) \rightarrow J'(1, 1)$
b. $K(-4, -1) \rightarrow K'(-5, 0)$

6. Triangle RST has vertices at $R(-2, 1), S(-1, 4)$, and $T(3, 2)$. Find the image triangle under the translation: x is increased by 2 and y is increased by 4.

a. Write the translation as a mapping rule.
b. Compare the slopes of $\overline{RS}$ and $\overline{R'S'}$.
c. Compare the lengths of $\overline{RT}$ and $\overline{R'T'}$.

7. Answer each using the mapping $(x, y) \rightarrow (x + 6, y + 2)$ and the points $A(-4, -1)$, $B(0, 1)$, and $C(-1, -2)$.

a. Find the coordinates of the image points.
b. Determine the slopes of $\overline{AA'}$, $\overline{BB'}$, and $\overline{CC'}$.
c. What do you notice about these slopes?
d. Determine the lengths of $\overline{AA'}$, $\overline{BB'}$, and $\overline{CC'}$.
e. What do you notice about these lengths?

8. Copy the diagram and use the properties of translations to draw the image under the transformation indicated by the arrow. (*Hint:* Find the translation that maps the point at the tail of the arrow to the point at the head of the arrow.)

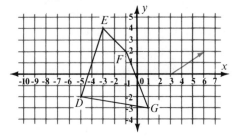

9. Triangle ABC has coordinates at $A(-2, 0)$, $B(1, -2)$, and $C(-4, -3)$.

a. Find the coordinates of the vertices of the image points A', B', and C' under the translation $(x, y) \rightarrow (x - 3, y - 1)$.
b. Describe the translation in your own words.
c. Find the slopes of $\overline{AB}$ and $\overline{AC}$.
d. What can be said about $\angle BAC$?
e. Find the slopes of $\overline{A'B'}$ and $\overline{A'C'}$.
f. What can be said about $\angle B'A'C'$?
g. Compare the measures of $\angle BAC$ and $\angle B'A'C'$.

10. Three of the vertices of parallelogram $ABCD$ are $A(0, 1), B(1, 4)$, and $D(5, 1)$.

a. Find the coordinates of C.
b. If the parallelogram is translated so that the side $\overline{AB}$ coincides with $\overline{CD}$, then find the coordinates of C' and D'.
c. Write the translation as a mapping.
d. Find the area of $ABC'D'$.

11. Triangle ABC, with vertices at $A(4, 3), B(7, 1)$, and $C(2, 0)$, is translated so that vertex B' is located at the origin.

a. Find the coordinates of A' and C'.
b. Show that $\triangle A'B'C'$ is a right triangle.
c. Find the area of $\triangle A'B'C'$.

11·3 Rotations

A design can be constructed by turning a shape about one point. This type of transformation is called a **rotation**.

Cut out of stiff cardboard a shape similar to $\triangle ABC$. Insert a pin through the cardboard near vertex A and place the triangle in a position so that side AB is close to horizontal. With your pencil trace an outline of $\triangle ABC$. Rotate the triangle a quarter turn and trace the figure again. Repeat this rotation two more times. The location of the pin is called the **centre of rotation**.

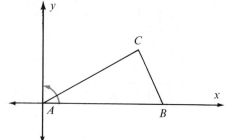

Arrows are used to indicate the direction of the rotation. Counterclockwise rotations are considered positive and clockwise rotations are negative.

Example 1

Triangle PQR has vertices at $P(1, 0)$, $Q(1, 4)$, and $R(-1, 4)$, and it is rotated $90°$ counterclockwise about the origin.

a. Plot the image triangle under this rotation.
b. Find the vertices of the image triangle.
c. Find a general mapping rule to describe this transformation.

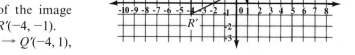

b. From the graph, the vertices of the image triangle are $P'(0, 1)$, $Q'(-4, 1)$, and $R'(-4, -1)$. Therefore, $P(1, 0) \rightarrow P'(0, 1)$, $Q(1, 4) \rightarrow Q'(-4, 1)$, and $R(-1, 4) \rightarrow R'(-4, -1)$.
c. The general mapping rule for a counterclockwise rotation of $90°$ about the origin is $(x, y) \rightarrow (-y, x)$.

Example 2

Triangle RST, with vertices at $R(3, 1)$, $S(4, 4)$, and $T(6, -2)$, is rotated $180°$ counterclockwise about the point $(1, 1)$. Find the coordinates of the vertices of the image triangle.

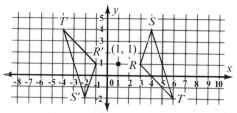

Rotate the triangle $180°$ to find the image points.
$R(3, 1) \rightarrow R'(-1, 1)$
$S(4, 4) \rightarrow S'(-2, -2)$
$T(6, -2) \rightarrow T'(-4, 4)$

By comparing the coordinates of the corresponding object points and image points, the mapping rule is $(x, y) \rightarrow (-x + 2, -y + 2)$.

> A rotation preserves length and angle measure; and the distances from the centre of rotation to a point and to its corresponding image are congruent.

Exercises

1. In Example 1, is side length and angle measure invariant? What conclusions can be drawn from this information about rotations? Explain.

2. Given any triangle, *ABC*, with the origin as the centre of rotation. Sketch the image under each rotation. (*Hint:* In which direction is a rotation positive? negative?)
a. 90°   **b.** 180°
c. 270°   **d.** −90°

3. Draw the image for a rotation of 90° and 180° about the point *A*.

a.

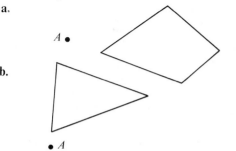

b.

4. Triangle *DEF* has vertices at *D*(0, −2), *E*(4, 0), and *F*(2, −5). Its image is found under a rotation of 90° about the origin.
a. Find the coordinates of the vertices of its image.
b. Describe the relation between the *x*-coordinates and the *y*-coordinates of each vertex and its image. Explain how this relation can be used to help draw the image of any shape under a 90° rotation about the origin.
c. Express this rotation as a mapping.

5. To locate the image of a point *P* under a rotation of 180°, draw a segment from the point *P* to the centre of rotation. Extend the segment through *P* to the point *P'* so that $\overline{PC} \cong \overline{P'C'}$, where *C* is the centre of rotation.
a. Use this method to draw the image of △*ABC* with vertices *A*(2, 1), *B*(3, 3), and *C*(6, 0) under a rotation of 180° about the origin.
b. Express a rotation of 180° about the origin as a general mapping rule.

6. Use the mappings from Exercises 4 and 5 to determine the coordinates of the images of these points under rotations of 90° and 180° about the origin.
a. *M*(−6, 8)   **b.** *N*(3, 2)   **c.** *P*(−1, −9)

7. Figure *ABCD* undergoes a rotation of 270° about the origin.

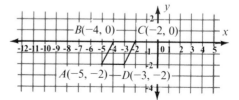

a. Find the coordinates of the vertices of its image.
b. Express a rotation of 270° about the origin as a mapping.

8. Use the mapping in Exercise 7 to determine the coordinates of the image points under a rotation of 270° about the origin.
a. *A*(5, −4)   **b.** *B*(−3, −10)   **c.** *C*(−7, 0)

9. If the coordinates of the vertices of the image triangle are *A'*(−3, 8), *B'*(3, 2), and *C'*(0, 4), then find the coordinates of the vertices of the original triangle under these mappings. In your own words, describe each rotation.
a. $(x, y) \rightarrow (y, -x)$
b. $(x, y) \rightarrow (-x, -y)$
c. $(x, y) \rightarrow (-y, x)$

10. Triangle *FGH* has vertices at *F*(1, 1), *G*(6, 3), and *H*(3, −2), and a centre of rotation at (2, 3). Triangle *FGH* undergoes a rotation of 90° about the origin.
a. Find the coordinates of the vertices of the image triangle.
b. Express this transformation as a mapping.

11. Points *U*(4, 1), *V*(1, 3), and *W*(7, 2) are transformed by a rotation of 180° with a centre of rotation at (1, 1).
a. Find the coordinates of the image points.
b. Express this transformation as a mapping.

12. Triangle *ABC* has vertices at *A*(−4, −1), *B*(−3, 4), and *C*(1, 2).

a. Graph the triangle and its image under a rotation of 90° about the origin.

b. Compare the triangles with respect to the length of the corresponding sides. What do you notice?

13. Triangle *FGH* has vertices at *F*(−2, −2), *G*(1, 4), and *H*(6, 2).

a. Compare the slopes of $\overline{FG}$ and $\overline{F'G'}$ under a rotation of 90° about the origin.

b. Compare the slopes of $\overline{FG}$ and $\overline{F'G'}$ under a rotation of 180° about the origin.

c. What conclusions can you make about slopes in rotations of 90° and 180° about the origin?

14. Triangle *PQR* has vertices at *P*(1, 4), *Q*(3, 5), and *R*(5, −2). The triangle undergoes a rotation of $(x, y) \rightarrow (y - 2, -x + 2)$.

a. Compare the lengths of the corresponding sides of the triangle and its image after the rotation.

b. Compare the slopes of the corresponding sides after the rotation.

15. Triangle *RST* has vertices at *R*(−2, 5), *S*(3, 4), and *T*(6, 1). After a rotation of $(x, y) \rightarrow (-y, x)$, compare the distances from the centre of rotation, (0, 0), to each of the vertices and their corresponding image points. What conclusions can you make?

16. The quadrilateral *DEFG* with coordinates *D*(−1, 2), *E*(0, 5), *F*(5, 4), and *G*(3, 3) is transformed under this mapping.

$(x, y) \rightarrow (-y + 3, x - 1)$

Compare the lengths of the sides of the quadrilateral and its image.

a. Are the lengths invariant?

b. Are the angle measures invariant? Explain.

17. Triangle *ABC*, with vertices *A*(0, 0), *B*(3, 5), and *C*(4, −2), is rotated 180° about the centre of rotation (−1, 3).

a. Copy the diagram and draw the image triangle.

b. Compare the distances from the centre of rotation to each of the vertices and their corresponding image points.

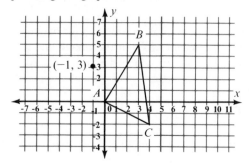

18. The image of △*JKL* is △*J'K'L'* under a $\frac{1}{4}$ rotation about the origin. Draw the triangles on a large sheet of graph paper so that the following construction may be completed.

a. Using compasses and a straightedge, construct the perpendicular bisectors of the line segments joining the corresponding vertices of the two triangles.

b. Describe the property that is illustrated in the constructions.

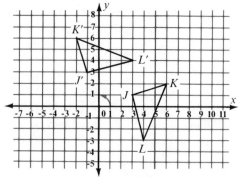

19. Triangle *PQR*, with vertices *P*(3, 2), *Q*(6, 5), and *R*(10, −4) is transformed under the mapping $(x, y) \rightarrow (-x + 2, -y - 2)$.

a. Determine the coordinates of the vertices of the image triangle.

b. On graph paper draw the triangle and its image. Use the construction described in Exercise 17 to determine the coordinates of the centre of rotation.

c. Use a protractor to measure the angles. Is angle measure preserved? Explain.

270

11·4 Reflections

Everyone has looked at themselves in a mirror. However, did you realize that the image you see is not the image that everyone else sees? By comparing your image in a mirror, and your image in a photograph, you will notice that the mirror image is a reflection of yourself.

In the reflections that are to be studied, the mirror or line of reflection will be placed in a variety of positions: the x-axis, the y-axis, the line $y = x$, and the line $y = -x$.

Example 1

Graph $\triangle RST$ having vertices at $R(-4, 3)$, $S(3, 6)$, and $T(-3, -2)$. Place a Mira along the line $y = x$ and draw the image of $\triangle RST$ as it would appear in the Mira.
a. Find the coordinates of the image triangle.
b. Write the general mapping rule.

a. From the graph, the vertices of the image triangle are $R'(3, -4)$, $S'(6, 3)$, and $T'(-2, -3)$.
b. The general mapping rule for a reflection in the line $y = x$ is $(x, y) \longrightarrow (y, x)$.

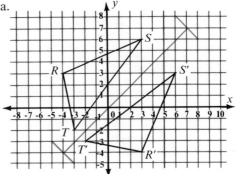

Example 2

Triangle ABC has vertices at $A(1, 1)$, $B(3, 4)$, and $C(6, 2)$. Draw the reflection of $\triangle ABC$ in the line $x = 0$ (the y-axis). Is this transformation an isometry?

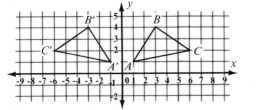

$$A(1, 1) \longrightarrow A'(-1, 1)$$
$$B(3, 4) \longrightarrow B'(-3, 4)$$
$$C(6, 2) \longrightarrow C'(-6, 2)$$
$$(x, y) \longrightarrow (-x, y)$$

Line Segment	AB	$A'B'$	AC	$A'C'$	BC	$B'C'$
Length	$\sqrt{13}$	$\sqrt{13}$	$\sqrt{26}$	$\sqrt{26}$	$\sqrt{13}$	$\sqrt{13}$
Slope	$\dfrac{3}{2}$	$-\dfrac{3}{2}$	$\dfrac{1}{5}$	$-\dfrac{1}{5}$	$-\dfrac{2}{3}$	$\dfrac{2}{3}$

Since the corresponding sides are congruent, the two triangles are congruent. Because the triangles are congruent, the corresponding angles are congruent. Therefore, a reflection in the y-axis will preserve length and angle measure and the reflection is an isometry.

> Any reflection is an isometry.

Although slope is not preserved, what pattern can be seen in the slopes of the corresponding sides? Will this same pattern of slopes be exhibited in a reflection in other lines? This pattern of slopes, as well as other properties, will be examined in the next example.

Example 3

Triangle PQR has vertices at $P(-6, 2)$, $Q(0, 8)$, and $R(2, 4)$. Triangle $P'Q'R'$ has vertices at $P'(2, -6)$, $Q'(8, 0)$, and $R'(4, 2)$.

a. Draw $\triangle PQR$ and $\triangle P'Q'R'$. Join the corresponding vertices.

b. Compare the slopes of the line segments joining the corresponding vertices.

c. Compare the slopes of the corresponding sides of each triangle. Is there a pattern?

d. Using compasses and a straightedge, construct the perpendicular bisectors of the lines joining the vertices.

e. Find an equation for the reflection line.

a.

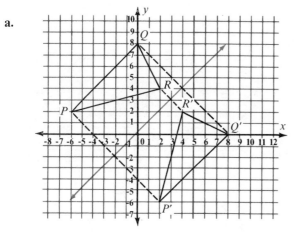

b. Using the slope formula, the slopes of the line segments joining the corresponding vertices are -1.

c. The slope of $\overline{PQ}$ is 1 and the slope of $\overline{P'Q'}$ is also 1.

The slope of $\overline{QR}$ is -2 and the slope of $\overline{Q'R'}$ is $\frac{-1}{2}$.

The slope of $\overline{PR}$ is $\frac{1}{4}$ and the slope of $\overline{P'R'}$ is 4.

There appears to be a pattern to the slopes of corresponding lines in a reflection. They are the reciprocals of each other.

d. The perpendicular bisectors of the lines joining the vertices are shown on the diagram.

e. Because the midpoints of the perpendicular bisectors lie on the line of reflection, we can find the equation of the line of reflection by finding the midpoints of any two of the bisectors. The midpoint of the third bisector can be used to verify our equation.

The midpoint of $\overline{PP'}$ is $(-2, -2)$ and the midpoint of $\overline{RR'}$ is $(3, 3)$.

Therefore, the slope of the line of reflection is 1.

$$1 = \frac{y - 3}{x - 3}$$
$$x - 3 = y - 3$$
$$y = x$$

Therefore, the line of reflection is the line $y = x$.

> Reflections preserve both angle measure and length, the line segments joining the corresponding vertices are parallel, the slopes of the corresponding sides are reciprocals, and the line of reflection is the perpendicular bisector of the lines joining corresponding vertices.

Exercises

1. The points $(4, 4)$, $(5, -7)$, and $(-3, 1)$ are transformed by a reflection in the x-axis.
a. Find the coordinates of the image points.
b. Describe this reflection as a mapping.

2. The points $(-1, -5)$, $(6, 2)$, and $(3, -8)$ are transformed by a reflection in the y-axis.
a. Find the coordinates of the images.
b. Describe the reflection as a mapping.

3. If the mapping for a reflection in the line $y = x$ is given as $(x, y) \rightarrow (y, x)$, then find the coordinates of the points whose images are $P'(-4, 10)$ and $Q'(3, 6)$.

4. The points $(-2, 4)$, $(3, 6)$, and $(1, -4)$ are reflected in the line $y = -x$.
a. Plot these points and graph the line $y = -x$.
b. Find the image points after a reflection in the line $y = -x$.
c. Describe the reflection in line $y = -x$ as a mapping.

5. Segment PR has endpoints at $P(5, 1)$ and $R(7, 4)$. Show that length is invariant under these reflections.
a. $(x, y) \rightarrow (-x, y)$ **b.** $(x, y) \rightarrow (x, -y)$
c. $(x, y) \rightarrow (y, x)$ **d.** $(x, y) \rightarrow (-y, -x)$

6. Triangle ABC has vertices at $A(-4, -1)$, $B(-1, 5)$, and $C(6, 2)$. Show that the line segments joining the corresponding vertices are parallel under a reflection in the y-axis.

7. Triangle FGH has vertices at $F(-6, -4)$, $G(2, 2)$, and $H(-1, -1)$. This triangle is transformed by a reflection in the x-axis.
a. Find the coordinates of the vertices of the image triangle.
b. Find the slopes of the corresponding sides of the two triangles.
c. Describe the pattern demonstrated using these slopes.

8. Triangle MNP has vertices at $M(-8, 6)$, $N(3, 9)$, and $P(0, -4)$ and is transformed under a reflection in the line $y = x$.
a. Find the coordinates of the vertices of the image triangle.
b. Show that the midpoints of the line segments joining the corresponding vertices lie on the line $y = x$.

9. Segment RS has endpoints at $R(-3, 8)$ and $S(-5, 1)$. Compare the slopes of $\overline{RS}$ and $\overline{R'S'}$ under these reflections.
a. $(x, y) \rightarrow (-x, y)$ **b.** $(x, y) \rightarrow (x, -y)$
c. $(x, y) \rightarrow (y, x)$ **d.** $(x, y) \rightarrow (-y, -x)$

10. Point $V(3, -5)$ is mapped onto $V'(-5, 3)$. Determine the equation of the line of reflection.

11. Triangle DEF has vertices at $D(-3, 5)$, $E(6, 8)$, and $F(9, 3)$. The image triangle under a reflection has vertices at $D'(-5, 3)$, $E'(-8, -6)$, and $F'(-3, -9)$.

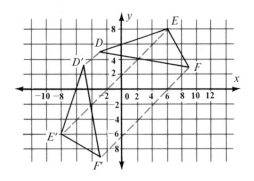

a. Find the coordinates of the midpoints of the two line segments DD' and FF'.
b. Find the equation of the line passing through these midpoints.
c. What is the particular significance of this line?

12. Triangle ABC, with vertices at $A(6, 2)$, $B(10, -4)$, and $C(2, -6)$, is transformed by the mapping $(x, y) \rightarrow (y + 2, x - 2)$.
a. Find the coordinates of the vertices of the image triangle.
b. Draw the two triangles.
c. Using compasses and a straightedge, construct the line of reflection.
d. What property has been used in this construction?
e. Find the equation of the line of reflection.

273

11·5 Invariance, Isometries, and Congruence

The three transformations (translations, rotations, and reflections) each have a number of common properties. A comparison of those properties will be made in this section.

The characteristics of a figure which are not changed in a transformation are invariant; while a transformation which preserves length is an isometry. In the previous sections, it was shown that translations, rotations, and reflections are all isometries. This chart shows some of the properties of transformations.

Properties of Transformations			
	Translation	Rotation	Reflection
Length	invariant	invariant	invariant
Angle measure	invariant	invariant	invariant
Slope	invariant	not invariant	not invariant
Segments joining corresponding points	parallel and congruent	no pattern	parallel
Perpendicular bisectors of the segments joining the corresponding points	perpendicular to the direction of the translation	all pass through the centre of rotation	coincide with the line of reflection
Note that the orientation, the direction of the vertex designation either clockwise or counterclockwise, is invariant in a translation and rotation, but is reversed in a reflection.			

Two figures are congruent if they have the same size and shape, or if there is some isometry that maps one shape onto the other. Since translations, rotations, and reflections maintain a figure's size and shape, each of these transformations would generate an image congruent to the object.

Translations and rotations create images while maintaining their orientation. Their images would be **directly congruent** to the object. However, reflections reverse the orientation and create images which are **indirectly congruent**.

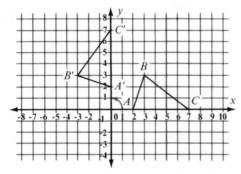

Rotation
Direct congruence

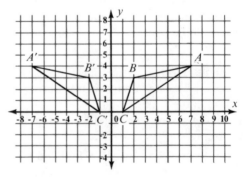

Reflection
Indirect congruence

Exercises

1. Refer to the object and its image as shown.

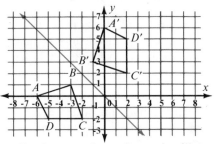

a. Describe the type of transformation illustrated.
b. Discuss the characteristics that are invariant.
c. Comment on the direction in which the vertices of the two quadrilaterals have been labelled.

2. If a transformation of $\triangle ABC \rightarrow \triangle A'B'C'$ preserves the slope and the length of the sides, then what is the nature of the transformation?

3. A triangle, with vertices at $J(0, 2)$, $K(4, 5)$, and $L(2, 0)$, is reflected in the line $y = x$.
a. Find the coordinates of J', K', and L'.
b. Show that the lengths are invariant.
c. Show that the slopes are not invariant.

4. Segment AB is rotated $180°$ about the centre of rotation, A. Explain how one might use the properties of a rotation to show that $\overline{AB}$ is congruent with $\overline{AB'}$.

5. Two points, $P(3, 3)$ and $Q(6, 4)$, are translated by decreasing both x and y by 2. Prove the quadrilateral formed by $PQP'Q'$ is a parallelogram.

6. Triangle ABC has vertices at $A(-1, 1)$, $B(-4, -2)$, and $C(-2, 2)$. It is reflected in the line $y = -x$. Show that $\triangle BB'C$ is isosceles.

7. Triangle ABC has vertices at $A(-4, -2)$, $B(-2, 2)$, and $C(0, 0)$. Triangle $A'B'C'$ is determined under the translation $(x, y) \rightarrow (-x, y)$.
a. Find the coordinates of the vertices of $\triangle A'B'C'$ and compare the lengths of the corresponding sides of the two triangles.
b. What conclusion can be drawn about the two triangles?

8. Describe which type of transformation has determined the image. Explain your answer.

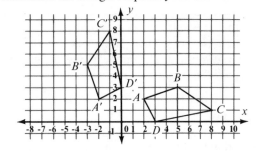

9. Consider the shapes on the coordinate grid below.

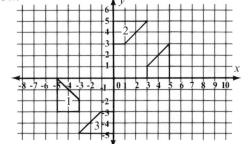

a. Find the transformation or series of transformations which will create the three images.
b. Indicate the type of congruence in each case.

10. A set of points in a quadrilateral is transformed under the mapping $(x, y) \rightarrow (-y, x)$.
a. Describe the transformation.
b. Will the congruence be direct or indirect?

11. Divide an equilateral triangle into 2 congruent parts.
a. Describe the transformation which maps one part onto the other.
b. Under these transformations, is there a direct or indirect congruence?
c. Repeat this process with 3 and then 4 congruent parts.

Using the Library

Write a report on the terms "googol" and "googolplex". In this report, include their meaning, where they are useful, and how the two terms were invented.

11·6 Images and Their Equations

In the previous sections, points contained in geometric figures and their transformations by isometries were studied. In this section, the transformation of the set of points defined by an equation will be examined. The image of any line under a transformation by an isometry will also be a line. The properties of a particular transformation can be used to determine the equation of the image line.

Under a translation, the points in the given line are transformed to another location as described by the mapping. Because slope is invariant in a translation, the slope of the image line will be the same as the slope of the given line. The equation of a line can be found if its slope and the coordinates of a point contained in the line are known.

Example

Find the equation of the image line formed when the set of points defined by the equation $2x - y = 3$ is translated by $(x, y) \rightarrow (x - 2, y + 4)$.

1. Understand the Problem

The object line is defined by the equation $2x - y = 3$.
The transformation is given by the mapping $(x, y) \rightarrow (x - 2, y + 4)$.
We must find an equation of the image line after the translation.

2. Develop a Plan

Since slope is invariant under a translation, the slope of the image line is the same as the slope of the object line. Therefore, we can find one image point and then use the point-slope process to find the equation of the image line.

3. Carry Out the Plan

The line $2x - y = 3$ can be written in the form $y = mx + b$ to find the slope.
$y = 2x - 3$
∴The required slope is 2.
A point on the object line can be the y-intercept, or $(0, -3)$.
$(0, -3) \rightarrow (-2, 1)$
$$\therefore 2 = \frac{y - 1}{x + 2}$$
$2x + 4 = y - 1$
$2x + 5 = y$

4. Look Back

Therefore the equation of the image line is $2x + 5 = y$.
Can we use this method with other isometries?

Although slope is not invariant in a rotation, rotating a line either 90° or 270° produces line segments which are perpendicular to each other; while rotating a line segment 180° produces parallel line segments.

Recall that reflecting lines in the x-axis or the y-axis produces line segments whose slopes are additive inverses.

Finally, reflecting in the lines $y = x$ or $y = -x$ produces lines whose slopes are additive inverses (reciprocals).

Exercises

1. Describe the relationship between the slope of a line and the slope of its image under a translation.

2. The equation of a line is $2x + 3y = 4$. If $8x + 12y = 2$ is the equation of the image under a translation, then show that slope has been invariant in this transformation.

3. The equation of a line is $6x - y = 4$. Find the equation of the image line under the following translations.

a. $(x, y) \rightarrow (x + 1, y + 4)$
b. $(x, y) \rightarrow (x - 3, y + 1)$
c. $(x, y) \rightarrow (x + 5, y - 1)$
d. $(x, y) \rightarrow (x, y + 6)$

4. A line whose equation is $5x + 2y = 1$ is transformed by a rotation of $270°$ about the origin.
a. Describe the relation between the slope of the image line and the slope of the object line.
b. Find the slope of the image line.
c. Find an equation for the image line.

5. Describe the relation between the slope of the image line and the slope of the object line for a rotation of $90°$ about the origin. Find the equation of each image line for a rotation of these object lines of $90°$ about the origin.

a. $x - 5y = -2$
b. $3x + 2y = 4$
c. $-4x + 2y = 9$
d. $x + y = 10$

6. A line whose equation is $2x + y = -6$ is transformed by a rotation of $270°$ with a centre of rotation at $(2, 0)$. Determine the equation of its image if the mapping for this rotation is given by $(x, y) \rightarrow (y + 2, -x + 2)$.

7. Describe the relationship between the slope of the image line and the slope of the object line for each transformation.
a. a reflection in the x-axis
b. a reflection in the y-axis
c. a reflection in the line $y = x$
d. a reflection in the line $y = -x$

8. The equation of a line is $5x + 3y = 8$.
a. Find the equation of the image line under a reflection given by the mapping $(x, y) \rightarrow (y, x)$.
b. Show that the slope of the line and the slope of its image are reciprocals.

9. A line whose equation is given by $3x - y = 10$ is transformed by a reflection in the y-axis.
a. Find the equation of the image line.
b. Find the coordinates of the point common to both lines.
c. Show that the slopes of the two lines are additive inverses. (*Hint:* Multiply the slopes together.)

10. A line whose equation is $6x + 2y = -5$ is transformed under the mapping $(x, y) \rightarrow (-y, -x)$. Find the equation of the image line.

11. The set of points in the line $4x - y = 5$ is translated by the mapping $(x, y) \rightarrow (x + 2, y - 6)$.
a. Find the equation of the image line.
b. Summarize the process by which the equation of the image was determined in the form "replace x by ■, and y by ■".

12. The points in a line are transformed by a rotation of $(x, y) \rightarrow (-x, -y)$.
a. Find the coordinates of any point, (a, b), under this mapping.
b. Since the coordinates of the image points are opposite in sign to those of the corresponding object points, the equation of the image line may be obtained by substituting what expressions for x and y in the original equation?

13. The points in a line are reflected in the x-axis.
a. Find the mapping for this transformation.
b. Find the coordinates of any point, (a, b), under this mapping.
c. The equation of the image line can be found by replacing the variables x and y in the original equation by what expressions?

14. A line is transformed by a reflection in the line $y = x$.
a. Find the general mapping.
b. Describe how to determine the equation and summarize it in the form "replace x by ■, and y by ■."

11·7 Composition

A plant may undergo a series of transformations in a cycle from plant to flower to seed and again to a plant. Just like the cycle of a plant through its various stages, the successive transformations of a geometric figure through different stages can be followed. In the diagram, $\triangle A'B'C'$ is the image of $\triangle ABC$ under a reflection in the line ℓ_1. Similarly, $\triangle A''B''C''$ is the image of $\triangle A'B'C'$ under a reflection in the line ℓ_2. Each reflection preserves the size and shape of its object and the final image and the object are directly congruent.

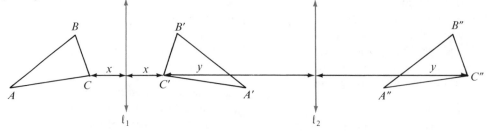

Other properties of a composition (series) of reflections can be seen by following the transformation of point C through its various stages.

A point and its image are equidistant from each line of reflection. From the diagram, the distance between C and C'' is $2x + 2y$. This implies that the total distance the object is transformed is twice the distance between the two parallel lines of reflection.

Also, the distance between the two lines of reflection is $x + y$.

A transformation may be composed of a combination of transformations.

Example 1

Answer each of the following by referring to the transformation of $\triangle RST$.

a. What type of transformation resulted in $\triangle R'S'T'$?

b. What type of transformation resulted in $\triangle R''S''T''$?

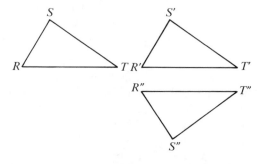

a. The image $\triangle R'S'T'$ is the result of a translation.

b. The image $\triangle R''S''T''$ is the result of a reflection of $\triangle R'S'T'$. The reflection line is parallel to the direction of the translation.

This composite transformation, in this case a translation followed by a reflection, is a **glide reflection**. Since the lengths and angle measures are invariant in a translation and reflection, those properties are maintained in a glide reflection.

Example 2

Triangle ABC has vertices at $A(5, 2)$, $B(8, -1)$, and $C(3, -2)$. Find the coordinates of the vertices of the image $\triangle A''B''C''$ after a reflection in the y-axis followed by a reflection in the x-axis.

Under a reflection in the y-axis, $(x, y) \rightarrow (-x, y)$, the coordinates would be found as $A(5, 2) \rightarrow A'(-5, 2)$, $B(8, -1) \rightarrow B'(-8, -1)$, and $C(3, -2) \rightarrow C'(-3, -2)$. Under the reflection in the x-axis, $(x, y) \rightarrow (x, -y)$, the coordinates would be found as $A'(-5, 2) \rightarrow A''(-5, -2)$, $B'(-8, -1) \rightarrow B''(-8, 1)$, and $C'(-3, -2) \rightarrow C''(-3, 2)$.

Exercises

1. Verify the coordinates of the composition in Example 2 by drawing the transformations on a grid. Find one transformation that will result in $\triangle ABC$ mapping directly onto $\triangle A''B''C''$.

2. Copy the figure and draw the image for each composition.

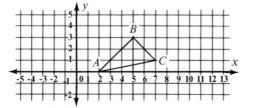

a. a rotation of 90° about the origin followed by a reflection in the x-axis

b. a reflection in the line $y = x$ followed by a reflection in the y-axis

c. a reflection in the x-axis followed by a rotation of 180° about the origin

d. a rotation of 180° about the point (2, 0) followed by a translation defined by the mapping $(x, y) \rightarrow (x + 4, y - 3)$

e. a translation defined by the mapping $(x, y) \rightarrow (x - 8, y)$ followed by a rotation of 180° about the origin

3. Draw a diagram similar to the one shown. Then draw the images after reflections in lines ℓ_1 and ℓ_2.

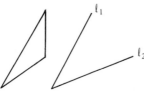

4. Draw $\triangle PQR$ with vertices at $P(-4, 6)$, $Q(-2, 2)$, and $R(-5, 0)$. Draw the image after a transformation defined by the mapping $(x, y) \rightarrow (x + 3, y - 2)$ followed by a reflection in the y-axis.

5. Find the coordinates of the image of the points $M(-4, 1)$ and $N(3, 8)$ under the series of transformations given.
a. $(x, y) \rightarrow (y, x)$ followed by $(x, y) \rightarrow (-x, -y)$
b. $(x, y) \rightarrow (x - 2, y + 1)$ followed by $(x, y) \rightarrow (x, -y)$

6. Triangle ABC with vertices at $A(1, 0)$, $B(3, 0)$, and $C(2, -2)$ undergoes two successive transformations. First, $(x, y) \rightarrow (x, -y)$, followed by $(x, y) \rightarrow (x - 4, y)$. Describe, in your own words, a single transformation or a series of transformations which would have the same result.

7. Refer to the two transformations of Exercise 6. Show that the transformations performed are commutative. (*Hint:* Recall that commutative means the transformations can be performed in any order.)

8. A line segment with endpoints at $F(-2, 4)$ and $G(1, -3)$ is transformed by two successive translations of $(x, y) \rightarrow (x + 2, y - 4)$ followed by $(x, y) \rightarrow (x + 5, y + 8)$.
a. Find the coordinates of the endpoints after the second translation.
b. Find the lengths of the line segments joining F and G to their respective final image points.
c. Find the slopes of these line segments.
d. Write a single mapping which describes this composition of transformations.

9. Triangle RST has vertices at $R(-2, -4)$, $S(3, 2)$, and $T(6, -1)$, and is transformed by a reflection in the y-axis followed by a rotation of 90° about the origin. Find the coordinates of the image triangle and compare the lengths and slopes of the corresponding sides of the two triangles.

10. In your own words, explain what is meant by the term "glide reflection".

279

11·8 Dilatations

A blueprint is a scale drawing. The actual size of the blueprint is not significant, but the relative sizes and the positions of its parts are important. A transformation which preserves the shape but not the size is a **dilatation**. A dilatation may be used to enlarge or reduce the object's size.

An enlargement of a photograph is identical to the original except for its size. The enlargement can be made 2, 3, or more times larger depending upon what is desired. In this section, some of the specific properties of dilatations will be examined.

Example 1

Triangle ABC is enlarged three times to form the image triangle $A'B'C'$. Compare the two triangles.

The corresponding sides have equal slopes and the lengths of the sides of the image triangle are three times the lengths of the corresponding sides of the object triangle. In a dilatation, slope, angle measure, and the orientation of vertices are preserved. The length changes by the **magnification** or **scale factor**. Since angle measure is preserved, the two triangles are similar. Therefore, the ratio of corresponding sides is constant.

$$(x, y) \longrightarrow (3x, 3y)$$

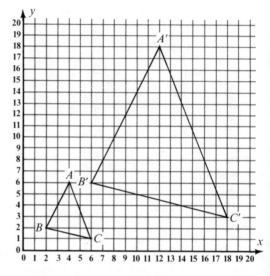

A transformation of $\triangle ABC$ to $\triangle A'B'C'$ such that $\overline{OA'} = k\overline{OA}$ and O, A, and A' are collinear is a dilatation. Point O is called the **dilatation centre** and k, any real number, is the scale factor. The sets of points O, B, B' and O, C, and C' will each be collinear. A dilatation with a scale factor of k and dilatation centre at the origin will be defined by the mapping $(x, y) \longrightarrow (kx, ky)$.

Example 2

The vertices of $\triangle ABC$ are $A(-1, -1)$, $B(1, 2)$, and $C(3, -2)$. Show that the ratio of the corresponding sides of $\triangle ABC$ and its image under a dilatation defined by $(x, y) \longrightarrow (2x, 2y)$ is constant.

The coordinates of $\triangle A'B'C'$ are found to be $A(-1, -1) \longrightarrow A'(-2, -2)$, $B(1, 2) \longrightarrow B'(2, 4)$, and $C(3, -2) \longrightarrow C'(6, -4)$. We wish to show that the ratio of the corresponding sides is constant.

$$\frac{\overline{AB}}{\overline{A'B'}} = \frac{\overline{BC}}{\overline{B'C'}} = \frac{\overline{AC}}{\overline{A'C'}}$$

$\overline{AB} = \sqrt{13}$ and $\overline{A'B'} = 2\sqrt{13}$.

$$\therefore \frac{\overline{AB}}{\overline{A'B'}} = \frac{1}{2}$$

Similarly, it can be shown that the ratio of the other pairs of corresponding sides is equal to one half.

Exercises

1. Copy the figure and draw its image under a scale factor of 2 and dilatation centre at the origin.

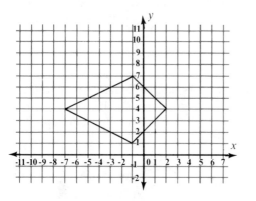

2. State the coordinates of the image points under the dilatation $(x, y) \rightarrow (3x, 3y)$.

a. $(-2, 5)$
b. $(0, 3)$
c. $(8, -1)$
d. $(4, 7)$

3. Draw $\triangle ABC$ with vertices at $A(-1, 3)$, $B(3, 4)$, and $C(0, 1)$. Under a scale factor of 2, and with a dilatation centre at the origin, find the coordinates of the vertices of $\triangle A'B'C'$.

a. Draw the object and the image triangles.
b. Is a dilatation an isometry? Explain.

4. Triangle PQR has vertices at $P(1, 4)$, $Q(5, 3)$, and $R(3, 1)$. Draw the image triangle under the dilatations defined by each.

a. $(x, y) \rightarrow (0.5x, 0.5y)$
b. $(x, y) \rightarrow (-2x, -2y)$
c. What is the geometric effect of a dilatation when $0 < k < 1$?
d. What is the geometric effect of a dilatation when $k < 0$?

5. Segment MN with endpoints at $M(-1, 1)$ and $N(2, 4)$ is dilatated using the mapping $(x, y) \rightarrow (4x, 4y)$. Compare the length of $\overline{MN}$ to the length of $\overline{M'N'}$.

6. Consider the line segments $\overline{AB}$ and $\overline{A'B'}$.

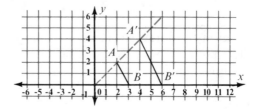

a. Find the magnification factor in the dilatation illustrated.
b. Show that the dilatation preserves the slope of the line segments.

7. Triangle ABC is transformed using the dilatation defined by $(x, y) \rightarrow (0.5x, 0.5y)$. Find the slopes of the segments AC and $A'C'$.

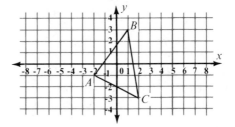

8. Summarize the properties of dilatations.

9. The image of $\triangle RST$ is formed by the dilatation $(x, y) \rightarrow (4x, 4y)$. Compare the lengths of the sides $R'S'$ and RS.

10. If the length of the image line segment $F'G'$ is 6 times longer than the line segment FG, then write the mapping which describes this dilatation.

11. Segment UV, with endpoints at $U(-3, 1)$ and $V(-2, 4)$, is transformed by the mapping $(x, y) \rightarrow (4x, 4y)$. Show that the ratio of $\overline{U'V'}$ to $\overline{UV}$ is equal to the scale factor.

12. How is the area of a triangle affected by a dilatation with each magnification factor k?

a. $k = 2$ **b.** $k = 3$ **c.** $k = n$

13. Find the equation of the image of the line $3x - 7y = 4$ under a dilatation of scale factor $\frac{3}{2}$.

281

11·9 Applications

Transformations are useful in solving many problems. A problem can either be solved, or reduced to a simpler problem, by applying the principles of transformations or using the properties that various transformations may have.

Example 1

In a game of snooker, it is desirable to leave your opponent with a shot that cannot be made directly. In other words, you snooker your opponent by having them hit a "bank shot". On the table shown, Ball 1 must be played so that it hits Ball 3 without hitting Ball 2. Find the path that the player must hit Ball 1 in order to hit Ball 3 first. Explain the reasoning behind this answer.

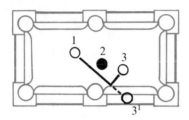

The side of the table, or the cushion, can be used as a line of reflection for Ball 3. By reflecting Ball 3 in this line, we find that the object and image balls are equidistant from the cushion. By taking aim at the image ball, Ball 3 will be struck without striking Ball 2.

Example 2

Consider the points $A(3, 7)$ and $B(5, 5)$. If N is a point on the x-axis such that the distance from A to N and from N to B is a minimum, then find the coordinates of N.

1. Understand the Problem
We are given two points and asked to find the coordinates of a point on the x-axis such that the distance from this point to each point is a minimum. Sketch a diagram to help summarize the information (Step 3).

3. Carry Out the Plan

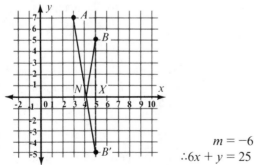

$$m = -6$$
$$\therefore 6x + y = 25$$

2. Develop a Plan
Reflect B in the x-axis and join A and B'. Remember, the shortest distance between two points is a straight line. Since the distance from the line of reflection to both B and B' is congruent, and the x-axis bisects $\overline{BB'}$, then $\triangle BNX \cong \triangle B'NX$. Therefore, $\overline{NB} \cong \overline{NB'}$ and N lies on the straight line formed by $\overline{AB'}$. Therefore, we can find the equation of $\overline{AB'}$ and then the x-intercept.

4. Look Back
The equation of $\overline{AB'}$ is $6x + y = 25$.
To find the x-intercept, let $y = 0$ and solve for x.
$$\therefore 6x = 25$$
$$x = \frac{25}{6}$$
Therefore, the point is $\left(\frac{25}{6}, 0 \right)$.

Exercises

1. To shoot a ball from point P to point Q, it is necessary to bounce the ball off the wall. Determine the path of the ball.

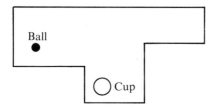

2. On a miniature golf course, the object is to hit the ball into the cup. Consider the layout below and determine where the ball should bounce off the wall to attempt a hole-in-one.

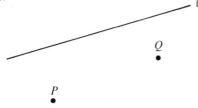

3. Apply reflections to find the shortest distance from point P to point Q if the path must touch the line ℓ.

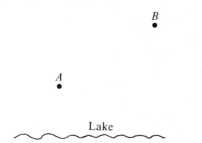

4. A pumping station is to be built at the edge of a lake to supply water to the two towns A and B. Find the location of the pumping station so that the total length of pipe is a minimum.

5. A supply boat at an ocean-drilling rig at P must transport some equipment from campsite A to site B and continue the trip to another drilling rig located at point Q. Determine the points on the shore of the bay where the boat would pick up the equipment from site A and would drop the equipment for site B in order for the distance travelled on water to be a minimum.

6. A runner in a race must run from the starting point, over to a fence, and on to the finish line. If this course was placed on a coordinate grid, the y-axis would be the fence, and the starting point and finish line would be placed at the points $(2, 5)$ and $(7, 12)$. At what point on the y-axis should the runner race to in order to result in the shortest distance possible?

7. A house is to be built at point B. Unfortunately, the nearest natural gas line is at point A and the pipe can only cross the road so that it is perpendicular to the road. Find the route that the pipe will take in order to produce the shortest length of pipe, and as a result, the least cost for the pipe.

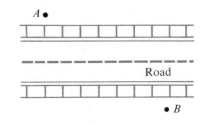

8. What are the next three numbers in this pattern?
2, 7, 4, 11, 6, 13, 8, ...

Braintickler

If three people eat three eggs in three minutes, then how many people eat 500 eggs in 500 min?

283

11·10 Deductive Reasoning

This chapter has introduced the properties of various transformations. In this section, these properties will be utilized in arriving at conclusions from a given set of conditions. This process is deductive reasoning.

To help you organize your thoughts, recall the four-step problem-solving method.

1. Understand the problem. State what is given and what is required.

2. Develop a plan. Outline what approach will be taken and the reasons for taking it.

3. Carry out the plan. Present your statements or proof indicating what properties have been used to arrive at each statement.

4. Look back. Check your results. State your final conclusion and verify your result.

Example

Segment AB is translated m units and relabelled $A'B'$. Prove that quadrilateral $ABB'A'$ is a parallelogram.

1. Understand the Problem
Segment AB is translated m units to form segment $A'B'$.
Prove that $ABB'A'$ is a parallelogram.
The fact that the translation is m units is extraneous information.

2. Develop a Plan
Use the properties of translations to prove that the opposite sides of the quadrilateral are parallel.

3. Carry Out the Plan

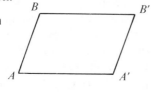

4. Look Back
Therefore, $ABB'A'$ is a parallelogram since the opposite sides are parallel.

Statement	Reason
1. $\overline{AB} \parallel \overline{A'B'}$	**1.** Slope is invariant under a translation.
2. $\overline{AA'} \parallel \overline{BB'}$	**2.** Line segments joining corresponding points in a translation are parallel.

There are many approaches which may be used in a proof. Some may utilize one particular property of transformations and some another property. It is important that you analyze the problem and develop a plan before attempting the proof.

Exercises

1. Statements made in a proof must be supported by evidence to show the validity of those statements. Properties of transformations may provide such evidence. List those properties which are invariant in each transformation.

a. translation   **b.** rotation
c. reflection   **d.** glide reflection
e. dilatation

2. The second step in the problem-solving model is to develop a plan. Explain what basic property must be shown to prove each of these statements.

a. 86 is an even number.
b. $\angle PQR$ is a right angle.
c. $ABCD$ is a quadrilateral.
d. $ABCD$ is a rhombus.
e. Triangle KLM is isosceles.
f. $\overline{AP}$ is a bisector of $\angle BAC$.

3. Segment RP is the perpendicular bisector of segment ST. Complete Step 1 and Step 2 of the four-step model in order to prove that $\overline{RS} \cong \overline{RT}$.

4. In the diagram, ℓ_1 is the perpendicular bisector of $\overline{DE}$ and ℓ_2 is the perpendicular bisector of $\overline{EF}$. Point A is the intersection of the lines ℓ_1 and ℓ_2. Copy and complete to prove that $\overline{AD} \cong \overline{AF}$.

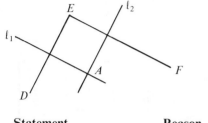

Statement	**Reason**
1. ℓ_1 is a line of reflection.	1. ▓▓▓▓▓▓
2. $\overline{AD} \cong \overline{AE}$	2. ▓▓▓▓▓▓
3. ℓ_2 is a line of reflection.	3. ▓▓▓▓▓▓
4. $\overline{AE} \cong \overline{AF}$	4. ▓▓▓▓▓▓
5. $\overline{AD} \cong \overline{AF}$	5. ▓▓▓▓▓▓

5. Segments JK and FK are reflected in the line ℓ. Prove that $\triangle JFK \cong \triangle J'F'K'$.

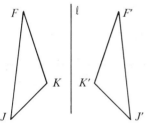

6. If segment AB is perpendicular to ℓ_1 and is reflected in the line ℓ_1, then prove that $\overline{AA'}$ is bisected by ℓ_1.

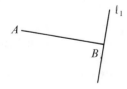

7. Given the right triangle ABC where $\angle ACB = 90°$, and $\triangle ABC$ is reflected about the line segment BC. Prove that $\triangle ABA'$ is an isosceles triangle.

8. In $\triangle PQR$, $\angle P \cong \angle R$ and $\overline{PT} \cong \overline{RT}$. Prove that $\overline{PQ} \cong \overline{QR}$.

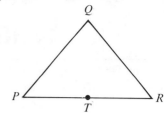

9. Triangle ABC is isosceles with $\overline{AB} \cong \overline{BC}$. If M is the midpoint of $\overline{AC}$, and the triangle is rotated 180° about the point M, then prove that the resulting quadrilateral is a rhombus.

10. In the diagram, $\triangle ABC$ is an isosceles right triangle where $\angle A = 90°$, $\overline{AB} \cong \overline{AC}$. It is rotated 90° about A so that $B'AC$ forms the base of a larger triangle. Prove that $\triangle B'BC$ is isosceles.

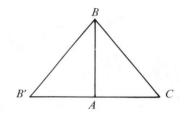

11. In the diagram, ℓ_2 is the image of ℓ_1 under the translation indicated by the arrow. Prove that the angles marked x and y are congruent.

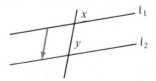

12. Prove that the adjacent angles (angles with a common side) of a parallelogram are supplementary (have a sum of 180°).

Historical Note

Pierre Varignon (1654-1722)
Pierre Varignon was a French mathematician who discovered a property of all quadrilaterals.

Draw various quadrilaterals and connect the midpoints of the four sides. Are the resulting figures parallelograms?

11·11 Computer Application — Transformations

Transformations can be demonstrated on the computer through the use of lo-resolution graphics. A lo-resolution graphics screen is divided into 40 columns and 40 rows labelled from 0 to 39. The screen for lo-resolution graphics is shown along with a reflection in the line $x = 20$.

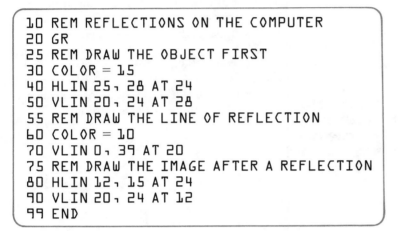

```
10 REM REFLECTIONS ON THE COMPUTER
20 GR
25 REM DRAW THE OBJECT FIRST
30 COLOR = 15
40 HLIN 25, 28 AT 24
50 VLIN 20, 24 AT 28
55 REM DRAW THE LINE OF REFLECTION
60 COLOR = 10
70 VLIN 0, 39 AT 20
75 REM DRAW THE IMAGE AFTER A REFLECTION
80 HLIN 12, 15 AT 24
90 VLIN 20, 24 AT 12
99 END
```

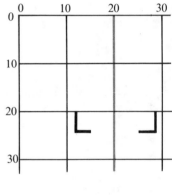

Exercises

1. What is the purpose of lines 20 and 30 in the program in the display?

2. Line 40 has the computer draw a horizontal line from column 25 to column 28 in row 24. Explain what lines 50, 70, 80, and 90 instruct the computer to do.

3. The command PLOT has the computer plot a point once you have given it the coordinates. Modify the program in the display by adding the command 35 PLOT 15, 30.

4. Write a program that will rotate the object from the program in the display 180° about the point (20, 20). (*Hint:* Draw the object and its image on grid paper first.)

5. What is the point (20, 20) called in the program of Exercise 4?

6. Modify your program from Exercise 4 so that it also shows the object and the images after rotations of 90° and 270°.

7. Write a program that will move the object from the program in the display to the left 8 units and up 4 units. (*Hint:* Draw the object and the image on paper before attempting to write the program.)

8. Serious consideration must be given to whether it is possible to create a truly intelligent machine. Write a short essay defending or rejecting the idea of a truly intelligent machine.

11·12 Chapter Review

1. Copy the triangle and draw the images for each transformation.

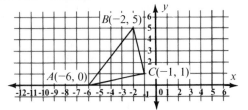

a. $(x, y) \rightarrow (x + 4, y - 3)$
b. a rotation of 90° about the origin
c. a reflection in the y-axis

2. Find the coordinates of the image points under each mapping.
a. $P(6, 2); (x, y) \rightarrow (x - 3, y + 2)$
b. $Q(0, -3); (x, y) \rightarrow (x + 5, y - 1)$

3. Triangle ABC has vertices at $A(-3, -2), B(1, 1)$, and $C(4, -1)$. The triangle is translated under the mapping $(x, y) \rightarrow (x + 2, y + 3)$. Show that the translation will preserve both length and slope.

4. Triangle DEF has vertices at $D(5, 3), E(4, -2)$, and $F(0, 0)$.
a. Find the coordinates of $\triangle D'E'F'$ under the mapping $(x, y) \rightarrow (x, -y)$.
b. Describe this transformation in your own words.
c. Show that the side lengths are invariant.

5. Parallelogram $ABCD$ has vertices at $A(-1, 5)$, $B(3, 5), C(2, -1)$, and $D(-2, -1)$. Apply a rotation of 180° about the origin to the parallelogram.
a. Compare the lengths of the corresponding sides of the two parallelograms to show that length is invariant.
b. Compare the slopes of $\overline{BC}$ and $\overline{B'C'}$.
c. Is slope preserved for rotations of 180° about the origin?

6. Determine the equation of the image line if the line defined by $2x + 7y = 2$ is reflected in the line $y = x$.

7. Given the equation $x + 3y = 2$, find the equation of the image line under the translation defined by this mapping.
$(x, y) \rightarrow (x - 3, y + 1)$

8. The points on the line defined by $y = 3x - 2$ are transformed under a rotation of 180° about the origin. Find the equation of the image line.

9. The points on the line AB with endpoints $A(2, 5)$ and $B(6, -3)$ undergo a reflection in the line $y = -x$ and a rotation of 90° about the origin. Find the equation of the image line.

10. Copy this diagram.

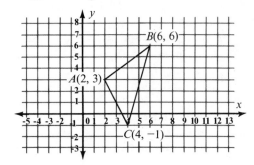

a. Draw the image of $\triangle A'B'C'$ under a translation $(x, y) \rightarrow (x - 2, y - 3)$.
b. Draw the image of $\triangle A'B'C'$ under a reflection in the x-axis.
c. Describe the results of the two transformations in your own words.
d. Show that length is invariant.
e. What other characteristics are invariant?

11. Triangle PQR has vertices at $P(-2, 2)$, $Q(0, -3)$, and $R(-3, -1)$. Show that under the mapping $(x, y) \rightarrow (-y, x)$, the two triangles are directly congruent.

12. Triangle FGH is an isosceles triangle with $\overline{FG} \cong \overline{GH}$. If the triangle is reflected in the line $\overline{FH}$, show that the figure $FGHG'$ is a rhombus.

287

11·13 Chapter Test

1. Copy the diagram and draw the image after each transformation. Describe each transformation in your own words.

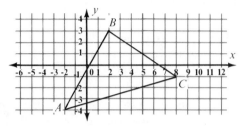

a. $(x, y) \rightarrow (x + 3, y + 2)$
b. $(x, y) \rightarrow (-x, -y)$
c. $(x, y) \rightarrow (y, x)$

2. Give the coordinates of the image after each transformation.
a. $A(-3, 7)$; x is decreased by 3, y is increased by 6
b. $B(4, 1)$; a rotation of 270° about the origin
c. $C(-5, -2)$; $(x, y) \rightarrow (-x, y)$
d. $D(8, -3)$; a reflection in the line $y = x$
e. $E(3, 1)$; $(x, y) \rightarrow (x - 5, y + 9)$
f. $F(4, 2)$; a rotation of 180° about the point $(1, 1)$
g. $G(-5, -6)$; a reflection in the x-axis
h. $H(-2, 4)$; a rotation of 90° about the point $(0, -2)$
i. $I(5, 0)$; $(x, y) \rightarrow (x + 4, y - 8)$

3. Describe each transformation in your own words.
a. $(x, y) \rightarrow (y, x)$ **b.** $(x, y) \rightarrow (-x, y)$

4. Triangle PQR has vertices at $P(1, 1)$, $Q(5, -2)$, and $R(-1, 0)$. The triangle is transformed under this mapping.
$(x, y) \rightarrow (-x, -y)$
Show that in this transformation both length and slope are invariant.

5. Segment AB has endpoints at $A(-1, 2)$ and $B(3, 5)$. Show that the length and the slope are invariant under this mapping.
$(x, y) \rightarrow (x + 4, y - 3)$

6. Given the equation $3x - 5y = 8$, find the equation of the image line under the translation defined by $(x, y) \rightarrow (x + 2, y - 1)$.

7. Find the equation of the image if the line defined by $8x + 3y = 12$ is rotated 90° about the origin.

8. Triangle ABC with vertices at $A(1, 3)$, $B(5, -1)$, and $C(0, -4)$ is subject to a glide reflection defined by these mappings.
$(x, y) \rightarrow (x - 3, y + 2)$
$(x, y) \rightarrow (-y, -x)$
Find the coordinates of the vertices of $\triangle A''B''C''$.

9. The equation $5x - y = 10$ is the image line after a glide reflection defined by these mappings.
$(x, y) \rightarrow (x - 2, y + 5)$
$(x, y) \rightarrow (x, -y)$
Find the equation of the original line.

10. Quadrilateral $ABCD$ has vertices at $A(0, 3)$, $B(4, 4)$, $C(5, -4)$, and $D(2, -2)$. The quadrilateral is rotated 90° about the origin. Compare the lengths of the corresponding sides to show that length is invariant in this rotation.

11. Triangle RST has vertices at $R(2, 3)$, $S(-3, -1)$, and $T(-1, 2)$. Determine whether $\triangle RST$ and its image under the mapping $(x, y) \rightarrow (y, -x)$ are directly or indirectly congruent.

12. Triangle DFG has vertices at $D(-3, -2)$, $F(-2, 2)$, and $G(-1, -1)$.
a. Draw $\triangle DFG$ and its image under this mapping.
$(x, y) \rightarrow (2x, 2y)$
b. Compare the slopes of $\overline{FG}$ and $\overline{F'G'}$.

13. Quadrilateral $ABCD$ is transformed under the mapping $(x, y) \rightarrow (4x, 4y)$. If $\overline{AB} = 7$ cm, $\overline{CD} = 18$ cm, and $\overline{B'C'} = 56$ cm, then find the lengths of $\overline{A'B'}$, $\overline{C'D'}$, and $\overline{BC}$.

DATA ANALYSIS

Tune Up

1. A survey showed that, on average, Canadian males bathe 1.8 times each week in the winter and 2.4 times each week in the summer. The same survey showed that, on average, Canadian females bathe 1.6 times each week during the winter and 2.2 times each week during the summer. The surveyor reached the conclusion that Canadian males bathe more than Canadian females. Comment on the results of the survey in light of the fact that the method used in the survey was a personal interview.

2. The population of a province was reported as 35 million. Five years later it was reported as 150 million.
a. Which census do you think was conducted for tax and military service and which was for financial assistance and famine-relief planning?
b. Explain your answer.
c. What problem in surveying does this case present?

3. Find the error in this report.
A leading medical researcher reported the results of a survey which found that one in twelve Canadians suffer from athlete's foot. Athlete's foot accounts for one third of all skin irritations. Therefore, one quarter of all Canadians suffer from the discomfort of chronic skin infection of the feet.

4. A salesperson for a nuts-and-bolts manufacturer approached the purchasing agent for a hardware company and offered their product at half price. The salesperson acknowledged that about 1% of the product is defective. How can the purchasing agent check the salesperson's claims without inspecting every nut and bolt?

5. You roll a die three times and get a two each time. Comment on the fairness of the die.

6. Comment on the truth of each statement.
a. A manufacturer knows that 0.02% of the bolts that are produced will be defective. The manufacturer has sold 9998 bolts without one being returned as defective. Therefore, by the laws of averages, the next two bolts sold will be defective.
b. The probability of rolling a two or a twelve with a pair of fair dice is $\frac{1}{18}$. A pair of dice have rolled between 3 and 11 on the last 34 rolls. Therefore, the next roll will be either a 2 or a 12.
c. The probability of drawing a heart from a well-shuffled deck of playing cards is 0.25. The last seven draws have not produced a heart. After each draw, the card was returned to the deck. Therefore, the next card drawn will be a heart.
d. A game consists of rolling two dice. A player wins when both dice show the same number. A player is "hot" and rolls three pairs in a row. Probability tells us that the next roll will be a win.

12·1 Charts, Graphs, and Tables

Statisticians, sales representatives, surveyors, and many other professionals use tables, charts, and graphs so that information can be presented, summarized, or checked easily.

For example, an angler may believe that the best time for fishing is at low tide. Finding the times for low tide could be done using a bar graph displaying high and low tides for every day in the week. Bar graphs can be used also by sales representatives to convince a company to purchase a certain type of video cassette based on sales.

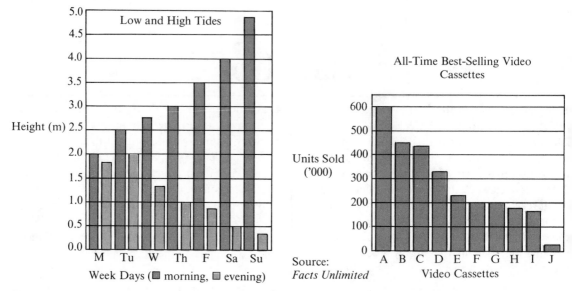

Reports and tables also are very useful in helping people keep track of an event or series of events. For instance, a stock-market report can help an investor keep track of the gains and losses of a particular stock or group of stocks.

Stock	Sales	High	Low	Close	Change	Year High	Year Low
Powr fin	26 395	$27\frac{3}{4}$	$27\frac{1}{2}$	$27\frac{5}{8}$		$28\frac{1}{8}$	$16\frac{3}{8}$
Prado ex o	7500	$19\frac{1}{2}$	18	$19\frac{1}{2}$	$+1\frac{1}{2}$	37	13
Prairie Oil	300	10	10	10		$10\frac{1}{2}$	$7\frac{1}{2}$
Precamb	14 100	$5\frac{3}{8}$	5	$5\frac{1}{8}$		$6\frac{5}{8}$	425
Princpl A	2375	$11\frac{3}{4}$	$10\frac{1}{2}$	$11\frac{1}{2}$	+1	$12\frac{1}{2}$	250
Provigo	58 370	$18\frac{5}{8}$	$18\frac{3}{8}$	$18\frac{1}{2}$	$+\frac{1}{8}$	20	$14\frac{5}{8}$
Que Sturg	3500	425	410	410	−10	$7\frac{1}{8}$	330
Quebcor	2941	$34\frac{1}{2}$	34	$34\frac{1}{4}$	$-\frac{1}{4}$	37	$12\frac{3}{4}$
Queenstak	8100	400	360	400	+30	$6\frac{1}{2}$	201

Exercises

Answer Exercises 1 to 14 using the tables and graphs in the display.

1. Which day of the week has the lowest tide?

2. If high tide is in the morning, and low tide is in the evening, would the angler in the display go fishing on Thursday morning or evening? Explain.

3. What happens to the low-tide heights as the week progresses?

4. If the angler's friend believes that high tide is the best part of the day to fish, which day(s) of the week affords her the best fishing?

5. What happens to the high-tide heights as the week progresses?

6. When would each of the anglers go fishing on Saturday?

7. If you were a video-store owner placing an order for 1000 cassettes, how many of each video cassette would you order to maintain the proportions shown in the bar graph?

8. List two disadvantages of a bar graph.

9. List two advantages of a bar graph.

10. Which stock showed the greatest gain during the week? the greatest loss?

11. What was the total increase in value of 1000 shares of Provigo during the week?

12. Which stock shows the best performance during the year?

13. Which stock shows the greatest range in price during the year?

14. If 3000 shares of Quebcor were bought at its lowest price and sold at its highest price during the year, what profit would be made?

15. Find the product of 1 and 142 857, 2 and 142 857, and 3 and 142 857.
a. Can you see a pattern?
b. Predict these products.
  i) 4 × 142 857   ii) 5 × 142 857
iii) 6 × 142 857
c. Use a calculator to find the products in part **b**.
d. Are your predictions reasonable?

16. A **circle graph**, sometimes called a **pie graph**, can be used to show the relative proportion of one quantity compared to another. For instance, a census taker may need to report on the distribution of the population across Canada by region. This population graph may help.

Distribution of Canadian Population 1981 Census

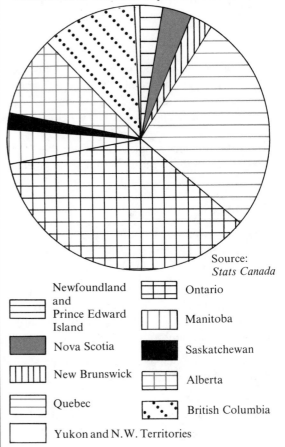

Source:
Stats Canada

▤ Newfoundland and Prince Edward Island	▦ Ontario
▨ Nova Scotia	▥ Manitoba
▥ New Brunswick	■ Saskatchewan
▤ Quebec	▦ Alberta
☐ Yukon and N.W. Territories	⠿ British Columbia

List two advantages and two disadvantages of this circle graph.

12·2 The Sample

To draw conclusions about a particular group, information must be obtained about it. One consideration in collecting information is the cost. Sampling the whole group is usually too expensive. Therefore, a cross section of the group is surveyed.

Example 1

There are 700 students at Lakeview High. Outline a method for the Student Council to determine if the students are in favour of a school uniform.

A list of all 700 students was obtained. The Student Council decided that due to absences, it was impractical to interview each student. A decision was made to send a questionnaire to 100 students. The problem facing them was which 100 students to choose in a **simple random sample**. In a simple random sample, each student must have an equal chance of being selected. A computer was used to assign each student a number from 100 through 800, and 100 three-digit numbers between 100 and 800 were picked at random. The numbers were matched against the numbers on the list, and these people received the survey.

These definitions will be helpful in your study of statistics.
Population — The group about which information is needed.
Sample — Part or all of the population used to obtain information about the whole group.
Strata — A particular group that is being sampled. This group has a common feature.

A **stratified random sample** is a sample taken by breaking the population into groups based on a special interest or common feature within the smaller group or strata.

Example 2

There are two other schools in the district, Oceanview, with 504 students, and Mountainview, with 1050 students. The Lakeview Student Council also want to know the overall percent of students in the district who favour a school uniform. Outline a procedure that could be used in the district.

The total population is all the students in the three schools. If a simple random sample plan is used, the survey might eliminate one of the schools from the sample. To be fair, the total population should be broken into smaller groups based on the school each student attends. This is a stratified random sample. The simple random sample plan is then used to sample Oceanview and Mountainview students.

The Student Council also realized that the sample size in each school must be proportional to that school's total population.

$$\frac{\text{Lakeview sample}}{\text{Lakeview population}} = \frac{\text{Oceanview sample}}{\text{Oceanview population}} \qquad \frac{\text{Lakeview sample}}{\text{Lakeview population}} = \frac{\text{Mountainview sample}}{\text{Mountainview population}}$$

$$\frac{100}{700} = \frac{s}{504} \qquad\qquad\qquad \frac{100}{700} = \frac{s}{1050}$$

$$s = 72 \qquad\qquad\qquad\qquad s = 150$$

The Student Council sampled 72 students from Oceanview and 150 students from Mountainview.

292

Exercises

1. Name the population in Example 1 in the display.

2. Name the population in Example 2.

3. What is the sample size in Example 1?

4. What is the sample size at Mountainview?

5. This statement appears in Example 2: "If a simple random sample plan is used, the survey might eliminate one of the schools from the sample." Explain.

6. Why do you think the Student Council ultimately decided to mail the questionnaire to students rather than asking them to respond at school?

7. What are some of the disadvantages to mailing a questionnaire for collecting data?

8. Would a response to the question in the display be valid if the respondent is interviewed in front of his/her friends? Explain.

9. Name the strata in Example 2.

10. A school contains 725 students, of which 360 are boys and 365 are girls. Devise a method to select a sample. The method used must allow you to tell whether the student selected is a boy or a girl.

11. Discuss the advantages and disadvantages of a stratified random sample over a simple random sample.

12. Suppose you are responsible for taking a poll for the next federal election.
a. Explain what a poll is.
b. Would you take a simple random sample or a stratified random sample to get the most accurate results? Explain.

13. A food processor has 40 large lots of canned soups awaiting shipment. Each lot is labelled with one of the numbers below.
301, 325, 341, 355, 379, 303, 327, 343, 361, 385, 305, 328, 345, 363, 386, 309, 329, 346, 365, 391, 311, 330, 347, 367, 392, 313, 332, 348, 369, 393, 321, 333, 350, 370, 397, 323, 337, 351, 371, 399
A simple random sample of four lots is to be chosen for inspection. How might the four lots be chosen at random?

14. A manufacturing plant employs 200 males and 50 females. A consulting firm takes a stratified random sample of 20 male and 20 female employees.
a. What is the chance that a male employee will be chosen?
b. What is the chance that a female employee will be chosen?
c. Each member of the sample is asked: "Are male employees in a job with this firm generally paid more than females with the same qualifications doing the same job?"
18 of the 20 females said yes.
6 of the 20 males said yes.
The consulting firm reported that, "24 out of 40 employees (60%) in the plant stated that males doing the same job with the same qualifications were paid more than females." Explain the error in this conclusion.

15. A committee of 12 is to be composed of representatives randomly chosen from the four regions of a province. North region has 640 members, East region has 720 members, West region has 240 members, and South region has 1200 members.
a. Describe how you could select the committee randomly from the whole population.
b. Select the committee using a stratified random sample representing each region proportionally. How many members of the committee are from each region?
c. Let members 0001 to 0640 be in the North region, those numbered 0641 to 1360 be in the East region, 1361 to 1600 be in the West region, and members 1601 to 2800 be in the South region. Compare how the different regions are represented in parts **a** and **b**.

12·3 The Survey

After deciding what group to survey, the kind of survey is determined. A **survey** is a method for collecting information from part or all of a population.

Example

The school board wanted to know about their high school students' career interests. What type of surveys might be used?

There are three types of surveys that are commonly used.

1. *Telephone Survey* — For this survey, a questionnaire is written, people are asked the questions over the phone, and the answers are recorded. One major problem is that people are often reluctant to express their opinions over the telephone.

2. *Mail Survey* — For this survey, a questionnaire is mailed and the recipients are asked to respond. However, this survey may be dismissed as "junk mail" and not returned.

3. *Personal Interview* — For this survey, interviewers are trained to administer a questionnaire in person. However, this type of survey often does not allow the person being interviewed to think about their response, and as a result, people sometimes feel pressured into giving an acceptable answer.

The school board realized that there are other factors that can influence the results and create a **bias**. A bias is not easily detectable and can result from the following sorts of errors.

1. *Coverage Error* — The inability to contact a part of the sample, or part of the samples' refusal to respond, can result in a bias since part of the target population will be omitted.

2. *Response Error* — Not responding honestly or correctly to questions on the survey will result in biased conclusions. For instance, people tend to give acceptable answers to sensitive social topics or succumb to peer pressure.

3. *Process Errors* — Errors may be made in repetitive tasks such as counting responses or entering the data into computers. These are often referred to as human errors.

The school board decided to ask the advice of a consultant in preparing the survey. Here are some of the hints that were given by the consultant.

1. Ensure that a good cross section of the population is surveyed.

2. Follow up the survey to ensure that all the sample members have responded.

3. Word the questions carefully to eliminate all ambiguities and to down play socially-sensitive subjects.

4. Ensure anonymity in the survey. Many people will not respond to a survey if they feel that anyone will know the identity of the respondent.

5. Try to ensure that the survey has multiple-choice questions and/or boxes to be checked. Many people will not take the time to write out answers.

6. In a telephone survey, tell the surveyors that they should avoid emphasizing any one word or phrase; and that if a respondent does not understand the question, the surveyor may read it again, but may not explain what the question means.

Exercises

1. Another error that can lead to a biased result is a **timing error**. For example, asking the owner of a factory if there should be tax benefits for factories at the time of year when taxes are payable may result in a biased opinion. Expand the list in the display to include other problems that may occur in a survey, and give an example of each type of problem.

2. List two advantages and two disadvantages of each type of survey.
a. telephone survey   **b.** mail survey
c. personal interview

3. Which survey in Exercise 2 do you think is least expensive? the most expensive? Explain.

4. Which survey in Exercise 2 do you think is the fastest? the slowest? Explain.

5. State whether each of the following words is vague or precise.
a. seven   **b.** often   **c.** many
d. none   **e.** quarter   **f.** exactly

6. State whether the answer to each question will be a fact or an opinion.
a. What is your age?
b. Should sixteen-year olds get an allowance?
c. What is the population of Canada?
d. What is the best musical group?
e. Are apples a better fruit than peaches?
f. Are McDougal hamburgers better than any other hamburger?

7. Explain the difference between "anonymous" and "confidential".

8. What disadvantage is there in making a survey anonymous?

9. What advantages and disadvantages are there in making a survey confidential?

10. Canada's widest survey is the census. Is the Canadian census confidential or anonymous?

11. Which survey errors could be caused in each of the following?
a. A survey of attitudes toward air travel immediately after a major air disaster.
b. Asking if the respondent is in favour of seat-belt laws as a means to reducing traffic fatalities.
c. A home telephone survey conducted during working hours.
d. A mail survey asking if the respondent supports raising the legal driving age.
e. Counting all the thumbtacks in a school while taking inventory.

12. Good survey questions do not influence the respondent or show a bias. Rephrase each question to remove the bias or potential influence on the respondent.
a. Do you favour the use of artificial sweeteners as a means to reduce tooth decay in children?
b. Should Canadians bow to the threats of foreigners and give up all their rights?
c. Do you agree with the doctors in the Canadian Medical Association that smoking is bad for your health?
d. Should the reckless and wealthy yacht owners be made to pay the expenses of search-and-rescue when they call for assistance at sea?
e. Should bike riders be allowed to endanger joggers by cycling on jogging paths?

13. Discuss the difference between the two wordings of the same question.
a. Are you in favour of adding to the tax laws a new law that will increase the number of taxes that we currently pay into … ?
b. Are you in favour of amending the tax laws to include one new law … ?

14. Design a school survey to determine each. Before you begin the survey, predict what the results will be and compare the final results to the prediction. Can you account for the differences by using the surveying problems given in the display?
a. student attitudes toward smoking
b. student preference in music
c. student plans for summer holidays
d. student interest in sports

12·4 Percent Frequency Table

The purpose of tallying and organizing data is to answer specific questions. A **percent frequency table** is one way of organizing the information. This organization allows us to determine the amount of information falling within a certain interval and to compare the results.

Example

Baseball's leading pitchers recorded these Earned Run Averages (ERAs) over a twenty-year period.

2.04, 1.73, 1.87, 1.12, 2.10, 2.81, 1.76, 1.98, 2.07, 2.28, 2.24, 2.52, 2.34, 2.43, 2.71, 2.21, 1.69, 2.40, 2.25, 2.48, 2.17, 2.03, 2.06, 1.60, 2.19, 2.56, 1.82, 1.91, 2.40, 2.49, 2.09, 2.34, 2.54, 1.74, 2.78, 2.47, 2.32, 2.96, 2.42, 2.79

a. How many of the leading pitchers had ERAs less than 2.0? less than 2.5?
b. What percent of the leading pitchers had an ERA less than 2.5?

An example of **interval**, or group, is shown by the inequality $1.00 \leq ERA < 1.50$, where 1.00 is the **lower class boundary**, 1.50 is the **upper class boundary**, and $\frac{1.00 + 1.50}{2} = 1.25$ is the **class mark**.

Interval	Tally	Frequency	Percent Frequency	Cumulative Percent Frequency
$1.00 \leq a < 1.50$	I	1	2.5	2.5
$1.50 \leq a < 2.00$	ℋℋ IIII	9	22.5	25
$2.00 \leq a < 2.50$	ℋℋ ℋℋ ℋℋ ℋℋ IIII	24	60	85
$2.50 \leq a < 3.00$	ℋℋ I	6	15	100

a. The number of pitchers with ERAs less than 2.0 is the sum of the frequencies of the first two classes, or $1 + 9 = 10$. The number of pitchers with ERAs less than 2.5 is the sum of the first three classes, or $1 + 9 + 24 = 34$.

b. The percent of the leading pitchers having ERAs less than 2.5 is the sum of the percent frequencies in the first three classes or the cumulative frequency of the third class $2.5 + 22.5 + 60 = 85$. Therefore, 85% of the leading pitchers have an ERA of less than 2.5.

The intervals in the table were found by establishing **lower** and **upper** limits for the range of the data and dividing the differences by four. The lower limit was established by rounding the least value (1.12) to 1.00. The upper limit was established by rounding the greatest value (2.96) to 3.00. The interval is $(3.00 - 1.00) \div 4 = 0.50$.

Exercises

Use the information in the display to solve Exercises 1 to 5.

1. How many pitchers have an ERA of less than 3.00?

2. What percent of the pitchers have an ERA of less than 1.50?

3. Find the class mark for each of the classes (intervals) in the percent frequency table.

4. What is the upper class boundary for the second class?

5. What is the lower class boundary for the fourth class?

6. Oil was discovered in an oil field at the following depths in metres.
353, 378, 381, 340, 337, 369, 385, 377, 362, 355, 357, 333, 366, 364, 351, 372, 359, 375, 342, 350, 356, 342, 327, 311, 360
a. Construct a percent frequency table. Group the data in classes with intervals of 10 m.
b. What is a "typical" depth to find oil?
c. The company reported to shareholders that the chances are better than 50% that the cost of drilling another well in this field will be less than $250 000. The cost of setting up and drilling a well was $700/m. Should the shareholders believe this statement? Explain.

7. The populations in thousands of 20 mid-sized Canadian cities are listed.
593, 542, 547, 155, 121, 135, 287, 170, 154, 233, 657, 284, 576, 304, 246, 278, 154, 164, 150, 585
a. Construct a percent frequency table based on this data. Group the data in class intervals of 100 000.
b. What are the upper and lower class boundaries of the data?
c. What is the range of the data?
d. What are the upper and lower limits of the data?
e. What percent of the cities listed are below a 600 000 population?
f. What percent of the cities listed are in the class $500 \le p < 600$?
g. How many cities are in the class $100 \le p < 200$?

8. The number of hamburgers sold daily by a fast-food outlet was recorded for one month. Construct a percent frequency table using class intervals of 150 hamburgers. Let the lower limit be zero.
392, 741, 895, 612, 771, 670, 411, 147, 971, 602, 580, 221, 141, 950, 845, 175, 300, 893, 575, 511, 215, 788, 475, 388, 866, 790, 452, 713, 137, 743
a. How many intervals will you use?
b. What are the boundaries, limits, and ranges for the data?
c. What percent of the days did the outlet sell between 450 and 600 hamburgers?
d. What percent of the month did the outlet sell less than 750 hamburgers per day?
e. What days of the week do you think the sixth class represents?
f. What fraction of the month did the outlet sell between 300 and 450 hamburgers?
g. How many hamburgers are sold on a "typical" day?
h. If a typical day has 2 shifts of 5 employees each, then how many staff members should a busy day have? a slow day?
i. If you are the manager of this outlet, then what days would you like to have off? Why?

9. The number of registered voters at each of 100 polling divisions in a provincial riding are listed.
474, 285, 289, 156, 247, 303, 506, 438, 452, 804, 207, 396, 236, 344, 423, 374, 515, 569, 219, 315, 378, 399, 405, 327, 399, 288, 317, 400, 449, 706, 347, 591, 363, 401, 389, 365, 323, 356, 313, 368, 322, 470, 295, 512, 362, 378, 315, 196, 404, 382, 434, 947, 342, 382, 382, 144, 318, 383, 486, 405, 251, 959, 303, 347, 451, 398, 261, 377, 324, 286, 373, 443, 261, 494, 387, 322, 334, 376, 409, 148, 148, 334, 317, 357, 360, 355, 201, 262, 279, 209, 454, 360, 417, 358, 402, 270, 369, 200, 653, 153
Total = 37 257
a. Construct a percent frequency table using class intervals of 100 voters.
b. What is the minimum number of polling divisions a political candidate will have to visit in order to visit 50% of the voters?
c. What can you conclude about the population in these polling divisions?

297

12·5 Bar Graphs and Histograms

The frequency table is just one way of organizing data. Data also can be organized and displayed graphically.

Example 1

A survey of the colours used in the flags of 180 countries produced the results in the frequency table. Display the results in a **bar graph**.

If the order of percent frequencies is not important, a bar graph can be used. This type of graph is especially effective when displaying data concerning unrelated amounts. The height of the bars indicates the percent frequency, and space is used between the bars.

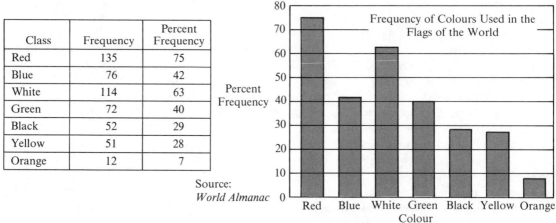

Class	Frequency	Percent Frequency
Red	135	75
Blue	76	42
White	114	63
Green	72	40
Black	52	29
Yellow	51	28
Orange	12	7

Source:
World Almanac

Example 2

The atomic masses of 105 known elements were grouped and displayed in the frequency table. Display the information in a **histogram**.

A histogram can be used to show order or relations in the data. In this case, the 105 elements are grouped into classes according to class boundaries in their atomic masses and a pattern emerges in the graph. A histogram is a bar graph in which no space is left between the bars.

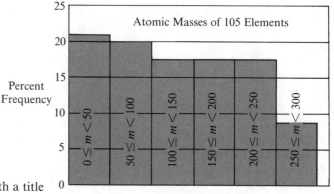

Interval	Percent Frequency
$0 \leq m < 50$	21
$50 \leq m < 100$	20
$100 \leq m < 150$	17
$150 \leq m < 200$	17
$200 \leq m < 250$	17
$250 \leq m < 300$	8

It is important that each graph have both a title and a source for the data.

Exercises

1. What information is missing in the histogram in Example 2?

2. State the interval size of the classes in Example 2.

3. State the class mark of the third class in Example 2.

4. State the upper class boundary and the lower class boundary of the sixth class of Example 2.

5. Would it be misleading to use bars of different widths in a bar graph or a histogram? Explain.

6. Would it be better to present the following data with a bar graph or a histogram? Explain.
a. the heights of the students in your class
b. the makes of cars in a parking lot
c. the marks of students on an examination
d. the number of volcanic eruptions for each decade of this century
e. the sales levels of the five leading toothpaste manufacturers

7. Construct a histogram for this data using class intervals of 100 km/h.
The cruising speed of 60 different two-engine aircraft:
824, 412, 442, 336, 266, 410, 386, 350, 756, 450, 418, 257, 257, 333, 296, 393, 927, 928, 370, 304, 257, 954, 408, 783, 475, 922, 384, 422, 555, 954, 435, 370, 450, 928, 563, 473, 290, 927, 352, 362, 797, 354, 473, 428, 556, 402, 344, 885, 924, 426, 402, 470, 330, 323, 885, 924, 842, 360, 386, 878

8. One bag contains eight red marbles and one blue marble. A second bag contains sixteen blue marbles and one red marble. A person reaches into each bag and pulls out one marble. Is it more likely that the marbles are both the same colour or different colours?

9. Construct either a histogram or a bar graph for each frequency table. Explain the reason for your choice.

a. the 42 tallest buildings in Toronto

Interval (m)	Frequency
$275 \leq h < 300$	20
$250 \leq h < 275$	13
$225 \leq h < 250$	2
$200 \leq h < 225$	2
$175 \leq h < 200$	0
$150 \leq h < 175$	2
$125 \leq h < 150$	2
$100 \leq h < 125$	1

b. early expeditions of arctic exploration

Interval (Century)	16th	17th	18th	19th	20th
Frequency	2	2	6	5	7

c. the length of the six longest rivers in Canada measured in kilometres

Mackenzie	4240	Saskatchewan	1939
St. Lawrence	3058	Churchill	1609
Nelson	2575	Fraser	1368

d. the leading uses of the home computer

Uses	Games	Business	Educational
Frequency	51	46	42

Uses	Word Pro.	Files	Calorie Count
Frequency	18	14	4

10. A biologist wanted to know how many seeds are in an average grapefruit. Forty grapefruits were selected at random and the seeds were counted. Display the results graphically.
4, 2, 0, 2, 3, 3, 3, 4, 2, 3, 4, 5, 0, 1, 3, 4, 6, 1, 5, 4, 3, 2, 0, 3, 2, 5, 3, 1, 3, 5, 1, 4, 3, 2, 5, 5, 4, 2, 1, 2

11. The average number of hours of sunshine, over a 14 a period at Frobisher Bay, North West Terrritories, was recorded.

Jan	Feb	Mar	Apr	May	Jun	Jul	Aug	Sep	Oct	Nov	Dec
35	88	181	234	185	165	210	193	78	59	43	16

a. Construct the appropriate display based on this data.
b. Explain the reasoning for your choice.

12·6 Stem and Leaf Tables

The **stem and leaf table** is another method for organizing, presenting, and analysing data.

Example

A survey of record prices from Roy's Record Emporium produced the following data. Construct a stem and leaf table and discuss the advantages of this type of presentation.

$13.00, $14.50, $9.99, $18.00, $19.99, $14.00, $13.99, $12.99, $17.99, $18.99, $14.00, $15.00, $15.00, $12.99, $11.00, $10.50, $8.99, $17.99, $16.99, $16.98, $15.98, $15.99, $16.00, $13.00, $13.98, $11.98, $11.99, $9.95, $20.00, $12.00, $10.00, $12.99, $10.99, $16.00, $17.98, $15.00, $12.00, $14.00, $14.75, $13.99, $13.98, $11.98, $14.99

Stem (dollars)	Leaf (cents)
8	99
9	95, 99
10	00, 50, 99
11	00, 98, 98, 99
12	00, 00, 99, 99, 99
13	00, 00, 98, 98, 99, 99
14	00, 00, 00, 50, 75, 99
15	00, 00, 00, 98, 99
16	00, 00, 98, 99
17	98, 99, 99
18	00, 99
19	99
20	00

This stem represents the class $14.00 \leq p < $15.00.

This leaf tells us there were two records priced in the $18.00 class; one at $18.00 and one at $18.99.

The stem represents the class chosen and the leaf indicates both the frequency and the precise value of the data in that class. The frequency in this case is the cents part of the price. The leaf portion of the table is written in increasing order of values from left to right.

There are three advantages to a stem and leaf table.

1. The data is preserved. Unlike other graphs, it is possible to identify the precise value of each item.

2. The specific pieces of data are not only preserved, but are also ordered. For instance, the highest and lowest record prices in each class can be identified quickly.

3. The general pattern of the distribution is also shown in this table. By examining the leaves, we can see that the prices tend to group in the $11 to $17 range, and that there are not many records priced outside of this range. In other words, it is an excellent way to summarize data.

Exercises

1. How many of the records from the example in the display are in each class?
a. $\$11 \leq p < \$12$
b. $\$19 \leq p < \$20$
c. $\$13 \leq p < \$14$

2. State the classes having each frequency.
a. 3 **b.** 6 **c.** 4 **d.** 1 **e.** 5

3. Construct a stem and leaf table for the ERA data in the display of Section 12·4.

4. Construct a stem and leaf table based on this data. These are the annual Canadian birth rates per thousand for twelve years.
10.7, 11.0, 14.5, 14.8, 12.9, 12.1, 10.4, 9.7, 12.4, 12.4, 11.9, 10.3

5. Construct a stem and leaf table based on the Canadian low temperature records by province.

Alberta	−61°C	New Brunswick	−47°C
B.C.	−59°C	Nova Scotia	−41°C
Manitoba	−53°C	Ontario	−58°C
Nfld.	−49°C	P.E.I.	−37°C
Quebec	−54°C	Saskatchewan	−57°C
N.W.T.	−57°C	Yukon	−63°C

6. Construct a stem and leaf table based on the greatest precipitation, in millimetres, in a 24 h period for 16 selected Canadian cities.

Calgary	32.4	Quebec	53.4
Charlottetown	42.8	Regina	73.6
Churchill	62.3	Saskatoon	96.6
Edmonton	42.5	Thunder Bay	38.9
Fredericton	58.9	Toronto	29.6
Halifax	90.7	Vancouver	46.6
Hamilton	49.0	Victoria	45.2
Ottawa	55.5	Winnipeg	47.2

a. What is the greatest frequency of precipitation? the least frequency?
b. What is the total precipitation that fell during the time of greatest frequency?

7. Anne-Nissa said that if you take her present age, triple it, add 30 to the result, take the square root of the next result, and subtract 12 from that result, then you will have zero. How old is Anne-Nissa?

8. Construct a double stem and leaf table based on the Runs Batted In (RBI) leaders over 35 a in the National and American leagues. Use stems of 10, 11, 12, ... (*Hint:* A double stem and leaf table has the stem in the middle and a leaf to the left and to the right.)
National League leading RBI totals:
126, 129, 127, 129, 109, 121, 143, 111, 120, 121, 121, 126, 105, 121, 106, 142, 142, 126, 149, 141, 153, 148, 120, 136, 130, 137, 118, 109, 119, 125, 121, 132, 130, 119, 91
American League leading RBI totals:
144, 112, 126, 122, 109, 129, 142, 119, 78, 139, 105, 126, 113, 133, 122, 145, 118, 117, 126, 126, 118, 118, 123, 116, 108, 109, 112, 130, 122, 119, 109, 114, 121, 139, 140

a. What is the greatest frequency of RBIs in each league?
b. Are they the same for each league?
c. What is the least frequency of RBIs in each league?

9. Construct a stem and leaf table based on the dates of the discovery of the 49 elements found during the 19th century.
1899, 1808, 1886, 1839, 1804, 1817, 1843, 1825, 1803, 1868, 1817, 1803, 1879, 1861, 1894, 1860, 1878, 1898, 1898, 1879, 1828, 1808, 1886, 1863, 1829, 1807, 1845, 1879, 1808, 1843, 1811, 1885, 1885, 1861, 1898, 1826, 1886, 1804, 1898, 1807, 1803, 1830, 1817, 1875, 1898, 1801, 1823, 1802, 1878

a. Which decade saw the greatest frequency of discovery?
b. Which decade saw the least frequency?
c. How many elements were discovered in the eighth decade of the 19th century?

10. These are examples of **oblong** numbers.
$1 \times 2 = 2; 2 \times 3 = 6; 3 \times 4 = 12$
Find the next three oblong numbers.

12·7 Measures of Central Tendency

It is useful to find a single value for a set of data that can represent the whole set. Examples are the **mean**, **median**, or the **mode** of the set. These values are called the **measures of central tendency**.

Example

A survey of the weekly television viewing time of 25 female and 26 male teenagers produced this data. Find the measures of central tendency for both male and female viewers.

Weekly Television Viewing Time in Hours	
Female	Male
29 21 23 31 20	32 20 26 24 16 25
32 20 26 33 18	23 19 22 23 26
27 25 25 32 16	35 10 27 26 31
14 27 19 23 15	19 28 30 31 32
24 27 20 24 35	25 29 34 15 22

The **mean** is the arithmetic average of each set of numbers and is determined by finding the sum of all the numbers in each set and dividing by the number of numbers. For females, the mean is $\frac{606}{25}$ or 24.24 h. For males, the mean is $\frac{650}{26}$ or 25 h.

The **median** is the middle number when the values are arranged in either ascending or descending order. If there is an even number of values, the median is the mean of the two middle values. For females, the median is 24 h. For males, the median is 25.5 h.

The **mode** is the most frequently occurring value in the set. The values 20 h and 27 h each occur three times in the data for females. This results in two modes for the television viewing time for females. This set of values is said to be **bi-modal**. For males, the mode is 26 h.

The mean, median, and the mode are all measures of central tendency. The use of one or another will depend on which measure is more meaningful in a particular situation. For example, suppose you watch a lot of television and are trying to convince your parents that your viewing habits are not unusual. If you are female, then what measure of central tendency will you use? In this case, you might argue that 27 h (the mode) is one of the most common viewing times.

On the other hand, if you are trying to convince your parents that girls do not watch much television throughout the week, then you might argue that 20 h (the other mode) is the most common viewing time.

Technically, both these claims are correct. However, each claim tends to bias the data in different directions. Which measure of central tendency might the girl's parents claim is the "most common" value for the viewing time?

Exercises

For each exercise in this section, use a calculator if one is available.

1. Use the data in the display to calculate the measures of central tendency for males and females combined. Compare them to the measures of central tendency for each separate group and note all similarities and differences.

2. Use the data in the display to present a brief argument to support each conclusion.
a. Males watch more television than females.
b. Females watch more television than males.

3. Using the data in the display, could you have predicted what the measures of central tendency would be for the whole population? Explain.

4. Every two hours, over an 18 h period, the number of yeast cells in a population was recorded.
20, 40, 105, 175, 160, 110, 40, 10, 5
a. Predict the measures of central tendency.
b. Calculate the measures of central tendency.
c. Were your predictions reasonable?

5. A survey of players in a baseball league revealed the following number of right-handed batters on each of twelve teams. Predict and find the mean, median, and mode for this data. Were your predictions reasonable?
24, 25, 27, 25, 25, 18, 21, 29, 23, 22, 26, 26

6. Create a set of data to show that the mean and the mode would be good measures of central tendency, but the median would not be.

7. What does "bi-modal" mean? Your explanation should include an example.

8. A long-playing record can play for as long as 30 min. A short-playing record can be as short as 2 min. However, they have one common feature: the number of grooves. How many grooves does each record have?

9. An automotive magazine conducted a survey of 45 makes and models of new cars. The interior sound level at 110 km/h was recorded in decibels, db.
72, 68, 74, 77, 74, 70, 72, 69, 75, 68, 85, 73, 76, 70, 72, 74, 73, 74, 75, 75, 75, 83, 77, 73, 74, 68, 68, 71, 72, 70, 73, 81, 73, 71, 76, 73, 75, 74, 72, 82, 72, 74, 75, 76, 69
a. Predict the measures of central tendency.
b. Calculate the actual measures of central tendency.
c. To convince people that the new cars had a low interior sound level, what might you do?

10. The same magazine reported the heights in centimetres of 46 different makes of sports cars. Find the mean, median, and mode for this data.
129, 133, 127, 129, 118, 130, 136, 127, 127, 133, 125, 123, 119, 129, 128, 119, 126, 130, 124, 132, 141, 128, 135, 127, 124, 126, 138, 113, 132, 125, 128, 131, 127, 132, 131, 132, 132, 130, 127, 118, 121, 112, 109, 125, 132, 106

11. A survey collected the heights in centimetres of 50 students. Find the mean, median, and mode for this data.
156.10, 157.48, 162.56, 165.10, 167.64, 168.91, 169.55, 169.90, 170.10, 171.00, 156.30, 158.00, 162.56, 165.50, 167.90, 169.00, 169.56, 169.90, 170.80, 172.00, 156.50, 158.30, 162.56, 165.50, 168.10, 169.00, 169.56, 169.90, 170.90, 172.50, 156.70, 158.70, 163.50, 165.50, 168.30, 169.20, 169.56, 169.90, 170.92, 173.00, 156.90, 159.00, 164.70, 166.00, 168.50, 169.30, 169.80, 169.90, 170.95, 175.00

12. You are 167.65 cm tall. Argue, using the data from Exercise 11, that you are taller than most people and that you are shorter than "most" people.

13. In a set of data the smallest number is decreased by 8 and the largest increased by 8. What changes occur to the measures of central tendency?

12·8 Weighted Mean

Sometimes data is already grouped, summarized, and displayed as in a bar graph, histogram, or frequency table. In these cases, a different method is used to find the measures of central tendency.

Example

The bar graph displays the number of fares sold in each class on a flight from Edmonton to Toronto. The airline sold 24 first-class seats at $493/each, 165 Connoisseur seats at $352/each, 64 Economy Senior's seats at $264/each, and 90 Economy Youth seats at $176/each. Find the mean and the mode for the set of data.

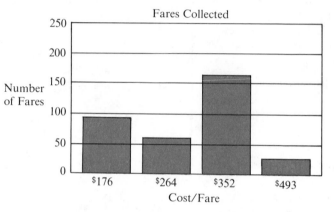

By interpreting the bar graph, we can determine that the mode for the set of data is $352. This is the highest bar, or the amount that occurs most often.

To find the mean amount paid for a seat, it is not appropriate to average the cost of the fares for each class because the fares are not evenly distributed. Therefore, the mean is calculated by dividing the total receipts from the flight by the total number of passengers. This is known as the **weighted mean**.

$$\text{Mean Fare} = \frac{90(176) + 64(264) + 165(352) + 24(493)}{343}$$

$$= \frac{102\,648}{343}$$

$$= 299.27 \qquad \text{The mean fare is } \$299.27.$$

Exercises

1. If 10 more passengers bought economy youth tickets for the flight, then how would this affect the mode? the mean?

2. Using the example in the display, suppose three stowaways were caught when the plane landed. How would this affect the mean and mode for the set of data?

3. The median for the data in the display is found in the usual way by arranging all the values in order and finding the middle value.
a. Find the median for the values in the display.
b. What is the best measure of central tendency, the median or the mean? Explain.

4. How do the median and the mode compare?

5. What percent of the passengers paid each fare?
a. First Class   **b.** Connoisseur
c. Economy Senior's   **d.** Economy Youth

6. What percent of the total fares were paid by each?
a. First Class   **b.** Connoisseur
c. Economy Senior's   **d.** Economy Youth

Copy and complete each table. Calculate the weighted mean and state the median and the mode.

7. Scores on a math test:

Score	Frequency
95	1
90	2
80	3
75	7
65	5
50	3
45	2
40	2
35	1
Total	

a. What would you predict for the score of a randomly-selected student? Explain.
b. What would you predict for the total score of three randomly-selected students? Explain.

8. Winning scores for the Canadian Open Golf Championship:

Score	Frequency
263	1
265	1
267	2
268	1
269	1
270	2
271	3
273	4
274	3
275	3
278	3
279	2
280	6
281	1
Total	

Use measures of central tendency to predict the winning score for next year. Justify your answer.

9. Ticket sales at a football game:

Ticket Price ($)	Frequency
16	15 300
13	22 400
7.5	10 800
5	8 300
Total	

If you wanted to sell the team to a prospective buyer, how would you present the data shown here? Use charts and diagrams if you feel they are necessary.

10. Apartment rental rate:

Rent/Month ($)	Frequency
350	3
450	20
475	35
500	40
550	31
590	10
625	6

You wish to raise the rent on a $480/month apartment. Develop an argument to present to the rent-review board. In this case, the tenant will also have a case to present against you. In your presentation, be prepared to defend your argument.

11. Thirty-six rolls of a pair of dice:

Number Turned Up	Frequency
2	1
3	2
4	3
5	4
6	5
7	6
8	5
9	4
10	3
11	2
12	1
Total	

In a dice game, you are required to throw a six or be eliminated from the game. What is the most likely sum of two dice on one throw?

12·9 Grouped Data

When investigating measures of central tendency for data having a large range, it is often useful first to group the data into classes. In grouped data of this kind, it is assumed that the values are evenly distributed within each class.

Example

A study of minimum-air-pollution reports from 30 cities produced data measured in micrograms per cubic metre. The data is summarized in this chart. Calculate the measures of central tendency for this data.

Class	Class Mark	Frequency	CM × F	Percent Frequency	Cumulative Percent Frequency
$0 \leq p < 10$	5	2	10	6.7	6.7
$10 \leq p < 20$	15	4	60	13.3	20
$20 \leq p < 30$	25	8	200	26.7	46.7
$30 \leq p < 40$	35	9	315	30	76.7
$40 \leq p < 50$	45	4	180	13.3	90
$50 \leq p < 60$	55	2	110	6.7	96.7
$60 \leq p < 70$	65	1	65	3.3	100
Total		30	940	100	

In this table, the class mark is the median of each class; while the column labelled CM × F is the total air pollution count for the class.

$$\text{Mean air-pollution count} = \frac{\text{total of (CM} \times \text{F)}}{\text{total frequency}}$$
$$= \frac{940}{30}$$
$$\doteq 31.3$$

The mean minimum air pollution of the 30 cities surveyed is approximately 31.3 $\mu g/m^3$.

The median lies between the 15th and 16th values which are found in the class $30 \leq p < 40$. The class width is 10. $(40 - 30 = 10)$

There are 9 values in this class and 14 values in the lower classes. The 15th value happens to be the first value, n, in the class $30 \leq p < 40$. The 16th value is the second value, $n + 1$, in the class.

Assuming even distribution of values in each class, the median is calculated as follows:

$$\text{(Lower class boundary)} + \frac{n}{9} \times \text{(class width)}$$

The 15th value is $30 + \frac{1}{9} \times 10 = 30 + \frac{10}{9}$ The 16th value is $30 + \frac{2}{9} \times 10 = 30 + \frac{20}{9}$
$$= 31.1 \qquad\qquad\qquad\qquad\qquad\qquad = 32.2$$

The mean of these two values is $\frac{31.1 + 32.2}{2} = 31.65$.

The **calculated median** is 31.65 $\mu g/m^3$.
The class or classes having the greatest frequency is called the **modal class**.
The modal class is $30 \leq p < 40$.

Exercises

1. In the example, explain why the median lies between the 15th and 16th values.

2. State the class width for each.
a. $0 \leq n < 5$ **b.** $2 \leq n < 4$
c. $-2 \leq n < 8$ **d.** $104 \leq n < 108$

3. Calculate the class mark, CM, for each.
a. $12 \leq n < 16$ **b.** $0 \leq n < 5$
c. $-8 \leq n < 0$ **d.** $23 \leq n < 33$

4. Explain how to find the class width.

5. Copy and complete the table. Calculate the mean, the median, and find the modal class.

Class	CM	Freq	CM × F	% Freq	Cum % Freq
$0 \leq n < 5$	2.5	5			
$5 \leq n < 10$	7.5	20			
$10 \leq n < 15$		20			
$15 \leq n < 20$		23			
$20 \leq n < 25$		24			
$25 \leq n < 30$		10			
$30 \leq n < 35$		4			
Total					

6. Copy and complete the table. Calculate the mean, the median, and find the modal class.

Canadian Traffic Fatalities by Age Group

Class	CM	Freq	CM × F	% Freq	Cum % Freq
$0 \leq n < 10$	5	102			
$10 \leq n < 20$		656			
$20 \leq n < 30$		962			
$30 \leq n < 40$		359			
$40 \leq n < 50$		262			
$50 \leq n < 60$		222			
$60 \leq n < 70$		160			
$70 \leq n < 80$		137			
$80 \leq n < 90$		74			
Total					

a. Predict and find the measures of central tendency for this data.
b. The age group that pays the most for car insurance, based on these figures is the 20 to 30 age group. Set up a display to argue that this group is not the most dangerous on the road.

Construct a frequency table for Exercises 7 to 11. Calculate the mean, the median, and find the modal class.

7. The marks, m, in percent for students. The first class is $20 \leq m < 30$.
84, 24, 72, 64, 42, 70, 99, 46, 63, 60, 60, 64, 74, 38, 64, 58, 26, 86, 62, 34, 78, 52, 56, 38, 58, 44, 78, 88, 87, 58

8. Hockey players total points, p. The first class is $0 \leq p < 10$.
4, 1, 17, 16, 5, 71, 10, 32, 72, 62, 75, 44, 80, 74, 72, 80, 67, 78, 72, 80, 47, 72, 77, 80, 20, 33

9. The low temperatures in degrees Celsius for January and February.
$-24, -23, -22, -25, -30, -5, -3, -8, -5, -3,$
$0, 2, 3, -4, -4, -3, -7, -10, -15, -21,$
$-37, -40, -41, -45, -30, -30, -26, -25, -25, -25,$
$-16, -8, -7, -3, -2, -1, -4, -4, -5, -8,$
$-10, -11, -10, -11, -10, -5, -16, -17, -5, -5,$
$-20, -30, -35, -31, -27, -26, -20, -31, -10, -8,$
$-5, 0$

10. The masses, w, of students in kilograms. The first class is $45 \leq w < 50$.
47, 72, 66, 62, 98, 84, 86, 76, 77, 73, 75, 50, 86, 47, 54, 77, 72, 72, 72, 68, 65, 66, 66, 62, 63, 55, 57, 63, 62, 61, 51, 74, 66, 67, 68, 62, 61, 56, 55, 99, 89, 66, 66, 63, 64, 64, 64, 61, 63, 60, 56, 57, 53, 67, 66, 66, 66, 50, 59, 59, 60, 61, 61, 64, 74, 72, 55, 55, 76, 66, 67, 60, 63, 84, 64, 64, 60, 55, 56, 57, 57, 52, 61, 74, 76, 66, 65, 66, 60, 60, 60, 61, 64, 63, 84, 72, 71, 61, 64, 63, 57, 56, 55, 79, 55, 70, 66, 67, 59, 73

12·10 Data Distribution

Data may be evenly or uniformly distributed. The shape of a graph often indicates the distribution of the data.

The monthly mean air temperature at a tropical location shows the distribution has no clear central tendency. The mode is equally likely to occur during any month. This is an example of **uniform distribution**.

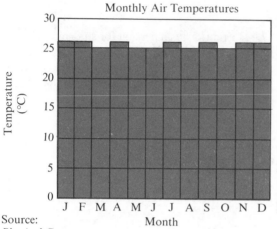

Monthly Air Temperatures

Source:
Physical Geo.

The hours of sunlight at 70°N latitude were recorded over a year. The histogram shows an example of a **normal** or **bell shaped** distribution.

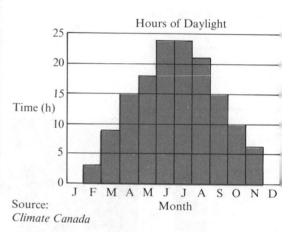

Hours of Daylight

Source:
Climate Canada

The number of snowfall days in Vancouver is displayed in the histogram. None of the measures of central tendency are representative of the number of snowfall days per month. This is called **bath tub** distribution due to its "bath tub" shape.

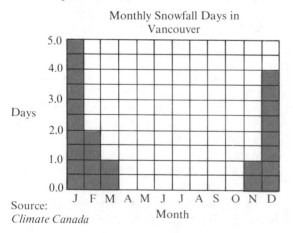

Monthly Snowfall Days in Vancouver

Source:
Climate Canada

A **frequency polygon**, or a line graph, can be used to show distribution. In this case, two lines show the distribution over two years.

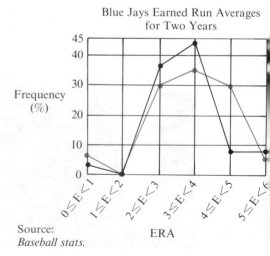

Blue Jays Earned Run Averages for Two Years

Source:
Baseball stats.

Exercises

Construct a histogram and name the type of distribution for each set of data. Calculate the mean and the median. Find the mode and comment on the central measures for each type of distribution with respect to appropriateness, meaningfulness, and reasonableness.

1. A parking-lot survey (percent use):

% Use	5	15	25	35	45	55	65	75	85	95
Class	0 to 9	10 to 19	20 to 29	30 to 39	40 to 49	50 to 59	60 to 69	70 to 79	80 to 89	90 to 100
Days	8	3	2	1	1	1	1	2	4	8

2. A two-week survey of air temperatures in a tropical country:

Day	1	2	3	4	5	6	7	8	9	10	11
Temp.	31	32	31	31	31	33	31	32	32	31	31

Day	12	13	14
Temp.	31	32	31

3. A survey of monthly rainfall in Timbo, measured in millimetres:

Month	J	F	M	A	M	J	J	A	S
Rain	0	0	30	60	160	220	310	370	250

Month	O	N	D
Rain	160	40	0

4. Results of a mathematics test:

Class Mark	5	15	25	35	45	55	65	75	85	95
Class	0 to 9	10 to 19	20 to 29	30 to 39	40 to 49	50 to 59	60 to 69	70 to 79	80 to 89	90 to 100
Freq.	1	3	7	12	18	20	14	7	3	1

5. A survey of the games won by the Calgary Commodores during a ten-week baseball season:

Week	1	2	3	4	5	6	7	8	9	10
Wins	7	3	2	1	1	1	2	3	4	8

6. A study of bacterial contamination of well water provided the following results.

Coliform Count/mL	0	1	2	3	4	5
Frequency	1	1	3	7	14	16

Coliform Count/mL	6	7	8	9	10
Frequency	22	16	13	5	3

7. A public health nurse examined 321 students and recorded their heights in centimetres.

Class Mark	165	170	175	180	185	190	195
Class	162.5 to 167.4	167.5 to 172.4	172.5 to 177.4	177.5 to 182.4	182.5 to 187.4	187.5 to 192.4	192.5 to 197.4
Freq.	10	29	72	98	69	31	12

8. The number of customers at a bank from 10:00 until 13:00 was recorded.

Class	$10:00 \leq t < 10:30$	$10:30 \leq t < 11:00$
	55	45

Class	$11:00 \leq t < 11:30$	$11:30 \leq t < 12:00$
	20	10

Class	$12:00 \leq t < 12:30$	$12:30 \leq t < 13:00$
	40	60

Draw frequency polygons (line graphs) for each set of data.

9. The daytime temperature affects the number of traffic accidents. The following data is a record of the number of accidents which occurred in a small town on days with the indicated temperatures.

Temp. (°C)	$-10 \leq t < -5$	$-5 \leq t < 0$	$0 \leq t < 5$
	15	10	4

Temp. (°C)	$5 \leq t < 10$	$10 \leq t < 15$	$15 \leq t < 20$
	1	1	2

Temp. (°C)	$20 \leq t < 25$	$25 \leq t < 30$	$30 \leq t < 35$
	5	8	12

a. List some of the ways the low temperatures might be a cause of accidents.
b. List some of the ways the high temperatures might be a cause of accidents.

12·11 Central Measures

The table summarizes the advantages and disadvantages of each measure of central tendency. These measures are all commonly referred to as **averages**.

Central Measure	Advantages	Disadvantages
Mean	Information is given about the sum of the values. It is easily computed. Most frequently used measure in statistical studies. Known commonly as arithmetic average.	May not be one of the values in the data set. Greatly influenced by extreme data values.
Median	Not greatly influenced by extreme data values. Gives the middle value in a set of data.	No information is given about the sum of the data values. Data values must be arranged in order.
Mode	Describes the most frequently occurring data value. Easy to locate in frequency tables, graphs, bar graphs, or histograms.	May be far from the centre of data values. May change greatly with new data values. May be more than one value and these values can vary greatly.

Example

The annual salaries of a group of baseball players on a team show 15 players at $70 000, 15 players at $100 000, and 1 player at $1 000 000. Find the three measures of central tendency and comment on each measure.

The weighted mean salary paid is $\dfrac{15(70\,000) + 15(100\,000) + 1\,000\,000}{31}$ or $114 516.12.

Only 1 player is paid over the mean salary. The $1 000 000 salary has increased the mean to a value well above the amount paid to all other players. Therefore, the mean is greatly influenced by this extreme value. However, if the total income of the team is of interest, then the mean would be an appropriate measure.

The median salary paid is $100 000 and is not influenced by the extreme salary of $1 000 000. The median, however, tells us nothing about the total salary paid to the team.

There are two mode salaries paid. The most appropriate use of the mode often occurs when most of the classes have many members and the extreme classes have very few. In this case, the modal values are $70 000 and $100 000. Neither will give a clear indication of the total salary of the team.

Exercises

For Exercises 1 to 7, consider each situation and name the most appropriate central measure. Explain your choice.

1. Before imposing a tax on residents of a town, the city council wanted to know the average personal income in order to estimate the tax base.

2. The Ministry of Health and Welfare wanted to know the average height of Canadian males and females.

3. A research scientist wanted to know the average monthly temperature at Aklavik, North West Territories.

4. A person interested in opening a restaurant wanted to know the most common country of origin for the people living in a town.

5. A site engineer had to submit a report on the depth needed to drill for oil in an oil field.

6. A sociologist studying the buying habits of people in a small town needed to know the income of a typical family.

7. A shoe-store owner was describing the average size of the shoes she sells.

8. The mean mass of 10 people in a boat is 65 kg. A 120 kg person gets into the boat. What is the new mean mass of the people in the boat?

9. An advertisement for sportswear reported that a survey had found that customers had a median income of $30 000/a and an average age of 25. Comment on why the median is reported for the income while the nature of the value of the age of the customer is not specified.

10. A real-estate agency conducted a survey and reported the median and mean values of residential property sold in a small town during the year were $86 279 and $81 592. Which is likely to be the median value? Explain.

11. The heights, in centimetres, of players on a basketball team are 178, 176, 218, 178, and 175.
a. If a coach wishes to intimidate the opposition, which central measure of the heights of the players would be announced?
b. If he wished to give the opposition a "false sense of security", which central measure would be reported?

12. A motorist set the cruise control on her car so that the number of vehicles passing her equalled the number of vehicles she passed. Had she set the speed at the mean, median or mode of the speed of the vehicles on the road? Explain.

13. A cyclist travelled at 15 km/h for 10 km, and then 25 km/h for another 10 km. What was the mean speed of the cyclist over the total distance?

14. The mean age of the members of the Royal Regiment at their 40th reunion was 67.7 a. At the 41st reunion a year later, the mean age was 67.2 a. Explain how the mean age could decrease as the regiment members got older.

15. The headlines on a newspaper article was "Average Canadian is a Caucasian female". Which measure of central tendency was the reporter most likely using?

16. On an examination only 10% of the 30 scores were above the mean. What percent of the scores were above the median?

17. A survey of median personal incomes omitted all the respondents whose income was zero.
a. Explain how a group median income could be less as the incomes of the members of the group increase.
b. Which central measure could correct this apparent problem?

18. The mean age of 29 students in a classroom is 15 a. A thirty-year-old teacher enters the room. What is the mean age of the people in the room?

12·12 Box and Whisker Plots

We cannot be positive about conclusions gathered from a survey because, generally, not every member of the population has been surveyed. However, it is possible to indicate a degree of confidence that an answer falls within a certain range. A **box and whisker plot** is one way of showing the confidence we have in a particular range of data.

Example

A machine produces red and blue marbles in an unknown ratio and deposits them in a large bin. A sample of 20 marbles is taken from the bin and 12 are red. What is the proportion of red to blue marbles in the bin?

In the original sample, 60% of the marbles are known to be red. To be sure of the red to blue marble ratio, we would have to remove all the marbles and count them individually. This could be very time-consuming. But, using a random number table, a simulation of the event of selecting 20 marbles, 100 times, can be set up. From the simulation, we can establish a degree of confidence that the actual ratio falls within a certain range of values.

Using the random number table at the back of the book, select 20 digits and record how many times the numbers from 1 to 6 appear. This will represent the red marbles; while the blue marbles will be represented by the numbers 7, 8, 9, and 0. This will give us a 60:40, red to blue ratio that was found in the original sample. The frequency table records 100 samples of size 20, with the number of times the red marbles appear recorded in the frequency row.

Red Marbles	0	1	2	3	4	5	6	7	8	9	10	11	12	13	14	15	16	17	18	19	20
Frequency	0	0	0	0	0	0	1	3	8	10	14	19	13	11	8	7	3	2	1	0	0

A histogram can be used to show this distribution. Notice that, in 90 trials, red marbles appeared from 8 to 15 times. From the frequency table and the histogram, we can predict with 90% confidence that the bin has between 40% and 75% red marbles. This 90% value is the **confidence interval** within which the conclusion can be stated. Notice that the confidence interval decreases with the range of ratios. For example, if the conclusion is that the bin has between 50% and 65% red marbles, then this only accounts for the trials where 10, 11, 12, and 13 red marbles appeared. Therefore, the confidence interval is 60%, since only 60 out of the 100 samples contained from 10 to 13 red marbles. Note also, that 10% of the time, the sample will not lie between 40% and 75%.

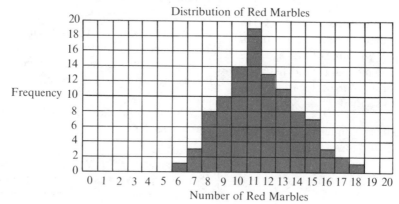

Distribution of Red Marbles

312

A box and whisker plot readily shows the confidence interval and the range of values in this interval. This plot shows the confidence interval of 90%, the box, and the values that appear in it.

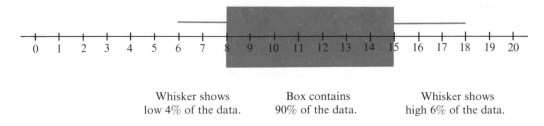

| Whisker shows low 4% of the data. | Box contains 90% of the data. | Whisker shows high 6% of the data. |

Notice that the values from 0 to 5, 19, and 20 did not occur in the trials. These values are in the **null class** of the set.

Exercises

1. In the example in the display, is a box and whisker plot or a histogram the best summary of the data? Explain.

2. Explain the terms "confidence interval" and "null class".

3. Construct a box and whisker plot that has a 75% confidence interval for the example.

4. Based on the simulation, how wide must the confidence interval be to be 100% confident of the conclusions? What is the conclusion that can be made with 100% confidence?

5. Can a box and whisker plot be affected by bias? Explain.

6. A random number table was used for the sample in the example. Explain how this table is used.

7. A sample size 20 is removed from a population containing an unknown number of green and white marbles. The sample contains 12 green marbles and 8 white marbles. As a class, run 100 trials using a random number table and pool the results in a frequency table.
a. For which percentages of the total population is this a common sample? Explain.
b. For which percentages of the total population is this a null sample? Explain.

8. Construct a box and whisker plot based on the frequency table from Exercise 7. Show five different confidence intervals and write the conclusions for each.

9. Construct two box and whisker plots based on the heights, in centimetres, of boys and girls in a Grade 10 class.
Girls:
144, 159, 163, 154, 160, 157, 155, 157, 161, 150, 152, 157, 157, 155, 157, 147
Boys:
148, 151, 154, 164, 158, 157, 155, 149, 144, 142, 151, 153, 157, 148, 152
a. Construct both box and whisker plots having an 80% confidence interval.
b. What is a "typical" height for girls? for boys?
c. Are the boys or girls "typically" taller in this class of students?

Using the Library

Statistics are used commonly in our everyday experience. Weather reports and polls are typical examples. Find how the government presented the statistics in the last census. Write a report summarizing the kinds of statistics presented, how the statistics were presented, and suggest any improvements that the government could make in the census. For example, one question recently removed from the English-speaking census was "can you read and write in English?"

12·13 Reliability of Predictions

The sample size of the Canadian Census is the entire population. This is a reliable but expensive and time-consuming way of gathering information. A small, and randomly chosen, sample of a population can be the basis for predictions about the whole population.

Predictions based on surveys or polls vary in reliability depending upon the size of the sample that is used. For example, suppose that a pollster stated that the Liberals were going to win a provincial election because 68% of the people surveyed would have voted Liberal at the time of the survey. However, if the pollster had surveyed only 100 people in one town, then the prediction is not reliable. On the other hand, if the survey had sampled 1000 people from every area in the province, the results are more reliable.

Exercises

1. Comment on the prediction based on the results of this survey.
49 out of 60 students at Rocky Mountain High brushed their teeth before leaving for school.
Prediction: Approximately 82% of all high-school students brush their teeth before leaving for school.

2. What affect would increasing the sample size in Exercise 1 have on the percent values for the entire population? Explain.

3. What affect does increasing the sample size have on the reliability of any prediction?

4. Which of these samples would yield a more reliable prediction? The question is: "What percent of students in a school have green eyes?" Explain.
2 students out of 20 had green eyes.
6 students out of 60 had green eyes.
11 students out of 100 had green eyes.

5. A farmer wishes to know how many head of cattle and how many hens he has. He knows that there are 125 heads and 350 feet altogether. How many of each kind of animal are there?

6. A pollster wanted to know if people preferred swimming in fresh water or salt water. She stood by the entrance of a swimming pool and asked every tenth person entering the pool which they preferred. She concluded that 90% of all people prefer swimming in fresh water. Is this a reliable conclusion?

7. What percent of Canadians will vote against the incumbent party in the next federal election?
13 out of 20 voters in a riding said that they would vote against.
38 out of 60 voters in a riding said that they would vote against.
31 out of 100 voters in a riding said that they would vote against.
a. Explain the reasons for the different results in the third poll.
b. If these were the only samples, would you predict that the incumbent party will win this election? Explain.

8. Design a questionnaire to help a shoe company decide what style of shoe to produce and how many of each size to produce.

Braintickler

Use the digits 1, 2, 3, 4, 5, 6, 7, 8, 9, and 0. Arrange them in order to make a sum of 1 using a maximum of one plus sign.

12·14 Selecting a Sample

How a sample is selected is an important consideration when surveying a population. These steps should be followed when gathering information about a population.

1. Decide on the population that is to be investigated.

2. Decide on the size of the sample.

3. Decide on the type of sample; whole population, a random sample, or a stratified random sample.

4. Avoid bias in sampling. (Refer to Section 12·3.)

Example

A random sample of 5 must be chosen from a group of 100 soldiers who have volunteered to take part in wilderness survival training. Design a plan to select 5 soldiers at random.

The target population is the 100 soldiers. One way of selecting a sample of 5, so that every soldier has an equal chance of being selected, is to list the soldiers in order alphabetically and to assign each soldier a two-digit number; 00, 01, 02, ... , 99. We could then use a random number table in two-digit groups to choose the soldiers whose numbers appear.

Exercises

For each of Exercises 1 to 9, comment on the plan for selecting a random sample and state how it can be improved.

1. How many raisins are in each box of Raisin Flake cereal?
Open one box of cereal and count the raisins.

2. How many people drink tea?
Ask 100 people at a coffee-producers' convention.

3. What is the most popular sport?
Ask 100 people leaving a basketball game.

4. How many Canadians are over 40 a old?
Ask the age of 20 people.

5. Check the condition of the tomatoes in a crate.
Squeeze the tomatoes on the top of the crate.

6. Check the manufacturer's inventory of nuts and bolts for defects.
Have a team of 5 workers examine every nut and bolt.

7. Determine if there is life on Mars.
Photograph 10% of the surface using a space probe.

8. Find the number of teenagers who play soccer in your province.
Take a random sample in the biggest city in your province.

9. Find public opinion about wages paid to a selected group of workers.
Ask the workers in that group.

10. Use a random number table to select three people from the following class list to report in Student Council meetings. Explain how you read the random number table.

Ambrose	Doberstein	Pebernat
Bidiuk	Gjesdal	Perrault
Blomgren	Hillis	Phye
Bossom	Jackson	Reich
Bramley	LaChapelle	Sedgwick
Carberry	Nap	Tjernqvist
Chowdhury	Nguyen	Turek
Coffey	Nickel	Vogel

12·15 Probability

There are certain expressions that we have all heard. For example: there is a 40% chance of rain; the probability of winning a lottery is 1 in 250 000; or the chance of drawing an ace from a well-shuffled deck is $\frac{1}{13}$.

Each of these is a **probability**, or measure of the chance that an **event** will occur. Testing the occurrence of an event takes place in an **experiment**, and the set of all possible outcomes to the experiment is the **sample space**. The **complement** of an event is the part of the sample space not in the event.

Probabilities range from a low of zero to a high of 1 or 100%. For example, there is a zero percent probability that a seven will be rolled using one fair die, but there is a 100% possibility that a number from 1 to 6 will appear.

If each event in the sample space of an experiment has an equal chance of occurring, then the outcomes are considered to be **equally likely**.

Example 1

A bag contains 5 red and 5 blue marbles. One marble is to be drawn at random from the bag. Is the probability of drawing a red marble equal to the probability of drawing a blue?

Since there is a $\frac{5}{10}$, (0.5), chance for each event, the events are equally likely.

Example 2

The numbers 10 to 19 inclusive are written on slips of paper, placed in a hat, and thoroughly mixed. What is the probability that a number drawn at random is an odd number? a prime number?

The sample space lists all the possible outcomes: {10, 11, 12, ... , 19}.
The probability of an event occurring is the ratio of the number of favourable outcomes to the number of possible outcomes.
The favourable outcomes for odd numbers (O) is the set {11, 13, 15, 17, 19}.
The favourable outcomes for prime numbers (A) is the set {11, 13, 17, 19}.

$$P(O) = \frac{5}{10}$$
$$= 0.5$$

The probability of an event E is written as P(E).

$$P(A) = \frac{4}{10}$$
$$= 0.4$$

The probability of drawing an odd number is 0.5 and the probability of drawing a prime number is 0.4.

This **tree diagram** shows the sample space and the probability of event O and $\bar{O}$ (complement of O).

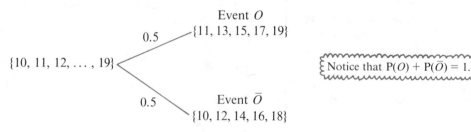

Event O
{11, 13, 15, 17, 19}

0.5

{10, 11, 12, ... , 19}

Notice that $P(O) + P(\bar{O}) = 1$.

0.5

Event $\bar{O}$
{10, 12, 14, 16, 18}

Exercises

1. State the complement of event O in Example 2 of the display.

2. Is each event equally likely to occur?
a. drawing a 5 of hearts from a well-shuffled deck of cards
b. a head turns up with one toss of a coin
c. drawing a black marble from a bag containing 1 black and 5 blue marbles
d. being born a male
e. drawing a card marked C from a hat containing 4 cards marked A, B, C, and D
f. rolling a one with a die which has its number dots grooved
g. a pitcher with a win/loss ratio of 0.333 winning the next game
h. a hockey player with a goal-scoring percent of 12, scoring with the next shot on goal

3. State the sample space, the event, and the complement for each of these experiments.
a. tossing a tail using a fair coin
b. drawing a diamond from a deck of well-shuffled cards
c. rolling a 3 with a fair die
d. having a friend randomly choose an odd digit
e. randomly choosing a vowel from the letters of the word CHANCE
f. rolling a 1, 2, 3, 4, 5, or 6 with a fair die

4. Calculate the probability for each event in Exercise 3.

5. Draw a tree diagram for each part of Exercise 3.

6. The letters of the word SUPERIOR are placed in a hat and one is drawn at random. Find the probability of each event. For example, P(S, U, P) means drawing either an S, a U, or a P $= \frac{3}{8}$.
a. P(P)   **b.** P(R)   **c.** P(N)
d. P($\overline{R}$)   **e.** P(vowel)   **f.** P(consonant)
g. P(S, U, P, E, R)   **h.** P(I, O, R)
i. P(S, U, P, E, R, I, O)   **j.** P(A)

7. Two coins are tossed. Calculate the probability for each event.
a. P(T, T) **b.** P(H, T) **c.** P(T, H) **d.** P(H, H)

8. A box contains 11 marbles. Three marbles are blue, 5 marbles are white, 2 marbles are green, and 1 marble is red. A marble is drawn from the box at random. Find the probability of each event.
a. P(B)   **b.** P($\overline{W}$)   **c.** P(R)   **d.** P(B, W)
e. P(G)   **f.** P(B, W, G) **g.** P($\overline{Y}$)
h. P(R, G)   **i.** P($\overline{B}$)   **j.** P(R, W)

9. Work with 10 000 mosquitoes produced the life-span data shown in the table. Find the probability that a mosquito will live to each age.
a. 2 weeks   **b.** 5 weeks
c. 7 weeks   **d.** 8 weeks

Age (weeks)	Mosquitoes Still Alive
0	10 000
1	8 000
2	7 500
3	6 900
4	6 500
5	5 000
6	3 000
7	1 500
8	100

Historical Note

Abraham De Moivre (1667-1754)
Abraham De Moivre was a French mathematician who lived and worked in London, England. His work was concentrated in the fields of trigonometry, probability theory, and annuities.

De Moivre's reputation was so great that in later years, Sir Isaac Newton, when questioned about his own work, answered, "Go to Mr. De Moivre; he knows these things better than I do."

Use the library and describe the theorem named after De Moivre.

12·16 Theoretical and Experimental Probability

Probabilities of real events can be affected by outside influences. If all external influences are eliminated, the theoretical probability of an event can be calculated.

> **Theoretical Probability** of Event, E.
>
> $P(E) = \dfrac{\text{number of favourable outcomes}}{\text{total number of possible outcomes}}$

Example 1

Find the theoretical probability of rolling a 3 with a fair die.

$P(3) = \dfrac{\text{number of favourable outcomes}}{\text{total number of possible outcomes}}$

$\quad = \dfrac{1}{6}$

The theoretical probability of rolling a 3 is $\dfrac{1}{6}$ or $16.\overline{6}\%$.

The experimental probability is obtained from repeated experiments.

> **Experimental Probability** of Event, E.
>
> $P(E) = \dfrac{\text{number of favourable outcomes}}{\text{number of experimental trials}}$

Example 2

Find the experimental probability of rolling a 3 with a fair die over 20 trials. The data collected is shown.

Trial	1	2	3	4	5	6	7	8	9	10	11	12	13	14	15	16	17	18	19	20
Outcome	4	5	1	3	2	4	6	1	3	1	6	5	5	6	6	1	4	5	3	2

$P(3) = \dfrac{\text{number of favourable outcomes}}{\text{number of experimental trials}}$

$\quad = \dfrac{3}{20}$

The experimental probability of rolling a 3 was found to be 15%.

The outcomes of the 20 rolls of a die are examples of **random** events. An event which occurs without prearrangement, plan, or design is **random**.

In performing experiments, it is important to control, minimize, or eliminate outside influences as much as possible. For example, in the experiment of rolling a die such factors as a rounded edge or even the varying masses of the dots on each face of the die may affect the results.

Exercises

1. Use the die from Example 2 in the display and calculate the experimental probability after 10 rolls. after 15 rolls.

2. Compare the experimental probability to the theoretical probability as the number of rolls increase in Example 2.

3. List two conditions surrounding each event that could cause variation in the experimental probability.
a. The player has a 31% chance of getting a hit next time at bat.
b. There is a 10% chance of rain tomorrow.
c. Mrs. Teshima will win the next election by a 20% margin.
d. The marksman will shoot a bull's-eye on the next shot.
e. There is a 75% chance that you will have more than one job during your lifetime.

4. Five slips of paper have the number 10 written on them. Fifteen slips of paper have the number 7 written on them. The slips of paper are placed in a bag and mixed.
a. What is the theoretical probability of drawing a 7? of drawing a 10?
b. Perform the experiment and record the results of 30 draws. Ensure that you replace the slip of paper and shake the bag before drawing the next slip of paper.
c. Calculate the experimental probability of drawing a 7 and of drawing a 10 using your results.
d. Compare the results of part **c** with the results in part **a**.

5. Record the results of 20 tosses of a coin. Calculate the experimental probability of tossing a head.
a. Compare your results with two classmates.
b. Compare your results with the theoretical probability for this event.

6. Find the value of the unit's digit for 7^{3274} without using a calculator or a computer.

7. Use a random number table for each experiment. Record the results of 20 trials and calculate the experimental probability for each. Compare your results with two classmates and the theoretical probability for each event.
a. A digit selected is even.
b. A two-digit number selected is greater than or equal to 80.
c. A composite number selected is between 30 and 51.

8. Conduct the experiment outlined to find the experimental probability that a family with two children will have each of the following.
a. two girls
b. one girl and one boy
c. two boys
Select 20 two-digit numbers from a random number table. Two odd digits represent two boys. An odd and an even digit represent a boy and a girl. Two even digits represent two girls.

9. The table shows the survival rates for Canadians in selected age groups.

| Age (years) | Surviving | |
	Male	Female
0	100 000	100 000
20	97 738	98 544
30	96 303	98 049
40	94 806	97 243
50	91 355	95 232
60	82 524	90 394
70	63 957	79 747
80	34 970	57 549

Use the table to calculate the probability of each.
a. a male living to age 80
b. a female living to age 80
c. a male of 20 living to age 60
d. a female of 20 living to age 60
e. a female of 60 living to age 80
f. a male of 40 living to age 70

10. Calculate the theoretical probability of rolling a 7 with two dice.

12·17 Independent and Dependent Events

Events may occur in succession. When the occurrence or nonoccurrence of the first event does not affect the occurrence or nonoccurrence of the second event, the events are **independent**. For example, there is a 50% probability that a newborn baby will be female. If the first born in a family is male, this in no way affects the probability for the gender of the next child born.

If the probability of two events is P(A) and P(B) respectively, then the probability that both events occur, P(A and B), is the product of the two individual probabilities.
P(A and B) = P(A) × P(B)

Example 1

A cookie jar contains 10 chocolate and 5 vanilla cookies of the same size and shape. A child reaches into the jar and randomly draws a cookie. The cookie is not the kind wanted so it is replaced and another is drawn. What is the probability that both cookies drawn are vanilla?

$$P(V \text{ and } V) = P(V) \times P(V)$$
$$= \frac{1}{3} \times \frac{1}{3}$$
$$= \frac{1}{9}$$

The probability that both cookies drawn are vanilla is $\frac{1}{9}$.

Example 2

If the first cookie drawn is vanilla and is eaten, what is the probability that both cookies drawn are vanilla?

Since the first cookie drawn is not replaced, the number of vanilla cookies left in the jar is 4. The probability that the second cookie is vanilla is represented by $P(V_1)$.

$$P(V_1) = \frac{4}{14} = \frac{2}{7}$$

The probability that both cookies are vanilla is

$$P(V \text{ and } V_1) = \frac{1}{3} \times \frac{2}{7}$$
$$= \frac{2}{21}$$

In this case, the probability of drawing two vanilla cookies is $\frac{2}{21}$.

The second case is an example of **dependent** events. Once the first cookie was drawn and eaten, then the probabilities changed for the next draw of a cookie. If the occurrence of the first event affects the occurrence of the second event, the events are **dependent**.

The tree diagrams show the probabilities for Examples 1 and 2.

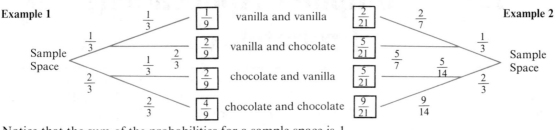

Notice that the sum of the probabilities for a sample space is 1.

Exercises

Refer to the examples in the display for Exercises 1 to 3.

1. If the first cookie drawn was replaced, then find each probability.
a. drawing a vanilla and then a chocolate cookie
b. drawing two chocolate cookies

2. Find the probability of drawing a chocolate and a vanilla cookie if the first cookie drawn is eaten.

3. Find the probability of drawing a vanilla and a chocolate cookie if the first cookie drawn is eaten.

4. State whether each statement is true.
a. A man tosses 15 heads in a row. The "law of averages" says the next toss will be a tail.
b. The sexes of successive newborn babies are independent.

5. There is a probability of $\frac{1}{10}$ that the brakes of a car sold at Lemon Used Car Sales are defective. There is a probability of $\frac{2}{5}$ that the horn is broken. Calculate the probability that a car has each problem.
a. both defective brakes and broken horn
b. defective brakes and a horn that works
c. brakes that work and a broken horn
d. both brakes and horn work

6. Draw a tree diagram to show the probabilities for Exercise 5.

7. In a lottery, a six-digit number is drawn. Which has the better chance of winning the lottery: 111 111 or 125 467? Explain your reasoning.

8. Suppose a jelly bean is drawn at random from a paper bag containing 10 black, 14 yellow, and 6 red jelly beans. The jelly bean is replaced and another is drawn. Calculate each probability.
a. P(B and B) **b.** P(B and Y) **c.** P(R and Y)
d. P(R and $\bar{R}$) **e.** P(R and B) **f.** P(B and R)
g. P(Y and Y) **h.** P(R and R) **i.** P(B and $\bar{B}$)

9. The first jelly bean drawn from the bag in Exercise 8 is eaten. A second jelly bean is drawn. Calculate each probability.
a. P(B and B) **b.** P(B and Y) **c.** P(R and Y)
d. P(Y and Y) **e.** P(R and B) **f.** P(R and R)

10. A bowl contains 3 white and 3 red marbles. The bowl is shaken and 3 marbles are drawn in succession without replacement. Calculate each probability.
a. P(W, W, W)   **b.** P(R, R, R)
c. P(W, R, W)   **d.** P(R, W, R)
e. P(W, W, R)   **f.** P(R, R, W)

11. Draw a tree diagram to illustrate all possible answers to Exercise 10.

12. A spacecraft has 3 independent computer guidance systems. The probability that each will fail is 10^{-3}. What is the probability that all three will fail?

13. The probability of a sharpshooter hitting a bull's-eye decreases with each shot. The probability is $\frac{9}{10}$ for the first shot, $\frac{7}{8}$ for the second shot, and $\frac{3}{4}$ for the third shot. Calculate the probability of hitting the bull's-eye in each case.
a. first and third shot **b.** second and third shot
c. first and second shot **d.** all three shots

12·18 Computer Application — Probability

The experimental probability for events can be simulated on the computer. The computer will simulate the roll of a die, flip of a coin, or even the deal of cards through the use of a built-in BASIC command called the RND(X) random number generator function. This function will have the computer pick a nine-digit random decimal between 0 and 1.

```
10 REM A PROGRAM THAT WILL FIND THE EXPERIMENTAL
15 REM PROBABILITY OF TOSSING A HEAD OR A TAIL WITH
20 REM A FAIR COIN USING 10 TOSSES OF A COIN
30 FOR X = 1 TO 10
40 LET TSS = RND(1)
50 IF TSS < = 0.5 THEN 70
60 LET H = H + 1
70 NEXT X
80 PRINT "PROBABILITY OF TOSSING A HEAD IS ": H / (X − 1)
90 PRINT "PROBABILITY OF TOSSING A TAIL IS ": 1 − H / (X − 1)
99 END
```

Exercises

1. State the purpose of line 40.

2. State the purpose of line 50.

3. Why does line 50 state that TSS must be less than or equal to 0.5?

4. Predict what the output of this program will be before it is run. Explain.

5. In line 80, the computer is told to divide by (X − 1). Why is this necessary?

6. What is the theoretical probability of tossing a head with a fair coin?

7. If line 30 was changed to FOR X = 1 TO 100, predict what would happen to the experimental probabilities. Justify your prediction.

8. Modify the program in the display to simulate the tossing of 200 coins. Have the computer tell the programmer how many heads and how many tails were tossed and find the experimental probability for each coin.

9. Modify the program in the display to simulate throwing a fair die 50 times. Find the experimental probability of rolling a 3. Compare this to the theoretical probability.

10. Modify the program of Exercise 9 to simulate throwing a pair of die 150 times. Have the computer calculate the probability of throwing a number greater than 8. How does this compare to the theoretical probability of throwing a number greater than 8?

11. Computers have been created to compete and win in all kinds of games. For example, the computers at the Ontario Science Centre are programmed to play tic-tac-toe against visitors. Is it possible to beat a computer that has been programmed to play such games? Explain.

12·19 Chapter Review

1. A stratified random sample of 30 members of a yacht club was planned. The club has 100 sailboat owners and 200 powerboat owners. Explain the method used to obtain the sample.

2. If the sample in Exercise 1 was proportional, then how many powerboat owners would be in the sample?

3. Explain the phrase "survey coverage error". Give an example.

4. List two advantages of a mail survey.

5. Construct a percent frequency table based on the number of ice-cream cones sold at a store during a month. Use an interval of $0 \leq n < 20$ for the first class.
82, 81, 105, 112, 45, 10, 108, 109, 92, 87, 67, 33, 111, 81, 75, 71, 68, 59, 60, 99, 100, 115, 118, 33, 101, 55, 80, 130, 114, 138

6. Construct a stem and leaf table based on maximum daily precipitation measured in millimetres during the month of November in selected Canadian cities.
11, 21, 12, 28, 19, 88, 29, 61, 68, 40, 36, 19, 31, 45, 35, 49, 24, 86, 46, 53, 55, 25, 16, 72, 79, 59, 99, 41

7. Find the mean, median, and mode for each.
a. marks on a mathematics examination
74, 77, 88, 80, 58, 89, 98, 70, 65, 63, 78, 46, 75, 82, 45, 91, 80, 67, 49, 82, 65, 85, 93, 63, 70, 81, 53, 54, 63, 70
b. masses of 25 students measured in kilograms
70, 63, 59, 66, 75, 62, 81, 73, 62, 65, 43, 57, 59, 69, 61, 67, 50, 66, 53, 56, 55, 61, 59, 57, 54

8. Construct a histogram and identify the type of distribution. Calculate the mean, the median, and the mode. Comment on the central measures for each type of curve.

Mean daily air temperatures in degrees Celsius at Halifax, N.S.:

Month	J	F	M	A	M	J
Temp.	−3.8	−4.2	−0.7	4	9	13.7

Month	J	A	S	O	N	D
Temp.	17.6	17.8	14.8	9.9	4.9	−1.1

9. For each event, find the sample space, the probability of each event, and the complement of each event.
a. tossing two heads with two coins
b. drawing a spade from a well-shuffled deck of cards
c. drawing a green marble from a bag containing 4 green and 4 white marbles
d. the day of the week the next birth will occur

10. State whether each event is equally likely to occur.
a. drawing the ace of spades from a well-shuffled deck of cards
b. drawing a red marble from a bag containing 12 red marbles and 10 white marbles
c. an eclipse of the moon will occur this month
d. the stock market average will change tomorrow
e. the next motorist to stop at an intersection will turn right

11. A marble is drawn from a bag containing 13 white, 10 blue, and 7 orange marbles. The marble is returned to the bag. The marbles are mixed and another drawn. Calculate each probability.
a. P(W and B) **b.** P(W and $\overline{O}$) **c.** P($\overline{B}$ and O)
d. P(W and W) **e.** P(B and O) **f.** P(W and $\overline{W}$)
g. P(B and W) **h.** P(G and O) **i.** P(W and O)

12. A marble is drawn from the bag in Exercise 11 and is not replaced. A second marble is then drawn. Calculate each probability.
a. P(B and B) **b.** P(B and W) **c.** P(B and O)
d. P(O and O) **e.** P(O and W) **f.** P(W and W)

323

12·20 Chapter Test

1. Study the graph and answer each question.

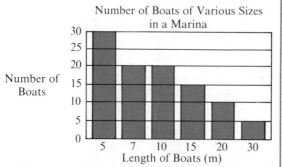

Number of Boats of Various Sizes in a Marina

a. How many boats are 15 m long?
b. How many boats are 5 m long?
c. What is missing in the graph?
d. Only 5 of the boats in the marina have what length?
e. What is the mode for boat lengths in the marina?

2. A stratified random sample of 20 members of a flying club was planned. The club has 15 float-plane owners and 80 wheel-plane owners. If the sample is taken correctly, then how many float-plane owners will be in the sample?

3. Explain what is meant by process errors in a survey.

4. Construct a stem and leaf table based on the ages of 25 people riding a bus.
11, 22, 33, 45, 52, 58, 49, 45, 36, 27, 22, 14, 37, 54, 53, 12, 34, 25, 54, 47, 22, 56, 28, 13, 45

5. Construct a histogram based on the data in the table.

Heights of Students (cm)	Frequency
$150 \leq h < 155$	1
$155 \leq h < 160$	2
$160 \leq h < 165$	5
$165 \leq h < 170$	10
$170 \leq h < 175$	5
$175 \leq h < 180$	2

6. Find the mean, median, and mode for the data on the masses of ten 10 kg bags of flour.
10.00, 9.82, 10.03, 10.10, 10.07, 10.02, 10.01, 10.07, 10.05, 9.98

7. Calculate the weighted mean from the data in the table.
Air temperatures in April:

Temperature	Frequency
−1°C	1
0°C	2
5°C	14
10°C	11
15°C	2

8. Construct a frequency table and find the modal class. Calculate the mean and median.
Concentrations of solutes in drinking water, mg/L. The interval in the first class is $0 \leq c < 50$.
44, 49, 51, 66, 89, 105, 107, 108, 120, 127, 135, 141, 143, 147, 149, 153, 159, 160, 170, 171, 171, 175, 183, 188, 189, 190, 190, 190, 191, 194, 195, 195, 198, 199, 199, 200, 200, 200, 203, 203, 209, 209, 210, 211, 212, 213, 215, 217, 222, 225, 230, 240, 240, 241, 241, 242, 242, 243, 243, 244, 245, 246, 247, 248, 249, 255, 260, 265, 271, 275, 279, 283, 285, 289, 291, 293, 295, 297, 298, 298, 298, 298, 299, 299, 299

9. The mean mass of 15 people is 80 kg. A 110 kg person is included in the group. Find the new mean mass.

10. State the sample space, event, and the complement of the event when drawing a red marble from a bag containing 6 red marbles and 6 white marbles.

11. The letters of the word TORONTO are placed in a hat and one is drawn at random. Find the probability of each event.
a. P(T)   **b.** P(N)   **c.** P(O)   **d.** $P(\bar{O})$
e. P(R)   **f.** P(V)   **g.** $P(\bar{V})$ **h.** $P(\bar{T})$

Cumulative Review Chapters 10–12

1. Where possible, write a logical conclusion for each set of statements. Indicate whether you arrived at your conclusion through inductive or deductive reasoning.
a. If the sun is shining, then we will play golf. The sun is shining.
b. The numbers 2, 3, 4, and 6 are all factors of 12.
c. Your grandmother hated math and your mother hated math.

2. Use the diagram to write the converse of each statement. Is each converse true? Explain.

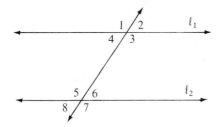

a. If $\ell_1 \| \ell_2$, then $\angle 1 \cong \angle 5$.
b. If $\ell_1 \| \ell_2$, then $\angle 3 + \angle 5 = 180°$.
c. If $\ell_1 \| \ell_2$, then $\angle 3 \cong \angle 6$.

3. Each pair of triangles has one pair of congruent angles. Which sides would have to be congruent in order to use the S.A.S. congruence postulate?

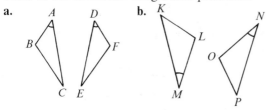

4. Each pair of triangles has one pair of congruent angles. Which pair of angles must be congruent in order to use the A.S.A. congruence postulate?

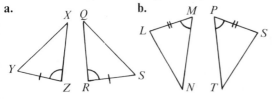

5. State the postulate or theorem that could be used to prove the triangles congruent.
a.

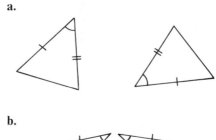

b.

6. Prove that $\triangle GPZ \cong \triangle ATW$.

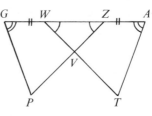

7. A teacher arranges 31 students in a circle. Each student is numbered consecutively from 1 to 31. The teacher starts at 1 and eliminates every third student until only student 6 and 27 remain. What was the number of the first student to be eliminated?

8. Consider an "if ... then" statement.
a. Which part represents the hypothesis and which part represents the conclusion?
b. Which part represents the given and which part represents the required?
c. Identify the given and required parts for each theorem.
 i) If a triangle is isosceles, then the altitude from the base bisects the vertex.
 ii) The longest side of a triangle is the side opposite the largest angle.

Cumulative Review Chapters 10-12

9. In the diagram, $\overline{AD} \| \overline{BC}$ and $\overline{DE} \cong \overline{BE}$.

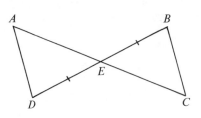

a. State the three pairs of angles which are congruent and give the reason for each.
b. State which pairs of sides are congruent and give a reason for each.
c. Which postulate or theorem could be used to prove that $\triangle ADE \cong \triangle CBE$? Is there more than one?
d. Prove that $\overline{AD} \cong \overline{BC}$.

10. In the diagram, $\overline{AD}$ does not bisect $\angle A$ and D is the midpoint of $\overline{BC}$.

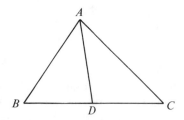

a. If indirect reasoning is to be used to prove that $\overline{AB} \cong \overline{AC}$, then what assumption would be made before the proof is started?
b. What two triangles can be proved congruent using the assumption from part **a** as one of the steps in the reasoning process?
c. What contradiction would be arrived at using the assumption from part **a**?

11. What is the median of a triangle? Prove that the median from the vertex of an isosceles triangle bisects that angle.

12. Prove that a triangle with sides of 12 cm, 17 cm, and 35 cm is a right triangle.

13. This circle has centre O.

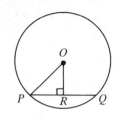

a. If the radius of the circle is 7 cm, and the length of the chord is 8 cm, then find the length of $\overline{OR}$.
b. If the radius of the circle is 12 cm, and the length of $\overline{OR}$ is 4 cm, then find the length of the chord.
c. If the length of $\overline{OR}$ is 14 cm, and the length of the chord is 18 cm, then find the radius of the circle.

14. Find the value of each indicated variable.

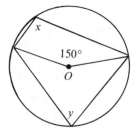

15. Use the diagram to answer each where $\overline{KT}$ is a tangent to the circle.

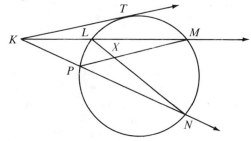

a. If $\overline{KT} = 15$ cm and $\overline{KP} = 12$ cm, then find the length of $\overline{PN}$.
b. If $\overline{LX} = 10$ cm, $\overline{XN} = 18$ cm, and $\overline{PX} = 9$ cm, then find the length of $\overline{XM}$.

Cumulative Review Chapters 10–12

16. Monica is approaching a football stadium that is in the shape of a circle with a radius of 100 m. She can see two gates to enter the stadium. If she takes the first gate that she comes to and walks in a straight line, then she would walk to the centre of the stadium. The second gate will take her to a point of tangency on the edge of the stadium. She walks 200 m to reach the gate. How far would the second gate take her?

17. Name the type of transformation shown by each.

a.   **b.**

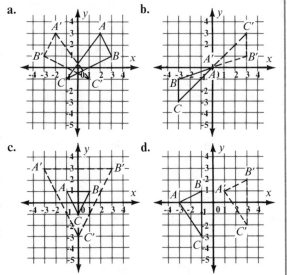

c.   **d.**

18. State the mapping that best describes the transformations shown in Exercise 17.

19. Copy the diagram and draw its image under each transformation.

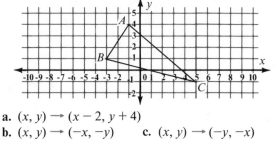

a. $(x, y) \rightarrow (x - 2, y + 4)$
b. $(x, y) \rightarrow (-x, -y)$ **c.** $(x, y) \rightarrow (-y, -x)$

20. State the image coordinates under each transformation.
a. $M(4, -2)$ is reflected in the y-axis.
b. $N(-7, 3)$ under the mapping $(x, y) \rightarrow (x + 3, y - 2)$.
c. $P(1, -4)$ is rotated $270°$ about the origin.
d. $Q(3, 5)$ under the mapping $(x, y) \rightarrow (-y + 2, -x + 4)$.

21. Use a triangle with vertices at $A(3, 5)$, $B(-2, 3)$, and $C(1, -2)$ to determine whether length, slope, and angle measure are invariant under each transformation.
a. $(x, y) \rightarrow (x - 3, y + 5)$
b. $(x, y) \rightarrow (-y, x)$
c. $(x, y) \rightarrow (-x, y)$
d. $(x, y) \rightarrow (3x, 3y)$

22. Which transformations studied so far are isometries?

23. Find the equation of the image of the line $3x - 2y = 5$ under each transformation.
a. $(x, y) \rightarrow (x - 3, y + 2)$
b. $(x, y) \rightarrow (1 - x, 2 + y)$
c. $(x, y) \rightarrow (y - 3, x + 1)$

24. Find the equation of the line of reflection when a line segment defined by the points $A(-2, 1)$ and $B(3, -2)$ is reflected using the mapping $(x, y) \rightarrow (2 - y, 2 - x)$.

25. Triangle ABC has vertices at $A(3, 2)$, $B(-4, -1)$, and $C(5, -1)$. Triangle $A'B'C'$ is formed by the transformation $(x, y) \rightarrow (2x, 2y)$.
a. Show that the perimeter of $\triangle A'B'C'$ is twice the perimeter of $\triangle ABC$.
b. Show that the area of $\triangle A'B'C'$ is four times the area of $\triangle ABC$.

26. Write the equation of the image line if the object line $3x + 2y = -5$ is transformed using a dilatation with a scale factor of 4.

327

Cumulative Review   Chapters 10–12

27. Copy the diagram. Show as many ways as you can for the white ball to hit the red ball without hitting the black ball.

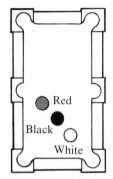

28. Rotate the triangle in Exercise 19 using the mapping $(x, y) \rightarrow (3 - x, 1 - y)$.
a. Find the coordinates of the image points.
b. Find the actual amount of rotation.
c. Find the rotation point.

29. A boy, 1.3 m tall, bounces a ball to his sister who is 1.7 m tall. They are standing 4 m apart and the ball rebounds at the same angle it was bounced. Where must the ball hit the ground if it is released from a height equal to the top of each person's head?

30. King, Amid, and Ishmail are a striker, a midfielder, and a goaltender on the Canadian National Soccer team, but not necessarily in that order. Also, there are three team officials with the same last names: Mr. King, Mr. Amid, and Mr. Ishmail.
Mr. Amid lives in Saskatoon.
The midfielder lives halfway between Edmonton and Calgary.
Mr. Ishmail earns $50 000/a.
The midfielder's nearest neighbour, one of the three officials, earns exactly three times as much as the striker.
King beats the striker at chess.
The official, whose last name is the same as the midfielder's, lives in Edmonton.
Who is the goaltender?

31. Quadrilateral *KRSM* is defined by the points $K(-1, -4)$, $R(1, 6)$, $S(8, 8)$, and $M(4, -12)$.
a. Prove that *KRSM* is a trapezoid.
b. If the trapezoid is transformed using the mapping $(x, y) \rightarrow (-y, -x)$, then prove that *K'R'S'M'* is also a trapezoid.

32. Construct a stem and leaf table based on the ages of these 30 people.
12, 13, 12, 15, 14, 12, 15, 11, 14, 13, 15, 12, 11, 14, 12, 15, 16, 12, 14, 12, 11, 12, 13, 12, 14, 16, 15, 13, 14, 13

33. Calculate the mean, median, and mode for the ages in Exercise 32.

34. A political science club has 43 members that are Conservative, 40 members that are Liberal, 24 members that are New Democrats, 8 members who are of the Social Credit party, and 35 who have no affiliation. A sample of 30 members of the club is needed for a survey.
a. How many Liberals should be chosen?
b. How many nonaffiliated members should be chosen?

35. A scientist was studying the suspended sediment load in 10 selected rivers. The data in parts per million was collected and reported.
140, 130, 110, 360, 220, 50, 180, 150, 240, 270
a. Graphically represent this data.
b. Explain why you chose the particular graph of part **a**.

36. Construct a frequency table based on this data. Calculate the mean, the median, and the modal class.
Ages of wedding guests. First class $0 \leq a < 10$.
11, 15, 1, 24, 1, 75, 65, 45, 45, 46, 47, 25, 25, 21, 21, 13, 14, 16, 5, 5, 16, 31, 22, 35, 44, 24, 24, 22, 42, 1, 2, 4, 18, 45, 26, 27, 22, 56, 58, 20, 62, 6, 7, 16, 43, 23, 34, 5, 4, 9, 21, 23, 46, 46, 52, 53, 56, 77, 52, 40, 42, 25, 46, 2, 6, 1, 45, 25, 56, 56, 7, 8, 9, 16, 21, 6, 17, 25, 24, 16, 42, 22, 15, 23, 23, 33, 23, 26, 23, 27, 26, 26, 24, 76, 79, 27, 25, 7, 21, 22

SELECTED TOPICS

Tune Up

1. Find the length of the unknown side correct to one decimal place.

a.

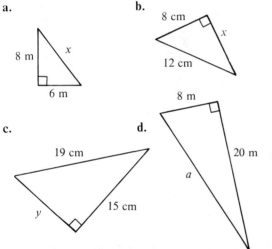

b.

c.

d.

2. Find the length of x correct to one decimal place.

a.

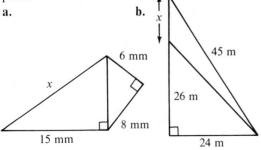

b.

3. Each edge of a cube has a length of 8 cm.
a. Find the length of the diagonal of one of the faces.
b. Find the length of the inside diagonal as a radical in simplest form.

4. The rectangular prism has sides of 3 cm, 4 cm, and 12 cm. Find the length of these diagonals.
a. $\overline{AC}$ **b.** $\overline{CD}$ **c.** $\overline{CE}$

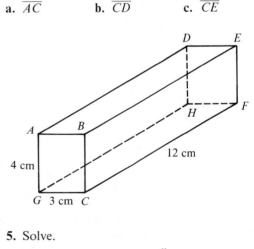

5. Solve.
a. $3x + 2 = 26$ **b.** $\dfrac{x}{6} = 14$
c. $\dfrac{27}{x} = 6$ **d.** $\dfrac{15}{22} = \dfrac{6}{x}$

6. Solve each system of equations.
a. $3x + 2y = 3$ **b.** $5m + 2n = -16$
$\quad\; x - 3y = -10$ $\qquad m - n = 1$

329

13·1 Similar Triangles

Two figures which have exactly the same shape may or may not have the same size. Such figures are said to be **similar** to each other.

Consider $\triangle ABC$. If the sides are all doubled in length, a similar triangle, $\triangle DEF$, will result. In both of these triangles, the corresponding sides are in proportion and the corresponding angles are congruent.

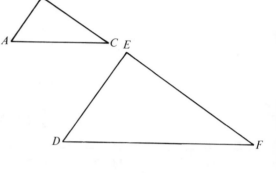

$\dfrac{\overline{AB}}{\overline{DE}} = \dfrac{\overline{AC}}{\overline{DF}} = \dfrac{\overline{BC}}{\overline{EF}}$ and $\angle A \cong \angle D, \angle B \cong \angle E, \angle C \cong \angle F$.

The similarity of the two triangles is written as $\triangle ABC \sim \triangle DEF$.

Example 1

Calculate the length of the indicated side. In the first case, $\triangle ABC \sim \triangle DEF$; in the second case, $\triangle ABC \sim \triangle ADE$.

a.

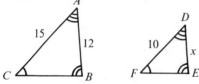

$\dfrac{15}{10} = \dfrac{12}{x}$
$15x = 120$
$x = 8$

Therefore, the length of the indicated side is 8 units.

b.

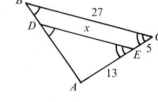

$\dfrac{18}{13} = \dfrac{27}{x}$
$18x = 351$
$x = 19.5$

Therefore, the length of the indicated side is 19.5 units.

Sometimes it is possible to use similar triangles to calculate distances which are difficult or impossible to measure directly.

Example 2

An electrical tower casts a shadow which is 24 m long. A post standing beside the tower is 1.8 m tall and casts a shadow 1.5 m long. How tall is the electrical tower?

By comparing the two triangles, we can see that they are similar.

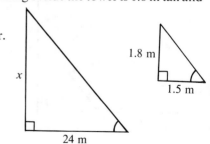

Therefore, $\dfrac{24}{1.5} = \dfrac{x}{1.8}$

$\qquad 1.5x = 43.2$ Cross multiply.

$\qquad\quad x = 28.8$

The tower is 28.8 m tall.

330

Exercises

1. For each pair of similar triangles, state the pairs of corresponding sides.

a.

b.

c.

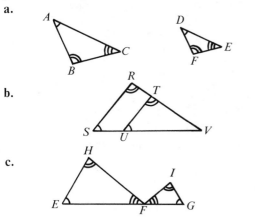

2. Find the lengths of the unknown sides of these similar triangles correct to one decimal place.

a.

b.

c.

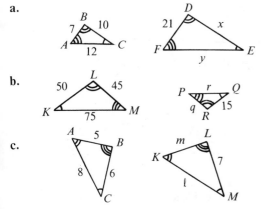

3. A ladder 5 m long reaches 4 m up a wall. How far would a ladder 6 m long reach up a wall if both ladders formed the same angle with the ground?

4. On a sunny day a tree 12.2 m tall casts a shadow 9.3 m long. How tall is a second tree which has a shadow 7.1 m long at the same time?

5. A plane is climbing at a uniform rate of 12 m for every 100 m it travels horizontally. What distance has the plane climbed when it has travelled a horizontal distance of 1 km?

6. Find the lengths of the unknown sides correct to one decimal place.

a.   **b.**

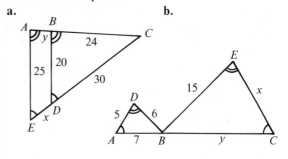

7. In order to calculate the distance across a river, a surveyor maps out the following diagram. Calculate the width of the river.

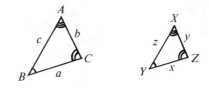

8. Given that $\triangle ABC$ and $\triangle XYZ$ are similar, with the lengths of the sides shown. Find the lengths of the unknown sides correct to one decimal place.

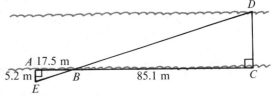

a. $a = 5,\ b = 7,\ c = 8,\ z = 16$
b. $a = 6,\ b = 8,\ c = 10,\ y = 2$
c. $a = 4,\ x = 10,\ y = 14,\ z = 16$
d. $y = 7\sqrt{3},\ a = 3,\ b = 2,\ c = 1$
e. $a = 3\sqrt{5},\ b = 2\sqrt{3},\ c = 2\sqrt{7},\ x = 5$

9. Two boys are playing table tennis. Kenji hits the ball directly above the end of the table from a height of 50 cm. On the return, Mike hits the ball directly above his end of the table from a height of 20 cm. The table is 2.8 m long. If the ball was hit in a straight line and the ball leaves the table at the same angle it hit the table, how far from Mike did the ball hit the table?

13·2 The Tangent Ratio

The height of a flagpole can be found by measuring its shadow and comparing it to the height and shadow of a post which we are able to measure.

$$\frac{\text{height of the flagpole}}{\text{length of flagpole's shadow}} = \frac{\text{height of the post}}{\text{length of post's shadow}}$$

The angle at the ground has been labelled θ (theta), a Greek letter pronounced tha'ta.

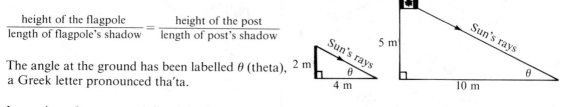

In previous chapters, we defined the sides with respect to the vertices of the triangle. In this section, the vertices will be defined with respect to an angle.

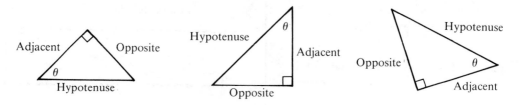

At different times of the day, the sun's rays will hit the ground at different angles.

Therefore, the ratio $\dfrac{\text{height of the flagpole}}{\text{length of flagpole's shadow}}$ will change as the angle θ changes.

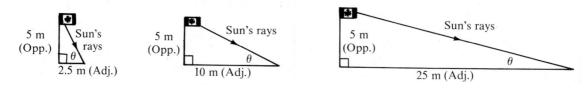

In any right triangle, the ratio of the side opposite the angle θ to the side adjacent to angle θ is called the **tangent** of the angle θ (abbreviated "tan θ").

> For any right triangle, $\tan \theta = \dfrac{\text{side opposite angle } \theta}{\text{side adjacent angle } \theta}$.

This implies that as long as the ratio of the opposite and adjacent sides of a triangle are constant, the tangent of an angle is also constant; and if the tangent of an angle is constant, then the ratio of opposite to adjacent sides is constant.

Example 1

Find tan θ for each of the three flagpoles above.

i) $\tan \theta = \dfrac{5}{2.5}$

$\quad = 2$

ii) $\tan \theta = \dfrac{5}{10}$

$\quad = \dfrac{1}{2}$

iii) $\tan \theta = \dfrac{5}{25}$

$\quad = \dfrac{1}{5}$

Calculators with trigonometric functions have circuits that evaluate the tangent ratios from a sub-routine. To find the tangent of 23°, enter 23 and press the tangent function $\boxed{\text{TAN}}$. The display will show 0.04244748. When this value is rounded to four decimal places, it is the same value as the one shown in the table at the back of the book.

Example 2

Use a calculator to find the tangent ratio for these angles. Round your answers to four decimal places.

a. 27°

tan 27° = 0.5095

b. 29°

tan 29° = 0.5543

c. 90°

tan 90° is undefined because an error will appear.

A calculator can also be used to find the measure of the angle (measure of θ) when the ratio is given. For example, if it is known that $\tan \theta = 1.1918$, then enter 1.1918 $\boxed{\text{INV}}$ $\boxed{\text{TAN}}$. The display will show 50.001099. This should be rounded to the nearest degree to give 50°. Note that your calculator may have a $\boxed{\text{MODE}}$ key rather than the $\boxed{\text{INV}}$ key. This allows the same calculator key to have two functions.

Example 3

Find the measure of θ in each.

a. $\tan \theta = 0.5095$

$\theta \doteq 27°$

b. $\tan \theta = 1.1106$

$\theta \doteq 48°$

c. $\tan \theta = \frac{12}{5}$

$= 2.4000$

$\theta \doteq 67°$

The values for the tangent ratio have been calculated for angles between 0° and 90° and may be found in the back of the book. Part of the table is shown. Notice that the tangent of 23° is 0.4245 which agrees with the value of your calculator rounded to four decimal places.

θ	tan θ
20°	0.3640
21°	0.3839
22°	0.4040
23°	0.4245
24°	0.4452

The ratios for given angles have been calculated. Therefore, it is possible to find the length of a side in a right triangle when one angle, and either an opposite or an adjacent side, are given.

Example 4

Find the value of the indicated side correct to one decimal place.

$\tan 69° = \dfrac{27}{x}$

$x = \dfrac{27}{\tan 69°}$

$x = \dfrac{27}{2.6051}$

$\doteq 10.4$

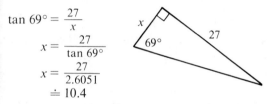

Using a calculator, the ratio is found by entering this sequence. 27 $\boxed{\div}$ 69 $\boxed{\text{TAN}}$ $\boxed{=}$ 10.364328

Example 5

Find the measures of θ and β correct to one decimal place.

$\tan \theta = \dfrac{12}{10}$

$= 1.2000$

$\theta \doteq 50°$

$\tan \beta = \dfrac{10}{12}$

$\beta \doteq 40°$

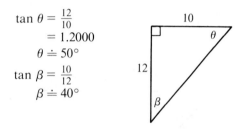

Exercises

1. Use the table at the back of the book to find a value for each.

a. tan 78°   **b.** tan 35°   **c.** tan 89°
d. tan 12°   **e.** tan 46°   **f.** tan 60°

2. Use the table at the back of the book to find the measure of each angle.

a. tan θ = 0.5543   **b.** tan θ = 1.1504

c. tan β = $\frac{4}{5}$ **d.** tan β = $\frac{1}{4}$

For the remainder of the exercises, use a calculator if one is available.

3. Find the value of each correct to four decimal places.

a. tan 53°   **b.** tan 17°   **c.** tan 44°   **d.** tan 89°

4. Find the measure of each angle to the nearest degree.

a. tan θ = 1.3764   **b.** tan θ = 0.4040
c. tan θ = 11.4300   **d.** tan θ = 0.1228

5. Find the value of each expression.

a. tan 30° + 1   **b.** tan 45° − 1

c. 2tan 60° − tan 75°   **d.** $\frac{1}{2}$(tan 25° − tan 30°)

e. (tan 60°)^2 **f.** 2tan^2 45° − 1

6. Find tan A and tan B for each triangle.

a.
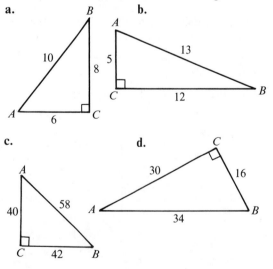

b.

c.

d.

7. Find the length of x correct to one decimal place.

a.
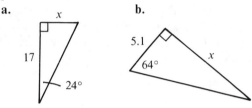

b.

8. Find the length of x correct to two decimal places.

a.
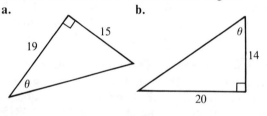

b.

9. Find the value of θ to the nearest degree.

a.
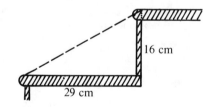

b.

10. On a set of stairs, the riser for each step is 16 cm while the tread is 29 cm. What angle do the stairs make with the floor?

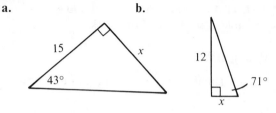

11. A road has a vertical rise of 8 m for every 200 m of horizontal distance. Find the angle of inclination (or the grade) of the road.

12. A guy wire supporting an electrical tower forms an angle of 71° with the ground. If the point where the wire is anchored is 23 m from the base of the tower, how high is the tower?

13·3 The Sine and Cosine Ratios

Daryl's kite string extends 73 m at an angle of 56° with the ground. How high is the kite above the ground?

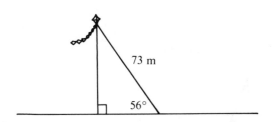

The tangent ratio for the angle cannot be used to find the height of the kite. But one of two other trigonometric ratios can be used to solve the problem. These two ratios are called the **sine** (sin) and **cosine** (cos) of an angle. Which of these ratios could be used to find the height?

$$\sin \theta = \frac{\text{side opposite angle } \theta}{\text{hypotenuse}}$$

$$\cos \theta = \frac{\text{side adjacent angle } \theta}{\text{hypotenuse}}$$

As is the case with the tangent ratio, the sine and cosine ratios do not depend on the position or size of the right triangle, only on the relationship of the sides to the given angle. This given angle is often referred to as the **reference** angle. In the three triangles shown below, the sine and cosine ratios for each triangle can be found by measuring the sides. You will notice that the ratios for the sines are the same.

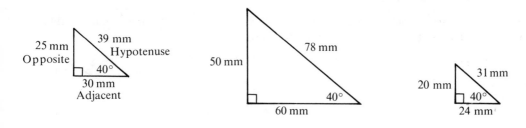

$$\sin 40° = \frac{25}{39}$$
$$= 0.64$$

$$\sin 40° = \frac{50}{78}$$
$$= 0.64$$

$$\sin 40° = \frac{20}{31.2}$$
$$= 0.64$$

Tables for sine and cosine are found at the back of the text.

Example 1

Use the table to find each value correct to four decimal places.

a. cos 34°   **b.** sin 31°   **c.** cos 30°

a. cos 34° = 0.8290
b. sin 31° = 0.5150
c. cos 30° = 0.8660

θ	sin θ	cos θ
30°	0.5000	0.8660
31°	0.5150	0.8572
32°	0.5299	0.8480
33°	0.5446	0.8387
34°	0.5592	0.8290

Example 2

Use the table at the back of the text to find the measure of each angle.

a. $\sin \theta = 0.5446$
$\quad \theta = 33°$

b. $\cos \theta = \frac{5}{6}$
$\quad \cos \theta = 0.8333$
$\quad \theta \doteq 34°$

Example 3

Triangle ABC has a right angle at A. Find the sine, cosine, and tangent ratios for angle C and angle B.

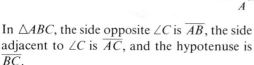

In $\triangle ABC$, the side opposite $\angle C$ is $\overline{AB}$, the side adjacent to $\angle C$ is $\overline{AC}$, and the hypotenuse is $\overline{BC}$.

$\sin C = \frac{5}{13}$, $\cos C = \frac{12}{13}$, $\tan C = \frac{5}{12}$

In $\triangle ABC$, the side opposite $\angle B$ is $\overline{AC}$, the side adjacent to $\angle B$ is $\overline{AB}$, and the hypotenuse is $\overline{BC}$.

$\sin B = \frac{12}{13}$, $\cos B = \frac{5}{13}$, $\tan B = \frac{12}{5}$

Example 4

Find the length of the unknown side x.

Since $29°$ is the measure of the reference angle, the side x is adjacent to the angle, and 15 units is the length of the hypotenuse, the cosine ratio should be used.

$\cos 29° = \frac{x}{15}$
$15(\cos 29°) = x$
$15(0.8746) = x$
$\quad\quad x \doteq 13.1$

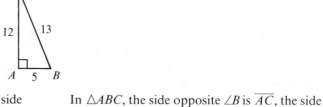

Therefore, the length of x is approximately 13.1 units.

The length of x also can be found on the calculator by keying in this sequence.

$15 \boxed{\times} \; 29 \; \boxed{\text{COS}} \; \boxed{=} \; 13.119295$

Example 5

Find the measure of the angle θ.

In this case, because θ is the reference angle and the opposite side and the hypotenuse are given, we can find the measure of θ using the sine ratio.

$\sin \theta = \frac{32}{45}$
$\sin \theta = 0.7111$

Using the tables, θ is approximately $45°$.

336

Exercises

1. Find each value using the table.
a. sin 36°   **b.** cos 73°   **c.** tan 57°
d. sin 89°   **e.** cos 43°   **f.** cos 90°

2. Find the degree measure of θ using the table.
a. sin θ = 0.4540   **b.** cos θ = 0.5592
c. sin θ = 0.9925   **d.** cos θ = 0.9925
e. sin θ = 0.3090   **f.** cos θ = 1.3795

For the remainder of the exercises, use a calculator if one is available.

3. Find a value for each.
a. cos 43°   **b.** sin 71°   **c.** cos 34°
d. sin 56°   **e.** cos 60°   **f.** sin 12°

4. Find the degree measure of angle θ.
a. sin θ = 0.2079   **b.** cos θ = 0.3584
c. sin θ = 0.7660   **d.** cos θ = 2.5678
e. sin $\theta = \frac{3}{4}$ **f.** cos $\theta = \frac{1}{7}$

5. Evaluate each expression.
a. cos 60° − sin 30°
b. cos 35° − 2sin 40°
c. sin 55° − cos 55° + tan 55°
d. tan 0° + sin 90° − cos 0°
e. $\frac{1}{2}$(sin 45° + cos 45°)
f. sin² 23° + cos² 23° (*Hint:* sin² 23° is the same as (sin 23°)².)
g. cos² (35°) − tan² (15°)
h. sin² 71° + cos² 71°

6. Find the ratio for sin A, cos A, tan A, sin B, cos B, and tan B in each.
a.   **b.**

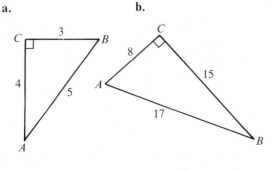

7. Calculate the value of x correct to one decimal place.
a.   **b.**

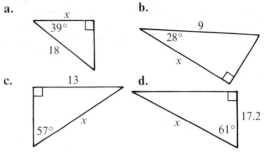

c.   **d.**

8. Find the degree measure of angle θ correct to one decimal place.
a.   **b.**

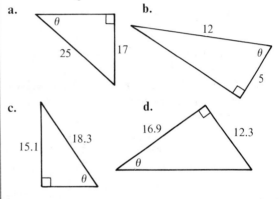

c.   **d.**

9. A road with an 8% grade has a rise of 8 m for every 100 m of road.
a. Find the angle the road makes with the horizontal.
b. What would be the angle for a road with a 12% grade?

10. Triangle ABC has a right angle at C. Find the value of all unknown sides and angles correct to one decimal place.
a. a if $\angle B$ = 19° and c = 23
b. b if $\angle B$ = 43° and c = 36
c. c if $\angle B$ = 29° and a = 7.2
d. c if $\angle A$ = 71° and a = 9.7

11. Copy and complete.
a. sin 30° = cos ■°   **b.** sin 45° = cos ■°
c. cos 23° = sin ■°   **d.** cos 54° = sin ■°
e. In general, cos x° = sin ■°.

13·4 Solving Right Triangles

Solving a right triangle means finding all the measures of missing sides and angles. This can be done using any of the three trigonometric ratios studied so far. Solving the triangle will require either the lengths of any two sides in the triangle, or the length of one side and the measure of one of the acute angles.

Example

Solve the triangle.

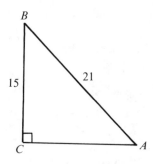

Since we know two sides in the triangle, it is possible to find either $\angle A$ or $\angle B$.

$\sin A = \frac{15}{21}$
$\sin A \doteq 0.7143$
$\quad A \doteq 46°$

Since $\angle A$ and $\angle B$ are complementary angles, then $\angle B \doteq 44°$.

There are two methods that can be used to solve for the third side of the right triangle. Since two sides have been given, the Pythagorean Theorem is one possibility. The other possibility is through the use of trigonometry.

1. Trigonometric ratios

$\cos 46° = \frac{b}{21}$
$21(\cos 46°) = b$
$\quad\quad b \doteq 14.6$

2. Pythagorean Theorem

$b^2 + 15^2 = 21^2$
$\quad b^2 = 21^2 - 15^2$
$\quad\quad b \doteq 14.7$

You will notice a difference in the values for b using the two methods. This difference occurs because we used an approximation for angle A. However, in this case, the difference of 0.1 is not significant.

Exercises

1. Solve these triangles.

a.   **b.**

c.   **d.**

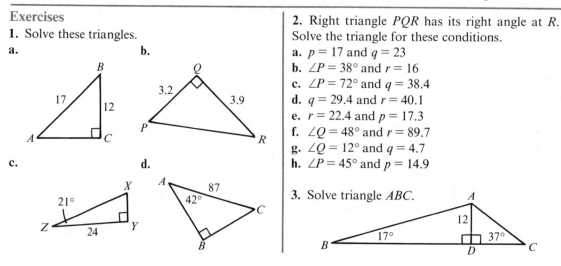

2. Right triangle PQR has its right angle at R. Solve the triangle for these conditions.
   a. $p = 17$ and $q = 23$
   b. $\angle P = 38°$ and $r = 16$
   c. $\angle P = 72°$ and $q = 38.4$
   d. $q = 29.4$ and $r = 40.1$
   e. $r = 22.4$ and $p = 17.3$
   f. $\angle Q = 48°$ and $r = 89.7$
   g. $\angle Q = 12°$ and $q = 4.7$
   h. $\angle P = 45°$ and $p = 14.9$

3. Solve triangle ABC.

13·5 Applications of Trigonometry

Trigonometry was first used extensively by navigators to determine distances and angles. Since that time, surveyors, architects, engineers, and other occupations have developed its uses. Two terms used extensively when describing problems with angles are **angle of elevation** and **angle of depression**.

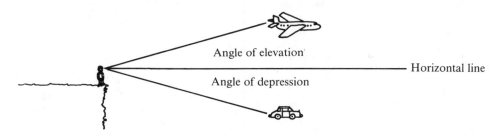

Example 1

A helicopter flying directly over a straight road spots a car ahead on the road. The helicopter is 150 m above the road and views the car at an angle of depression of 29°. At that instant, how far is the helicopter from the car?

Understand the Problem

Interpret the problem by drawing a simple diagram. Why is the angle of depression equal to ∠C in the diagram?

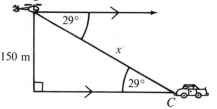

Develop and Carry Out the Plan

The diagram suggests the use of the sine ratio since the opposite side and an angle are given.

$$\sin 29° = \frac{150}{x}$$
$$x = \frac{150}{\sin 29°}$$
$$x \doteq 309$$

Look Back

The helicopter is approximately 309 m from the car.

Example 2

Two towers on a bridge are 21 m apart. From the top of the shorter tower, the angle of elevation to the top of the other tower is 64°, while the angle of depression to the bottom of the tower is 39°. Find the height of the taller tower.

Consider the two right triangles separately.

$$\tan 64° = \frac{x}{21} \qquad \tan 39° = \frac{y}{21}$$
$$21(\tan 64°) = x \qquad 21(\tan 39°) = y$$
$$x \doteq 43 \qquad\qquad y \doteq 17$$

The height of the tower is approximately 60 m.

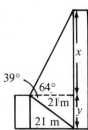

339

Exercises

1. Find the height of a kite above the ground if the kite string extends 500 m and the string makes an angle of 55° with the ground.

2. The shadow of a school flagpole is 37 m when the angle of elevation of the sun is 41°. Find the height of the flagpole.

3. An extension ladder 11 m long is placed against a building with the foot of the ladder 2.5 m from the wall.
a. What angle does the ladder make with the ground?
b. How high up the wall of the building will the ladder reach?

4. A guy wire supporting an electrical tower forms an angle of 54° with the ground. If the point where the wire is anchored is 17 m from the base of the tower, then find the length of the guy wire.

5. A straight road has an angle of elevation of 7°. What is the increase in elevation for a distance of 1 km along the road?

6. A plane leaves the ground and climbs steadily at an angle of 11°. Find the vertical height of the plane after it has travelled a horizontal distance of 2 km.

7. The angle of depression of a submarine going into a dive is 18°. After the submarine has vertically dropped 150 m, how far has it travelled?

8. A rectangle measures 13 cm by 8 cm.
a. Find the angle between the longest side and the diagonal.
b. Find the length of the diagonal in the rectangle.

9. The equal sides in an isosceles triangle measure 18 cm while the equal angles measure 61°.
a. Find the height of the triangle.
b. Find the length of the third side.
c. Find the area of the triangle.

10. A cliff is 75 m above sea level. From the top of the cliff, a ship directly out from the base of the cliff is viewed at an angle of depression of 29°.
a. How far is the ship from the base of the cliff?
b. How far is the ship from the top of the cliff?

11. By how many metres does the shadow cast by a 180 m high church spire lengthen as the sun sinks from an angle of elevation of 66° to an angle of elevation of 43°?

12. From the top of a 150 m tall office building, the angle of depression to the top of a second building is 16°. The angle of depression to the base of the second building is 57°. Find the height of the second building.

13. In the World Cup Downhill held at the Panorama Ski Resort, the skiers raced 3514 m down the face of the mountain. If the vertical height of the ski course was 984 m, then what was the average angle of elevation of the mountain?

14. A farmer has a field with four pumps that he uses to water his cattle. The pumps form a square 1 km on a side. If the farmer wishes to build a road to join all four pumps, then how should he do it to have the shortest possible road?

15. The area of a circle circumscribed about a regular hexagon is 300π. Find the area of the hexagon.

16. Two trees are 150 m apart. From a point halfway between the two trees, the angle of elevation of their tops is 15° and 20°.
a. How much taller is one tree than the other?
b. Where would a person have to stand in order to have the angles of elevation to the top of each tree the same?

Braintickler

How could you cut a hole in a sheet 20 cm by 30 cm so that you could crawl through the hole without ripping the paper?

13·6 Matrices

One of the problems that businesses face is the systematic handling of large amounts of data. Matrices are one method that allows the orderly arrangement and handling of data. The terminology and rules that are used in dealing with matrices, as well as the application of matrices, will be presented.

A **matrix** is any rectangular array of numbers. The plural of "matrix" is "matrices".

This chart represents the results of the first half of the season for the Westmount Soccer League as well as its corresponding matrix.

Team	Wins	Losses	Ties
Blues	13	2	3
Colts	11	5	2
Kickers	8	4	6
Saints	3	11	4

$$\text{Rows} \longrightarrow \begin{bmatrix} 13 & 2 & 3 \\ 11 & 5 & 2 \\ 8 & 4 & 6 \\ 3 & 11 & 4 \end{bmatrix} \text{Columns} \downarrow$$

Each element of a matrix is called a **component**, and each component has a definite meaning. For example, the component in row 3 and column 2 represents the losses in the first half of the season for the Kickers. The size of a matrix is the **order** of the matrix and is given by first describing the number of rows which run horizontally and then the number of columns which run vertically. The order of the Westmount Soccer League matrix is 4×3 (read "4 by 3").

Example 1

Find the order of each matrix.

$$A = \begin{bmatrix} 5 & 2 & -1 \\ -2 & 7 & 2 \\ -9 & 3 & 8 \end{bmatrix} \qquad B = \begin{bmatrix} 7 \\ 5 \\ -7 \\ 14 \end{bmatrix} \qquad C = \begin{bmatrix} 1 & -3 & 6 & 12 \\ 0 & 7 & -1 & 3 \end{bmatrix} \qquad D = \begin{bmatrix} 7 & 3 \end{bmatrix}$$

Matrix A is a **square** matrix with an order of 3×3.
Matrix B is a **column** matrix with an order of 4×1.
Matrix C has an order of 2×4.
Matrix D is a **row** matrix with an order of 1×2.

Two matrices are said to be **equal** if and only if they have the same order and the corresponding components are the same.

Example 2

Find the value of the variables so that the matrices are equal.

a. $\begin{bmatrix} 2 & 1 \\ y & 5 \end{bmatrix} = \begin{bmatrix} 2 & x \\ -3 & z \end{bmatrix}$ **b.** $\begin{bmatrix} 5 & -7 & m \\ -2 & 2k & 5n \end{bmatrix} = \begin{bmatrix} 5 & -7 & 6 \\ p & 8 & -15 \end{bmatrix}$ **c.** $\begin{bmatrix} -5 & 3 \\ y & 4 \end{bmatrix} = \begin{bmatrix} -5 & x \\ -3 & 7 \end{bmatrix}$

a. $x = 1$, $y = -3$, and $z = 5$.
b. $m = 6$, $k = 4$, $n = -3$, and $p = -2$.
c. These two matrices cannot be made equal because $4 \neq 7$ for the bottom right components.

341

The results for the second half of the Westmount Soccer League are summarized below.

Team	Wins	Losses	Ties
Blues	11	5	2
Colts	10	5	3
Kickers	6	6	6
Saints	2	11	5

The results of each half of the league as well as the final results for the year are all expressed as matrices.

$$
\begin{bmatrix} 13 & 2 & 3 \\ 11 & 5 & 2 \\ 8 & 4 & 6 \\ 3 & 11 & 4 \end{bmatrix} + \begin{bmatrix} 11 & 5 & 2 \\ 10 & 5 & 3 \\ 6 & 6 & 6 \\ 2 & 11 & 5 \end{bmatrix} = \begin{bmatrix} 24 & 7 & 5 \\ 21 & 10 & 5 \\ 14 & 10 & 12 \\ 5 & 22 & 9 \end{bmatrix}
$$

The final matrix is the sum of the first two matrices. The sums were found by adding the corresponding components of the first two matrices. In order to add matrices, they must be of the same order. When the matrices are of the same order, they are said to be **conformable for addition**.

Example 3

Add. If the matrices are not conformable, explain why.

a. $A + E$ **b.** $C + D$ **c.** $A + B$ **d.** $B + D$

$$
A = \begin{bmatrix} 7 & -1 & 5 \end{bmatrix}
$$

$$
B = \begin{bmatrix} 7 \\ 4 \\ 1 \end{bmatrix} \quad C = \begin{bmatrix} 8 & -1 & 3 \\ -4 & 2 & 0 \\ -3 & 0 & -1 \end{bmatrix} \quad D = \begin{bmatrix} -4 & 6 & -8 \\ -2 & -5 & 8 \\ 4 & 12 & 17 \end{bmatrix} \quad E = \begin{bmatrix} -3 & 4 & 6 \end{bmatrix}
$$

a. $A + E = \begin{bmatrix} 4 & 3 & 11 \end{bmatrix}$

b.
$$
C + D = \begin{bmatrix} 4 & 5 & -5 \\ -6 & -3 & 8 \\ 1 & 12 & 16 \end{bmatrix}
$$

Parts **c** and **d** are not conformable for addition because the order of the matrices is not the same.

Subtraction of matrices is performed by subtracting the corresponding components. As with addition, the order of the matrices being subtracted must be the same.

Example 4

Using the matrices of Example 3, find a single matrix that will represent $3C - D$.

When multiplying a matrix by a number, multiply each component of the matrix by that number. The number that multiplies each component is a **scalar**.

$$
3C = \begin{bmatrix} (3 \times 8) & (3 \times -1) & (3 \times 3) \\ (3 \times -4) & (3 \times 2) & (3 \times 0) \\ (3 \times -3) & (3 \times 0) & (3 \times -1) \end{bmatrix} = \begin{bmatrix} 24 & -3 & 9 \\ -12 & 6 & 0 \\ -9 & 0 & -3 \end{bmatrix}
$$

$$
3C - D = \begin{bmatrix} 24 - (-4) & -3 - (6) & 9 - (-8) \\ -12 - (-2) & 6 - (-5) & 0 - (8) \\ -9 - (4) & 0 - (12) & -3 - (17) \end{bmatrix} = \begin{bmatrix} 28 & -9 & 17 \\ -10 & 11 & -8 \\ -13 & -12 & -20 \end{bmatrix}
$$

Exercises

1. State the order of each of the matrices.

$$A = \begin{bmatrix} 3 & 5 & -9 \end{bmatrix}$$

$$B = \begin{bmatrix} 0 & 5 & -7 & 8 \\ -2 & 5 & -3 & 11 \\ -7 & 5 & 3 & -4 \\ 8 & 25 & 6 & -4 \end{bmatrix}$$

$$C = \begin{bmatrix} 4 & 6 \\ 0 & 0 \\ 3 & 41 \\ -1 & 0 \\ -3 & 5 \end{bmatrix}$$

$$D = \begin{bmatrix} 4 & -6 \\ -9 & 51 \end{bmatrix}$$

$$E = \begin{bmatrix} 0 & 0 & 1 \\ 1 & 0 & 1 \end{bmatrix}$$

$$F = \begin{bmatrix} -3 & 2 & 7 & -12 \end{bmatrix}$$

2. Use the matrices of Exercise 1, as well as those given below, to find a single matrix to represent the sum or difference indicated.

$$K = \begin{bmatrix} -2 & 5 \\ -4 & 1 \\ 2 & 7 \\ 1 & 0 \end{bmatrix}$$

$$L = \begin{bmatrix} 0 & -3 & 6 & -2 \\ -4 & 6 & -6 & 11 \\ 0 & 3 & 0 & 21 \\ -2 & -3 & 0 & 4 \end{bmatrix}$$

$$M = \begin{bmatrix} -4 \\ -1 \\ 9 \\ 8 \\ -4 \end{bmatrix}$$

$$N = \begin{bmatrix} -1 & 3 & -2 \end{bmatrix}$$

$$P = \begin{bmatrix} 6 & -7 \\ -1 & 0 \\ 11 & -51 \end{bmatrix}$$

a. $A + N$
b. $B + L$
c. $C + K$
d. $P + D$
e. $A + F$
f. $N - A$
g. $B - L$
h. $K - C$
i. $P - D$
j. $3A - 2N$
k. $3B + 2L$
l. $2C + K$

3. Use the matrices in Exercises 1 and 2 to find a single matrix to represent the sum indicated.
a. $N + A$
b. $L + B$

4. Compare your answers in Exercise 3 with parts a and b in Exercise 2, respectively. Is the addition of matrices commutative?

5. Use the matrices in Exercises 1 and 2 to comment on the truth of each statement.
a. $2(B + L) = 2B + 2L$
b. $5(A + N) = 5A + 5N$
c. $-3(P + D) = -3P - 3D$
d. Write a general statement concerning the distributive property of a scalar with two matrices.

6. Find the additive inverse for this matrix.

$$\begin{bmatrix} -5 & 7 \\ 4 & -6 \end{bmatrix}$$

7. Two bicycle factories, A and B, each make four different models of bicycles: a standard model, a luxury model, a deluxe model, and a super-deluxe model. Factory A manufactured 1700 standard, 1200 luxury, 1000 deluxe, and 500 super-deluxe models. Factory B manufactured 1300 standard, 1000 luxury, 800 deluxe, and 400 super-deluxe models.

a. Construct a 2×4 matrix to summarize this information using the first row for Factory A and the second row for Factory B and the first column for the standard models, the second for the luxury models, etc.

b. From your matrix give the following information and describe how you obtained it.
  i) How many standard models were manufactured altogether?
  ii) How many bicycles were manufactured in Factory B?
  iii) How many bicycles were manufactured in both factories in total?

8. Find the values of the variables that will make the matrices equal.

a.
$$\begin{bmatrix} 5 & x & 7 \\ -3 & 12 & z \end{bmatrix} = \begin{bmatrix} -y & 4 & 7 \\ k & 3m & 6 \end{bmatrix}$$

b.
$$\begin{bmatrix} (2x + 1) & (2y - 4) \\ (3m - 2) & (7 - 5n) \end{bmatrix} = \begin{bmatrix} 13 & -16 \\ 19 & -23 \end{bmatrix}$$

9. Four friends, Twyla, Susan, Mike, and Paul, have had a dispute. Twyla talks only to Susan and Mike. Susan talks only to Paul. Mike talks to Twyla and Paul. Paul talks to everyone. Set up a 4×4 matrix to give the lines of communication by filling in the chart below. Put a 1 for "talks to" and a 0 for "does not talk to". Assume no one talks to themselves.

	Twyla	Susan	Mike	Paul
Twyla				
Susan				
Mike				
Paul				

13·7 Multiplication of Matrices

If points in the Westmount Soccer League are awarded on the basis that each team receives 2 points for a win, 0 points for a loss, and 1 point for a tie, the points gained by each team can be calculated using matrix multiplication.

$$A = \begin{bmatrix} 2 \\ 0 \\ 1 \end{bmatrix}$$ This matrix represents the points gained per game.

$$B = \begin{bmatrix} 24 & 7 & 5 \\ 21 & 10 & 5 \\ 14 & 10 & 12 \\ 5 & 22 & 9 \end{bmatrix}$$ This matrix represents the wins, losses, and ties for the season.

The total points for each team is found by taking the product of matrix B and matrix A.

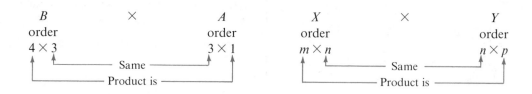

$$BA = \begin{bmatrix} 24 & 7 & 5 \\ 21 & 10 & 5 \\ 14 & 10 & 12 \\ 5 & 22 & 9 \end{bmatrix} \times \begin{bmatrix} 2 \\ 0 \\ 1 \end{bmatrix} = \begin{bmatrix} 24 \times 2 + 7 \times 0 + 5 \times 1 \\ 21 \times 2 + 10 \times 0 + 5 \times 1 \\ 14 \times 2 + 10 \times 0 + 12 \times 1 \\ 5 \times 2 + 22 \times 0 + 9 \times 1 \end{bmatrix} = \begin{bmatrix} 48 + 0 + 5 \\ 42 + 0 + 5 \\ 28 + 0 + 12 \\ 10 + 0 + 9 \end{bmatrix} = \begin{bmatrix} 53 \\ 47 \\ 40 \\ 19 \end{bmatrix}$$

Each component in the product matrix is the sum of the products of the components in a row matrix of B and the corresponding components in a column matrix A.

Note that a 4×3 matrix was multiplied by a 3×1 matrix giving a product that was a 4×1 matrix.

$$
\begin{array}{ccc}
B & \times & A \\
\text{order} & & \text{order} \\
4 \times 3 & & 3 \times 1
\end{array}
\qquad
\begin{array}{ccc}
X & \times & Y \\
\text{order} & & \text{order} \\
m \times n & & n \times p
\end{array}
$$

Same — Product is

Same — Product is

Two matrices **conform** for multiplication when the number of columns in the first matrix is the same as the number of rows in the second matrix.

Example

At a Dual Swim Meet between Western and Central, the following results were obtained.

School	Firsts	Seconds	Thirds	Fourths	Fifths
Western	12	8	7	11	14
Central	8	12	13	9	6

Two scoring systems were suggested.

1. 5 points for first, 4 for second, 3 for third, 2 for fourth, and 1 for fifth.

2. 7 points for first, 5 for second, 3 for third, 2 for fourth, and 1 for fifth.

Find which system will favour Central and which system will favour Western.

Matrix A represents the placing of the teams, while Matrix B represents the point-scoring possibilities.

$$A = \begin{bmatrix} 12 & 8 & 7 & 11 & 14 \\ 8 & 12 & 13 & 9 & 6 \end{bmatrix} \qquad B = \begin{bmatrix} 5 & 7 \\ 4 & 5 \\ 3 & 3 \\ 2 & 2 \\ 1 & 1 \end{bmatrix} \qquad AB = \begin{bmatrix} 149 & 181 \\ 151 & 179 \end{bmatrix}$$

Multiplying matrix A times matrix B will give the points each team would receive under both scoring systems.

Therefore, Western will be favoured by system 2 and Central by system 1.

Exercises

1. Under what conditions are matrix addition and multiplication conformable?

2. Multiply a 2×3 matrix by a 5×2 matrix.
a. What will be the order of the product?
b. Describe how you would obtain the element in the second row and first column of the product.

3. If A is a 5×4 matrix and B is a 4×5 matrix, then find
a. the order of AB.   **b.** the order of BA.

4. In the example in the display, why was A multiplied by B and not B multiplied by A?

5. Find the indicated product matrix where possible. If it is not possible, explain why.

$$A = \begin{bmatrix} 5 & -1 & 3 \\ 0 & 3 & 2 \end{bmatrix} \qquad B = \begin{bmatrix} -2 & 4 \\ 4 & -1 \\ -1 & 0 \end{bmatrix}$$

$$C = \begin{bmatrix} -3 & -4 \\ -6 & 3 \end{bmatrix} \qquad D = \begin{bmatrix} 7 & -2 \end{bmatrix}$$

a. AB **b.** CA **c.** BA **d.** AC
e. CD **f.** BC **g.** DA **h.** DC
i. $C^2 \, (C \times C)$ **j.** C^3

6. Is $AB = BA$? Is matrix multiplication commutative?

$$A = \begin{bmatrix} 2 & -1 \\ 5 & -2 \end{bmatrix} \qquad B = \begin{bmatrix} -3 & 1 \\ 2 & -4 \end{bmatrix}$$

7. Find a matrix B, such that

$$\begin{bmatrix} -4 & 3 & 0 \\ 2 & -1 & -1 \\ -3 & 0 & 1 \end{bmatrix} \times B = \begin{bmatrix} -4 & 3 & 0 \\ 2 & -1 & -1 \\ -3 & 0 & 1 \end{bmatrix}$$

The matrix you have found is called the **identity** matrix.

8. Find AB and BA.

$$A = \begin{bmatrix} 1 & 0 \\ 0 & 1 \end{bmatrix} \qquad B = \begin{bmatrix} -1 & 0 \\ 0 & -1 \end{bmatrix}$$

9. Find the product. What is the name of the first matrix?

$$\begin{bmatrix} 1 & 0 \\ 0 & 1 \end{bmatrix} \times \begin{bmatrix} -5 & 4 \\ 2 & 3 \end{bmatrix}$$

Historical Note

Arthur Cayley (1821-1895)
Arthur Cayley was born in 1821 in Richmond, England, and graduated from Trinity College in Cambridge in 1842.

Cayley concentrated his work in matrix algebra. In matrices, he created an algebra with laws structurally different from those of "regular" algebra. One of the differences was that matrices do not follow the commutative law.

Can you find other differences between the algebra of matrices and the algebra you have studied in your mathematics courses?

13·8 Inverse of a Matrix

In the real number system, the identity element for multiplication is 1. Similarly, with square matrices there is an identity matrix, I, such that $A \times I = A$.

If $A = \begin{bmatrix} 5 & -1 \\ -2 & 3 \end{bmatrix}$, then $\begin{bmatrix} 5 & -1 \\ -2 & 3 \end{bmatrix} \times I = \begin{bmatrix} 5 & -1 \\ -2 & 3 \end{bmatrix}$.

As was seen in the previous section, the only matrix that satisfies this equation is $I = \begin{bmatrix} 1 & 0 \\ 0 & 1 \end{bmatrix}$. This is the **identity matrix** under multiplication.

In the real number system, the inverse of any number, k, under multiplication is $\frac{1}{k}$, $k \neq 0$. Similarly, for a square matrix, A, there is an inverse, written A^{-1}, such that $AA^{-1} = A^{-1}A = I$, where I is the identity matrix under multiplication.

Example 1

If $A = \begin{bmatrix} -3 & 5 \\ -2 & 3 \end{bmatrix}$, then find A^{-1}.

AA^{-1} is the identity matrix.

$\therefore \begin{bmatrix} -3 & 5 \\ -2 & 3 \end{bmatrix} \times \begin{bmatrix} a & b \\ c & d \end{bmatrix} = \begin{bmatrix} 1 & 0 \\ 0 & 1 \end{bmatrix}$ By solving for a, b, c, and d, the inverse matrix can be found.

$-3a + 5c = 1$
$-2a + 3c = 0$ Solve the systems by one of the methods
$-3b + 5d = 0$ presented in Chapter 9.
$-2b + 3d = 1$

Therefore, $a = 3$, $c = 2$, $b = -5$, and $d = -3$, and the inverse matrix A^{-1} is $\begin{bmatrix} 3 & -5 \\ 2 & -3 \end{bmatrix}$.

Example 2

Solve the system of equations. $4x + y = -5$
$2x + y = -1$

Set up matrices representing the system.

$A = \begin{bmatrix} 4 & 1 \\ 2 & 1 \end{bmatrix}$ $B = \begin{bmatrix} -5 \\ -1 \end{bmatrix}$ A is the **coefficient matrix**.

If the system of equations $AX = B$ has a unique solution, then by multiplying both sides of this equation by A^{-1}, the solution of the system becomes $A^{-1}B$.

$A^{-1} = \begin{bmatrix} \frac{1}{2} & \frac{-1}{2} \\ -1 & 2 \end{bmatrix}$ $A^{-1}B = \begin{bmatrix} \frac{1}{2} & \frac{-1}{2} \\ -1 & 2 \end{bmatrix} \times \begin{bmatrix} -5 \\ -1 \end{bmatrix} = \begin{bmatrix} -2 \\ 3 \end{bmatrix}$

Therefore, the solution to the system of equations is $x = -2$ and $y = 3$.

Exercises

1. Find the inverse matrix of each if it exists.

a. $\begin{bmatrix} -5 & 3 \\ 6 & -4 \end{bmatrix}$ **b.** $\begin{bmatrix} 7 & -3 \\ 4 & -2 \end{bmatrix}$

c. $\begin{bmatrix} 4 & 5 \\ 1 & 1 \end{bmatrix}$ **d.** $\begin{bmatrix} -6 & -2 \\ 3 & 1 \end{bmatrix}$

e. $\begin{bmatrix} \frac{1}{2} & \frac{3}{4} \\ \frac{-1}{2} & \frac{1}{4} \end{bmatrix}$ **f.** $\begin{bmatrix} \frac{2}{3} & \frac{5}{6} \\ \frac{-1}{2} & \frac{-3}{4} \end{bmatrix}$

g. $\begin{bmatrix} \frac{-5}{3} & \frac{2}{5} \\ \frac{-3}{2} & \frac{-21}{25} \end{bmatrix}$ **h.** $\begin{bmatrix} -\sqrt{5} & 3\sqrt{2} \\ \sqrt{10} & -4 \end{bmatrix}$

2. Why does the inverse of the matrix not exist in part **d** of Exercise 1?

3. Find the inverse of each matrix if it exists.

a. $\begin{bmatrix} -12 & 5 \\ 2 & -1 \end{bmatrix}$ **b.** $\begin{bmatrix} 9 & -7 \\ 4 & -3 \end{bmatrix}$

c. $\begin{bmatrix} \frac{3}{2} & \frac{7}{4} \\ \frac{-1}{3} & \frac{-1}{3} \end{bmatrix}$ **d.** $\begin{bmatrix} \frac{-1}{3} & \frac{3}{4} \\ \frac{5}{6} & \frac{-15}{8} \end{bmatrix}$

4. Solve each system of equations using the inverse-matrix method.

a. $3x - 2y = -9$
$\quad 4x - 3y = -13$

b. $2a - 3b = 5$
$\quad -a + 2b = -2$

c. $x + y = 5$
$\quad 2x - y = 7$

d. $3k - 2m = -6$
$\quad 6k - 4m = 4$

e. $8x - 6y = -1$
$\quad 2x + y = 1$

f. $3d + 5e = 0$
$\quad 2d + e = \frac{-7}{15}$

5. Explain why the inverse-matrix method cannot be used to solve Exercise 4, part **d**.
a. Use one of the algebraic methods from Chapter 9 to solve part **d**.
b. Graph the system of equations in Exercise 4, parts **b** and **d**, and use these graphs to explain your answers.

6. Solve each system of equations. (*Hint:* Write each equation with integral coefficients before attempting to solve.)

a. $a + b = 7$
$\quad \dfrac{a}{3} + \dfrac{b}{4} = 2$

b. $\dfrac{1}{2}x - \dfrac{2}{3}y = 6$
$\quad \dfrac{1}{4}x + \dfrac{1}{3}y = -1$

c. $\dfrac{a+3}{3} = 1 + \dfrac{3b-1}{5}$
$\quad \dfrac{2-3a}{4} = 5 + \dfrac{b+3}{6}$

d. $\dfrac{1}{2}x + 3 = \dfrac{7-2y}{2}$
$\quad \dfrac{8x-9}{8} = \dfrac{1}{2}y - 2$

7. Using multiplication, determine if the given matrices are inverses of each other.

a. $\begin{bmatrix} 1 & 2 \\ 3 & 4 \end{bmatrix}$ $\begin{bmatrix} 4 & -3 \\ -3 & 1 \end{bmatrix}$

b. $\begin{bmatrix} 1 & 2 \\ 2 & 3 \end{bmatrix}$ $\begin{bmatrix} -3 & 2 \\ 2 & -1 \end{bmatrix}$

c. $\begin{bmatrix} 1 & 2 & 3 \\ 2 & 4 & 5 \\ 3 & 5 & 6 \end{bmatrix}$ $\begin{bmatrix} 1 & -3 & 2 \\ -3 & 3 & -1 \\ 2 & -1 & 0 \end{bmatrix}$

d. $\begin{bmatrix} -2 & -1 & 4 \\ 1 & 1 & 0 \\ 4 & 2 & -10 \end{bmatrix}$ $\begin{bmatrix} -5 & 3 & 4 \\ 5 & 2 & 0 \\ -1 & 2 & 2 \end{bmatrix}$

8. For each problem, write two equations with two variables and solve the system of equations using matrices.
a. Two numbers have a sum of 11 and a difference of 7. Find the two numbers.
b. Paul has $2.05 in nickels and dimes. There are 29 coins in total. How many of each does he have?
c. A boat, propelled by a constant force, travels 120 km upstream in 3 h and returns in 2 h. What is the velocity of the boat relative to the water, and what is the velocity of the current?

9. Under what conditions will the inverse of a matrix not exist?

10. Why do only square matrices have inverses?

11. Use an algebraic method to show that the solution of the system $ax + by = m$ and $cx + dy = n$ is
$$\frac{1}{ad - bc}\begin{bmatrix} d & -b \\ -c & a \end{bmatrix}\begin{bmatrix} m \\ n \end{bmatrix}.$$

13·9 Transformation of Matrices

Any operation in which there is a one-to-one correspondence between the points of an object and a corresponding image is called a **transformation**. Matrices are useful for performing transformations algebraically. Addition of matrices produces translations while multiplication of matrices produces other transformations, such as reflections, rotations, and dilatations.

When a matrix is used to represent points on a plane, the coordinates of the points are written in vertical form. For example, a triangle has vertices at $A(-1, 2)$, $B(-5, 4)$, and $C(1, 6)$. These three coordinates are represented by matrix Y.

$$Y = \begin{bmatrix} -1 & -5 & 1 \\ 2 & 4 & 6 \end{bmatrix}$$

When a constant is added to each x- and y-value of the ordered pair, the sum is the image under the translation.

Example 1

Find the image of $\triangle ABC$ given $A(-1, 2)$, $B(-5, 4)$, and $C(1, 6)$ under the translation $(x, y) \rightarrow (x+4, y-5)$.

The translation matrix, T, is $\begin{bmatrix} 4 & 4 & 4 \\ -5 & -5 & -5 \end{bmatrix}$.

Add the object and translation matrices and find the resulting image.

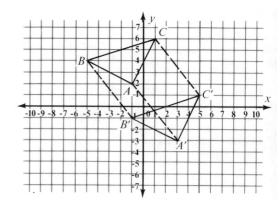

$$\begin{bmatrix} -1 & -5 & 1 \\ 2 & 4 & 6 \end{bmatrix} + \begin{bmatrix} 4 & 4 & 4 \\ -5 & -5 & -5 \end{bmatrix} = \begin{bmatrix} 3 & -1 & 5 \\ -3 & -1 & 1 \end{bmatrix}$$

The image points of the new triangle are $A'(3, -3)$, $B'(-1, -1)$, and $C'(5, 1)$. Plotting the triangles on a grid produces this graph.

Example 2

Reflect the triangle in Example 1 by multiplying the object matrix, Y, by the reflection matrix, T, of

$$\begin{bmatrix} 1 & 0 \\ 0 & -1 \end{bmatrix}.$$

$$TY = \begin{bmatrix} 1 & 0 \\ 0 & -1 \end{bmatrix} \times \begin{bmatrix} -1 & -5 & 1 \\ 2 & 4 & 6 \end{bmatrix} \quad \text{Notice the order in which the matrices are multiplied.}$$

$$= \begin{bmatrix} -1 & -5 & 1 \\ -2 & -4 & -6 \end{bmatrix}$$

348

$A(-1, 2)$ has been transformed to $A'(-1, -2)$, $B(-5, 4)$ has been transformed to $B'(-5, -4)$, and $C(1, 6)$ has been transformed to $C'(1, -6)$.

The graph of the object and the image for Example 2 is shown. Triangle ABC has been transformed to triangle $A'B'C'$ through a reflection in the x-axis. Therefore, multiplication by the transformation matrix, T, causes a reflection in the x-axis and is equivalent to the transformation $(x, y) \rightarrow (x, -y)$.

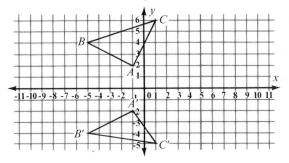

Example 3

Rotate the triangle in Example 1 by multiplying the object matrix, Y, by the rotation matrix,

$$R = \begin{bmatrix} -1 & 0 \\ 0 & -1 \end{bmatrix}.$$

$$RY = \begin{bmatrix} -1 & 0 \\ 0 & -1 \end{bmatrix} \times \begin{bmatrix} -1 & -5 & 1 \\ 2 & 4 & 6 \end{bmatrix}$$

$$= \begin{bmatrix} 1 & 5 & -1 \\ -2 & -4 & -6 \end{bmatrix}$$

$A(-1, 2)$ has been transformed to $A'(1, -2)$, $B(-5, 4)$ has been transformed to $B'(5, -4)$, and $C(1, 6)$ has been transformed to $C'(-1, -6)$. The graph of the object and the image is shown. This is a 180° rotation of triangle ABC about the origin. Therefore, multiplication by the transformation matrix, R, causes a 180° rotation about the origin and is equivalent to the transformation $(x, y) \rightarrow (-x, -y)$.

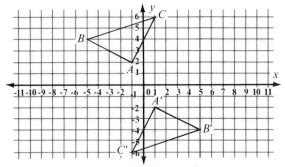

Using the patterns developed so far, the transformation matrix equivalent to a dilatation will be

$$\begin{bmatrix} \pm k & 0 \\ 0 & \pm k \end{bmatrix}.$$

Exercises

1. Write each set of ordered pairs in matrix form.
a. {(−5, 2)}
b. {(3, −1), (−6, 2)}
c. {(−1, −1), (5, 0), (7, 3)}

2. Find the image of △ABC with vertices at A(−2, 5), B(1, 3), and C(5, −2) under each transformation matrix. Draw the object and the image on a grid.

a. $\begin{bmatrix} 3 & 3 & 3 \\ -4 & -4 & -4 \end{bmatrix}$ **b.** $\begin{bmatrix} -2 & -2 & -2 \\ 5 & 5 & 5 \end{bmatrix}$

3. Find and plot the image of each line segment after a reflection in the x-axis.
a. A(−3, 1), B(2, −4)
b. K(4, −2), L(5, 2)
c. P(−4, −1), Q(3, 2)

4. Find the transformation matrix for a reflection in the y-axis. Check your hypothesis using the point (3, 2).

5. Find and plot the image of each triangle after a reflection in the y-axis.
a. A(3, 0), B(4, 3), C(−1, 2)
b. K(−1, −1), L(2, −3), M(4, 1)
c. P(5, 3), Q(−2, −6), R(3, −1)

6. Find the image of each set of points using this transformation matrix.

$T = \begin{bmatrix} -1 & 0 \\ 0 & -1 \end{bmatrix}$

Graph each set of points and show their image. Comment on the type of reflection.
a. {A(−4, 1), B(1, 5)}
b. {E(3, −2), F(1, −4), G(−3, −2)}

7. Use the triangle whose vertices are the ordered pairs (1, 2), (−2, −1), and (3, −2). Find the image points under each product transformation and graph the set of points. Comment on the effect that each product transformation matrix has on the points.

a. $\begin{bmatrix} 3 & 0 \\ 0 & 1 \end{bmatrix}$ **b.** $\begin{bmatrix} 1 & 0 \\ 0 & 3 \end{bmatrix}$ **c.** $\begin{bmatrix} 3 & 0 \\ 0 & 3 \end{bmatrix}$

8. Use the triangle whose vertices are the ordered pairs (1, 1), (4, 1), and (1, 5). Find image coordinates under each transformation matrix.

a. $\begin{bmatrix} 0 & 1 \\ -1 & 0 \end{bmatrix}$ **b.** $\begin{bmatrix} -1 & 0 \\ 0 & -1 \end{bmatrix}$ **c.** $\begin{bmatrix} 0 & -1 \\ 1 & 0 \end{bmatrix}$

Graph the set of points. What type of transformation is each? How many degrees about the origin has each transformation matrix rotated the original triangle?

9. Write the transformation matrix described by each.

a. a reflection in the x-axis
b. a reflection in the y-axis
c. a reflection in the line y = x
d. a dilatation by a scale factor of 4
e. a stretch in the x direction of 3
f. a stretch in the y direction of 2
g. a 90° clockwise rotation about the origin
h. a 180° clockwise rotation about the origin
i. a 270° clockwise rotation about the origin

10. If a property is preserved under a given transformation, that property is **invariant**. Copy and complete the table by filling in the invariant properties.

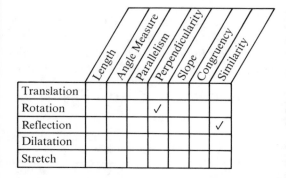

	Length	Angle Measure	Parallelism	Perpendicularity	Slope	Congruency	Similarity
Translation							
Rotation				✓			
Reflection							✓
Dilatation							
Stretch							

11. The coordinates of rectangle ABCD are at A(−1, 2), B(−4, 2), C(−4, 4), and D(−1, 4). Draw the rectangle and its image after each transformation on a coordinate grid. Predict the location of the image points before multiplying.

a. $\begin{bmatrix} 1 & 0 \\ 0 & -1 \end{bmatrix}$ **b.** $\begin{bmatrix} -1 & 0 \\ 0 & 1 \end{bmatrix}$ **c.** $\begin{bmatrix} 0 & 1 \\ 1 & 0 \end{bmatrix}$

13·10 Volume and Surface Area I

The surface area and volume of objects is often considered in making decisions regarding the packaging of material.

Example

Calculate the volume and surface area of a cereal box that is 6.6 cm deep, 20.3 cm wide, and 27.3 cm high.

Volume = 6.6 × 20.3 × 27.3
      = 3657.654

> The volume of any rectangular prism is the product of the length, width, and height.

The volume of the cereal box is approximately 3658 cm³.

The surface area is found by finding the sum of the areas of all six sides.

Area of one side is 6.6 × 20.3 or 133.98 cm².
Area of a second side is 6.6 × 27.3 or 180.18 cm².
Area of a third side is 20.3 × 27.3 or 554.19 cm².

The surface area of the object is 2(133.98 + 180.18 + 554.19) or 1736.7 cm².

Exercises

1. Use the net to find the dimensions of the box.

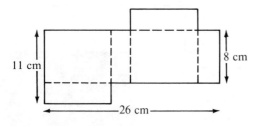

2. Find the amount of material used in this soap box.

3. Find the volume of each rectangular prism.

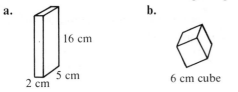

a. 16 cm, 5 cm, 2 cm

b. 6 cm cube

4. How much greater is the volume of a cube 13.5 cm on each side than that of a 12 cm by 13.5 cm by 15 cm rectangular prism?

5. Use a 2 cm by 5 cm by 7 cm rectangular prism to investigate the effect that each has on the total surface area.
a. doubling each of the three dimensions
b. tripling each dimension
c. In general, what effect will increasing the dimensions by a factor of n have on the surface area?

6. What effect do the changes in Exercise 5, parts **a** and **b**, have on the volume of the prism? In general, what effect will increasing each dimension by a factor of n have on the volume?

7. A marine biologist pumped 8000 L of water into an aquarium. Find the area of the base of the aquarium if the water level rose 1 m and the sides are perpendicular to the base.

351

13·11 Volume and Surface Area II

A cylinder is commonly used as a container for liquid substances.

Example

Find the volume (or capacity) and the surface area of a soft-drink can with a diameter of 6 cm and a height of 11.8 cm.

$V = Bh$ *B is the area of the base.*
$\quad = \pi r^2 \times 11.8$
$\quad = (3.14)(3^2)(11.8)$
$\quad = 333.468$

The volume of the cylinder is approximately 333.5 cm³.

The surface area of the cylinder is given by the expression $2\pi r^2 + 2\pi rh$.

$S.A. = 2\pi r^2 + 2\pi rh$
$\quad\quad = 2\pi(3)^2 + 2\pi(3)(11.8)$ *The length of the rectangle equals the circumference of the can.*
$\quad\quad = 18\pi + 70.8\pi$
$\quad\quad = 88.8\pi$

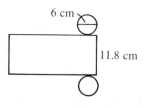

The surface area of the cylinder is approximately 278.8 cm².

Exercises

1. Calculate the volume and surface area of each.
a. a juice can with a diameter of 6 cm and a height of 11.8 cm
b. a paint can that is 20.8 cm high with a diameter of 18 cm

2. A cylindrical oil-storage tank is 28 m high and 16 m in diameter. It costs $0.75/m² to paint it with a protective paint. Find the cost of painting the outside top and walls.

3. A 0.75 km long cylindrical drainage system is laid under a new street. It consists of sections that are 20 m long and 4 m in outside diameter.
a. How many sections will be required to complete the job?
b. Find the surface area of the entire system.

4. What area of pavement is covered by one revolution of a roller that is 3.4 m long and 2.1 m in diameter?

5. Copy and complete the chart for these cylinders.

Diameter	Height	Volume	Surface Area
5 cm	7 cm		
10 m	7 m		
5 mm	14 mm		
10 mm	14 mm		
15 cm	7 cm		

6. Using the results from Exercise 5, describe the effect each of these changes has on the volume and surface area of a cylinder.
a. doubling the height, doubling the diameter, and doubling both the height and diameter
b. tripling the height, tripling the diameter, and tripling both the height and diameter
c. dividing both the height and diameter by 2

7. A culvert is a hollow cylinder commonly used to carry water under a highway or railway. A 20 m cement culvert has an inner diameter of 2.4 m and an outer diameter of 2.5 m. Find the volume of cement that forms the culvert.

13·12 Volume and Surface Area III

A sphere is a shape such as a balloon or a tennis ball. In this section, the formulas for the volume and surface area of a sphere will be introduced.

Example

Calculate the volume and surface area of a spherical balloon with a radius of 11 cm.

The volume of a sphere is found using the formula $V = \frac{4}{3}\pi r^3$.

The volume of the balloon is $\frac{4}{3}\pi \times 11^3$ cm³ or approximately 5572 cm³.

The surface area of a sphere is found using the formula $S.A. = 4\pi r^2$.
The surface area of the balloon is $4\pi(121)$ or approximately 1520 cm².

Exercises

1. Find the volume and surface area of a basketball 24 cm in diameter.

2. Calculate the volume of a hemisphere with a radius of 3 m. (*Hint:* A hemisphere is half of a sphere.)

3. Find the volume and surface area of each.
a. a spherical balloon 18 cm in diameter
b. a soccer ball with a 10 cm radius
c. a glass sphere with a circumference of 21π cm

4. A leather basketball is 24 cm in diameter. How many square centimetres of leather covers the ball?

5. The surface areas of two spheres are in a ratio of 64:27. Find the ratio of their radii.

6. A sphere just touches the top, bottom, and sides of a cylinder. Find the ratio of the volume of the sphere to the volume of the cylinder.

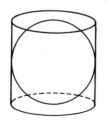

7. List the volumes of these four containers.
a. large cylinder   **b.** sphere
c. small cylinder   **d.** cone

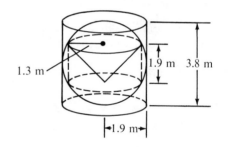

8. What effect will doubling the diameter of the sphere have on its volume?

9. Find the ratio of the volume of a sphere to the volume of a cylinder if the sphere fits tightly into the cylinder.

10. Which is larger?
a. the volume of a sphere with a diameter of 2 m or the volume of a hemisphere with a radius of 2 m
b. the surface area of a sphere with a radius of 10 cm or the surface area of a hemisphere with a radius of 20 cm
c. the surface area of a sphere with a diameter of x cm or the surface area of a cube with a side length of x cm

13·13 Volume and Surface Area IV

There is a unique relationship that exists between the volume of a cone and the volume of a cylinder when they have equal bases and heights. This same relationship also holds between a pyramid and a prism when they have equal bases and heights.

The contents of 3 pyramids (or 3 cones) are required to fill a prism (or cylinder) with the same base and height.

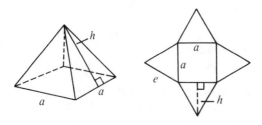

Therefore, the volume of a pyramid is one third the area of the base times the height.

Volume of a pyramid $= \frac{1}{3}lwh$

Therefore, the volume of a cone is one third the area of the base times the height.

Volume of a cone $= \frac{1}{3}\pi r^2 h$

Seoui and Cyndi decided to work together to find the formulas for the surface area of the pyramids and cones. They drew three nets.

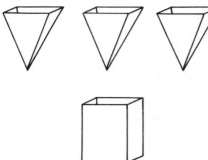

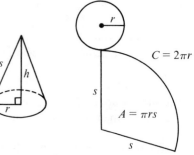

The surface area of this pyramid is found by finding the sum of the individual areas. This pyramid has a slant height of h units and a side length of a units.

$S.A. = $ Area of base $+$ Area of 4 sides

$= a^2 + \frac{4ha}{2}$

$= a^2 + 2ha$

$= a(a + 2h)$

The surface area of the cone is the sum of the area of the base and the area of the slant side. This cone has a slant side length of s units and a radius of r units.

$S.A. = $ Area of base $+$ Area of slant side

$= \pi r^2 + \pi rs$

$= \pi r(r + s)$

354

Exercises

1. Calculate the volume of each figure.

a.

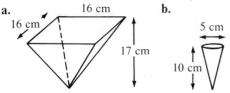

16 cm / 16 cm / 17 cm

b.

5 cm / 10 cm

2. Find the volume of a conical holding tank 6 m in diameter and 10 m in height.

3. Find the volume of the flower pots. Each is cut from a cone and the resulting shape is called a **frustum**.

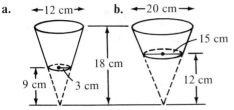

a. ←12 cm→ 9 cm / 3 cm / 18 cm

b. ←20 cm→ 15 cm / 12 cm

4. Calculate the surface area of these closed square-based pyramids.

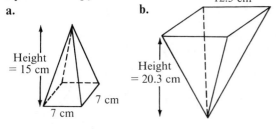

a. Height = 15 cm / 7 cm / 7 cm

b. 12.5 cm / Height = 20.3 cm

5. A pyramid has a vertical height of 10 cm and a 5 cm square base.
a. Use the Pythagorean Theorem to calculate the slant height.
b. Find the surface area of each triangular face.
c. Find the surface area of the whole pyramid.

6. A pyramid, with a square base of 12 cm and a height of 10 cm was cut in half. The top of this new truncated pyramid is also square and has a side length of 4 cm.
a. Draw a diagram to show this shape.
b. Calculate the volume and the surface area of this shape.

7. Calculate the surface area of each ice-cream cone.
a. 7 cm high with a 5 cm diameter
b. 12 cm high with a radius of 3 cm

8. A plastics company manufactures orange conical pylons with an open base for construction markers. Each pylon is 25 cm high and has a 12 cm diameter. Find the surface area of each pylon.

9. The surface area of an open frustum can be determined by subtracting the missing part from the entire cone.
$$S.A. = \pi sr - \pi s_1 r_1$$
$$= \pi(sr - s_1 r_1)$$
Find the surface area of this frustum.

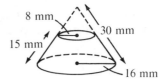

8 mm / 30 mm / 15 mm / 16 mm

10. If the dimensions of the original cone are not given, the surface area of the open frustum is calculated using the formula $S.A. = \pi s(r_1 + r_2)$. Find the surface area of this cone.

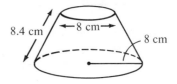

8.4 cm / ←8 cm→ / 8 cm

11. Find the surface area of each.

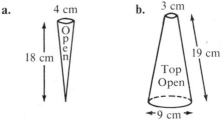

a. 4 cm / 18 cm / Open

b. 3 cm / 19 cm / Top Open / ←9 cm→

12. Calculate the surface area of each.
a. a closed cone 12 cm high with a diameter of 10 cm
b. a closed frustum with a slant height of 8.4 cm and radii of 4 cm and 9 cm

355

13·14 Combinations of Shapes

There are many objects that are formed by combining two or more geometric shapes. Some of those objects are shown.

1. A Swimming Pool — A pool is often constructed with a shallow end that gets progressively deeper. This type of pool is a combination of a trapezoidal prism and a rectangular prism.

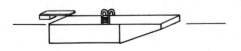

2. An Observatory — An observatory, used mainly by astronomers, is often in the shape of a cylinder and a hemisphere.

3. A Rocket — The Apollo rockets were designed for space exploration. They were a combination of a cylinder and a cone.

4. A Water Tower — The water tower is the shape of a cylinder and a sphere.

Exercises

1. Sketch five other objects that could be the combination of two or more three-dimensional objects.

2. Locate shapes in your area that combine two or more common geometric shapes, or find pictures that illustrate such combinations.

3. Calculate the surface area of these shapes.

a.

$r = 0.25$ m
3 m
3.5 m
2 m
4 m

b.

8 m
21 m
16 m

4. Calculate the volume of each.

a.

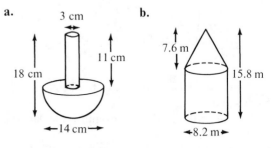

3 cm
11 cm
18 cm
14 cm

b.

7.6 m
15.8 m
8.2 m

Using the Library

The ancient Greeks built the Parthenon using three-dimensional geometry. The Parthenon has structures that appear parallel but that are not in reality. Write a short report on this phenomenon and any other architectural techniques that are unique to the Parthenon.

13·15 Packaging

There are a number of elements that must be considered when designing a box for packaged materials. These include the strength of the box, nature of the contents, storage, stacking in displays, and the price of the materials for the box.

Example

Determine the ratio of material (surface area) to volume for each package and identify the most cost-efficient container. They all have a capacity of 1728 cm³.

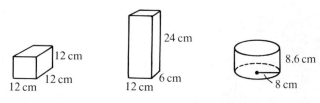

The most cost-efficient package is the one in which the ratio of surface area to volume is the smallest. In this case, the cylinder has the smallest surface area at 834 cm² and is the most efficient package.

Exercises

1. Find the cost of a large cylindrical container that is 8 m high and has a 4 m diameter. The material for the container costs $2.63/m².

2. Each package has the same volume.

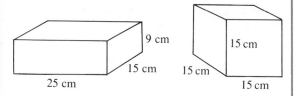

a. Find the volume.
b. Find the surface area of each package.
c. Which package is the most efficient?

3. Each package has the same surface area. Find the most efficient package.

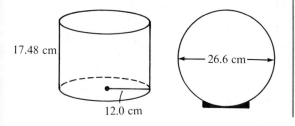

4. Establish dimensions for three packages in the shape of a cone, a cylinder, and a sphere to have approximately the same volume. Identify the package that is most efficient.

5. Find the ratio of surface area to volume for a cylindrical container.

6. Find the ratio of surface area to volume for each cylinder.
a. height is one third the radius
b. height is one half the radius
c. height is equal to the radius
d. height is twice the radius
e. height is three times the radius
f. height is four times the radius

7. Which of the cylinders in Exercise 6 would be the most efficient?

8. Find the most efficient container.
a. a rectangular prism 13 cm by 15 cm by 4 cm
b. a rectangular prism 6 cm by 12 cm by 14 cm

9. Write a short report discussing advantages and disadvantages of containers shaped as cones, spheres, rectangular prisms, and cylinders.

357

13·16 3D Sketching

The sketching of three-dimensional objects requires the use of two special rules.

1. Lines that are parallel in the object are drawn to look parallel in the sketch.

2. All hidden lines are drawn as broken or dotted lines.

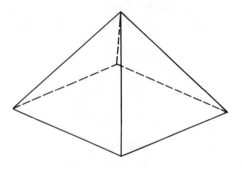

In the sketch of the pyramid, broken lines are shown even though they are hidden in the photograph. These broken lines are also parallel to the solid lines that are visible in the photograph.

A three-dimensional object often has to be viewed from several different angles in order to draw it.

Consider the three-dimensional object shown. If this object was placed in a transparent box, and the image of each side transposed to the sides of the box, then an accurate representation of the top, front, and side views would be visible. Generally, these three views are enough to give an accurate representation of what an object actually looks like when there are lines or sides that cannot be seen.

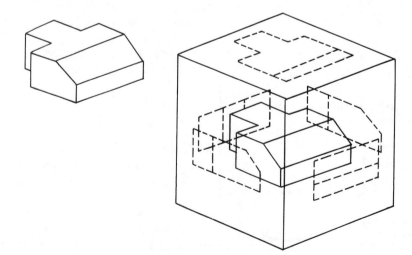

Exercises

1. Use the conventions of parallel lines and hidden lines to draw a three-dimensional representation of a detergent box.

2. Copy this sketch of an open strawberry flat. Convert edges in view to solid lines and leave the hidden edges as broken lines.

3. Copy this sketch of a truncated pyramid and add the dotted lines that indicate hidden edges.

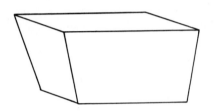

4. Sketch each shape.
a. a cube
b. a pyramid
c. an open frustum
d. a triangular prism

5. Copy this drawing, then draw the views of the object from all sides on the faces of a transparent box.

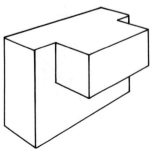

6. Draw separate top, front, and side views of this object.

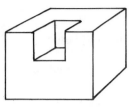

7. Draw a three-dimensional sketch of an object with these top, front, and side views.

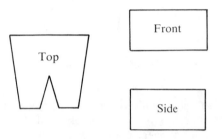

8. Examine some of the techniques used by artists to enhance the realism of three-dimensional sketches. Consider the use of shading and vanishing points. Consider the work of Hogarth (1697-1794) and Dürer (1471-1528).

Braintickler

Identify as many five-letter words as you can by selecting letters from successive vertices of this three-dimensional structure.

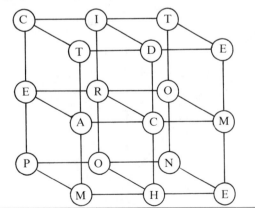

359

13·17 Symmetry in Three Dimensions

The points that make up a three-dimensional object are often related to each other. When this is the case, the object has **symmetry**.

If the shape can be "sliced" into two congruent halves, it has **plane symmetry**. For example, a perfectly-formed bowling ball has plane symmetry.

If the shape can be formed by revolving a two-dimensional object around one axis, then it has **rotational symmetry**. For example, a perfectly-formed cylinder has rotational symmetry.

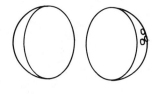

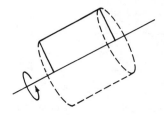

A shape has **point symmetry** if every point on the object can be reflected through the centre onto a corresponding point on the object. For example, the cylinder and the bowling ball both have point symmetry as every point on the surface has a corresponding point equidistant from the centre.

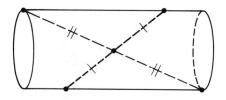

Example

Draw a cone. Identify and illustrate the symmetries of the cone.

A cone has rotational symmetry because it can be generated by revolving a triangle around an axis. It also has plane symmetry because any vertical plane through its centre will cut it into two congruent halves.

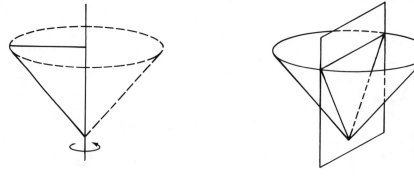

Exercises

1. In your own words, define for three-dimensional shapes, the terms "rotational symmetry", "point symmetry", and "plane symmetry". Give an example of each.

2. If an object has plane symmetry, does it automatically have point symmetry? Explain.

3. Give an example of an object that has plane symmetry, rotational symmetry, and point symmetry.

4. For an object to have plane symmetry, it must have one side congruent to the other side. What does this imply about the location of the plane?

5. Which of these shapes has plane symmetry? Identify and indicate the number of planes of symmetry the shape has.

a. Rectangular prism **b.** Frustum **c.** Cylinder

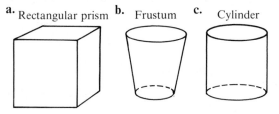

6. Identify the shapes that have rotational symmetry.

a. Cone **b.** Rectangular prism **c.** Sphere

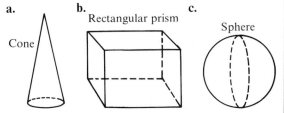

7. Describe the location of the point of symmetry, if there is one, for each object.

a. Cube **b.** Sphere **c.** Cone

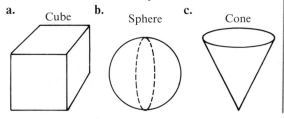

8. Draw the two-dimensional shape that is rotated to generate these three-dimensional objects.

a. Cone **b.** Frustum

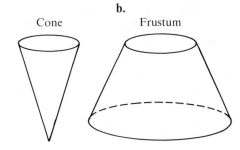

9. Copy and complete the missing half of each object if the object has plane symmetry.

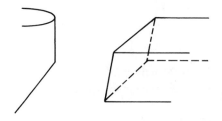

10. A ski patrol was on a routine check of a ski run. While observing the slope, they discovered a unique situation with an oak tree. There were two single ski tracks; one on each side of the tree. What explanation could there be for this phenomenon?

11. You have been offered a partnership in a small business. The current owner will allow you to run the business but she expects a certain percent of what the business makes. The percent is equal to the number of hundreds of the profit made every month. For example, if you make $1800 in a month, then you must give her 18%. Find the most that the business can earn for you to receive the maximum profit for the month.

12. Describe the planes of symmetry for each.
a. a cube **b.** a sphere

13. Describe completely the symmetries of the combinations of shapes identified in the display from Section 13·14.
a. the swimming pool **b.** the observatory
c. the rocket **d.** the water tower

13·18 Introduction to Vectors

A ship sails south for 50 km. A car travels east at 120 km/h. Martha exerts a force of 490 N directed downward.

Each of these quantities may be represented by **vectors**. A vector has both **magnitude** and **direction**. Vectors are represented in diagrams as arrows called **directed line segments**. A vector from A to B is represented as $\overrightarrow{AB}$, where A is the starting point of the vector, called the **tail** or **initial point**, and B is the **head** or **terminal point**. The head of the vector also shows the direction of the vector.

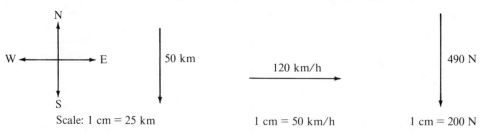

Scale: 1 cm = 25 km   1 cm = 50 km/h   1 cm = 200 N

John has $120 in the bank. Paul is 2 a old. Terri has a mass of 52 kg. A car is travelling at 105 km/h. Each of these statements involves only magnitude and are called **scalars**.

Example 1

Use a vector to represent each.

a. a displacement of 30 km east

b. a velocity of 250 km/h southwest

a.

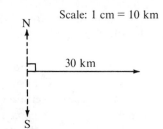

Scale: 1 cm = 10 km

b.

Scale: 1 cm = 100 km/h

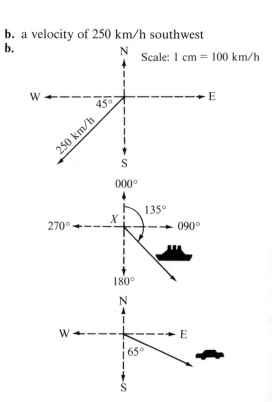

Directions for vectors are commonly given in two ways. In navigations, bearings are used. North is 000°. Moving clockwise, all other directions are assigned a three-digit number in degrees up to 359°. For example, due east is 090°, and southwest is 225°. In the diagram, a ship moving from X is said to have a bearing of 135°.

Standard direction is a second method. Direction is measured from north or south and the number of degrees to the east or west. The angle is always less than 90°, and east or west are given as E or W. The car in the diagram is moving S65°E.

Example 2

Draw a diagram to represent each using the scale given.
a. a displacement of 40 km on a bearing of 240°
b. a velocity of 30 km/h in a standard direction of N75°W

a.

b.

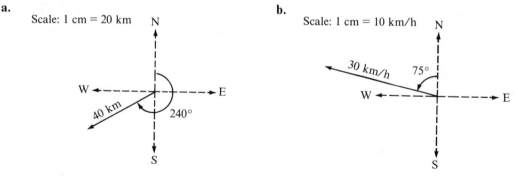

If two cars are travelling at 90 km/h east on a four-lane highway, they both have the same velocity and direction. They are **equivalent vectors**.

The vectors in Example 2 have been represented geometrically. Any vector that is represented geometrically has its tail at the origin and its head at the terminal point. Vectors also can be represented algebraically. For example, $\vec{a} = [5, 2]$. The first member of this ordered pair is the **horizontal component**, while the second member is the **vertical component**.

Example 3

Given the points $A(-3, 4)$ and $B(2, 1)$, express $\overrightarrow{AB}$ as an algebraic vector, and find its magnitude.

In the vector $\overrightarrow{AB}$, A is the tail and B is the head of the vector. Since an algebraic vector must have its tail at the origin, the vector must be translated to the right 3 units and down 4 units. This will move the head of the vector to the point $(5, -3)$. Therefore, $\overrightarrow{AB}$ can be represented algebraically as $[5, -3]$.

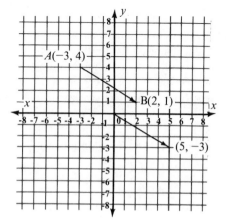

The magnitude of the vector is found using the Pythagorean Theorem.

$$\overrightarrow{AB} = [5, -3]$$
$$|\overrightarrow{AB}| = \sqrt{5^2 + (-3)^2}$$
$$= \sqrt{34}$$

The magnitude of $\overrightarrow{AB}$ is $\sqrt{34}$ units.

Exercises

1. Identify each as a vector, scalar, or neither. Explain your answers.
a. an aircraft flying at 560 km/h
b. a boy running east at 8 km/h
c. a translation of [4, −2]
d. a sale of $42
e. the wind blowing from the north
f. a car travelling with 6 passengers
g. a distance of 750 m
h. time moving forward
i. a force of 300 N

2. Write each bearing as a standard direction. The first one is done for you.

$300° = N60°W$

a. 030°   **b.** 140°
c. 180°   **d.** 240°
e. 325°   **f.** 089°

3. Write each standard direction as a bearing.
a. N65°E   **b.** S20°E
c. SE   **d.** due east
e. S40°W   **f.** N25°W

4. Draw a diagram to represent each vector. Indicate a scale where necessary.
a. a displacement of 200 m due north
b. a velocity of 75 m/s on a bearing of 160°
c. a force of 700 N in a direction of S40°E
d. a velocity of 300 km/h in a direction of N30°W
e. [5, 3]
f. [−4, 3]
g. a displacement of 25 cm on a bearing of 220°

5. Find the magnitude of each vector.
a. [−8, 10]   **b.** [6, −3]
c. [1, −4]   **d.** [5, 12]

6. Write each vector in the diagram as an algebraic vector and find its magnitude.

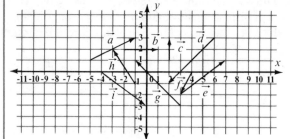

7. Which pairs of vectors appear to be equivalent?
a.

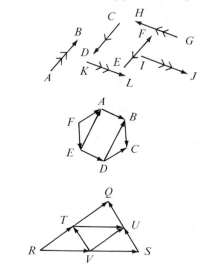

b.

c.

8. Divide a rectangle into four right triangles using only two lines.

9. Given the four points $A(5, 2)$, $B(−1, −2)$, $C(−5, 4)$, and $D(3, −2)$, represent each as an algebraic vector and find its magnitude.
a. $\vec{AB}$ **b.** $\vec{DC}$ **c.** $\vec{CA}$
d. $\vec{BD}$ **e.** $\vec{BA}$ **f.** $\vec{DA}$

10. Given two points $A(x_1, y_1)$ and $B(x_2, y_2)$, show that $\vec{AB} = [(x_2 − x_1), (y_2 − y_1)]$.

11. A vector has been described as "the physical representation of something that cannot be seen." Do you agree with this definition based on your understanding of vectors? Explain.

13·19 Addition of Vectors

Since vectors represent displacements in a certain direction, displacement vectors can be combined to find a total displacement from a fixed or initial starting point.

Example 1

A student is on his way home from school. He walks 3 km north and 4 km east.
a. How far is he from the school?   **b.** Find the direction of his home from the school.

a. Using the Pythagorean Theorem, we will find that the student is 5 km from the school.
b. The angle between the north vector and the displacement vector d can be measured using a protractor. The angle measure is 53°. Therefore, the student's home is N53°E from the school.

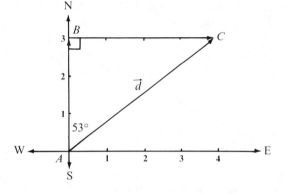

In Example 1, the first vector drawn is 3 km N and the second vector drawn is 4 km E. The head of the first vector is joined to the tail of the second vector. These two vectors create a third displacement vector from the tail of the first vector to the head of the second vector. This displacement vector is the **sum** of the two individual vectors.

> The addition of vectors can be determined by placing the head of the first vector to the tail of the second vector. This is the **triangle law** of addition. The sum vector is from the tail of the first vector to the head of the second.

Example 2

Find each sum from the diagram.
a. $\overrightarrow{AB} + \overrightarrow{AD}$ **b.** $\overrightarrow{BC} + \overrightarrow{BH}$ **c.** $\overrightarrow{AC} + \overrightarrow{AG}$ **d.** $\overrightarrow{GA} + \overrightarrow{GH}$

If two vectors are arranged tail to tail, they may be added by using a second method called the **parallelogram law** of addition. Complete the parallelogram started by the two vectors that are joined "tail to tail". The sum of the two vectors is the diagonal of the parallelogram.
a. $\overrightarrow{AB} + \overrightarrow{AD} = \overrightarrow{AE}$ This is found by completing parallelogram $ABED$ where the diagonal is $\overrightarrow{AE}$.
b. $\overrightarrow{BC} + \overrightarrow{BH} = \overrightarrow{BI}$
c. $\overrightarrow{AC} + \overrightarrow{AG} = \overrightarrow{AI}$
d. $\overrightarrow{GA} + \overrightarrow{GH} = \overrightarrow{GB}$

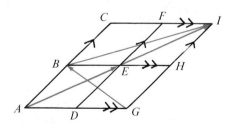

Exercises

1. Copy the vectors $\vec{a}$ and $\vec{b}$ and draw a diagram to find the sum of $\vec{a} + \vec{b}$ using both the triangle law and the parallelogram law of addition.

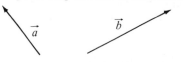

2. A grasshopper jumps from point A to point B, then to point C, then to point D, and so on. Find a single vector that will represent the sum of the five vectors shown. (*Hint:* Recall that the resultant vector is the vector that shows the magnitude and distance an object is away from the starting point.)

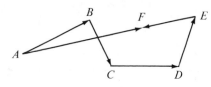

3. Use a ruler and protractor to make scale drawings.
a. A girl rides her bicycle to a store which is 12 km south of her house. She then cycles 7 km east to visit a friend. How far is it across country from her house to her friend and in what direction?
b. An aircraft flying due north at 500 km/h, encounters an easterly wind blowing at 100 km/h. Find the aircraft's resultant velocity and direction relative to the ground.

4. Consider the two diagrams showing airplane flights between various centres. Express each flight as a single vector.

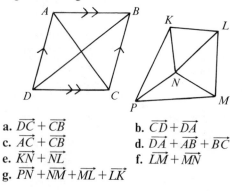

a. $\overrightarrow{DC} + \overrightarrow{CB}$
b. $\overrightarrow{CD} + \overrightarrow{DA}$
c. $\overrightarrow{AC} + \overrightarrow{CB}$
d. $\overrightarrow{DA} + \overrightarrow{AB} + \overrightarrow{BC}$
e. $\overrightarrow{KN} + \overrightarrow{NL}$
f. $\overrightarrow{LM} + \overrightarrow{MN}$
g. $\overrightarrow{PN} + \overrightarrow{NM} + \overrightarrow{ML} + \overrightarrow{LK}$

5. Add the vectors to find a single vector representation of each sum.
a. $[3, 5] + [5, 7]$ **b.** $[-1, 6] + [6, -3]$
c. $[2, -7] + [-3, 2]$ **d.** $[4, 8] + [-3, -8]$
e. $[4, -5] + [-2, -9] + [-7, 3]$
f. $[-2, 1] + [4, -7] + [-2, 6]$
g. $[15, -23] + [-22, 17] + [12, -6]$

6. Using a coordinate grid, illustrate Exercise 5, parts **a**, **b**, and **c**, using both the triangle law and the parallelogram law.

7. Find $[a, b]$.
a. $[a, b] + [3, -1] = [-5, 7]$
b. $[-9, 12] + [a, b] + [5, -3] = [-4, 6]$
c. $[-5, 2] + [a, b] = [-7, 3] + [2, 1]$

8. Use a ruler and protractor to make scale drawings.
a. Two boys each tie a rope to a wagon in order to pull it. Both exert a force of 600 N. One pulls northeast while the other pulls northwest. In which direction will the wagon move? What single force could replace the forces of the two boys?
b. A boat sails N30°E from a pier for 20 km. It then turns and sails due south for 15 km. Find the distance and direction the boat takes from the pier.
c. A ship wishes to travel from Lizard Island to Snake Bay on a bearing of 250°. The captain knows there is an ocean current moving from a bearing of 120° at 4 km/h. If the ship is to travel at 12 km/h, relative to the shore, in which direction should the ship be steered and with what speed should the motors be driven?

9. Find the additive inverse of each vector. (*Hint:* The additive inverse of a vector is a vector that, when added, produces $[0, 0]$.)
a. $[5, 2]$ **b.** $[-7, -3]$
c. $[-5, 3]$ **d.** $[x, y]$

10. Subtract the vectors.
a. $[7, 12] - [3, 7]$
b. $[-9, 5] - [-8, -13]$
c. $[-6, 9] - [7, -3]$
d. $[3, -5] - [-6, -2]$

13·20 Scalar Multiplication

A girl pulling a sled with a force of 500 N, 30° above the horizontal, is helped by three other friends who also exert a force of 500 N, 30° above the horizontal. The total force on the sled is now 2000 N in a direction 30° above the horizontal.

This situation illustrates the multiplication of a vector by a scalar. In the first case, 4×500 N, 30° above the horizontal. The direction of the vector remains the same but the magnitude is multiplied by the scalar.

Example

Multiply the vector $\vec{a} = [-1, 2]$ by 3.

$$3\vec{a} = 3[-1, 2]$$
$$= [-3, 6]$$

Comparing the magnitudes of $[-1, 2]$ and $[-3, 6]$,

$$|\vec{a}| = \sqrt{(-1)^2 + 2^2} \qquad |3\vec{a}| = \sqrt{(-3)^2 + 6^2}$$
$$= \sqrt{1 + 4} \qquad\qquad = \sqrt{9 + 36}$$
$$= \sqrt{5} \qquad\qquad\quad\; = \sqrt{45}$$
$$\qquad\qquad\qquad\qquad\quad = 3\sqrt{5}$$

The magnitude of $3\vec{a}$ is three times the magnitude of $\vec{a}$.

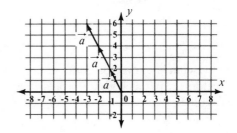

If $\vec{v} = [a, b]$, then $k\vec{v} = [ka, kb]$.

Exercises

1. Multiply each vector by 5.

a. 40 N downward

b. 150 m/s on a bearing of 070°

c. 7 m at an angle of 15° to the vertical

d. $[-5, 3]$ **e.** $[7, 8]$ **f.** $[-6, 0]$

2. If $\vec{u} = [3, 4]$ and $\vec{v} = [-2, 4]$, then find each resultant vector.

a. $3\vec{u}$ **b.** $5\vec{v}$ **c.** $-2\vec{u}$

d. $2\vec{u} + 3\vec{v}$ **e.** $-4\vec{u} + 2\vec{v}$ **f.** $0\vec{v}$

3. If $\vec{w} = [-6, 2]$, then illustrate each product on a Cartesian coordinate grid.

a. $2\vec{w}$ **b.** $-3\vec{w}$ **c.** $-\frac{1}{2}\vec{w}$

4. What is the effect of multiplying a vector by a negative scalar?

5. If $\vec{x} = [6, -3]$, then find $|\vec{x}|$ and compare it with the magnitude of each scalar product.

a. $2\vec{x}$ **b.** $-3\vec{x}$ **c.** $-\frac{4}{3}\vec{x}$

6. What is the effect on the magnitude of a vector when it is multiplied by a negative scalar?

7. From the diagram, express each vector in terms of $\overrightarrow{OB}$ and $\overrightarrow{OF}$. The first one is done for you.

$$\overrightarrow{OK} = \tfrac{3}{2}\overrightarrow{OF} + \overrightarrow{OB}$$

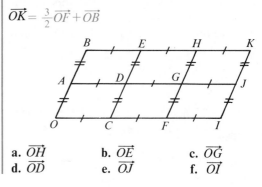

a. $\overrightarrow{OH}$ **b.** $\overrightarrow{OE}$ **c.** $\overrightarrow{OG}$

d. $\overrightarrow{OD}$ **e.** $\overrightarrow{OJ}$ **f.** $\overrightarrow{OI}$

13·21 Vector Proofs

In previous chapters, various forms of proofs such as inductive proofs, deductive proofs, and indirect proofs have been presented. Some of the methods of coordinate geometry also were used to prove certain deductions. Vectors allow us to prove some of the deductions that were proved in other sections using other means and for many proofs that are not easily done using other methods.

Certain statements that are made using vectors have definite implications when applied to geometry.

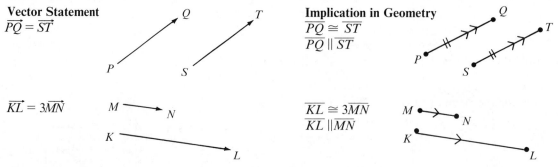

Vector Statement
$\vec{PQ} = \vec{ST}$

Implication in Geometry
$\overline{PQ} \cong \overline{ST}$
$\overline{PQ} \parallel \overline{ST}$

$\vec{KL} = 3\vec{MN}$

$\overline{KL} \cong 3\overline{MN}$
$\overline{KL} \parallel \overline{MN}$

Since two equivalent vectors, or one vector being a scalar multiple of a second vector, implies that the two vectors are parallel, vector proofs appear to be readily useful in proving that segments are parallel to each other, or a scalar multiple of each other.

Example

In $\triangle ABC$, M and N are the midpoints of $\overline{AB}$ and $\overline{AC}$ respectively. Prove that $\overline{MN}$ is parallel to $\overline{BC}$ and that $\overline{MN} \cong \frac{1}{2}\overline{BC}$.

GIVEN: Triangle ABC with M and N midpoints of $\overline{AB}$ and $\overline{AC}$ respectively.

REQUIRED: To prove that $\overline{MN} \cong \frac{1}{2}\overline{BC}$ and that $\overline{MN}$ is parallel to $\overline{BC}$.

PROOF: In order to prove that $\overline{MN} \parallel \overline{BC}$ it will be necessary to prove that $\overline{BC} \cong \overline{MN}$ or that $\overline{BC} \cong k\overline{MN}$.

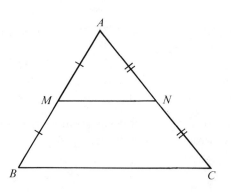

1. In $\triangle AMN$, $\vec{MN} = \vec{MA} + \vec{AN}$.
2. In $\triangle ABC$, $\vec{BC} = \vec{BA} + \vec{AC}$.
3. Since M is the midpoint of $\overline{AB}$ and N is the midpoint of $\overline{AC}$, $\overline{MA} \cong \overline{BM}$ and $\overline{NA} \cong \overline{CN}$.
4. Therefore, $\vec{BA} = 2\vec{MA}$, $\vec{AN} \cong \vec{NC}$, and $\vec{AC} = 2\vec{AN}$.
$\vec{BC} = 2\vec{MA} + 2\vec{AN}$
$\quad = 2(\vec{MA} + \vec{AN})$
$\quad = 2\vec{MN}$
5. Since $\vec{BC}$ is a scalar multiple of $\vec{MN}$, $\overline{BC} \parallel \overline{MN}$.
6. Since $\vec{BC} = 2\vec{MN}$, $\vec{MN} = \frac{1}{2}\vec{BC}$.

Therefore, $\overline{MN} \cong \frac{1}{2}\overline{BC}$.

368

Exercises

1. Express each vector as the sum of two other vectors using the diagram.

a. $\overrightarrow{DA}$ **b.** $\overrightarrow{CD}$ **c.** $\overrightarrow{CB}$
d. $\overrightarrow{AB}$ **e.** $\overrightarrow{DB}$ **f.** $\overrightarrow{BC}$

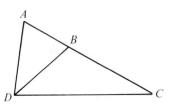

2. Express each vector in terms of $\vec{m}$ and $\vec{n}$ from parallelogram $QRST$.

a. $\overrightarrow{TR}$ **b.** $\overrightarrow{TQ}$ **c.** $\overrightarrow{SR}$
d. $\overrightarrow{ST}$ **e.** $\overrightarrow{RQ}$ **f.** $\overrightarrow{RT}$

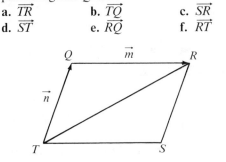

3. In parallelogram $ABCD$, M and N are the midpoints of $\overline{AB}$ and $\overline{CD}$ respectively.
a. Express $\overrightarrow{AN}$ in terms of two other vectors.
b. Express $\overrightarrow{MC}$ in terms of two other vectors.

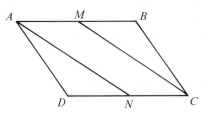

For Exercises 4 to 9, prove each deduction using a vector proof.

4. Using the diagram in Exercise 3, prove that $\overline{AN} \cong \overline{MC}$ and $\overline{AN} \parallel \overline{MC}$.

5. In $\triangle ABC$, M and N are trisection points of $\overline{AB}$ and $\overline{AC}$ respectively. Prove that $\overrightarrow{MN} \parallel \overrightarrow{BC}$ and $\overline{MN} \cong \frac{1}{3}\overline{BC}$.

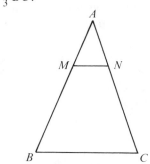

6. Quadrilateral $ABCD$ is a rectangle. Points E and F are the midpoints of $\overline{AD}$ and $\overline{BC}$ respectively. Prove that $\overline{EF} \cong \overline{AB}$ and $\overline{EF} \parallel \overline{AB}$.

7. If the diagonals of a quadrilateral bisect each other, then the quadrilateral is a parallelogram.

8. Prove the converse of Exercise 7.

9. Arusha says that she has built a polyhedron with five triangular faces, four quadrilateral faces, and two pentagonal faces. How do you know that Arusha has made a mistake?

10. In a new version of Canadian football, a touchdown is worth eight points with the possibility of adding two points for a convert after a touchdown; a field goal is worth five points. If single points have been eliminated, then what is the largest score that may not be made?

Braintickler

Find the pattern that a fly would trace as it crawls from the centre of a bicycle wheel out to the rim as the bicycle travels along a road.

13·22 Vectors in Three Dimensions

A painter walks 30 m due north from his truck, climbs 15 m up a vertical ladder, and then walks 10 m due east along a scaffold to begin painting. The sum of the three vectors which represents each displacement is a **three-dimensional vector**.

The triangle law and parallelogram law for the addition of vectors both apply to three-dimensional vectors. However, they may have to be applied more than once to find a single vector that is representative of the displacement.

In order to graph the worker's displacement, an ordinary coordinate plane cannot be used. Instead, a three-dimensional diagram is set up. Picture the diagram as being a rectangular solid in which you are walking along the edges. This diagram illustrates the path taken by the painter as well as the sum of the three vectors.

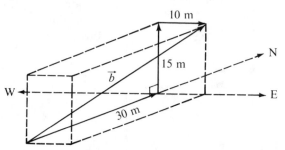

The distance the painter is from his initial starting point is the **resultant** vector, and can be found by finding the sum of the two individual displacements.

Let the resultant vector formed by the painter going 30 m north and 10 m east be $\vec{a}$.

$$|\vec{a}| = \sqrt{30^2 + 10^2}$$
$$= \sqrt{900 + 100}$$
$$= \sqrt{1000}$$
$$= 10\sqrt{10}$$

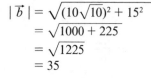

Vector a has a magnitude of $10\sqrt{10}$ m.

Let the vector representing the displacement of vector a and 15 m up a vertical ladder be $\vec{b}$.

$$|\vec{b}| = \sqrt{(10\sqrt{10})^2 + 15^2}$$
$$= \sqrt{1000 + 225}$$
$$= \sqrt{1225}$$
$$= 35$$

The worker is 35 m from the original starting point.

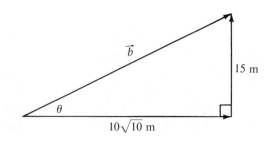

These two steps could also have been done in one step by finding the distance using a **Pythagorean Triple**.

$$|\vec{b}| = \sqrt{30^2 + 15^2 + 10^2}$$
$$= \sqrt{900 + 225 + 100}$$
$$= \sqrt{1225}$$
$$= 35$$

This assumes that the starting point is at (0, 0, 0).

Therefore, the worker is 35 m from his truck.

To find the direction of the resultant vector, draw a scale diagram in two dimensions for vector a and measure the angle with a protractor. Measuring this angle gives a direction of approximately 25°.

All the properties that were introduced with two-dimensional vectors are also properties of three-dimensional vectors.

If $\vec{x} = [a, b, c]$, then $|\vec{x}| = \sqrt{a^2 + b^2 + c^2}$.

Example

Represent $\vec{b} = [3, 2, 4]$ on a three-dimensional coordinate grid and calculate $|\vec{b}|$.

There are points which are outside the x-y plane. Therefore, a third axis, called the z-axis, is added to graph the third component in the vector. To graph $\vec{b}$, move 3 units along the x-axis, 2 units parallel to the y-axis, and 4 units parallel to the z-axis. Vector b is shown on the grid.

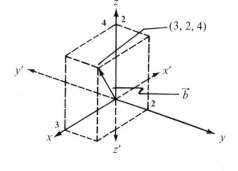

$$|\vec{b}| = \sqrt{3^2 + 2^2 + 4^2}$$
$$= \sqrt{9 + 4 + 16}$$
$$= \sqrt{29}$$

The length of $\vec{b}$ is $\sqrt{29}$ units.

If $A(x_1, y_1, z_1)$ and $B(x_2, y_2, z_2)$ are any two points, $\overrightarrow{AB} = [(x_2 - x_1), (y_2 - y_1), (z_2 - z_1)]$.

Exercises

1. Graph each vector and find its magnitude.
a. [3, 4, 12]   b. [−2, 1, 5]
c. [1, 0, −3]   d. [−4, −2, 4]

2. Given three points $A(-1, 5, 3)$, $B(3, 2, -4)$, and $C(-5, 5, 2)$, express each as one ordered triplet and find its magnitude.
a. $\overrightarrow{AB}$ b. $\overrightarrow{AC}$ c. $\overrightarrow{BC}$
d. $\overrightarrow{BA}$ e. $\overrightarrow{CA}$ f. $\overrightarrow{CB}$

3. Find the sum or difference.
a. [5, 9, 23] + [12, 7, 11]
b. [−4, 5, −8] − [2, −7, −4]
c. [−6, 0, 18] + [−17, −2, 1] − [3, −1, 2]

4. An airplane travels according to the vector [300, 500, 50], while the wind travels according to the vector [60, 20, −3]. Find the resultant direction of the airplane.

371

13·23 Computer Application — Trigonometric Functions

Mitch left his trigonometric tables at home on the day of his mathematics examination. However, he remembered that his teacher had said that all the angles on the exam were between 47° and 62° and that the computer had these functions built into its memory. He went to the computer and entered this program.

```
10 REM A TRIG TABLE FOR THE ANGLES 47 TO 62 DEGREES
20 PRINT "ANGLE"; "    SINE"; "    COSINE"; "   TANGENT"
30 LET X = 47
35 LET K = X * 3.14159 / 180
40 LET SI = INT(100000 * SIN(K) + 0.5) / 100000
45 LET CO = INT(100000 * COS(K) + 0.5) / 100000
50 LET TA = INT(100000 * TAN(K) + 0.5) / 100000
60 PRINT " "; X; "    "; SI; "    "; CO; "   "; TA
70 LET X = X + 1
80 IF X > 62 THEN 99
90 GOTO 35
99 END
```

In this program, line 35 converts the degree measure to radian measure so that the computer can understand what ratio the user would like to find.

Exercises

1. Enter the program from the display and run it on the computer. Compare the output from this program with the table at the back of the book. Are they the same?

2. Modify the program from the display so that it uses a FOR ... NEXT statement instead of the IF ... THEN statement.

3. Using increments of 30°, write a program to find the sine, cosine, and tangent ratios of angles from 0° to 360°. Use these values to graph each function on a Cartesian coordinate grid. Use the horizontal axis for degrees and the vertical axis for the values of sine, cosine, and tangent.

4. One train of thought on the rapidly expanding field of computer technology is that the computer companies, instead of just selling software and hardware to clients, should help organizations adjusting to the new technology. They should be addressing their client's concerns about the new and ever-changing technology. Write a short essay either defending or rejecting this argument.

5. Write a program that will solve a right triangle with side lengths of 1 unit and 2 units.

6. Modify the program from Exercise 5 so that it also draws the triangle on the screen. (*Hint:* Recall how to use the graphics mode on the computer.)

13·24 Scatterplots

There are many ways to organize and display information. For example, bar graphs and histograms are graphical representations of information. Another graphical representation is the **scatterplot**. A scatterplot (sometimes called a **scatter diagram**) is a graph representing the relationship between two variables which can be measured.

Example

Ms. Alexandria, the local aerobics instructor, conducted an experiment to compare various people's heartbeat per minute with the number of steps that the person walks in one minute. The information that she collected is shown in the table. Draw an appropriate scatterplot to display the information.

Person	1	2	3	4	5	6	7	8	9	10
Number of Steps/min	10	17	38	21	45	16	19	24	14	20
Heartbeat/min	64	59	75	70	75	62	60	68	61	60

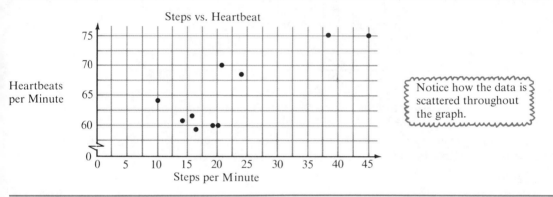

Notice how the data is scattered throughout the graph.

Exercises

1. Explain why the name "scatterplot" is appropriate for the graph.

2. Two people who walked 17 steps per minute recorded different heartbeats per minute. Can you account for this difference?

3. Consider the scale on each axis. Are they appropriate for what is being measured? If so, explain why. If not, what scale do you feel is more appropriate and explain why.

4. Another aerobics instructor examined the data and concluded that the heartbeat increases with the rate of walking. Do you agree with this conclusion? Explain.

5. A peach farmer in the Niagara Peninsula recorded the overnight temperature and the number of peaches per hectare that were damaged.

Temperature	Damaged Peaches per Hectare
20°C	17
19°C	10
22°C	15
15°C	21
17°C	16
15°C	20
12°C	24
22°C	4
18°C	12
20°C	8

Draw a scatterplot to represent this information.

13·25 Interpreting Data — Scatterplots

A complete scatterplot can reveal more information about a set of data when the graph is considered as a whole as opposed to examining the individual ordered pairs.

Example 1

The year-end statistics for 18 professional hockey players were compiled and a scatterplot was drawn for the number of points scored versus the number of penalty minutes. What conclusions can be drawn?

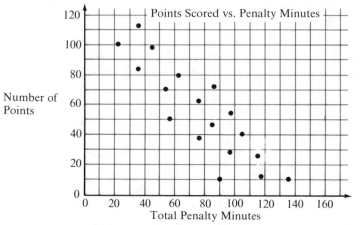

By investigating the pattern as a whole, we can see that the more penalty minutes a player has, the less likely it is for the player to score points. Although this graph does not fall on a straight line exactly, it does appear that the number of points scored decreases as the number of penalty minutes increases. This type of scatterplot is said to have a **negative** (or **inverse**) **correlation**.

Example 2

On the same hockey team, the relationship between a player's mass and the total number of penalty minutes was also examined and a scatterplot was drawn for the data. What conclusions can be drawn from the graph?

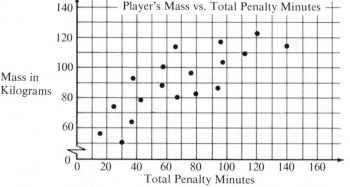

As is the case with Example 1, the ordered pairs do not fall onto a straight line exactly, although a pattern does appear to exist. It appears that a player's penalty minutes increases with the mass of the hockey player. This type of scatterplot shows a **positive** (or **direct**) **correlation**.

Exercises

1. In your own words, explain negative correlation and positive correlation.

2. Which of these scatterplots appears to have a positive correlation, a negative correlation, or a zero correlation?

a.

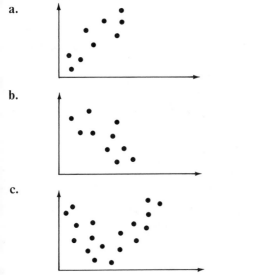

b.

c.

3. A scatterplot shows a relationship between two variables only. It is often necessary to consider other factors that can influence the conclusions. For instance, in Example 1, the amount of ice time a player receives can directly affect both the number of points scored and the penalty minutes. Suggest two factors that can influence the conclusions drawn for Example 2.

4. Which of these can be displayed using a scatterplot?
a. If the relationship cannot be presented using a scatterplot, then explain why.
b. Also explain whether each would likely be a negative correlation or a positive correlation.
 i) level of education versus annual income
 ii) amount of studying done and the score on the last English test
 iii) the length of time a pot of water is boiling versus the temperature of the water
 iv) height of students versus their IQ scores
 v) height of students versus their mass

5. What outside influences would result in a different conclusion than the one you reached in Exercise 4, part **i**?

6. A scatterplot can be used to compare two different sets of data relating the same two variables. This scatterplot compares the population of Bacteria *A* and Bacteria *B* at various temperatures.

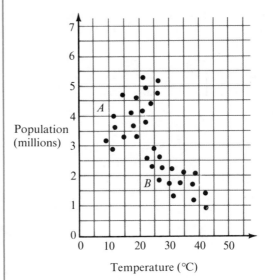

Temperature (°C)

a. Is there a negative correlation, a positive correlation, or zero correlation between the population of Bacteria *A* and the temperature of the culture? Bacteria *B* and the temperature of the culture?
b. Which bacteria has the greatest population?
c. What conclusions can be drawn from the scatterplot about the relationship between Bacteria *A* and the temperature? Bacteria *B* and the temperature? Explain.
d. What reasons, besides temperature, could explain the conclusions you have drawn in part **c**?

7. Give an example of a relationship that would give each type of scatterplot.
a. a positive correlation
b. a negative correlation
c. no correlation

8. A scatterplot is said to have a 100% perfect correlation. Can all the points of this scatterplot be joined by the same straight line? Explain.

13·26 The Line of Best Fit

A straight line can be drawn in relation to a series of points on a scatterplot. This line is drawn so that all the points lie near or on the line. This is a way to estimate visually and linearly the relationship between two variables.

Example

A basketball team recorded the number of points each player scored versus the number of shots they took. The data is shown in the table. Draw a scatterplot for the information and estimate the **line of best fit** for the information.

Shots	25	32	24	15	54	67	34	24	31	19	40	60	10	30	50
Points	40	54	36	24	80	108	60	30	40	34	50	75	20	45	85

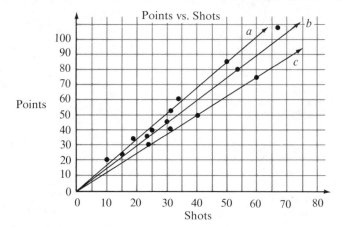

When drawing the line of best fit, the line should have as many points above it as below it, and in this case, it is reasonable to assume that it passes through the origin. Three attempts have been made for the line of best fit. Line *b* is used as the most probable line.

Method 1

Let *P* represent the points scored.
Let *s* represent the number of shots taken.

Find the equation of the line by estimating two points on the line. The points (15, 24) and the origin were chosen.

$$m = \frac{24 - 0}{15 - 0}$$
$$= 1.6$$
$$\therefore P = 1.6s$$

Method 2

Use the **median fit line** to find an equation of the line. Arrange the data, in order, into equal groups with an odd number of values and find the median of each.

10 15 <u>19</u> 24 24   25 30 <u>31</u> 32 34   40 50 <u>54</u> 60 67
20 24 <u>30</u> 34 36   40 40 <u>45</u> 54 60   50 80 <u>85</u> 75 108

Notice the median values are (19, 30), (31, 45), and (54, 85). Draw a line through the two extreme median points and find an equation of that line. In this case, the extreme points are (19, 30) and (54, 85).

$$m = \frac{85 - 30}{54 - 19} = 1.57$$
$$\therefore P = 1.57s$$

Using the estimate that has been drawn as the line of best fit, it appears that the team will score on the average, about 1.6 points for every shot that is taken. However, remember that the line you draw as the line of best fit is only an estimate and not an exact representation.

Exercises

1. The line of best fit is often stated as an estimate of the relationship between two variables.
a. Explain this statement.
b. Explain why lines *a* and *c* are not as good a fit as line *b*.

2. Explain the meaning of the median fit line.

3. The line of best fit relates one variable in terms of another variable. If a player on the team in the display takes 75 shots, then about how many points will the player score? Explain.

4. If the player in Exercise 3 had scored 44 points, then how many shots will the player probably have taken? Explain.

5. Define the terms "interpolation" and "extrapolation" and explain how each could be used in the example. Refer to Chapter 8 if necessary.

Exercises 6 to 16 refer to this table of values. Use a calculator for all the exercises if one is available.

Study Time for an Exam (h)	2	4	3	6	12	1	3	9	5	3.5
Score (%)	44	71	98	55	87	50	66	71	70	60

6. Construct a scatterplot to display this information for the two variables. Place the score on the vertical axis and the time studied on the horizontal axis.

7. In order to find an equation of the line of best fit, is it always reasonable to assume that the line will pass through the origin? In other words, if a student does not study for the exam, will that student receive a mark of 0%?

8. Sketch the line of best fit through the points on your scatterplot and find an equation for it.

9. Find the slope of the median fit line. Is this slope comparable to the slope you found in Exercise 8?

10. Does this scatterplot show a positive correlation between the number of hours studied and the score on the exam? Explain.

11. Find an equation for the line of best fit using the slope from Exercise 9.

12. According to your scatterplot, what is the maximum number of hours that should be studied in order to receive a mark of 100% on the exam? a mark of 50% on the exam?

13. Use interpolation or extrapolation to estimate the following.
a. the mark a student could expect to receive after studying for 1 h
b. the mark a student could expect to receive after studying for 0.5 h
c. the probable number of hours a student studied if he/she received a mark of 40%
d. the probable number of hours a student studied if he/she received a mark of 82%

14. What conclusions can be made about the correlation between the total number of hours studied and the mark received on the exam?

15. A positive correlation was found between a person's height and a person's mass for statistics taken at the last Olympics. However, this correlation was not as strong when this same relationship was tested in the city of North Bay. Give reasons why this correlation would not be as strong.

13·27 Interpretation

Scatterplots and the line of best fit can be used to give an accurate estimate of how one variable is related to another. However, they can also give an inaccurate estimate of trends due to short term "fluctuations" which can be attributed to outside factors. To interpret the statistics with some degree of accuracy, it is often necessary to account for or "even out" these fluctuations.

Consider a city that relies on seasonal tourist trade for much of its economy. It can experience a rise in unemployment during a certain period of time even though its economy is not changing from year to year. This rise in unemployment can be interpreted as an unemployment problem when in fact as soon as the season begins again, the employment situation will return to normal. In this instance, the unemployment statistics are **seasonally adjusted**. These statistics are adjusted to account for the seasonal employment situation.

Example 1

The unemployment rate at a popular tourist resort in February is 7.4%. Research into the unemployment rates for each month of the last fifteen years revealed that the unemployment rate for February is 1.11 times higher than the yearly average. Find the seasonally adjusted unemployment rate for February.

$$\text{Seasonally Adjusted Rate} = \frac{\text{Monthly Average}}{\text{Average Rate Higher}}$$
$$= \frac{7.4}{1.11}$$
$$= 6.67$$

Therefore, the seasonally adjusted average for February shows an unemployment rate of approximately 6.67%.

The scatterplot, the median fit line, and the seasonally adjusted average are tools used by people in an attempt to predict future outcomes. Successful prediction is particularly important for economic planning and in shares and commodity trading.

When attempting to predict the future outcomes, trends and cycles are looked for in past events. A **trend** is said to be a "persistent long-term movement"; while a **cycle** is an "up-and-down" movement of inconsistent length and duration. A sequence of measurements of the same variable, made at definite or consistent time periods, is a **time series**.

The manner in which previous trends and cycles are interpreted is left up to the individual. The following example shows two different ways in which statistics can be interpreted. There are many others.

Example 2

A farmer must decide which crop to plant during the summer of 1987. The market suggests that wheat will be the most profitable crop to harvest during the summer and corn will be the least profitable. The farmer realizes that to grow corn, there must be an average rainfall of 30 mm/summer, while wheat needs an average monthly rainfall of 35 mm/summer. The farmer decides to check the average summer rainfall for the years 1980 to 1985 in order to decide which crop to grow during the summer. Use the scatterplot shown to help the farmer decide which crop to grow during the summer.

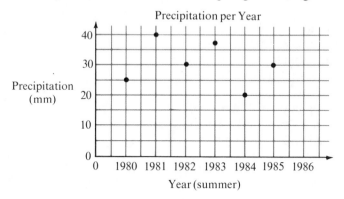

Precipitation per Year

Although there are a number of ways to interpret the data, only two are shown.

1. The farmer may look at the most basic of all measurements, the measure of central tendency. Two measures that can be used are the mean and the median.

The median is $\frac{30 + 30}{2}$ or 30 mm/summer.

The mean measurement is $\frac{25 + 40 + 30 + 36 + 20 + 30}{6}$ or 30.16 mm/summer.

Using either of these two measures, it would seem likely that the farmer would grow corn as opposed to wheat.

2. A second method of interpretation is to find an equation to estimate the median fit line. There are two variables being related in the scatterplot and an equation is a possibility.

Let P represent the precipitation.
Let Y represent the year that precipitation is being estimated.
Place the data into two groups of three each and draw the line through the median points of the groups.

1984	1980	1982		1985	1983	1981
20	25	30		30	36	40

Therefore, the median points are (1980, 25) and (1983, 36).

$$m = \frac{36 - 25}{1983 - 1980} = 3.67$$

Using the point (1980, 25), the equation of the line can be found as $P = 3.67Y - 7241.6$. Substituting the year 1987 into the equation, the estimated precipitation is 50.69 cm for the summer and the farmer should grow wheat during the summer.

Exercises

1. Are seasonally adjusted unemployment figures an accurate indication of whether a particular economy is in trouble? Explain.

2. A ski resort area reported that there is an unemployment rate of 12.2% for the months of June, July, and August. They also noted that this is 1.64 times higher than the average yearly unemployment figures for the last eight years. Find the seasonally adjusted unemployment rate for this time period.

3. For the ski resort owners to show a profit, the seasonally adjusted unemployment rate for the ski resort should be no more than 7.75%. Using the information in Exercise 2, is the ski resort a profitable venture? Explain.

4. Is each of these a trend, a cycle, or a time series? Explain your reasoning.
a. the winning times in a local car race have been increasing every year since 1948
b. the inflation rate for each month of the year 1982 varied from a low of 1.8% in March to a high of 4.9% in July
c. the unemployment rate was measured for each month of each year from 1970 to 1975 and the statistics were published as a line graph
d. a publisher reported a sales increase of 2.6%/a for each of the last 10 a

5. If you were the farmer in Example 2, would you grow corn or wheat during the summer of 1987? Explain.

6. What other factors are there to help determine if there is enough precipitation in order to grow corn successfully?

7. Redraw the scatterplot of Example 2 with this information: 1976 — 35 mm/a; 1977 — 28 mm/a; 1978 — 21 mm/a; 1979 — 41 mm/a.
Using this added information, will the farmer wish to grow corn or wheat in the summer of 1987? Explain.

8. This table shows the year and the winning average speed for a road race in Hamilton over the first ten years the race was held.

Year	Average Speed (km/h)
1970	125
1971	128
1972	126
1973	130
1974	141
1975	138
1976	158
1977	155
1978	139
1979	171

a. Draw a scatterplot for the data.
b. What do you think the winning average speed for 1990 will be given the scatterplot and the table of values? Explain how you arrived at this answer.
c. Predict what the winning average speed would have been for this road race in 1968 if the race had been run then. Explain how you arrived at this answer.

9. The inflation rate for North America has been steadily climbing for the last ten years. Is this a trend or a cycle? Explain.

10. What are some of the trends and cycles that you would look for if you were to play the stock market?

Using the Library

Research the Consumer Price Index. Report on what it is; how it is used to determine whether increases in a person's salary are enough to cover the inflation rate for a certain time period; what 100 will mean for a certain year; and give an example of what a person's salary should be in 1985 if their 1975 salary was $18 000.

13·28 Correlation — Estimate or Guess

When an equation for the line of best fit is estimated, and a high positive correlation is found between the two variables, there is not necessarily a "cause and effect" relationship between the two variables. In other words, an increase in one variable does not necessarily result in a similar increase in the other variable, even when a high correlation exists.

Generally, when there is a high positive correlation between two variables, we assume that there is a connection between the variables. In fact, many advertisements are designed to exploit this assumption. Advertisers wish the consumer to believe that an increased use of their product will result in a positive outcome.

Example

A newspaper reported that during the last fifteen years, as the city police department's total salary increased, the number of crimes committed per capita also increased. The article concluded that lowering the salary of every officer would also lower the crime rate.

a. Is this conclusion reasonable?

b. Give some possible reasons that could explain the increase in crime statistics over the fifteen-year period.

a. The reporter in this article has made a conclusion based on statistics. However, there is no likely correlation between salaries and crime rates even though a high positive correlation has been reported to exist between the two variables. Therefore, it is reasonable to assume that all the variables were not taken into account.

b. There are many reasons that could explain this situation. For instance, an increase in crime could result in an increased hiring of police officers. Due to inflation, the police department's total salary could be increasing. There could also be economic factors in the community that cause the crime rate to go up, or this relationship may be a coincidence and the increase in crime could have happened regardless of the salaries of police officers. Can you think of other reasons?

Graphs that show a high positive correlation between two variables will always be used to draw conclusions and make predictions about certain events. However, these same conclusions and predictions can later prove to be incorrect or illogical if **all** the variables responsible for the prediction are not examined. In such cases, what appears to be a reasonable estimate can often be no more than a guess or an illogical conclusion.

Exercises

Exercises 1 to 4 report observed happenings which were presented as cause and effect relations. Explain whether this is a reasonable association. If not, what are some of the factors that could produce the associations?

1. A hospital reported that the number of cases of flu for their bedridden patients increased with the number of oranges served with the meals.

2. A study among editors found a high positive correlation between the size of the editor's foot and the average annual salary.

3. A report showed that there was a strong positive correlation between the number of years a person stays in school and their average annual salary.

4. A used-car sales representative found that there was a strong negative correlation between the age of a car and its eventual resale value.

Exercises 5 to 8 describe a possible association. Predict whether a positive, negative, or zero correlation exists between the two variables. Explain why you made the particular prediction.

5. A study is made to relate the number of reporters working on a newspaper and the newspaper's total annual sales.

6. A study was done to relate the average winning speeds at the Indianapolis 500 and the year that the race took place.

7. A study was done to relate the height of various people and their actual mass.

8. A study was done to relate the number of males in a university education course who later went on to become high school mathematics instructors.

9. Sometimes the correlation between two variables can change over a period of time. These are examples of such a phenomenon. Give possible explanations for the changing of the correlation.
a. Twenty years ago, a university graduate could start in business earning an annual salary higher than the national average. Now, there is little correlation between the university graduate and the initial starting salary (compared with the national average).
b. One hundred years ago there was little or no correlation between the age of a person and the likelihood of having lung disease. Today, age and lung disease have a fairly strong positive correlation.

10. A scatterplot can be made for the various yearly record times for the marathon run from 1884 to 1979. Using this scatterplot, a year can be found for the running of the marathon in one minute. Would this be a reasonable prediction?

Braintickler

Two baseball players wish to be the starting outfielder in the playoffs. Player A is a rookie and Player B is a veteran. The coach told the rookie that if he has a better batting average, then he will start in the playoffs, but each player would need 250 at bats to determine the best batter. At playoff time, the rookie had a better batting average than the veteran; 0.324 to 0.316. When the playoffs started, the veteran was started against both left-handed pitchers and right-handed pitchers because the veteran had the better average against both. The rookie demanded to see the statistics and was presented with this chart.

	Left-handers	Right-handers	Total
Player A	$\frac{6}{25} = 0.24$	$\frac{75}{225} = 0.333$	$\frac{81}{250}$
Player B	$\frac{28}{100} = 0.280$	$\frac{51}{150} = 0.340$	$\frac{79}{250}$

Can you explain why the rookie's overall statistics were better than the veteran's, but not his individual statistics. You may wish to use your library and research **Simpson's Paradox**.

13·29 Chapter Review

TRIGONOMETRY

1. If $\triangle MNP$ is similar to $\triangle RST$, then find the length of the missing sides correct to one decimal place.

a. $m = 4$, $n = 7$, $p = 8$, $r = 12$

b. $r = 12$, $s = 15$, $t = 20$, $n = 10$

2. Find the value of x correct to one decimal place.

a.   **b.**

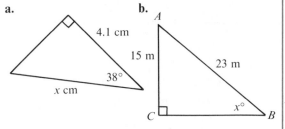

3. Given $\triangle ABC$ with the right angle at A.

a. Find $\angle B$ if $c = 31.6$ m and $b = 28.2$ m.

b. Solve the triangle if $a = 32.3$ units and $b = 26.6$ units.

4. A telephone post snaps in the wind and touches the ground 7 m from its base. If the top of the post forms an angle of $49°$ with the ground, then what was the original height of the post?

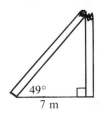

5. Two hunters in a forest become separated. Both are able to see a fire-lookout tower. The first hunter spots the tower at an angle of elevation of $19°$, while the second sees the tower at an angle of elevation of $7°$.

a. If the tower is 75 m high, then what is the closest the two hunters could be to each other?

b. What is the greatest distance they could be apart?

MATRICES

1. State the order of each matrix.

$$A = \begin{bmatrix} -7 & 4 & -6 & -1 \\ 0 & -2 & 8 & -4 \end{bmatrix} \qquad B = \begin{bmatrix} -5 \\ -6 \\ 1 \end{bmatrix}$$

$$C = \begin{bmatrix} -1 & 8 & -3 \\ 0 & -5 & 6 \\ -2 & 0 & 2 \end{bmatrix} \qquad D = \begin{bmatrix} 0 & -4 \\ -1 & 3 \\ 11 & -5 \end{bmatrix}$$

2. Using the matrices of Exercise 1 as well as the matrices given below, find the sum or difference indicated.

$$F = \begin{bmatrix} -4 & 2 \\ 7 & -6 \end{bmatrix} \qquad G = \begin{bmatrix} 3 & -5 & -6 \\ -1 & 0 & 8 \end{bmatrix}$$

$$H = \begin{bmatrix} 3 & -5 \\ -2 & 0 \\ 6 & -9 \end{bmatrix} \qquad J = \begin{bmatrix} -5 & -4 & 1 \\ 7 & -5 & -1 \\ 3 & 0 & 3 \end{bmatrix}$$

a. $H - D$ **b.** $G + D$ **c.** $J - C$

d. $3A$ **e.** $2C + J$ **f.** $D - 5H$

3. Find the value of the variables that will make the matrices equal.

$$\begin{bmatrix} -3 & 2a & 4b \\ 3c & -d & 7e \end{bmatrix} \quad \begin{bmatrix} -3 & -12 & 28 \\ -9 & -18 & -35 \end{bmatrix}$$

For Exercises 4 and 5, use the matrices in Exercises 1 and 2.

4. Find the product matrix and state the order of each.

a. GB **b.** JH **c.** GD

d. F^2 **e.** HA **f.** JB

g. FG **h.** $(GJ)H$ **i.** $G(JH)$

5. Find the inverse matrix of H.

THREE-DIMENSIONAL GEOMETRY

1. Construct a net for each.

a. a 6 cm × 4 cm × 2 cm rectangular prism

b. an open cone with a slant height of 5 cm and a diameter of 2 cm

2. Calculate the surface area of each. Use a calculator if one is available.

a. a closed cylinder 16 cm tall having a diameter of 6.2 cm

b. a sphere with a diameter of 18 cm

c. an open cone with a slant height of 12 cm and a diameter of 5 cm

3. Half of a spherical satellite is to be covered with a protective heat shield. Find the cost of the shield if the satellite has a diameter of 8 m and the shield costs $0.85/cm².

4. Find the cost of material necessary for a cylindrical container standing 8 m tall and having a radius of 2 m. The cost of the material is $2.63/m².

5. Calculate the volume of each.

a. a cylinder 3 m tall with a 1.2 m diameter

b. a cone standing 7 cm tall having a 15 cm diameter

c. a sphere with a radius of 14 cm

6. Define and give an example of each.

a. plane symmetry

b. rotational symmetry

c. point symmetry

7. Sketch and label three different three-dimensional containers having a volume of approximately 1500 cm³. Identify the most efficient container with respect to packaging a product.

8. Draw the top, front, and side views of this object.

VECTORS

1. Identify as a vector, scalar, or neither.

a. a hot-air balloon drifting east at 6 km/h

b. a racing bike with a mass of 8 kg

c. a car racing at 300 km/h on a bearing of 175°

d. a cross-country skier heading S35°E

2. Represent each by a vector. State the scale where necessary.

a. a force of 150 N directed 45° above the horizontal

b. a displacement of 60 cm N55°W

c. a translation of [−4, 7]

3. Consider the vectors shown.

a. Write the components of each vector.

b. Find each vector's magnitude.

c. State which vectors are equivalent.

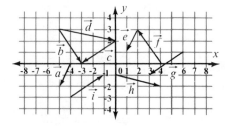

4. Express each as a single vector. Show the resultant vector on a coordinate grid.

a. [−3, 2] + [−5, −7]

b. [4, −5] + [−3, 4]

c. [5, −7] + [−2, 5] + [−3, 2]

5. Perform each addition using a scale diagram. State the magnitude and direction of the sum.

a. 25 km/h due north + 45 km/h due east

b. 2 m/s on a bearing of 030° + 6 m/s on a bearing of 140°

c. 3 m N + 6 m E + 5 m W

6. If $\vec{u} = [−2, 5]$ and $\vec{v} = [5, 1]$, then find each.

a. $2\vec{u}$ **b.** $−3\vec{v}$ **c.** $2\vec{u} + 3\vec{v}$ **d.** $\vec{u} − 3\vec{v}$

7. If $\vec{a} = [−3, 4, −7]$ and $\vec{b} = [1, 3, −1]$, then find each.

a. $2\vec{a} + \vec{b}$ **b.** $3\vec{b} − \vec{a}$

13·30 Chapter Test

TRIGONOMETRY

1. Find the length of x in the pair of similar triangles correct to one decimal place.

2. Find the value of sin A, sin B, cos A, cos B, tan A, and tan B for each triangle.

a. **b.**

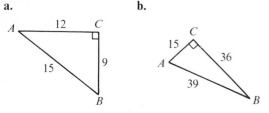

3. From a point 450 m from its base, the angle of elevation of the top of the City Hall tower is 15°. Find the height of the tower.

4. A seaplane is 6 km from shore flying at an altitude of 1000 m directly towards the shore. If it starts to climb at an angle of 25° with respect to the horizontal, then find the reading on the altimeter when it crosses the shoreline correct to the nearest ten metres.

5. A waterwheel is shown in the diagram. Calculate the height of the buckets $A, B, C,$ and D above the water when the wheel is in the position shown.

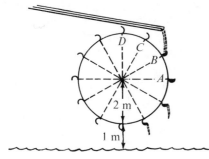

MATRICES

Use these matrices to answer Exercises 1 to 6.

$$A = \begin{bmatrix} 3 & 1 & -2 \\ 1 & 4 & 0 \\ 0 & 3 & -2 \end{bmatrix} \qquad B = \begin{bmatrix} -1 & 4 & 3 \\ 2 & 0 & 5 \\ -6 & 9 & -1 \end{bmatrix}$$

$$C = \begin{bmatrix} 1 & -4 \\ -1 & 2 \\ 0 & 3 \end{bmatrix} \qquad D = \begin{bmatrix} 8 & -1 \\ -3 & 5 \\ -6 & 2 \\ 0 & 1 \end{bmatrix}$$

$$E = \begin{bmatrix} 6 & -2 \\ 0 & -3 \end{bmatrix} \qquad F = \begin{bmatrix} -3 & 4 & -1 \end{bmatrix}$$

1. Find a single matrix to represent each sum or difference of matrices.

a. $2A - 3B$ **b.** $-5C$

2. State the order of each matrix.

a. C **b.** B **c.** F
d. DE **e.** FA **f.** FC

3. Find E^{-1}.

4. Find the product matrix.

a. AB **b.** BA **c.** DE
d. A^2 **e.** FC **f.** $(AC)E$

5. Show that $(E)(E^{-1}) = I$.

6. Is matrix multiplication commutative? associative?

7. Consider these matrices.

$$X = \begin{bmatrix} 1 & 2 & 3 \\ 1 & 3 & 4 \\ 1 & 4 & 3 \end{bmatrix} \qquad Y = \begin{bmatrix} \frac{7}{2} & -3 & \frac{1}{2} \\ -\frac{1}{2} & 0 & \frac{1}{2} \\ -\frac{1}{2} & 1 & -\frac{1}{2} \end{bmatrix}$$

Show by multiplication that X and Y are inverse matrices.

THREE-DIMENSIONAL GEOMETRY

1. Calculate the surface area of each.
a. a rectangular prism that measures 17 cm × 24 cm × 12 cm
b. a cylinder with a height of 3 m and having a diameter of 1.5 m
c. a cone 12 cm high and having a radius of 12 cm
d. a sphere with a radius of 6.4 m

2. Calculate the volume of each.
a. a cylinder 12 m high and 15 m in diameter
b. a cone with a height of 16 cm and a radius of 8 cm
c. a sphere with a diameter of 12.8 m

3. A water tower is formed by combining a cylinder supporting a sphere. Find the amount of water the tower can hold if the cylinder has a diameter of 18 m, stands 35 m tall, and the sphere has a diameter of 28 m.

4. Calculate the volume of this solid.

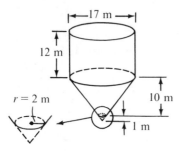

5. Draw a three-dimensional sketch of the object having these top, front, and side views.

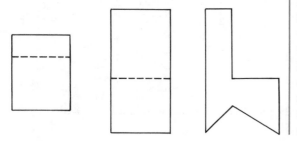

VECTORS

1. Express each bearing as a standard direction.
a. 065°   **b.** 135°   **c.** 290°

2. Express each standard direction as a bearing.
a. N85°E   **b.** S35°W   **c.** N25°W

3. For each vector give its component vector, graph it on a coordinate grid, and find its magnitude.
a. $\vec{AB}$ with $A(-5, 3)$ and $B(2, -1)$
b. $\vec{PQ}$ with $P(3, 7)$ and $Q(-4, 11)$
c. $\vec{KL}$ with $K(3, 2, 5)$ and $L(1, 3, 6)$

4. The diagram shows a square-based right pyramid. State any vectors equivalent to each of the following.

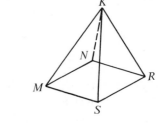

a. $\vec{SM}$ **b.** $\vec{KR}$
c. $\vec{MN}$ **d.** $\vec{KN} + \vec{NR}$
e. $\vec{KM} - \vec{KN}$ **f.** $\vec{RN} - \vec{RK}$
g. $(\vec{KN} + \vec{NR}) + \vec{RS}$ **h.** $\vec{KN} + (\vec{NR} + \vec{RS})$

5. Three forces all act at right angles to each other. If the forces are 10 N, 12 N, and 16 N respectively, then find the magnitude of a single force which could replace the three individual forces.

6. Use a scale drawing to answer each.
a. A plane heads in a direction S40°E at 500 km/h. A wind blowing from S30°W at 80 km/h blows the plane off course. Find the velocity and direction the plane is travelling relative to the ground.
b. A miner walks 75 m due west from the mining office, takes a vertical elevator 60 m into a mine-shaft, and then walks 40 m due south in a horizontal tunnel. How far is the miner from the mining office?

Powers, Roots, 1-100

n	$\sqrt{n}$	n	$\sqrt{n}$
1.0	1.0000	5.5	2.3452
1.1	.0488	5.6	.3664
1.2	.0954	5.7	.3875
1.3	.1402	5.8	.4083
1.4	.1832	5.9	.4290
1.5	1.2247	6.0	2.4495
1.6	.2849	6.1	.4698
1.7	.3038	6.2	.4900
1.8	.3416	6.3	.5100
1.9	.3784	6.4	.5298
2.0	1.4142	6.5	2.5495
2.1	.4491	6.6	.5690
2.2	.4832	6.7	.5884
2.3	.5166	6.8	.6077
2.4	.5492	6.9	.6268
2.5	1.5811	7.0	2.6458
2.6	.6125	7.1	.6646
2.7	.6432	7.2	.6833
2.8	.6733	7.3	.7019
2.9	.7029	7.4	.7203
3.0	1.7321	7.5	2.7386
3.1	.7607	7.6	.7568
3.2	.7889	7.7	.7749
3.3	.8166	7.8	.7928
3.4	.8439	7.9	.8107
3.5	1.8708	8.0	2.8284
3.6	.8974	8.1	.8460
3.7	.9235	8.2	.8636
3.8	.9494	8.3	.8810
3.9	1.9748	8.4	.8983
4.0	2.0000	8.5	2.9155
4.1	.0248	8.6	.9326
4.2	.0494	8.7	.9496
4.3	.0736	8.8	.9665
4.4	.0976	8.9	2.9833
4.5	2.1213	9.0	3.0000
4.6	.1448	9.1	.0166
4.7	.1679	9.2	.0332
4.8	.1909	9.3	.0496
4.9	.2136	9.4	.0659
5.0	2.2361	9.5	3.0822
5.1	.2583	9.6	.0984
5.2	.2804	9.7	.1145
5.3	.3022	9.8	.1305
5.4	2.3238	9.9	3.1464

n	n^2	n^3	$\sqrt{n}$	$\sqrt[3]{n}$	n	n^2	n^3	$\sqrt{n}$	$\sqrt[3]{n}$
1	1	1	1.000	1.000	51	2 601	132 651	7.141	3.708
2	4	8	1.414	1.260	52	2 704	140 608	7.211	3.733
3	9	27	1.732	1.442	53	2 809	148 877	7.280	3.756
4	16	64	2.000	1.587	54	2 916	157 464	7.348	3.780
5	25	125	2.236	1.710	55	3 025	166 375	7.416	3.803
6	36	216	2.449	1.817	56	3 136	175 616	7.483	3.826
7	49	343	2.646	1.913	57	3 249	185 193	7.550	3.849
8	64	512	2.828	2.000	58	3 364	195 112	7.616	3.871
9	81	729	3.000	2.080	59	3 481	205 379	7.681	3.893
10	100	1 000	3.162	2.154	60	3 600	216 000	7.746	3.915
11	121	1 331	3.317	2.224	61	3 721	226 981	7.810	3.936
12	144	1 728	3.464	2.289	62	3 844	238 328	7.874	3.958
13	169	2 197	3.606	2.351	63	3 969	250 047	7.937	3.979
14	196	2 744	3.742	2.410	64	4 096	262 144	8.000	4.000
15	225	3 375	3.873	2.466	65	4 225	274 625	8.062	4.021
16	256	4 096	4.000	2.520	66	4 356	287 496	8.124	4.041
17	289	4 913	4.123	2.571	67	4 489	300 763	8.185	4.062
18	324	5 832	4.243	2.621	68	4 624	314 432	8.246	4.082
19	361	6 859	4.359	2.668	69	4 761	328 509	8.307	4.102
20	400	8 000	4.472	2.714	70	4 900	343 000	8.367	4.121
21	441	9 261	4.583	2.759	71	5 041	357 911	8.426	4.141
22	484	10 648	4.690	2.802	72	5 184	373 248	8.485	4.160
23	529	12 167	4.796	2.844	73	5 329	389 017	8.544	4.719
24	576	13 824	4.899	2.884	74	5 476	405 224	8.602	4.198
25	625	15 625	5.000	2.924	75	5 625	421 875	8.660	4.217
26	676	17 576	5.099	2.962	76	5 776	438 976	8.718	4.236
27	729	19 683	5.196	3.000	77	5 929	456 533	8.775	4.254
28	784	21 952	5.292	3.037	78	6 084	474 552	8.832	4.273
29	841	24 389	5.385	3.072	79	6 241	493 039	8.888	4.291
30	900	27 000	5.477	3.107	80	6 400	512 000	8.944	4.309
31	961	29 791	5.568	3.141	81	6 561	531 441	9.000	4.327
32	1 024	32 768	5.657	3.175	82	6 724	551 368	9.055	4.344
33	1 089	35 937	5.745	3.208	83	6 889	571 787	9.110	4.362
34	1 156	39 304	5.831	3.240	84	7 056	592 704	9.165	4.380
35	1 225	42 875	5.916	3.271	85	7 225	614 125	9.220	4.397
36	1 296	46 656	6.000	3.302	86	7 396	636 056	9.274	4.414
37	1 369	50 653	6.083	3.332	87	7 569	658 503	9.327	4.431
38	1 444	54 872	6.164	3.362	88	7 744	681 472	9.381	4.448
39	1 521	59 319	6.245	3.391	89	7 921	704 969	9.434	4.465
40	1 600	64 000	6.325	3.420	90	8 100	729 000	9.487	4.481
41	1 681	68 921	6.403	3.448	91	8 281	753 571	9.539	4.498
42	1 764	74 088	6.481	3.476	92	8 464	778 688	9.592	4.514
43	1 849	79 507	6.557	3.503	93	8 649	804 357	9.644	4.531
44	1 936	85 184	6.633	3.530	94	8 836	830 584	9.695	4.547
45	2 025	91 125	6.708	3.557	95	9 025	857 375	9.747	4.563
46	2 116	97 336	6.782	3.583	96	9 216	884 736	9.798	4.579
47	2 209	103 823	6.856	3.609	97	9 409	912 673	9.849	4.595
48	2 304	110 592	6.928	3.634	98	9 604	941 192	9.899	4.610
49	2 401	117 649	7.000	3.659	99	9 801	970 299	9.950	4.626
50	2 500	125 000	7.071	3.684	100	10 000	1 000 000	10.000	4.642

Random Numbers

1	67983	60852	09916	43596	20363	53315	37287	07662	26401	28650
2	19010	91956	31795	41845	25190	06991	66521	93755	02166	79003
3	41830	13963	52289	51633	77785	31712	93500	19449	77822	36645
4	50115	21246	09195	09502	53413	26357	63992	52872	42570	80586
5	22712	09067	51909	75809	16824	41933	97621	68761	85401	03782
6	82806	82277	88300	29832	22806	92486	36042	34590	55743	85297
7	68885	23670	25151	14619	33069	05296	14748	43282	62802	30626
8	41971	29316	23695	60065	62854	01237	72575	98475	61743	66763
9	86818	10485	28018	57382	70220	77420	94651	05024	24716	63746
10	61411	17729	56740	10634	56007	05873	36764	41765	97918	49916
11	20240	11618	52392	19715	20334	01124	39338	73458	63616	72057
12	47935	98490	99047	20071	81921	13627	99672	26523	53766	01219
13	28555	86201	62668	98919	54425	52470	21863	38900	96199	02418
14	59767	56647	35868	12109	29037	72768	45163	69121	72091	48070
15	99784	67224	77465	88593	61371	05036	41838	02224	34532	14840
16	69823	11868	50659	64782	20491	11303	41774	80579	09599	00703
17	89585	58666	00566	73433	67326	86922	42271	45800	59208	94299
18	93707	06735	84194	51810	19421	68021	05152	06217	57168	95760
19	04063	28256	83450	70758	00038	24278	55795	30155	78395	65622
20	89294	03751	09422	22965	09888	95835	80131	65972	16145	59876
21	60301	16519	51348	36322	70572	48637	05309	08369	79567	67699
22	74006	15355	95718	91467	30481	31576	84764	67417	19343	01920
23	86117	80403	42385	64085	70178	07265	87005	48570	25755	81223
24	87860	70624	75971	40430	43435	34945	70220	32445	18369	01990
25	10484	39599	04817	06980	22037	43080	52425	77667	67793	92230
26	45635	80376	17981	83957	91343	18249	85861	90149	59239	10040
27	89884	99155	65450	31432	60782	51442	31091	91187	81633	54164
28	08854	49077	20318	73772	85867	61524	78601	92812	34536	97897
29	43755	12282	84744	58693	25640	66247	58618	40854	85560	00699
30	36381	94203	18050	28540	97769	63915	65191	04638	76462	13106
31	05478	49611	27465	72222	56456	82646	09667	43683	33611	15020
32	30900	37036	68577	43276	57609	88486	16952	46799	49171	19846
33	87097	50134	42000	51378	60900	70086	51319	51408	85037	15608
34	84951	45154	20051	46979	79305	46375	16686	96475	54604	14795
35	52243	19460	67237	95379	78426	75457	05919	05828	13052	51831
36	48397	03688	27314	19086	58154	56293	78283	87702	17610	97741
37	36108	73699	01494	88477	18706	86938	40590	38087	22757	04249
38	73798	17752	23699	42632	77518	34777	66590	12061	35079	14551
39	26577	40103	74102	06328	43037	77254	78000	61577	41810	85898
40	81004	57367	28642	02357	23267	76973	29206	69086	42603	49297

Sines, Cosines, and Tangents 0°-90°

Degrees	Sine	Cosine	Tangent	Degrees	Sine	Cosine	Tangent
0°	0.0000	1.0000	0.0000	45°	0.7071	0.7071	1.0000
1°	0.0175	0.9998	0.0175	46°	0.7193	0.6947	1.0355
2°	0.0349	0.9994	0.0349	47°	0.7314	0.6820	1.0724
3°	0.0523	0.9986	0.0524	48°	0.7431	0.6691	1.1106
4°	0.0698	0.9976	0.0699	49°	0.7547	0.6561	1.1504
5°	0.0872	0.9962	0.0875	50°	0.7660	0.6428	1.1918
6°	0.1045	0.9945	0.1051	51°	0.7771	0.6293	1.2349
7°	0.1219	0.9925	0.1228	52°	0.7880	0.6157	1.2799
8°	0.1392	0.9903	0.1405	53°	0.7986	0.6018	1.3270
9°	0.1564	0.9877	0.1584	54°	0.8090	0.5878	1.3764
10°	0.1736	0.9848	0.1763	55°	0.8192	0.5736	1.4281
11°	0.1908	0.9816	0.1944	56°	0.8290	0.5592	1.4826
12°	0.2079	0.9781	0.2126	57°	0.8387	0.5446	1.5399
13°	0.2250	0.9744	0.2309	58°	0.8480	0.5299	1.6003
14°	0.2419	0.9703	0.2493	59°	0.8572	0.5150	1.6643
15°	0.2588	0.9659	0.2679	60°	0.8660	0.5000	1.7321
16°	0.2756	0.9613	0.2867	61°	0.8746	0.4848	1.8040
17°	0.2924	0.9563	0.3057	62°	0.8829	0.4695	1.8807
18°	0.3090	0.9511	0.3249	63°	0.8910	0.4540	1.9626
19°	0.3256	0.9455	0.3443	64°	0.8988	0.4384	2.0503
20°	0.3420	0.9397	0.3640	65°	0.9063	0.4226	2.1445
21°	0.3584	0.9336	0.3839	66°	0.9135	0.4067	2.2460
22°	0.3746	0.9272	0.4040	67°	0.9205	0.3907	2.3559
23°	0.3907	0.9205	0.4245	68°	0.9272	0.3746	2.4751
24°	0.4067	0.9135	0.4452	69°	0.9336	0.3584	2.6051
25°	0.4226	0.9063	0.4663	70°	0.9397	0.3420	2.7475
26°	0.4384	0.8988	0.4877	71°	0.9455	0.3256	2.9042
27°	0.4540	0.8910	0.5095	72°	0.9511	0.3090	3.0777
28°	0.4695	0.8829	0.5317	73°	0.9563	0.2924	3.2709
29°	0.4848	0.8746	0.5543	74°	0.9613	0.2756	3.4874
30°	0.5000	0.8660	0.5774	75°	0.9659	0.2588	3.7321
31°	0.5150	0.8572	0.6009	76°	0.9703	0.2419	4.0108
32°	0.5299	0.8480	0.6249	77°	0.9744	0.2250	4.3315
33°	0.5446	0.8387	0.6494	78°	0.9781	0.2079	4.7046
34°	0.5592	0.8290	0.6745	79°	0.9816	0.1908	5.1446
35°	0.5736	0.8192	0.7002	80°	0.9848	0.1736	5.6713
36°	0.5878	0.8090	0.7265	81°	0.9877	0.1564	6.3138
37°	0.6018	0.7986	0.7536	82°	0.9903	0.1392	7.1154
38°	0.6157	0.7880	0.7813	83°	0.9925	0.1219	8.1443
39°	0.6293	0.7771	0.8098	84°	0.9945	0.1045	9.5144
40°	0.6428	0.7660	0.8391	85°	0.9962	0.0872	11.4301
41°	0.6561	0.7547	0.8693	86°	0.9976	0.0698	14.3007
42°	0.6691	0.7431	0.9004	87°	0.9986	0.0523	19.0811
43°	0.6820	0.7314	0.9325	88°	0.9994	0.0349	28.6363
44°	0.6947	0.7193	0.9657	89°	0.9998	0.0175	57.2900
45°	0.7071	0.7071	1.0000	90°	1.0000	0.0000	undefined

Glossary

Abscissa The horizontal or x-coordinate of an ordered pair plotted on a Cartesian coordinate grid.

Base of a power The repeated factor in a power.

Bearing A method of giving direction by degree measurements from north.

Biased sample A sample in which certain members do not have an equal chance of being selected.

Box and whisker plot A graphic representation of confidence intervals and extreme values of a population.

Centroid The point of intersection of the medians of a triangle.

Circumcentre The intersection point of the perpendicular bisectors of the sides of a triangle. This point is the centre of the circumscribed circle of the triangle.

Collinear points Points which lie on the same straight line.

Complement of an event That part of a sample space not in the event.

Complementary angles Two angles the sum of whose measures is $90°$.

Concurrent Lines passing through the same point.

Confidence interval A range of values, for which we may be a stated percent sure, that the mean value of a population lies.

Conjugate radical A pair of irrational numbers whose product is a rational number.

Constant of proportionality The common ratio between two variables in a direct variation.

Continuous In a set of points there is always another point between any two given points.

Coplanar Three or more points or lines which lie in the same plane.

Degree of a polynomial The degree of a polynomial is the greatest sum of the exponents of the variables in any one term of the polynomial.

Dependent equations A system of linear equations that has infinitely many solutions.

Dependent event Event B is dependent on event A if the occurrence of event B requires the occurrence of event A.

Dilatation A transformation in which the image is similar in shape to the object. The image may be a reduction or enlargement of the object.

Direct congruence A direct congruence of figures is a congruence in which the order of labels on corresponding vertices is in the same direction.

Direct variation A relation in which the pairs of values have a constant ratio.

Domain The set of all first elements or abscissas in a relation.

Equally likely Event A is equally likely as Event B if event A has the same chance of occurring as event B and vice versa.

Equation A mathematical sentence containing an equal sign separating two expressions which designate the same number.

Equidistant To say that A and B are equidistant from C means that A and B are the same distance from C.

Equivalent equations Equations with the same solution set.

Exponent In a power, it tells how many times the base is used as a factor.

Exterior angle The angle formed outside a polygon between the extended side and the side adjacent to the extended side of the polygon.

Extraneous root A solution of an equation which will not satisfy the original equation.

Extrapolation The process of using the pattern in sets of data to estimate unknown values beyond the range of the known values.

Glide-reflection A composition of transformations in which one transformation is followed by one or more transformations.

Incentre The point of intersection of the bisectors of the angles of a triangle. This point is the centre of an inscribed circle in the triangle.

Inconsistent equations A system of equations that has no solution.

Independent equations A system of linear equations that has exactly one solution.

Independent event Event B is independent of event A if the occurrence of event B does not effect the probability of event A.

Index See *Exponent*. Also, the root to which a radicand is taken.

Indirect congruence An indirect congruence of figures is a congruence in which the order of labels on corresponding vertices is not in the same direction.

Integers The positive and negative Natural Numbers plus zero. $\{\ldots, -3, -2, -1, 0, 1, 2, 3, \ldots\}$

Interpolation The process of using the pattern in sets of data to estimate unknown values between known values.

Invariant property A property of a shape which does not change under a transformation.

Inverse variation A relation in which pairs of values have a constant product.

Irrational Numbers Real Numbers which cannot be written as a ratio.

Isometry An isometry is any transformation which preserves length.

Like terms Like terms are monomials that contain exactly the same variables raised to the same degree.

Linear pair Two angles that have a common side and the other sides are opposite rays.

Linear relation A relation changing at a constant rate; the graph is a straight line.

Magnitude The length of a vector or a line segment.

Matrix A rectangular array of numbers.

Mean The arithmetic mean is the sum of n numbers divided by n.

Mean proportional In the proportion $\frac{x}{y} = \frac{y}{z}$, y is the mean proportional.

Median The middle number in a set of numbers arranged in order. The arithmetic mean of the two middle numbers when there is an even number of numbers.

Median of a triangle A line segment from one vertex to the midpoint of the opposite side.

Mode The most frequently occurring number in a set.

Natural Numbers Members of the set of numbers $\{1, 2, 3, \ldots\}$.

Numerical coefficient The numerical coefficient is the number factor of a monomial.

Opposite rays Two rays which form a straight line.

Ordinate The vertical or y-coordinate of an ordered pair plotted on a Cartesian coordinate grid.

Origin The basic reference point on a coordinate system. It is the point $(0, 0)$ in the Cartesian coordinate system.

Orthocentre The point of intersection of the altitudes of a triangle.

Parameter An arbitrary constant.

Partial variation A relation in which pairs of values in a linear pattern are without a constant ratio; the graph does not go through the origin.

Polynomial A polynomial is an algebraic expression which contains one or more terms.

Population The group of objects or people about which information is to be gained.

Postulate A statement accepted as true without proof.

Power An expression written with a base and an exponent. 4 written as a power of 2 is 2^2.

Principal root The positive square root of a number.

Probability A ratio of the number of ways an event can occur to the number of possible outcomes.

Proportion Two or more equal ratios.

Radical The root of a quantity denoted by an expression written under the radical sign, $\sqrt{}$.

Radical, mixed A product of a quantity and a radical. For example, $3x\sqrt{2y}$.

Radical, pure A radical where the quantity under the radical sign does not have a factor which is a perfect square.

Radicand The expression under the radical sign.

Range The set of all second elements or ordinates in a relation.

Rational Numbers Numbers which can be written as a ratio whose numerator is an integer and whose denominator is a nonzero integer.

Ray A half line which includes an initial point and all the points on one side of it.

Real Numbers The set of numbers composed of the rational and irrational numbers.

Reflection A transformation in which the image is produced by flipping the object over a line to produce a symmetrical pattern.

Resultant The sum of two or more vectors.

Rotation A transformation in which the points in an object are turned a specific amount around a fixed point.

Sample space Part of a whole population.

Scalar A quantity which has only magnitude.

Scientific notation A number written in the form $a \times 10^n$, where $1 \leq a < 10$.

Simple random sample A sample of a population in which each member has an equally likely chance of being selected.

Skew lines Nonintersecting, nonparallel lines in three-dimensional space.

Stratified random sample Combined simple random samples taken in proportion on subgroups of a population.

Supplementary angles Two angles the sum of whose measures is 180°.

System of equations Two or more equations written in the same variables.

Tangent A line or line segment that intersects a circle at only one point.

Theorem A general statement which must be proved before it is accepted as true.

Transformation A correspondence or mapping of points in a plane to produce an image of those points.

Translation A motion in which each point in an object is moved the same distance and in the same direction.

Transversal A line or line segment that intersects two or more lines at unique points.

Tree diagram A diagram, in the shape of branching lines, showing all possible outcomes of a certain event.

Vector A quantity which has both magnitude and direction.

Whole Numbers Members of the set of numbers $\{0, 1, 2, 3, \ldots\}$.

Zeros Zeros of a polynomial are the values of the variable which would make the value of the polynomial equal to zero.

Answers

Chapter 1

Page 1 1. 3 2. a. iv b. v, ii, vi c. vii d. vi e. ii f. viii g. i h. iii 3. a. 498 b. 100 4. a. 6 b. 180 5. 2 roasts, 6 steaks 6. a. $n-1$ b. $n+1$ 7. Answer may vary. 8. Answer may vary.

Page 2 1. a. 2105 b. 32 c. 5014 d. 2330 e. 1818 f. 1275 g. 121 h. 132 2. a. 125 b. 2318 c. 3 435 195 d. 103 e. 0 f. 520 g. 0 3. 10 400 000 4. 0 5. a. 1040 b. 208 6. $n+1$

Page 3 1. a. -28 b. -7 c. -21 d. -10 e. -52 f. -15 g. -33 h. -62 i. -21 j. -87 2. a. -160 b. 114 c. 2 d. -198 e. -31 f. -47 g. -1 h. 16 3. a. 37°C b. 40°C c. 17°C d. 67°C 4. a. 28°C b. 14°C/min 5. 729, 15 625, Answers may vary. 6. 60 m **BRAINTICKLER** 1184, 1210

Pages 4-5 1. a. 30 b. 315 c. 408 d. 72 2. a. $-\frac{1}{2}$ b. $\frac{1}{3}$ c. $-\frac{1}{9}$ d. $\frac{1}{4}$ e. $-\frac{1}{6}$ f. $-\frac{1}{3}$ 3. a. 1 b. $\frac{1}{4}$ c. $-\frac{6}{5}$ d. $-\frac{1}{6}$ e. $\frac{7}{6}$ f. $\frac{25}{8}$ g. $-\frac{9}{4}$ h. $-\frac{73}{15}$ 4. a. $\frac{4}{12}$ b. $\frac{3}{12}$ c. $\frac{10}{12}$ 5. a. $4\frac{5}{12}$ b. 6 c. $6\frac{3}{4}$ 6. $1\frac{11}{12}$ h 7. $\frac{9}{20}$ 8. a. $\frac{2}{5}$ b. $\frac{1}{2}$ c. $-\frac{1}{12}$ d. $\frac{10}{99}$ e. $\frac{7}{24}$ f. $-\frac{1}{15}$ 9. a. $\frac{25}{32}$ b. $-\frac{30}{11}$ c. $\frac{2}{3}$ d. -1085 e. -82 f. 6 10. a. $-\frac{1}{5}$ b. $\frac{2}{3}$ c. $\frac{9}{19}$ d. $-\frac{5}{34}$ e. $-\frac{4}{3}$ f. $\frac{1}{5}$ 11. $\frac{200}{3}$ 12. a. $\frac{3}{25}$ b. $\frac{25}{3}$ c. -15 d. 0 e. $\frac{1}{12}$ f. $-\frac{2}{3}$ g. $-\frac{5}{23}$ h. $-\frac{47}{57}$ i. $-\frac{5}{11}$ j. -26 k. $\frac{75}{32}$

Pages 6-7 1. So that the answer is universal. 2. a. 28 b. 9 c. 4 d. 1 e. 20 f. 15 g. 3 h. 3 i. 20 j. 27 k. 47 l. 0 3. a. -6 b. -12 c. 0 d. 2 e. -1 f. 14 g. -7 h. 14 i. 4 j. -12 4. a. -6 b. -1 c. $-\frac{1}{4}$ d. 1 e. 0 f. $4\frac{1}{5}$ g. -1 h. $\frac{4}{27}$ 5. -15 m 6. e 7. 8 ha 8. a. -1 b. -40 c. -6 d. 19 e. -11 f. $\frac{1}{2}$ g. 6 h. 0 i. 72 j. 57 9. a. 0 b. $\frac{21}{32}$ c. 4 d. 4 e. -80 10. e 11. a. $\frac{39}{14}$ b. $8\frac{1}{25}$ c. -3 d. 2 e. $\frac{25}{27}$ 12. Answer will vary. **BRAINTICKLER** Pick one of the guards. Ask, "If I was to ask your friend if (one of the roads) is the way home, what would he say?" If Yes, do not take the road; if No, take the road.

Page 8 1. a. -7 b. 8 c. $\frac{1}{2}$ d. -420 e. $\frac{121}{21}$ f. $\frac{5}{17}$ 2. a. 125 b. 115 c. 150 d. 100 e. 0 f. 85, The student gets 0. 3. a. $2\frac{1}{10}$ b. $-1\frac{11}{14}$ c. $-\frac{9}{10}$ d. $6\frac{1}{4}$ e. $-9\frac{3}{10}$ f. $3\frac{15}{56}$ 4. $\frac{x^2+3}{y+1}$ 5. $v = 73.5$ m/s, $d = 275.625$ m 6. a. 122.376 b. 128.69 c. 142.49 d. 169.71 e. 189.74 f. 232.38

Page 9 1. a. 17 b. 3 c. 543 d. 007 e. 97 f. 07 2. a. $9.\overline{7}$ b. $36.0\overline{35}$ c. $-271.\overline{876}$ 3. Decimal: $0.\overline{63}$, $0.\overline{07}$, $14.\overline{142\,857}$, $0.291\overline{6}$, $0.0\overline{36}$ Period: 63, 07, 142 857, 6, 036, Length of Period: 2, 2, 6, 1, 3 4. Accuracy: 0.242 647 1, 0.242 774 6, 0.204 023, 0.410 256 4 5. a. 42 g for \$1.75 b. 25 L for \$12.48 c. 172 kg for \$21.07 d. 37.9 mL for \$0.72 e. 350 mg for \$16.77 6. 0.052 631 578 947 368 421

Pages 10-11 1. a. $\frac{2}{5}$ b. $\frac{13}{25}$ c. $2\frac{1}{4}$ d. $-\frac{1}{500}$ e. $\frac{5}{8}$ f. $\frac{9}{200}$ 2. a. $6.\overline{6}, 66.\overline{6}, 666.\overline{6}$ b. $25.\overline{3}, 253.\overline{3}, 2533.\overline{3}$ c. $-87.\overline{2}, -872.\overline{2}, -8722.\overline{2}$ d. $9.\overline{9}, 99.\overline{9}, 999.\overline{9}$ e. $0.\overline{4}, 4.\overline{4}, 44.\overline{4}$ f. $-121.\overline{21}, -1212.\overline{12}, -12\,121.\overline{21}$ g. $-137.\overline{87}, -1378.\overline{78}, -13\,787.\overline{87}$ h. $-10.\overline{01}, -100.\overline{1}, -1001.\overline{1}$ i. $3.12\overline{45}, 31.2\overline{45}, 312.\overline{45}$ 3. a. $9x$ b. $99x$ c. $900x$ 4. a. $\frac{1}{9}$ b. $\frac{1}{3}$ c. $\frac{5}{9}$ d. $\frac{7}{9}$ e. $1\frac{2}{3}$ f. $4\frac{2}{9}$ 5. $\frac{7}{9}$ 6. $\frac{59}{90}$ 7. $\frac{5}{18}$ 8. a. $\frac{7}{33}$ b. $\frac{5}{11}$ c. $\frac{127}{999}$ d. $\frac{131}{99}$ e. $-7\frac{61}{99}$ f. $\frac{14}{33}$ g. $-4\frac{91}{99}$ h. $3\frac{287}{450}$ i. $\frac{863}{900}$ j. $\frac{982}{2475}$ k. $\frac{8227}{9990}$ l. $\frac{17\,264}{24\,975}$ 9. 6 10. 5 11. $36\frac{2}{3}$ m 12. Answers may vary. 13. $20\frac{20}{99}$ cm 14. $133\frac{5}{7}$ m 15. 400 cm 16. $73\frac{1}{3}$ 17. 20 000 18. $6\frac{3}{4}$ mm 19. a. 0.037 037 037 b. yes c. Answers may vary.

Pages 12-13 1. Natural Numbers' Column: y, y, n, n, y, y, n, n, y, y, n, n, n, n, n, n, n, y Whole Numbers' Column: y, y, n, n, y, y, n, n, y, y, n, n, y, y, n, n, n, n, y Integers' Column: y, y, y, n, y, y, n, n, y, y, n, n, y, y, y, y, n, y Rationals' Column: y, y, y, y, n, n, y, n, n, y, y, y, y, y, y, y, y, y, y 2. Answers will vary. 3. Answers will vary. 4. a. 60 b. 1900 c. 36.7, distributive property 5. a. commutative b. identity c. identity d. inverse e. commutative f. identity g. density h. inverse i. density j. commutative k. distributive 6. a. not closed b. not closed c. closed d. closed 7. a. no b. no

c. no **d.** yes **8.** Answers may vary. **9. a.** $-\dfrac{7}{12}$ **b.** $\dfrac{9}{5}$
c. $\dfrac{5}{4}$ **d.** $\dfrac{100}{1027}$ **e.** $-\dfrac{5}{19}$ **f.** -1 **10. a.** $n+1$ **b.** $n-1$
c. $n+3$ **d.** $n+2$ **e.** $n+2$ **f.** n^2+n **g.** $2n+1$ or
$n+(n+1)$ **h.** $\dfrac{2n+1}{2}$ or $\dfrac{n+(n+1)}{2}$ **11. a.** $0.\overline{8}$ **b.** $3.\overline{9}$
12. a. $4.\overline{3}$ **b.** $-0.\overline{8}$ **13. a.** $1.\overline{3}$ **b.** $0.1\overline{3}$ **c.** $0.8\overline{13}$
d. $0.6\overline{813}$ **e.** $0.0\overline{81}$ **f.** $0.0\overline{37}$ **14. a.** $5n+5$ **b.** $-3x-9$
c. n^2+4n **d.** $5x$ **e.** $8x+8y$ **f.** $-5x^3-5x^2-35x$
15. Answers may vary. **16. a.** $17+19=36$,
$29+19=48$ **b.** yes **c.** yes

Pages 14-15 **1. a.** rational **b.** irrational **c.** rational
d. rational **e.** irrational **f.** irrational **g.** rational
h. rational **i.** irrational **j.** irrational **k.** irrational
l. irrational **2. a.** $\sqrt{3}$ **b.** 2 **c.** 25 **d.** $\sqrt{13}$ **3.** product
of roots, $\dfrac{a}{b}$, by substitution, $\dfrac{a^2}{b^2}$, a is a multiple of 3,
$9n^2=3b^2$, b^2, b is a multiple of 3, contradiction, of a
rational, irrational **4.** See answers. **5.** See answers.
6. Answers may vary. **7.** Answers may vary.
8. Answers may vary. **9.** $3\sqrt{2}$ m **10. a.** yes **b.** yes
c. yes **d.** no **11.** $4\sqrt{10}$ m or 12.65 m **12.** $8\sqrt{2}$ m or
11.3 m **13.** 17.9 km **14.** $\sqrt{13}$ or 3.6 **15.** yes
16. 3.605 551 3... **a.** irrational **b.** irrational **c.** No,
they are independent sets.

Page 16 **1.** Answers may vary. **2. a.** F **b.** T **c.** T
d. F **e.** F **f.** F **g.** F **h.** T **i.** F **j.** T **k.** T **l.** F
3. Answers may vary. **4. a.** T **b.** F **c.** T **d.** T **e.** F
f. F **g.** F **h.** T **i.** T **j.** T

Page 17 **1. a.** $x=15$ **b.** $x=21$ **c.** $x=7$ **d.** $x=64$
e. $x=2$ **f.** $x=-8$ **g.** $x=12$ **h.** $x=0$ **2. a.** $x=7$
b. $x=4$ **c.** $x=5$ **d.** $x=3$ **e.** $x=\dfrac{1}{4}$ **f.** $x=\dfrac{1}{2}$
g. $x=\dfrac{5}{11}$ **h.** $x=3$ **i.** $x=0$ **j.** $x=5$ **k.** $x=\dfrac{1}{2}$
l. $x=-4$ **m.** $x=-4$ **n.** $x=0$ **o.** $x=-5$ **p.** $x=-\dfrac{5}{2}$
q. $x=1$ **r.** $x=1.99$ **3. a.** $x=9$ **b.** $x=-11$ **c.** $x=48$
d. $x=18.5$ **e.** $x=1.2$ **f.** $x=0.36$ **g.** $x=\dfrac{7}{3}$ **h.** $x=9.3$
4. a. $x=4$ **b.** $x=1$ **c.** $x=21$ **d.** $x=2$ **e.** $x=25.2$
f. $x=30$ **g.** $x=6$ **h.** $x=15\dfrac{2}{9}$ **5. a.** equals

b. subtracted, equals, equals **c.** If equals are
multiplied by equals, the products are equal. **d.** If
equals are divided by equals, the quotients are
equals.

Page 18 **1.** 11 **2.** Best = 22, Banting = 29
3. $L=18$, $W=8$ **4.** 550 km/h **5.** 20°, 40°, 120°
6. 187, 189 **7.** $A=64$, $B=16$, $C=128$ **8.** Answers
may vary. **9.** Seminaire de Quebec 1663, King's
College 1788 **10.** 0.5 L of oil

Page 19 **1. a.** $a=x+y$ **b.** $a=t-x$ **c.** $a=\dfrac{r}{2}$

d. $a=\dfrac{y-x}{-5}$ **e.** $a=\dfrac{d}{t}$ **f.** $b=5d$ **g.** $c=\dfrac{d}{5}+2$
h. $c=mt-t$ **i.** $a=-2x$ **j.** $c=\dfrac{\pi-A}{2}$ **k.** $a=4n-m$
l. $b=\dfrac{h}{6}$ **m.** $c=\dfrac{s+r}{3}$ **n.** $a=\dfrac{-t}{3t-1}$ **o.** $b=\dfrac{3x-2\pi}{2}$
p. $a=4(x-y)$ **2.** $2a-4$, b, 36, 36, $\dfrac{4h+36}{18}$
a. $ab=36$, $a=\dfrac{36}{b}$ **b.** $(a-6)(b-3)=9$,
$a-6=\dfrac{9}{b-3}$, $a=\dfrac{6b-9}{b-3}$ **3. a.** $h=\dfrac{A}{b}$ **b.** $t=\dfrac{d}{v}$
c. $k=pv$ **d.** $R=\dfrac{F}{n}$ **e.** $I=-\dfrac{E}{R}$ **f.** $w=\dfrac{V}{lh}$ **g.** $\pi=\dfrac{C}{2r}$
h. $h=\dfrac{2A}{b}$ **i.** $a=\dfrac{F}{m}$ **j.** $t=\dfrac{i-p}{rp}$ **k.** $v=\sqrt{ar}$
l. $l=\dfrac{xYA}{F}$ **m.** $g=\dfrac{v^2}{2h}$ **n.** $H_2=\dfrac{JH_1-W}{J}$
o. $v_2=v_1-\dfrac{Q}{c}$ **p.** $f=\dfrac{uv}{u-v}$ **q.** $c=\sqrt{\dfrac{E}{m}}$ **r.** $1=\dfrac{gT^2}{4\pi^2}$
4. 2500 **5.** 2750, 4125, 6875 **6.** 32 cm

Pages 20-22 **1. a.** 0.16, $\dfrac{4}{25}$ **b.** 0.69, $\dfrac{69}{100}$ **c.** 3.2, $\dfrac{16}{5}$
d. 0.01, $\dfrac{1}{100}$ **e.** 0.005, $\dfrac{1}{200}$ **f.** 0.000 03, $\dfrac{1}{100\,000}$
2. a. 52 **b.** 130 **c.** 104 **d.** 91 **e.** 39 **f.** 156 **3. a.** 1040
b. 867 **c.** 1300 **d.** 910 **e.** 975 **f.** 1200 **4. a.** 4.3 **b.** 6.5
c. 10.9 **d.** 13 **e.** 30.4 **f.** 39.1 **5. a.** 37 **b.** 31.45 **c.** 725
d. 24 **e.** 15.4 **f.** $16.\overline{6}$ **6. a.** 3360 **b.** 60 000 **c.** 126 000
d. 232.75 **7.** 2.3793 m³ **8.** 40% **9.** 68 kg **10.** $138
11. $56 **12.** total reduced $16.56, final price $19.44
13. total reduced $460.80, final price $499.20
14. a. 48% **b.** 47.75% **c.** 34.75% **d.** 66% **e.** 39.55%
15. $604.80 **16.** 64.3% **17.** $2.16 **18. a.** $130
b. 50% **19. a.** $725 **b.** 20% **20. a.** $36, $336, 10.7%
b. 1.275, 14.025, 9.1% **c.** 6.80, 49.30, 13.8%
d. 16.96, 42.40, 40% **e.** 0.26, 5.46, 4.76% **f.** 5.43,
20.93, 26% **21.** $9846 **22. a.** 121 300 **b.** $100 000
23. a. 24.4% **b.** 31.5% **c.** 20% **24.** col. 4: 119.10,
0.12, 0.5, 7.15, 126.25; col. 5: 126.25, 0.12, 0.5, 7.57,
133.82; col. 6: 133.82, 0.12, 0.5, 8.03, 141.85
25. a. $14 079.97 **b.** 52 192.60 **c.** 4 500 191.43

Page 23 **1. a.** $x=6$ **b.** $x=46$ **c.** $x=27\dfrac{3}{7}$ **d.** $x=10$
e. $m=13$ **f.** $r=-\dfrac{1}{15}$ **g.** $x=\dfrac{8}{5}$ **2. a.** 60 **b.** $\dfrac{1}{5n}$
c. 33.5 **d.** 25 **e.** $3\dfrac{1}{3}$ **3. a.** $w=\dfrac{Al_1w_1}{A_1l}$ **b.** $C_1=\dfrac{Cr_1}{r}$
c. $r=\dfrac{er_1}{(E-e)}$ **d.** $R=\dfrac{sC-rT}{sT}$ **4.** 30, 20 **5.** 135, 225
6. 145.6 **7.** The dealer lost 4 per cent. **8.** $\dfrac{45}{63}$
9. 513 918 km²

Pages 24-25 **1. a.** -1.414, -1.3, -1, $-\dfrac{1}{2}$, $\sqrt{2}$, $4\dfrac{3}{7}$
b. $\dfrac{7}{13}$, $\dfrac{5}{9}$, $\dfrac{8}{11}$, $\dfrac{11}{15}$, $\dfrac{5}{6}$, $\dfrac{6}{7}$, $\dfrac{7}{8}$ **c.** 0.45, $0.45\overline{3}$, 0.453,
0.4534, 0.453 453, 0.453 453 **d.** 0.010,

0.010 010 001..., 0.010 101 101 110...,
0.011 011 101 111..., 0.101 101 110... **e.** 0.58,
0.581 581 158 111, 0.581 81, 0.581 811 811 181

2. a. $>$ **b.** $>$ **c.** $<$ **3. a.** {..., 5, 6, 7} **b.** {..., 1, 2, 3, 4}
c. {−1, 0, 1, 2, ...} **d.** {0, 1, 2, 3, ...} **e.** {..., −6, −5, −4}
f. {..., −4, −3, −2} **4. a.** {5, 6, 7, ...} **b.** {..., −6, −5, −4} **c.** {..., −4, −3, −2} **d.** {−2, −1, 0, ...}

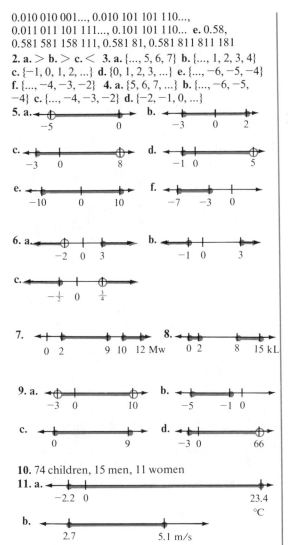

5. a. −5, 0 **b.** −3, 0, 2
c. −3, 0, 8 **d.** −1, 0, 5
e. −10, 0, 10 **f.** −7, −3, 0

6. a. −2, 0, 3 **b.** −1, 0, 3
c. $-\frac{1}{2}$, 0, $\frac{3}{4}$

7. 0 2, 9 10 12 Mw **8.** 0 2, 8, 15 kL

9. a. −3, 0, 10 **b.** −5, −1, 0
c. 0, 9 **d.** −3 0, 66

10. 74 children, 15 men, 11 women
11. a. −2.2, 0, 23.4 °C
b. 2.7, 5.1 m/s

13. a. $-8 \leq x \leq 2$ **b.** $9 < x < 12$ **c.** $2 \leq x \leq 5$
d. $-3 \leq x \leq 7$ **e.** $2 < x \leq 4$ **f.** $2 < x \leq 5$
g. $-6 < x < 5$ **h.** $2 < x \leq 5$ **i.** $x \leq 2$ **j.** $x > 2$

Page 26 **1.** brackets, exponents, left to right multiplication and division, left to right addition and subtraction **2. a.** $\wedge$ **b.** $+$ **c.** $*$ **d.** $/$ **3. a.** 45, 54, 686 **b.** Answers may vary. **c.** Answers may vary. **4.** reset memory **5.** outputs answer **6.** documentation **7.** $(6 + 12) * 4$

Page 27 **1. a.** 588 **b.** 39 **c.** 0 **d.** 289 **e.** 1100 **2. a.** −11 **b.** −36 **c.** −18 **d.** −4 **3.** Mon. 3174, Tues. 6038.88, Wed. 6598.47, Thurs. 7120.80, Fri. 3918.51, Total $26 850.66 **4.** −241 831 **5.** −22

6. a. −15 **b.** 1 **c.** 0 **d.** $\frac{-5}{2}$ **7.** 19.5 km **8. a.** Larry 1.80, Curly 1.35, Moe 2.70 **b.** no **9. a.** $4620 **b.** $14 687.50 **c.** $2019.23 **10. a.** $\frac{4}{9}$ **b.** $\frac{27}{100}$ **c.** $\frac{82}{99}$ **d.** $\frac{323}{900}$ **11.** $\frac{7}{9}$ **12.** 8.77% **13. a.** $96 536.78 **b.** $101 201.76 **14.** 11.7 m

Page 28 **1.** 26 **2.** $3319.50 **3. a.** 7 **b.** −143 **c.** 5 **d.** −53 **4.** −37 **5. a.** $\frac{34}{77}$ **b.** $\frac{-275}{16}$ **c.** $\frac{-27}{19}$ **6.** $-\frac{6}{13}$
7. a. 21 **b.** $-\frac{1}{10}$ **8.** $0.0\overline{17}$ **9.** 45 min **10.** $6900
11. a. $\frac{23}{99}$ **b.** $\frac{288}{495}$ **12. a.** 172.80 **b.** 18.75 **c.** 2.857 14%
13. $\frac{11}{60}$ **14.** $-8a - 8b$ **15.** −12 **16.** −6 **17.** $r = 2$
18. $\frac{48}{7}$, $\frac{36}{7}$ **19.** $a = \frac{7(\pi + c)}{5}$ **20.** 42.8% **21.** 26
22. $\sqrt{39}$ **23.** 150 332 **24.** no **25. a.** inverse **b.** closure **c.** distributive

26. −2, −1, 0, 1

27. −4, −3, −2, −1, 0, 1, 2

Chapter 2

Page 29 **1.** once **2.** hammer $10.50, nails $0.50 **3.** holes **4.** 124 **5.** 90 **6.** 1. mustard, relish, onion; 2. mustard, relish, onion; 3. nothing **7.** 9 **8.** orange, green, blue, red, white **9.** 2:1 **10.** 31 **11.** 9

Pages 30-31 **2.** made $8000 **3.** 11 turtles, 7 geese **4.** 14 by 4 **5.** 286 **6.** Cut out a 4×7 and a 2×7 piece. **7.** 60 **8.** 5 min **9.** 4722 or 9033 **10.** 36 **11.** 0, 1, 2, 3, 4 **12.** 36

Pages 32-33 **2.** number of years between perihelions **3.** crane operator's regular wage **4.** how large is a batch of pickles **5.** how big is the bucket **6.** Excess info: # of jumps and spectators, 45 s, 320 km/h; height of free fall 2.33 km **7.** Excess info: # of employees, weekly payroll, cost of skis; 44% **8.** $1373.69 **9.** indeterminate **10.** insolvable **11.** 7.5 L **12.** 140 km icy roads; 280 km dry roads

Pages 34-35 **1.** no **2. a.** 666 **b.** 0 **3.** 256 **4.** 89 cm **5.** 1980 m **6.** 465 **7. a.** 16 777 216 **b.** $355 505.38 **c.** 333.52 km **8.** Answers may vary. **9.** $4960 **10.** Answers may vary. **11.** 12 **12.** $187 **13.** 32 768 **14.** 101 123... **15.** 360°

Pages 36-37 **2.** McKay **3.** 14 **4.** 72 **5.** shovel is 5 pears; hatchet is 4 pears; fishing rod is 2 pears **6.** 8
7. Miss Rightside
(doctor)

Mr. Leftbank   Miss Downey
(actor)   (lawyer)

Mr. Uptown
(artist)

8. 200

Pages 38-39 **2. a.** 0.5 L left **b.** yes **3.** Wanetta $\frac{1}{2}$, Sam $\frac{1}{4}$, Dino $\frac{1}{12}$, Charlie $\frac{1}{6}$ **4.** 1st, $1289.25
5. a. 445.50 **b.** 11.1% **6. a.** yes **b.** 1.2 × 1.2
7. a. 811.25 km **b.** 1875 L **8.** $5 + \sqrt{5}, 5 - \sqrt{5}$
9. Example: 22 + 8 **10.** 93 **11.** 50 **12.** 3 **13.** 155 pencils, 30 students **14.** 500 **15.** 6 L **16.** 100 kg

Pages 40-41 **1.** entrances in middle of sides **2.** 16
3.
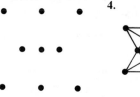
4.

5. 50 km **6.** 13 **7.** divide the perimeter by 8
8. 450 m **9. a.** 64 **b.** Answers may vary. **10.** 38
11. $(2\pi - 4)$ cm² **12.** 25π cm² **13.** 86 m
14.

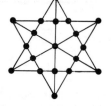

15. 255 m²

Page 42 **1.** 2 m **2. a.** 70 s **b.** 70 m, 14 m
3. a. 63.64 **b.** 38.64 **c.** 25 **d.** 8.53 **4.** $\sqrt{3} \doteq 1.75$, $\sqrt{5} \doteq 2.24$, $\sqrt{8} \doteq 2.83$ **5.** $\sqrt[3]{4} \doteq 1.6$, $\sqrt[3]{5} \doteq 1.7$, $\sqrt[3]{7} \doteq 1.9$ **6.** 12 of each

Page 43 **1.** Answers may vary. **2.** 4 004 001
3. 1240 **4.** 28.28 m **5.** 77, 90, 170 **6.** 1770
7. 36 min

Page 44 **1.** $\frac{1}{2^{12}}$ **2.** 192 **3.** $189 **4.** 250 adults, 170 students **5.** $S - 17, Q - 24, B - 34, D - 9$ **6.** 29

Page 45 **1.** added instead of subtracted
2. Example: other tracks faded **3.** 91 **4.** 60
5. Answers may vary. **6.** a cylinder cut along a side diagonal

Pages 46-47 **1.** Answers may vary. **2.** 40-car train leaves 30 cars in the siding and backs up with 10 cars. 36-car train then pushes the 30 cars out of

the way. First train goes into the siding to let other train pass. **3.** 3 **4.** Empty 5 L into 3 L twice. The overflow is 4 L. **5.** Borden, container, Victoria to Honolulu, Laurier, tanker, Vancouver to Yokohama, MacDonald, grain carrier, Prince Rupert to Bombay **6.** Check 3 against 3. If one pile of 3 is heavier, check one coin against another in this pile. If both piles of 3 are the same mass, check one coin against another in the third pile of 3. **7.** 90 hens, 10 cows **8.** Wong, Captain; Lewis, Navigator; Holm, Flight Engineer; Clarke, Attendant; Tidski, First Officer **9.** Terry
10. Answers may vary. **11.** 31 **BRAINTICKLER**
$9 \div 9 + 99$

Pages 48-49 **1.** 7 h **2.** 76 000 **3.** 17 **4.** 8; 16
5. Mai is the singer from Alpha High **6.** 259.2
7. 35 km/h **8. a.** 4096 **b.** 4^{n-1}; $\frac{4^{n+1} - 1}{3}$ **9.** 4
10. 870 **11.** 28 **12.** 40 min **13.** 35 **14.** $200
15. 14

Page 50 **1.** 20 has the user input a number; 30 does the calculations; 60 continues the loop if the request is Y **2.** 20 NUMBER TO BE ROUNDED • 30 X • 40 "ANSWER IS "; ANS • 60 AN$, 20
3. Answers may vary. **4.** 10 INPUT "NUMBER TO BE ROUNDED "; X • 20 INPUT "TO WHAT ACCURACY "; Y • 30 LET ANS = INT(X ∗ Y / 0.5) / Y • 40 PRINT ANS • 50 END

Page 51 **1.** 613 **2.** 32 **3.** 50 **4.** Alfred is Captain, Bingo is the engineer, Cedric is the cook, Donovan is the deckhand, Cedric and Donovan are brothers, Bingo is Donovan's son and Cedric's nephew **5.** 3 for $1.13 **6.** 25% **7.** 4% **8.** $7\frac{1}{2}$ min **9.** $14
10. 9 h 57 min **11.** 10 elephants and 20 storks
12. 2485 **13.** 30 × 64 **14.** **15.** 204

Page 52 **1.** understand the problem; develop a plan; carry out the plan; look back **2.** 20 **3.** 12
4. 45; 5 × 6 = 30, 3025; 6 × 7 = 42, 4225; etc. **5.** 66
6. a. $61 - 4n = 85$; $n = -6$ **b.** $25q + 5n = 650$
c. $v = \frac{d}{t}$ **7.** 9 m **8.** approx. 8.5 billion **9.** 41.35%
10. 16 pizzas, 30 hotdogs **11.** mass of strawberries in a jam jar **12.** Answers may vary. **13.** 50
14. 15 min

Chapter 3

Page 53 1. a. 5 b. −13 c. 18 d. −4 e. 35 f. 10
g. 31 h. 3 i. 35 j. 9 k. 16 l. 41 m. −15 2. a. 10
b. 24 c. 11 d. 12 3. a. $\frac{4}{3}$ b. $\frac{3}{40}$ c. $\frac{-1}{15}$ d. $\frac{6}{7}$ e. $\frac{29}{45}$
f. $\frac{23}{40}$ g. $7\frac{9}{16}$ 4. a. 3 b. 4 c. 5 d. 2 e. −15 f. 5 g. $\frac{6}{5}$
h. 1 5. a. 18 b. 36 c. −1 d. 7 6. a. positive
b. negative

Pages 54-55 1. a. 2^{11} b. 3^{23} c. p^{15} d. m^{15} e. $24m^{12}$
f. $36x^{15}$ g. r^{4n+1} h. $y^{(a+5)}$ 2. a. 7^3 b. 5^6 c. n^2 d. q^{16}
e. $5s^6$ f. $-7r^6$ g. z^{2b} h. r^{p+2} i. $-(m+n)^3$ 3. a. 2^6
b. 5^6 c. $-a^{20}$ d. c^{20} e. $16x^{12}$ f. $-27a^{15}$ g. q^{x^2} h. s^{4s^2-1}
4. a. a^6b^9 b. x^9y^{12} c. x^4y^8 d. m^9n^3 e. $81p^8q^{24}$
f. $49x^{14}y^{10}z^2$ g. $k^{4b}m^{8b}$ h. $r^{4m^2+6m}s^{4m^2-6m}$ 5. a. $\frac{1}{16}$
b. $-\frac{27}{64}$ c. $\frac{x^{12}}{y^6}$ d. $\frac{b^4}{(b+c)^4}$ e. $\frac{125m^9}{8n^6}$ f. $\frac{-8r^{15}}{27s^9}$ g. $\frac{p^n}{q^{2n}}$
h. $\frac{m^{8n^2+4n}}{n^{12n^2-4n}}$ 6. $4a^6$ 7. $14k^7m^3$ 8. a. $6x^3y^7$ b. $35p^4q^6$
c. x^6y^5 d. $-24p^4r^4q^2$ e. $5xy^2$ f. $3a$ 9. a. x^5y^4
b. $72a^{10}b^9c^8$ c. x^{20} d. a^2b^2 e. x^9y^3 f. $k^4m^4n^8$ 10. a. 12
b. 216 c. 17 d. −343 11. a. c^{6m} b. h^{4k} c. 1 d. a^{2m+2}
e. k^{9m} f. z^{4a+b} 12. $\frac{21}{2}(a+b)^7(b+c)^7$ 13. $2p^2q$
14. $3^{33} = 3^{27} = 7\,625\,597\,484\,987$, $(3^3)^3 = 19\,683$
15. a. 2^{12} b. 3^4 c. 2^{-11} 16. $2^{-11} = \frac{1}{2^{11}}$

Pages 56-57 1. a. $\frac{1}{8}$ b. 2 c. $\frac{1}{9}$ d. $-\frac{1}{9}$ e. $\frac{1}{9}$ f. 1
g. −1 h. 1 i. 27 j. −25 k. 10 l. 2500 2. a. $\frac{1}{x^2}$ b. y^3
c. $\frac{3}{y^4}$ d. $\frac{n^4}{m^2}$ e. $\frac{7b^2}{a^3}$ f. $\frac{-3}{x}$ g. $\frac{3m^2}{b^2}$ h. $\frac{b^2}{a^2}$
3. a. $\frac{2k^2p^4}{m^3n^2}$ b. m^2n^3 c. $\frac{b}{ac}$ d. $\frac{1}{9y^2}$ e. $\frac{8x^{12}}{y^9}$ f. $\frac{-1}{27a^3b^6}$
g. mn^2 h. $\frac{p^4q^2}{m^2}$ 4. a. $\frac{1}{m^7}$ b. $\frac{n}{m^6}$ c. x^2 d. $6p^8$ e. $\frac{1}{ab^5}$
f. a^6 g. m^6 h. $\frac{-6m^2q^6}{p^5}$ 5. a. $\frac{k^{10}}{2m^7}$ b. $\frac{4}{9a}$ c. r^5 d. $\frac{m^6}{25n^4}$
e. $\frac{x^2y^2}{4}$ f. $\frac{y^6}{6u^4}$ 6. a. $\frac{7x}{4}$ b. $2y^3$ c. $\frac{w^5}{128}$ d. $\frac{r^3}{p^2q}$ e. $\frac{4b}{a^6}$
f. x^3y^{13} 7. a. $\frac{1}{4}$ b. 1 c. 4 d. $\frac{3}{2}$ e. −8 f. $-\frac{4}{3}$ g. $\frac{1}{27}$
h. $-\frac{3}{4}$ 8. a. x^{3k} b. x^{r-1} c. p^{5r} d. q^{r+11} e. p^{2a^2+6a} f. t^4
9. 2

Page 58 1. a. 7.86×10^2 b. 6.74×10^7 c. 2.3×10
d. 5.462×10^{11} e. 7.9×10^0 f. 2.003×10^{10}
g. 8.6×10^3 h. 8.0225×10^{13} i. 5.67×10^{-2}
j. 2.3×10^{-10} k. 3.0×10^{-5} l. 7×10^{-13} m. 3.4×10^4
n. 2.15×10^{-3} o. 1.006×10^0 p. 1×10^{-1}
2. a. 53 000 000 b. 258 000 000 000 000
c. 0.000 073 81 d. 0.000 000 000 09 e. 34.67 f. 4.92

g. 0.473 92 h. 387.4567
i. 0.000 000 000 000 000 000 000 071 j. 0.006
k. 0.005 67 l. 0.000 000 3 3. a. 3.1×10^{-17},
0.000 000 000 000 000 031 b. 4.78×10^9,
4 780 000 000 c. 4.16×10^{13}, 41 600 000 000 000
d. 2.4×10^{-31},
0.000 000 000 000 000 000 000 000 000 24
4. a. 5.4, 15 b. 7.61, 09 c. 3.7, −05 d. 6.98, −53
5. 3^{50}

Page 59 1. a. 3.2×10^{17} b. 1.12×10^{10}
c. 1.32×10^{-9} d. 1×10^{17} e. 2×10^{-6} f. 5×10^{10}
2. a. 1.5 b. 2×10^{-11} c. 5×10^{-2} d. 2×10^{10}
e. 2×10^6 f. 2.0689×10^{10} 4. $3^3 - 3$
5. a. 1.99×10^{-23} b. 4.8×10^8 c. 1.97×10^4
d. 5.56×10^2 e. 4.32×10^7

Pages 60-61 1. a. 3 b. 7 c. 10 d. 12 e. 12 f. 14
2. a. 12 b. 16 c. 15 d. 6.32 e. 8.37 f. 31.62 g. 0.2
h. 0.095 i. 0.007 3. a. $2\sqrt{2}$ b. $3\sqrt{2}$ c. $4\sqrt{2}$
d. $5\sqrt{3}$ e. $4\sqrt{6}$ f. $12\sqrt{2}$ 4. a. $x\sqrt{2}$ b. $2x^2\sqrt{3y}$
c. $3ab\sqrt{3b}$ d. $m^2n\sqrt{mn}$ e. $3k^3\sqrt{7}$ f. $7a^4\sqrt{3a}$
g. $15x\sqrt{x}$ h. $4x^2\sqrt{11}$ i. $8a^3b^4\sqrt{3a}$ j. $7k^2m^5\sqrt{m}$
k. $2ab\sqrt{11b}$ l. $r^6s^6\sqrt{7s}$ 5. a. $\sqrt{12}$ b. $\sqrt{45}$ c. $\sqrt{294}$
d. $\sqrt{1008}$ e. $\sqrt{275}$ f. $\sqrt{288}$ g. $\sqrt{216}$ h. $\sqrt{224}$
i. $\sqrt{2a^2}$ 6. a. $\sqrt{3a^2b^4}$ b. $\sqrt{50x^3y^2}$ c. $\sqrt{12c^3}$ d. $\sqrt{8}$
e. $\sqrt{\frac{125}{9}}$ f. $\sqrt{\frac{9}{7}}$ g. $\sqrt{\frac{3x^3}{2}}$ h. $\sqrt{\frac{2a^3}{3b}}$
i. $\sqrt{50r^7s^4}$ 7. a. $4\sqrt{2}$ b. $6\sqrt{3}$ c. $30\sqrt{2}$ d. $10\sqrt{2}$
e. $16\sqrt{3}$ f. $15\sqrt{3}$ g. $12\sqrt{2}$ h. $49\sqrt{2}$ i. $9\sqrt{5}$ 9. a. 5
b. 3 c. $2\sqrt[3]{5}$ d. $2\sqrt[4]{2}$ e. $3\sqrt[3]{2}$ f. $2\sqrt[4]{7}$ g. $4\sqrt[3]{5}$
h. $5\sqrt[4]{2}$ i. $4x\sqrt[3]{5y}$ 10. no real root for a negative
number 11. $15\sqrt{2}$ cm 12. $2\sqrt[3]{175}$ m or 11.19 m
13. $10\sqrt{15}$ or 38.73 cm³ 14. 90 cm³ 15. If index is
even, then x must be positive; if index is odd, then x
can be negative. 16. a. 14, 30, 54 b. 22, 70, 150
c. $4n + 2$, $2n^2 + 4n$, $6n^2$

Pages 62-63 1. a. $8\sqrt{7}$ b. $-3\sqrt{11}$ c. $38\sqrt{3}$
d. $5\sqrt{6}$ e. $-2\sqrt{10}$ f. $109\sqrt{15}$ g. $5\sqrt[3]{2}$ h. $5\sqrt[4]{6}$
2. a. $\sqrt{3}$ b. $6\sqrt{11}$ c. 0 d. $-8\sqrt{6} + 2\sqrt{7}$
e. $4\sqrt{2} + 15\sqrt{5}$ f. $2\sqrt{13} - 7\sqrt{14} + 3\sqrt{15}$
3. a. $2\sqrt{10}$ b. $8\sqrt{2}$ c. $5\sqrt{7}$ d. $\sqrt{11}$ e. $3\sqrt{5}$
f. $-2\sqrt{3}$ 4. a. $13\sqrt{10}$ b. $7\sqrt{2}$ c. $-3\sqrt{2}$ d. $15\sqrt{3}$
e. $-8\sqrt{7}$ f. $-3\sqrt{6}$ g. 0 h. $43\sqrt{13}$ 5. $9\sqrt{5}$
6. a. $14\sqrt{7} - 14\sqrt{2}$ b. $18\sqrt{3} - 14\sqrt{5}$
c. $17\sqrt{7} - 47\sqrt{2}$ d. $30\sqrt{5} - 41\sqrt{3}$
e. $6\sqrt{7} + 11\sqrt{11}$ 7. a. $9\sqrt{5}$ b. 20.1 8. a. $-2\sqrt{6x}$
b. $\sqrt{7d} + 10\sqrt{5d}$ c. $-3x\sqrt{x} + y\sqrt{y}$ d. $8a\sqrt{6}$
e. $5x\sqrt{5}$ 9. a. $\frac{13\sqrt{6}}{20}$ b. $\frac{13\sqrt{7}}{7}$ c. $4\sqrt{2}$ d. $\frac{\sqrt{6}}{2}$
e. $10\sqrt{2} - 10\sqrt{6}$ 10. $2\sqrt{17} + 2\sqrt{5}$, save 0.72 km
11. $\frac{2225}{4}\pi$ m²

Pages 64-65   **1. a.** $\sqrt{21}$ **b.** $\sqrt{30}$ **c.** $\sqrt{143}$ **d.** $\sqrt{30}$ **e.** $\sqrt{102}$ **f.** $\sqrt{42}$ **2. a.** $6\sqrt{2}$ **b.** $4\sqrt{6}$ **c.** $3\sqrt{5}$ **d.** $7\sqrt{3}$ **e.** $10\sqrt{2}$ **f.** 11 **3. a.** $15\sqrt{10}$ **b.** $-15\sqrt{42}$ **c.** $28\sqrt{51}$ **d.** $105\sqrt{2}$ **e.** 120 **f.** -24 **4. a.** $2\sqrt{13}\,\text{km}^2$ **b.** $52\,\text{km}^2$ **5. a.** $\sqrt{10}+\sqrt{14}$ **b.** $\sqrt{21}+13\sqrt{7}$ **c.** $2\sqrt{15}-4\sqrt{10}$ **d.** $2\sqrt{39}-\sqrt{13}$ **e.** $18\sqrt{2}+30\sqrt{6}$ **f.** $45\sqrt{5}-6\sqrt{3}$ **6. a.** $\sqrt{6}+6\sqrt{3}-5\sqrt{2}-30$ **b.** $-1-\sqrt{5}$ **c.** $36-16\sqrt{11}$ **d.** $\sqrt{15}+\sqrt{35}-\sqrt{6}-\sqrt{14}$ **e.** $-34-2\sqrt{2}$ **7.** $2\sqrt{6}$ **8. a.** -1 **b.** 3 **c.** -1 **d.** 37 **e.** 16 **f.** 8 **9. a.** $\sqrt{5}-1$ **b.** $\sqrt{3}+\sqrt{6}$ **c.** $2\sqrt{7}+8$ **d.** $5\sqrt{2}-3\sqrt{7}$ **10.** $A=3+\sqrt{6}=5.45$, $P=4\sqrt{3}+8\sqrt{2}=18.2$ **11. a.** $3+2\sqrt{2}$ **b.** $14-6\sqrt{5}$ **c.** $56+12\sqrt{3}$ **d.** $162-60\sqrt{2}$ **e.** $16+8\sqrt{3}$ **f.** $16-2\sqrt{55}$ **g.** $14+6\sqrt{2}-6\sqrt{3}-2\sqrt{6}$ **h.** $17+2\sqrt{10}+4\sqrt{5}+10\sqrt{2}$ **i.** $25-12\sqrt{3}+6\sqrt{2}-2\sqrt{6}$ **12. a.** $24\sqrt{3}$ **b.** $7+5\sqrt{2}$ **c.** $38-17\sqrt{5}$ **d.** $43\sqrt{7}-66\sqrt{3}$ **13.** $2\sqrt{3}$ **14.** $\sqrt{2}+1$

Page 66   **1. a.** 3 **b.** 4 **c.** 5 **2. a.** $\sqrt{5}$ **b.** $\sqrt{2}$ **c.** 3 **d.** 2 **e.** $5\sqrt{5}$ **f.** $7\sqrt{2}$ **g.** $6\sqrt{6}$ **h.** $2\sqrt{5}$ **i.** $-\dfrac{4\sqrt{3}}{3}$ **3. a.** $\dfrac{\sqrt{3}}{3}$ **b.** $\dfrac{5\sqrt{7}}{7}$ **c.** $3\sqrt{2}$ **d.** $2\sqrt{7}$ **e.** $\dfrac{\sqrt{10}}{4}$ **f.** $\dfrac{4\sqrt{15}}{5}$ **g.** $\sqrt{5}$ **h.** $2\sqrt{3}$ **i.** $\dfrac{5\sqrt{6}}{4}$ **4.**

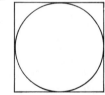

area of base $\sqrt[3]{25}$ **5.** 6 cm   **6.** $\sqrt[3]{5}$ m, **7. a.** $\dfrac{9\sqrt{2}+4\sqrt{3}}{6}$ **b.** $\dfrac{2\sqrt{15}+15}{30}$ **8. a.** $\dfrac{3+2\sqrt{3}}{3}$ **b.** $\dfrac{\sqrt{10}-2}{2}$ **c.** $5\sqrt{2}-\sqrt{10}$

Page 67   **1. a.** -2 **b.** 13 **c.** 31 **d.** -19 **2. a.** $-1+\sqrt{2}$ **b.** $\dfrac{-12-4\sqrt{2}}{7}$ **c.** $10-5\sqrt{3}$ **d.** $3-3\sqrt{3}$ **e.** $\dfrac{45-15\sqrt{7}}{2}$ **f.** $\dfrac{-\sqrt{5}-1}{2}$ **3. a.** $-5\sqrt{3}-9$ **b.** $15-10\sqrt{2}$ **c.** $\dfrac{25\sqrt{7}+5\sqrt{77}}{14}$ **d.** $\dfrac{40-12\sqrt{5}}{11}$ **e.** $\dfrac{24-4\sqrt{15}}{7}$ **f.** $\dfrac{4+8\sqrt{10}}{-39}$ **4.** $\dfrac{14\sqrt{6}+21\sqrt{2}}{6}$ **5. a.** $-\sqrt{2}-\sqrt{3}$ **b.** $\dfrac{3-\sqrt{6}}{5}$ **6. a.** $\dfrac{-5-3\sqrt{3}}{2}$ **b.** $\dfrac{-5-7\sqrt{5}}{11}$ **c.** $\dfrac{43-10\sqrt{2}}{17}$ **7. a.** $5\sqrt{a}$ **b.** $\dfrac{-9-3\sqrt{b}}{18-2b}$ **c.** $\dfrac{\sqrt{x}+2x}{1-4x}$

Pages 68-69   **1. a.** $(\sqrt[3]{2})^1,\ \sqrt[3]{2^1}$ **b.** $(\sqrt[3]{5})^2,\ \sqrt[3]{5^2}$ **c.** $(\sqrt{4})^1,\ \sqrt{4^1}$ **d.** $\dfrac{1}{\sqrt[4]{6^3}},\ \dfrac{1}{(\sqrt[4]{6})^3}$ **e.** $\sqrt[7]{8^4},\ (\sqrt[7]{8})^4$ **f.** $\dfrac{1}{\sqrt{4^5}},\ \dfrac{1}{(\sqrt{4})^5}$ **g.** $\sqrt[5]{x^3},\ (\sqrt[5]{x})^3$ **h.** $\dfrac{1}{\sqrt[3]{a^4}},\ \dfrac{1}{(\sqrt[3]{a})^4}$ **i.** $\sqrt[8]{y^3},\ (\sqrt[8]{y})^3$ **2. a.** $14^{\frac12}$ **b.** $4^{\frac32}$ **c.** $6^{\frac52}$ **d.** $7^{\frac13}$ **e.** $2^{\frac15}$ **f.** $3^{\frac14}$ **g.** $x^{\frac25}$ **h.** $c^{\frac73}$ **i.** $q^{\frac35}$ **3. a.** 4 **b.** 9 **c.** 7 **d.** $\dfrac{1}{8}$ **e.** $\dfrac{1}{7}$ **f.** 3 **g.** -2 **h.** 2 **i.** 2 **j.** -5 **k.** -3 **l.** 3 **4. a.** 16 **b.** 8 **c.** 27 **d.** 32 **e.** 4 **f.** 81 **g.** 25 **h.** 64 **i.** 32 **5. a.** $\dfrac18$ **b.** $\dfrac14$ **c.** $\dfrac19$ **d.** $\dfrac13$ **e.** $\dfrac{1}{1000}$ **f.** $\dfrac16$ **g.** $\dfrac{1}{32}$ **h.** $\dfrac{1}{25}$ **i.** $-\dfrac18$ **j.** $\dfrac{1}{1728}$ **k.** $\dfrac{1}{81}$ **l.** $-\dfrac17$ **6.** $-\dfrac23$ **7.** $-\dfrac34$ **8. a.** 8 **b.** $\dfrac19$ **c.** 27 **d.** $\dfrac43$ **e.** $\dfrac49$ **f.** $\dfrac{125}{8}$ **g.** $\dfrac{8}{27}$ **h.** $\dfrac23$ **i.** $\dfrac{625}{16}$ **9. a.** 9.7 **b.** 403.3 **c.** 44.1 **10. a.** -18 **b.** 8 **c.** $-57\dfrac34$ **d.** $-33\dfrac13$ **11. a.** $x^{\frac34}$ **b.** 1 **c.** $r^{\frac{9}{20}}$ **d.** $a^{\frac32}b^2c^{\frac12}$ **e.** $k^{\frac78}$ **f.** $\dfrac{1}{x^2y}$ **g.** $b^{\frac12}$ **h.** $\dfrac{1}{y^{\frac{5}{12}}}$ **i.** $a^{\frac45}$ **j.** $k^3m^{\frac92}n^{\frac32}$ **k.** $\dfrac{r}{s^2}$ **l.** $c^{\frac{4}{15}}$ **m.** $\dfrac{1}{k^{\frac52}m}$ **n.** $\dfrac{a^{\frac13}c^{\frac43}}{b^{\frac13}}$ **o.** a^6b^9 **p.** $a^{\frac58}$ **q.** c^3 **r.** $\dfrac{r^6s^3}{t^6}$ **s.** $\dfrac{a^6b^{15}}{c^4}$ **t.** $\dfrac{1701x^{10}}{8y^9}$ **12. a.** 2 **b.** 4 **d.** 1024 **e.** 2^n

Page 70   **1. a.** 4, 2, 2 **b.** 25 **c.** $\varnothing$ **d.** $\varnothing$ **e.** 9 **2. a.** 2, 5, $2x-3$, 14 **b.** 2 **c.** 5 **d.** 16 **e.** 7 **3. a.** $\left\{\dfrac{11}{2}\right\}$ **b.** $\{75\}$ **c.** $\{7\}$ **d.** $\{15\}$ **4.** can't have a root to a negative number **5. a.** $\{19\}$ **b.** $\{7\}$ **c.** $\{3\}$ **d.** $\{8\}$ **e.** $\{8\}$ **6. a.** 3, 2 **b.** $\varnothing$ **c.** 1 **d.** 2, 4 **e.** $\dfrac32$ **f.** $\dfrac13$, $\dfrac23$ **g.** $\dfrac54$, 1 **h.** $\dfrac43$
BRAINTICKLER One, Two, Three, Four, Five, Six, Seven, Eight, ...

Page 71   **1. b.** $5\sqrt{2}$, $5\sqrt{2}$ **c.** $10\sqrt{2}$ **d.** 4.1 **2.** train **3. a.** $10\sqrt{10}$, 31.6 **b.** 5 **c.** $5\sqrt{13}$, 18.0 **d.** $24\sqrt{3}-26$, 15.6 **4.** $90-10\sqrt{41}$, 26.0 **5. a.**

b. $4:\pi$ **6. a.** 5 **b.** $4\sqrt{10}$ **c.** 13 **7.** $\sqrt{3}-\sqrt{15}$ **8.** $\dfrac{-14\sqrt{5}-7}{19}$

Page 72   **1. a.** Reads DATA on line 50. **b.** Reads DATA on line 80. **2.** Brackets to the power N, then multiplied by T. **3.** 1612.5, 1828.1569 **4.** same **5.** Semicolon causes the value of the variables to be printed next to the literal. **6. a.** Line 50 DATA 15750, 0.1225, 5 **b.** Line 50 DATA 1000, 0.115, 5 **7. i)** Delete 20-50 and 90, change 80 to DATA 1000, 0.1225, 2, 25 **ii)** Delete 20-50 and 90, change 80 to DATA 1000, 0.1225, 4, 25

Page 73 1. a. 4^{12} b. r^{20} c. $30x^{10}$ d. m^{2x} e. $\frac{1}{5}$ f. $2x^2$
g. $8x^{12}y^{18}$ h. $\frac{4p^2}{3q^8}$ 2. a. $\frac{1}{m^5}$ b. $\frac{98}{b}$ c. $\frac{1}{y^6x^4}$ d. $\frac{2a^2b^5}{c}$
3. a. $\frac{1}{27}$ b. $-\frac{9}{16}$ c. 27 d. 62 500 4. a. 11 b. 7 c. 6
d. 21.19 e. 7.82 f. 28.50 g. 59.24 h. 2374.82 i. 19.93
5. a. 12 b. $\frac{13}{4}$ c. 1 d. $6\sqrt{3}$ 6. a. 5.6×10^4
b. 3×10^{-3} c. 7.2×10^8 d. 5.6×10^{-2} e. 4×10^{-7}
f. 3.2×10^0 g. 2×10^{11} h. 1.8×10^0 7. a. 470 000
b. 0.053 8. a. $2\sqrt{10}$ b. $9x\sqrt{2}$ c. $25\sqrt{2}$ d. $2x\sqrt[3]{7x}$
9. a. $4\sqrt{7}$ b. $18\sqrt{2}$ c. $7\sqrt{3}$ d. $3\sqrt{5}$ e. $3\sqrt{5}-\sqrt{6}$
f. $9\sqrt{7}-19\sqrt{3}$ g. $-ab\sqrt{ab}$ 10. a. $\sqrt{33}$ b. $6\sqrt{3}$
c. $-30\sqrt{3}$ d. $20\sqrt{6}$ e. $6+6\sqrt{3}$ f. $10\sqrt{21}+25\sqrt{14}$
g. $7-3\sqrt{3}$ h. $20\sqrt{6}-8\sqrt{2}-15\sqrt{3}+6$
i. $11-4\sqrt{3}+6\sqrt{2}-2\sqrt{6}$ j. $49-12\sqrt{5}$
k. $6a+\sqrt{ab}-b$ 11. 27π cm², 84.8 cm² 12. a. 3
b. $\sqrt{15}$ c. $3\sqrt{6}$ d. $4\sqrt{5}$ e. $\frac{\sqrt{14}}{2}$ f. $\frac{2\sqrt{42}}{9}$
g. $\frac{15\sqrt{2}+2\sqrt{6}}{6}$ h. $-2-\sqrt{3}$ i. $\frac{\sqrt{7}-1}{3}$ 13. a. $\sqrt[3]{5^2}$
b. $\sqrt[5]{13^3}$ c. 3 d. 2197 e. $\frac{1}{27}$ f. $\frac{1}{7}$ 14. a. $x^{\frac{5}{3}}$ b. $a^{\frac{1}{4}}$
c. $b^{\frac{1}{2}}$ d. $p^{\frac{3}{10}}$ e. a^3b^2 f. $\frac{1}{r^{\frac{1}{8}}s^{\frac{1}{3}}}$ g. $\frac{1}{m^{\frac{3}{2}}n^2}$ h. $x+x^{\frac{3}{2}}$

Page 74 1. a. 5^{11} b. m^{14} c. $30y^6$ d. t^{4x-y} e. $3y^5$
f. $\frac{2}{r^{4b}}$ g. x h. $\frac{9a^{12}b^4}{c^4}$ 2. a. $\frac{3y}{x^6}$ b. $\frac{27x}{25}$ c. a^mb^m
d. $\frac{b^4}{a^4b^6}$ 3. a. $\frac{1}{25}$ b. 2500 c. 25 d. 343 e. $\frac{9}{4}$ f. $\frac{8}{125}$
4. a. 7 b. $\frac{2}{9}$ c. 25 d. 19 5. a. 4.4 b. 1948.4 c. 30.0
6. a. 7.2×10^{-5} b. 8.3×10^5 c. 1.7×10^1
d. 8.7×10^{-2} e. 1.3×10^6 f. 1.5×10^{-7} g. 1.4×10^{-13}
h. 5×10^{-5} 7. a. 0.000 093 1 b. 1 200 000
8. a. 6.75×10^{-6} b. 1.48×10^8 9. a. $2\sqrt{14}$
b. $6ab\sqrt{3a}$ c. $12\sqrt{2}$ d. $2y\sqrt[4]{2y^2}$ 10. a. $22\sqrt{6}$
b. $-8\sqrt{3}$ c. $16\sqrt{11}$ d. $2\sqrt{6}$ e. $12\sqrt{3}-2\sqrt{2}$
f. $11\sqrt{2}-5\sqrt{7}$ g. $6xy\sqrt{xy}$ 11. a. $\sqrt{14}$ b. $5\sqrt{2}$
c. $-8\sqrt{15}$ d. $126\sqrt{2}$ e. $24-4\sqrt{3}$ f. $12\sqrt{10}-6\sqrt{3}$
12. $\frac{\pi}{3}(10\sqrt{5}+4\sqrt{30})$, 46.36 13. a. $\sqrt{10}$ b. $\sqrt{13}$
c. $2\sqrt{7}$ d. $6\sqrt{2}$ e. $\frac{\sqrt{42}}{7}$ f. $\frac{\sqrt{55}}{2}$ g. $\frac{5\sqrt{3}-6\sqrt{2}}{3}$
h. $\frac{16-17\sqrt{2}}{7}$ i. $\frac{34+8\sqrt{14}}{5}$ j. $\frac{11\sqrt{ab}+15+2ab}{25-4ab}$
14. a. $\sqrt{7}$ b. $\sqrt[5]{12^2}$ c. 27 d. 27 e. $\frac{1}{32}$ f. $\frac{1}{16}$ 15. a. 36

b. 16 c. 37 d. 12 e. $\pm2\sqrt{3}$ f. $\frac{3}{2}$

Cumulative Review Chapters 1-3

Pages 75-78 1. a. three hundred eighty-three thousand, three hundred seventy-five b. $25
2. $22 500 3. 0 4. 1 5. {18, 19, 20, 21, 22, 23, 24, 25} 6. a. 1-10, 18, 19, ... 7. 5040 8. a. 216 b. 3294
c. 0 d. 829 9. a. 121 b. 272 10. a. -37 b. -7
c. -15 d. -24 e. -98 f. 32 11. a. -80 b. -126
c. 134 d. -1 12. $y>x$ 13. a. -1100 b. 0
c. -10 m/min 14. a. 4+16+36 b. 100+9+1
c. 64+25+4 d. 144+1 15. a. -14 000 b. division
c. $2000 16. a. positive b. negative
17. a. -0.333... m/s² b. -10 m/s² c. 1 m/s²
d. 0.5875 m/s² 18. a. $\frac{4}{5}$ b. -14 c. -105 19. a. $\frac{-1}{7}$
b. $\frac{7}{6}$ c. $\frac{5}{16}$ 20. a. 2 b. $\frac{1}{11}$ c. -5 21. a. 15 b. 0
c. 55 22. a. $\frac{-5}{36}$ b. $\frac{9}{8}$ c. $\frac{-5}{8}$ 23. a. $\frac{-10}{11}$ b. $\frac{16}{3}$
24. a. 0.6 b. 0.777... c. 0.6767... d. 0.666...
e. 0.0808... f. 4.5454... g. 2.522 727 272...
h. 2.3737... 25. a. $\frac{5}{9}$ b. $\frac{2}{5}$ 26. 3.541 666... km/h
27. 0.619; 0.599; 0.642; 0.665; 0.542; 0.680 28. 2; 3;
4; 1 29. a. $\frac{31}{99}$ b. $\frac{23}{990}$ c. $\frac{113}{900}$ 30. 135% 31. 7.36
32. a. $20.63 b. $61.87 33. Boston; New York;
Toronto; Detroit; Kansas City; Cleveland;
Minnesota; Milwaukee; Texas; Oakland; Seattle;
Baltimore; Chicago; California 34. a. 25%
b. $240.00 35. a. $446.25 b. $531.25 36. a. $9
b. 50% 37. 0.049% 38. $200 39. $640
40. $849.29 41. $1378.84 42. $7310.41 43. 52%
44. a. identity b. inverse c. commutative 45. a. 9
b. -5 c. 6 d. no solution e. 16 f. 2 g. 15 46. 0.45 L
47. a. $c+b$ b. $\frac{d}{3}$ c. $\frac{x}{5}+2$ d. $\frac{t}{1-2t}$ 48. a. $\sqrt{\frac{A}{\pi}}$
b. $\frac{1}{pr}$ c. $\sqrt[3]{\frac{4}{3\pi}}$ d. $\frac{fu}{u+1}$ 49. $340 000, $204 000,
$136 000 50. a. $E<B$ b. 12 000 51. a. 13 cm
b. 11 m 52. a. 7^2+7^4 b. 1 c. $2m$ d. $\frac{1}{4^2}$ e. 9
f. $\frac{1}{x^4y^6c^2}$ 53. a. 0 b. 9 54. 5.7×10^7 55. 0.006 73
56. $4xy\sqrt{3y}$ 57. a. $2\sqrt{10}$ b. $14\sqrt{2}$ c. 12 d. $15\sqrt{6}$
58. a. $\frac{\sqrt{15}}{3}$ b. $-(1+\sqrt{2})^2$ 59. a. 8 b. 5 60. Throw
the rope across the pond leaving one end of it on
each side. The worker then drags the other end
around the pole so that both ends are on the same
side of the pond. Tie the knot. 61. 7 62. 40 min
63. 256 64. Bob +$2; Al -$7; Charles -$3;
David +$8

Chapter 4

Page 79 1. a. $2\times2\times2\times2\times2$ b. $2\times2\times5$
c. $5\times5\times5$ d. $2\times3\times x\times x$ e. $2\times2\times3\times3\times3$
f. $-(2)(2)(3)(a)(a)(b)(b)$ 2. a. 5^7 b. 6^3 c. 2^{10} d. 3^2
3. a. $5xy^2, -2xy^2, 4xy^2$ b. $pq^3, -pq^3$ 4. a. $15x-10$
b. $-4x-28$ c. $6x-15$ d. $6a-15b+3c$
5. $P=25x-y$, let $x=3, y=4$; then $P=71$
6. a. $3p-q$ b. $3a^2-5b$ c. $13m+14n$ 7. a. -22
b. 50 c. -50 d. 228 8. a. $2x^2-x-15$
b. $4x^2+4x+1$ c. $25x^2-4$ d. $4xy+5x-12y-15$
9. a. $a-4b$ b. $5p+9pq$ 10. a. $(a+b)(a-b)$
b. $(x-12)(x+1)$ c. $18x(2x-y)$ d. $(m-7)(m+5)$
e. $(u+16v)(u+v)$ f. $(2p+q)(2p-q)$

Page 80 1. a. binomial b. variables c. constant or
monomial 2. a. 23 b. -0.5 c. 1 d. $6\sqrt{2}$ e. 24 f. 4^3
g. $\frac{5}{3}$ h. $\frac{3}{2}$ i. -2 j. $\frac{4}{5}$ 3. a. $5x$ b. $-3x^2$ c. xz d. $\frac{x}{9}$
4. a. trinomial, 3 b. binomial, 0 c. not a
polynomial, radical d. monomial, 5 e. trinomial,
15 f. monomial, 0

Page 81 1. a. -3 b. 14 c. 5 d. -3 e. 32 f. 20
g. -43 h. 18 2. a. -122 b. -92 c. -32 d. 36 e. 28
f. 228 3. a. 44 b. 30 c. 2 d. 24 e. 52 f. 4
4. \$122.40 5. 55 cm² 6. 50.2 m 7. 2.2 s 8. 5
9. 720^0 10. $2n-4, 12$ 11. 10 12. 64

Pages 82-83 1. a. 2 b. 4 c. 4 d. 7 2. a. 3 b. 2 c. 1
d. 0 3. a. $5+xy^2$ b. $9-x^2y^2+4x^3$
c. $8xy-5x^2+x^3y^2$ d. $-4+5xy+x^2+2x^3$ 4. a. 3rd,
x^3+5x^2-6x+8 b. 1st, $-x+2\sqrt{3}$ c. 4th,
$8x^4-3x^3-2x^2+10$ d. Zero, 74 e. 5th, x^5+14x
f. 3rd, $4x^3-x^2+7xy$ g. 5th, $9x^4y-5x^2y^2+xy^3$
h. 6th, $6x^4+3x^3y^3-2x-10y^4$ 5. a. *not* third degree
b. binomial, $xy+4x^2y$ c. trinomial, $3y^2-5xyz+x^2$
d. trinomial, $5-2x+x^3$ e. *not* third degree
f. trinomial, $-7xy^2+2x^2y+x^3$ g. monomial, $10x^3$
h. *not* third degree 6. $\frac{k}{2}+2$ 7. $w=\frac{p+3}{5}$ 8. $2x^2$
9. 3 10. 2 12. a. 28.5 b. illicit 13. a. 5 b. 8 c. $2x^2$
d. $2y^3$ e. trinomial

Pages 84-85 1. a. $3a, 5a; 5a^2, a^2; 12ab, 7ab$ b. $8m^2$,
$4m^2; -15mn, mn$ c. $22pk, -8pk$ d. $6x^2, 9x^2; xy^2$,
$14xy^2$ 2. a. $4ab+4bc$ b. $22xy+8xz-4yz$
c. $4m^2+7mn+2n^2$ d. $9x^2y^2+6x^2y-10xy^2$
e. $-rt-7st+16rs$ f. $-11cw+cx$
g. $-3m^2+16mj-5f^2$ h. $4x^2y^2+4x^2y-xy^2$
i. $13a^2-4ab-4b^2c$ j. $7p^3+4pq^2-2q^2$
3. a. $-4x-6y$ b. $2a-5b$ c. $-3x^2-9x+15$
d. $-x^2+y^2$ e. $5x^2+2xy-16y^2$ f. $-8ab-3bc+5ac$
4. a. $-2x-5y$ b. $-3a^2+19$ c. $10ab-3bc+7ac$
d. $-x^2+15x-12$ e. $-3r^2-4rs-14s^2$
f. $-2x^2+9x-7$ g. $-4x^2-3x+14$ h. $6x^2-24x+6$
i. $-4y^2+2yz-15z^2$ j. $6x^3+9x^2-x+20$
5. $(12x+4y)$ km 6. a. $8x+2y$ b. $3a-5b$

c. $8a-2b+9c$ d. $12x^2+7x+4$ e. $-3x+6y-2z$
f. $10a^2-15a+14$ 7. a. 53 b. -38 c. 4 d. -30 e. 61
f. -12 g. 24 8. a. x^3+4x^2-x+3
b. $x^4-2x^3+3x^2-3$ c. $x^2+6x+10$ d. $5x+5$
e. $-3x^2+4x+4$ f. $4x^2-6x-10$ g. $-5x^2-x+3$
9. a. $7x^2+3$, 2nd b. $9x+14$, 1st c. $-5x^2-3x-12$,
2nd d. $x-2$, 1st e. 4, zero 10. $17x-15$
11. $6x^2+12x-2$ 12. $9a-10b$ 13. $4a+9b-13c$
14. $5x+3$ 15. 3 trials 16. $\overline{AB}=8y-3x$,
$\overline{AC}=5y-2x$ 17. Column 1: $6x, x$; Column 2: $4x$,
$7x$; Column 3: $14x$

Pages 86-87 1. a. $10xy$ b. $14ac$ c. $12a^3$ d. $12x^3y^5$
e. $6a^7b^6$ f. $-36x^8y^6$ g. $-80p^7q^{11}$ h. $60r^6s^8$
2. a. $5a^2-25ab$ b. $4mp+12np$ c. $-18x+6y$
d. $16x^2-40x$ e. $-10a+2b$ f. $12a^3+21a^2b$
g. $8a^3-2a^2+4a$ h. $-10x^3+5x^2y-5xy^2$
i. $15x+3x^2-9x^3$ j. $6x^4-8x^3+12x^2$
k. $-52p^2-24p^3+20p^4$ 3. a. $9x^4y^2$ b. $4a^2b^6$ c. $4x^3y^2$
d. $-5x^8y^2$ e. $320a^5b^5$ f. $48x^5y^3$ g. $4x^6y^{10}$ h. $-2p^8q^4$
4. a. $22x-19$ b. $19a+26b+7c$ c. $-4p-13q$
d. $38x-20y$ e. $3a-45b$ 5. a. $12a+9b+7c$
b. $52x+19y-8z$ c. $10x^2-7x+4$
d. $25a+24b-19c$ e. $-3x^2+9$ f. $21x^2+10xy+2y^2$
g. $8a^2+4ab+12b^2$ 6. a. $-2x^2+8x$
b. $40a-36b-4ab$ c. $18x^2+x$
d. $-x^3+19x^2+42x-12$ e. $-a^2-34ab-4b^2$
7. a. 33 b. 30 c. 400 d. 219 e. 250 8. a. $6x+6$
b. $4y-36x$ c. $40ab-70ac$ d. $18x+270$ e. $22x+69$
9. $12x-9y$ 10. $\pi(16a-6b)$ 11. $2l+2w+6$
12. 400 13. $10x-10y$ 14. a. $15x^3-18x^2+3x$, 3
b. $2x^6+5x^4$, 6 c. $-12x^4+8x^2$, 4

Pages 88-90 1. $2x^2+12x+18$ 2. x^2+5x+4
3. $2x^2+5x+2$ 4. $x^2-2x+3x-6; x^2+x-6$
5. a. $x^2-2x-48$ b. x^2-3x-4 c. $x^2+6x-27$
d. x^2-4x-5 e. $x^2-5x-14$ f. $x^2+7x+12$
g. x^2-6x+5 h. $x^2+6x-16$ i. $x^2+6x-40$
j. $x^2-9x+18$ 6. a. $2x^2+13x+15$ b. $5x^2-19x-4$
c. $16x^2-30x-25$ d. $2x^2+11x-6$
e. $20x^2-47x+21$ f. $9x^2-10x-16$ g. $18x^2-9x-5$
h. $2x^2+3x-27$ i. $12x^2+17x+6$ j. $6x^2+23x-4$
7. Count starts with #15. 8. a. $2x^2+xy-15y^2$
b. $x^2-6xy+8y^2$ c. $2x^2+13xy+6y^2$
d. $12a^2-7ab+b^2$ e. $10m^2-7mn-6n^2$
f. $8p^2+15pq-2q^2$ 9. a. $12x^3+28x^2-x+10$
b. $2x^3-x^2-11x-12$ c. $5t^3-9t^2-8t+12$
d. $2n^4+7n^3+n^2+20n$ e. $20x^3-7x^2y-xy^2+2y^3$
10. a. $8k^2+12k-19$ b. $7x^2-7x-3$
c. $-4x^2-x-22$ d. $3p^2-3p-16$ e. $16x^2-10x-2$
f. $-m^2-16m+14$ g. $10x^2+10x-11$
h. $2x^2+4xy-2y^2$ 11. $30x^2+30xy-8y^2$
12. $\frac{1}{2}(10x^2+3xy-18y^2)$ 13. $(2l-8)l=A$
14. $2n-15$ 15. a. i) $A+B$ ii) $A^2+2AB+B^2$
iii) $A^3+3A^2B+3AB^2+B^3$

b. $(A + B)^4 = A^4 + 4A^3B + 6A^2B^2 + 4AB^3 + B^4$
16. $(24x^2 - 13x + 65)$ **17. a.** $6x^2 - 9x - 60$
b. $-12p^2 - 22p + 4$ **c.** $5x^2 - 15x - 90$
d. $48 - 88x + 24x^2$ **e.** $-18a^2 - 21a - 6$
f. $20t^2 + 12t - 144$ **g.** $-8m^2 - 10m + 12$
h. $30 - 3x - 6x^2$ **18. a.** $7x^2 - 41x - 26$
b. $14p^2 + 7p - 39$ **c.** $14x^2 - 2x + 2$ **d.** $2x^2 - 35x + 98$
19. a. $13x^3 - 7x^2 + 44x + 12$
b. $-7n^3 - 13n^2 + 24n - 144$ **c.** $6x^3 - 9x^2 - 17x + 20$
d. $-9x^3 + 54x^2 - 30x + 12$ **20. a.** -44 **b.** 208 **c.** -55
d. 12 **e.** -25 **21.** $3a^2 + 8ab - 3b^2$
22. $10x^2 + 5xy - 38y^2$ **23.** $(25q + 10d + 5n)$ cents
24. 7.5 h **25.** $\left(\dfrac{y - x}{xy}\right)$ tanks/h **26.** 1.5 km/h
27. $(m + 5)(n + 5) = m^2 + 5m + 5n + 25$

Pages 91-92 **1.** $4a^2 + 4ab + b^2$ **2. a.** $x^2 - 6x + 9$
b. $4p^2 + 4p + 1$ **c.** $16x^2 - 40x + 25$ **d.** $9x^2 + 24x + 16$
e. $25n^2 + 20n + 4$ **f.** $36y^2 - 12y + 1$ **g.** $a^2 + 16a + 64$
h. $81x^2 - 36x + 4$ **3. a.** $4b^2 - 25$ **b.** $36x^2 - 1$
c. $x^2 - 9$ **d.** $81m^2 - 4$ **e.** $16q^2 - 25$ **f.** $9x^2 - 64$
4. a. $25x^2 - 4y^2$; 88 **b.** $16x^2 + 8xy + y^2$; 121
c. $9x^2 + 24xy + 16y^2$; 324 **d.** $x^2 - 4y^2$; -32
e. $64 - 48y + 9y^2$; 196 **f.** $1 + 10x + 25x^2$; 81
g. $4x^2 - 81$; -65 **h.** $36x^2 - 60xy + 25y^2$; 9
5. $\dfrac{1}{2}(5x + 3)^2 = \dfrac{1}{2}(25x^2 + 30x + 9)$
6. a. $3x^2 + 30x + 75$ **b.** $8x^2 - 24x + 18$
c. $3a^3 - 18a^2 + 27a$ **d.** $24t^3 + 24t^2 + 6t$ **e.** $36x^2 - 4$
f. $-2n^2 + 8$ **g.** $5k^3 - 80k$ **h.** $12p^3 - 75p$
7. a. $3x^2 - 17x + 43$ **b.** $12y^2 + 12y - 18$
c. $13a^2 - 50a + 100$ **d.** $24x^2 + 12x - 28$
8. a. $r^3 - 7r^2 + 8r + 16$ **b.** $12x^3 + 8x^2 - x - 1$
c. $2x^3 - 11x^2 - 8x + 80$ **d.** $-24a^3 + 294a$
e. $8k^3 - 3k^2 - 128k + 48$ **f.** $18u^3 + 45u^2 - 8u - 20$
9. a. $x^2 + 2xy + y^2 + 2xz + 2yz + z^2$
b. $4x^2 - 4xy + y^2 - 4xz + 2yz + z^2$
c. $a^2 + 2ab + 6ac + b^2 + 6bc + 9c^2$
d. $p^2 - 2pq + 4pr + q^2 - 4qr + 4r^2$
e. $4u^2 - 4uv - 12u + v^2 + 6v + 9$
f. $9m^2 - 6mn + n^2 + 12mp - 4np + 4p^2$
10. a. $V = \pi(4x - 5)^2(2x + 9) =$
$\pi(32x^3 + 64x^2 - 110x + 225)$
b. $S.A. = 2\pi(4x - 5)^2 + 2(2x + 9)(4x - 5)$
HISTORICAL NOTE a. 28 **b.** 126

Page 93 **1. a.** $8a$ **b.** $7xy$ **c.** $12m^2n^3$ **d.** $9rst^2$
e. $-18a^2bc^3$ **f.** $15xy^2$ **g.** $-15pq^2$ **2. a.** 60 **b.** $8x$
c. $13ab$ **d.** 54 **e.** $5x^2y$ **f.** $78a$ **g.** $45mn^2$ **h.** $12st^3$ **3.** 53
4. 501 **BRAINTICKLER a.** no **b.** yes **c.** no **d.** yes

Pages 94-95 **1. a.** $5x$ **b.** $3a$ **c.** $4x$ **d.** $2x$ **e.** $3p$ (or
$-3p$) **f.** $6a^2$ **g.** 4 **h.** $2xy$ **2. a.** $a + 4b$ **b.** $6x^2y$
3. a. $x(x - y + 6z)$ **b.** $3(2x^2 + 3x - y)$
c. $2a(5 + b - 2c)$ **d.** $5a(2a - 3b + 1)$
e. $-xy(x + 2y - z)$ **f.** $2y(2x^2 - 6y - z)$ **4. a.** $3(x - 2y)$
b. $5a(p + q)$ **c.** $-8m(1 + 3mx)$ **d.** $\pi r(5 - 3r)$

e. $xy(x + y - 1)$ **f.** $12(1 + 5ab)$ **g.** $2(2x + m + n)$
h. $x(x - 30a + 6b)$ **i.** $2xy(m - 4n + 1)$
j. $4ab^2(3a - 5b + 2)$ **5. a.** $(x + y)(2a - 3b)$
b. $(m + 5)(x - 3)$ **c.** $(2x - 1)(a + b)$ **d.** $(3x + 1)(a - 1)$
e. $(x + 5)(1 + y)$ **f.** $3(a - 2b)(2x^2 + 1)$
g. $5(m + 4)(3x - 1)$ **h.** $x^2(4a - b)(x + y)$
i. $(x - 2)(5a - 3b + 1)$ **j.** $(6x - 5)(x + y - 6z)$
6. a. i) $12x, 3y, 3$ **ii)** $12x, 4xy^2, 4x$ **iii)** $3y, 4xy^2, y$
b. i) $5p^2q, 2q, q$ **ii)** $5p^2q, 8pq^2, pq$ **iii)** $2q, 8pq^2, 2q$
c. i) $6u^3v, 10u^2v, 2u^2v$ **ii)** $6u^3v, 9uv, 3uv$ **iii)** $10u^2v,$
$9uv, uv$ **d. i)** $5m^2n, 12m, m$ **ii)** $5m^2n, 7mn^2, mn$
iii) $12m, 7mn^2, m$ **e. i)** $5ab^2, -15a^2b^2, 5ab^2$ **ii)** $5ab^2,$
$60b^3c^2, 5b^2$ **iii)** $-15a^2b^2, 60b^3c^2, 15b^2$ **f. i)** $5(x - 2y),$
$(x - 2y), (x - 2y)$ **ii)** $3x(x + 2y), (x + 2y)(x - 2y),$
$(x + 2y)$ **g. i)** $6pq, 3(2p + 3q), 3$ **ii)** $6pq,$
$2p(p + 2q)(2p + 3q), 2p$ **iii)** $3(2p + 3q),$
$2p(p + 2q)(2p + 3q), (2p + 3q)$ **7. a.** $(m + 6)(m + n)$
b. $(x - 2)(x + y)$ **c.** $(n + 3)(5m - 2)$ **d.** $(x - 6)(2y - 1)$
e. $(a - 5)(y - 3)$ **f.** $(x - 3)(x^2 + 2)$
g. $(4a + b^2)(a - 5b)$ **h.** $(3a - b^2)(a^2 + 8b)$
i. $(5m + 3n)(5m - 2n^2)$ **j.** $3(r + 2q)(2p - 3q)$
k. $2x(y + 4)(5x - y^2)$ **l.** $a(4x - 5a)(3x + 2b)$
m. $5m(m - 3)(2n + 1)$ **n.** $4pq(q - 2p)(p + 3)$
8. a. $\dfrac{27\pi x^2}{4}$ cm^2 **b.** $(2x + 3)^2(4 - \pi)$ cm^2
9. $\dfrac{1}{2}(x - 2)(4x + y)$ **10.** $329 + 14.1(N - 35)$
11. $7.98(p + q)$ **12.** $\dfrac{5}{2}M$ **13.** $\$1333.33$ **14.** $5w + 2t,$
$4w + 3t, 3w + 4t, 2w + 5t$ **15.** 3 times

Pages 96-97 **1. a.** $3, 4$ **b.** $4, 9$ **c.** $-5, 6$ **d.** $5, -6$
e. $4, 12$ **2. a.** $14a, -4a$ **b.** $-22x, -x$ **c.** $-3m, 2m$
d. $6x, -2x$ **e.** $2p, 5p$ **3. a.** $(x + 3)(x + 1)$
b. $(a - 6)(a - 1)$ **c.** $(y + 6)(y - 3)$ **d.** $(x + 2)(x - 6)$
e. $(x - 11)(x - 2)$ **f.** $(b + 9)(b - 2)$ **g.** $(x + 7)(x - 4)$
h. $(a - 21)(a - 1)$ **i.** $(p - 8)(p + 2)$ **j.** $(x + 6)(x - 5)$
k. $(t + 5)(t + 4)$ **l.** $(u - 18)(u + 2)$
4. a. $(x - 4y)(x + 3y)$ **b.** $(a + 6b)(a + b)$
c. $(p + 16q)(p - 3q)$ **d.** $(m + 5n)(m + 6n)$
e. $(x - 7z)(x - 3z)$ **f.** $(a - 21d)(a + 3d)$
g. $(x + 3y)(x + 8y)$ **h.** $(x - 3y)(x - 5y)$
i. $(r - 4s)(r - 3s)$ **j.** $(a + 3b)(a + b)$
k. $(p + 2q)(p + 4q)$ **l.** $(u + 6v)(u + 2v)$
5. a. $3(x + 2)(x - 1)$ **b.** $2(x + 5)(x - 2)$
c. $a(x + 4)(x + 3)$ **d.** $5(x + 3)(x + 1)$
e. $2(x - 6)(x - 2)$ **f.** $4(x - 4)(x + 1)$
g. $-3(x + 3)(x - 5)$ **h.** $2x(x + 1)(x + 6)$
i. $2r(r + 4s)(r + s)$ **j.** $p(p + 8q)(p - 3q)$
6. a. $(xy + 5)(xy - 3)$ **b.** $(x + 6yz)(x - 2yz)$
c. $(a^2 + 2b)(a^2 + b)$ **d.** $(xy - 6)(xy - 4)$
e. $(2 + mn)(9 - mn)$ **f.** $(ab - 8c)(ab + 2c)$
g. $(x^2y + 5)(x^2y + 7)$ **h.** $(a - 8bc)(a + 2bc)$ **7. a.** $\pm6,$
±26 **b.** $\pm8, \pm10, \pm17$ **c.** $\pm1, \pm19, \pm41$ **d.** $\pm1, \pm4,$
±11 **e.** $\pm10, \pm22$ **f.** $\pm3, \pm6, \pm18, \pm39$ **8.** There are
chairs in 2 of the corners only. They are common to
2 rows only. **9. a.** $(a - 8)(a + 5)$

b. $(x + 2y)(x + 15y)$ **c.** $(mn - 6)(mn + 2)$
d. $x(x + 17y) + 30y$ or $x^2 + y(17x + 30)$
e. $(8 - x)(4 - x)$ **f.** $(a - 9b)(a - b)$ **g.** $(x - 2)(x - 18)$
h. $(x + 7y)(x + 3y)$ **i.** $(bc - 12)(bc + 2)$
j. $2(p + 25)(p + 1)$ **k.** $3(a - 8)(a + 1)$
l. $-5(x + 3)(x - 1)$ **m.** $x(x - 9)(x + 7)$
n. $2a(a + 10)(a + 3)$ **o.** $4(p - 2)(p - 4)$
p. $-x(a - 14)(a + 4)$ **q.** $3(x + 18y)(x - 2y)$
r. $5(n + 3m)(n + 12m)$ **10. i)** 5, $(x - 1)(x - 5)$ **ii)** 8,
$(x - 2)(x - 4)$ **iii)** 9, $(x - 3)(x - 4)$ **iv)** -7,
$(x - 7)(x + 1)$ **11. a.** $(x^2 - 8)(x^2 + 5)$
b. $(a^2 + 10)(a^2 + 2)$ **c.** $(m^2 + 4)(m^2 - 3)$
d. $(p^2 - 18)(p^2 + 2)$ **e.** $(k^2 - 14)(k^2 - 2)$
f. $(x^2 + 14)(x^2 + 3)$ **g.** $(a^2 - 5b)(a^2 + b)$
h. $(r^2 - 4t)(r^2 - 9t)$ **i.** $(u^2 - 6v^2)(u^2 + 5v^2)$
j. $(p^2 - 11q^3)(p^2 + 2q^3)$ **12.** 13 min **13.** Answers
may vary.

Pages 98-99 **1. a.** 3, 18 **b.** -11, 12 **c.** -16, -9
d. -4, 14 **2. a.** ± 7, ± 11 **b.** ± 3, ± 7, ± 17 **3. a.** $2x$,
$x + 5$, $x + 5$, $x + 5$ **b.** $(2x + 1)(x + 2)$
c. $(3x - 4)(x - 3)$ **d.** $(4x + 5)(2x - 3)$
e. $(3x + 1)(2x + 3)$ **f.** $(6x + 1)(2x + 3)$
g. $(3x - 5)(2x - 3)$ **4. a.** $(5x + y)(x - 5y)$
b. $(2a + b)(a + 2b)$ **c.** $(3m - 2n)(6m + n)$
d. $(4x - 5y)(3x - y)$ **e.** $(2x - 9y)(x - 4y)$
f. $3(5x + 7)(x + z)$ **g.** $(3a - 2b)(2a + 7b)$
h. $(10p - 3q)(p + 2q)$ **5. a.** $2(4x + 3)(x - 2)$
b. $y(5x + 1)(x - 2)$ **c.** $3(3x - 1)(2x - 1)$
d. $5(4x + 1)(3x - 2)$ **e.** $a(2x + 3)(x + 6)$
f. $2x(2x - 5)(4x + 3)$ **g.** $3(3a - 5b)(a + 4b)$
h. $2p(p^2 - 5pq^2 - 6q^3)$ **6. a.** $(4x + 4y + 3)(x + y - 1)$
b. $(4p + 2q + 5)(2p + q - 3)$
c. $(5x - 15y - 2)(x - 3y + 2)$
d. $(3a - 3b - 2)(2a - 2b + 1)$
e. $(m + 2n - 6)(m + 2n - 4)$
f. $2(10x + 2y - 3)(5x + y + 1)$
g. $3(2a + 2b - 1)(2a + 2b + 5)$ **7. a.** $(4x + 3)(5x - 1)$
b. $(x + 12)(x + 1)$ **c.** $(6x + 1)(2x - 3)$
d. $(x - 9)(x - 3)$ **e.** $2(2a + 1)(a + 5)$ **f.** $(6 - x)(3 + 5x)$
g. $3(2p + 11)(p - 5)$ **h.** $(9x - 5)(2x + 3)$
i. $(5y - 9)(2y - 1)$ **j.** $x(x + 2)(x + 20)$
k. $(p - q - 6)(p - q + 1)$ **l.** $3y(3x - 1)(9x - 5)$
8. $(3x - 5)$ **9.** A possible answer is 7.
10. a. $(2a^2 + 5b^2)(2a^2 - 3b^2)$ **b.** $(3u^2 + v^2)(u^2 - 3v^2)$
c. $(5m^2 + 3n^2)(m^2 + n^2)$ **d.** $(2r^2 + s^2)(6r^2 - 5s^2)$
e. $(2p^2 - q^2)(3p^2 + 4q^2)$ **f.** $(2x^2 - 7y^2)(x^2 - 3y^2)$
g. $(8r^2 - 3t^2)(2r^2 - 3t^2)$ **h.** $(2a^2 - c^2)(a^2 + 6c^2)$
11. a. $(5a + 2)(3a - 1)$ **b.** $(3x - 4)^2$
c. $(2m + 5n)(m - 2n)$ **d.** $(4p^2 + q^2)(2p^2 + q^2)$
e. $(6r + s)(r - 2s)$ **f.** $(6x - 3y)(x + 3y)$
g. $(2ab + 3c)(ab + 4c)$ **h.** $2m(m - 2n)(2m - 5n)$
i. $(3a + 9b + 1)(a + 3b - 1)$
j. $(2x - y + 1)(10x - 5y + 2)$ **12.** {1, 2, 3, 4} or {5, 6,
7, 8} **13.** 5 times **14.** $2400.00

Pages 100-101 **1. a.** $16y^2$, $3x$, $3x$, $4y$ **b.** $9x^2$, 5, $3x$,

5 c. $81r^2$, $2p$, $9r$, $2p$ **d.** 2, $2x$, 1, $2x$ **e.** $27x^2$, y, $3x$, y
f. 5, $2x$, $2x$, 1 **2. a.** $(4x - 1)(4x + 1)$
b. $(a + 2b)(a - 2b)$
c. $(9m + 6n)(9m - 6n) = 9(3m + 2n)(3m - 2n)$
d. $(x + 3y^2)(x - 3y^2)$ **e.** $(8 + p)(8 - p)$
f. $(7r + 11s)(7r - 11s)$ **g.** $(2x^2 + 9)(2x^2 - 9)$
h. $(a + bc)(a - bc)$ **i.** $(3a + 10b^3)(3a - 10b^3)$
j. $(2x^4y^2 + 1)(2x^4y^2 - 1)$ **k.** $(7 + 4d^8)(7 - 4d^8)$
l. $(12x + 5)(12x - 5)$ **m.** $(a^2 + 13)(a^2 - 13)$
n. $(pq^2 + r)(pq^2 - r)$ **3. a.** $3(2x + 5)(2x - 5)$
b. $a(a + b)(a - b)$ **c.** $5(3m + 2)(3m - 2)$
d. $6(x + 6y^2)(x - 6y^2)$ **e.** $x(x + 8)(x - 8)$
f. $2x^2(x + 15)(x - 15)$ **g.** $a(a^2 + 1)(a + 1)(a - 1)$
h. $8x^2(4x^3 + 1)(4x^3 - 1)$ **i.** $2a^2(a + 3)(a - 3)$
j. $3xy(2x + 1)(2x - 1)$ **4. a.** $(x^2 + 1)(x + 1)(x - 1)$
b. $(9a^4 + 4b^2)(3a^2 + 2b^2)(3a^2 - 2b^2)$
c. $(a^2 + 9y^2)(a + 3y)(a - 3y)$
d. $(16x^6 + y^4)(4x^3 + y^2)(4x^3 - y^2)$
e. $(p^2 + 9)(p + 3)(p - 3)$
f. $(x^2 + 4y^8)(x + 2y^4)(x - 2y^4)$
g. $2(x^4 + 1)(x^2 + 1)(x + 1)(x - 1)$
h. $(4 + x^6)(2 + x^3)(2 - x^3)$ **5. a.** $(x + y + z)(x + y - z)$
b. $(3a + b + 2c)(3a + b - 2c)$
c. $(x - 5y + 3z^2)(x - 5y - 3z^2)$ **d.** $4(a - b)(a - 2b)$
e. $(5x + 6y)(5x - 4y)$ **f.** $-(2x + y)(4x + y)$
g. $(3a + 2b - 6c)(3a - 2b + 6c)$ **h.** $(7 + 2x)(1 - 2x)$
i. $8n(m - 2n)$ **j.** $9(x + 1)(x - 9)$ **k.** $3x(4 - 3x)$
l. $(6p + q + 4t)(6p - q - 4t)$ **6. a.** $(3a - 2b)(a + 4b)$
b. $4(2x + 3)(x - 1)$ **c.** $-(2p + 7q)(4p - 5q)$
d. $-(6x + 1)(4x - 5)$ **e.** $9(4a + 7)$
7. a. $(2x^2 + 1)(x + 2)(x - 2)$ **b.** $(a^2 + 3)(a + 3)(a - 3)$
c. $(3p^2 + 2q^2)(p + q)(p - q)$
d. $(3m^2 + 2n^2)(m + 2n)(m - 2n)$
8. a. $(x^2 + 3x - 2)(x + 1)(x + 2)$
b. $(2a^2 - 5a - 2)(2a - 1)(a - 2)$
c. $(3p^2 - 4p + 4)(3p + 2)(p - 2)$
d. $(5 - 7t - 2t^2)(5 + 2t)(1 + t)$
e. $(3t + 2)(t + 1)(3t + 1)(t - 2)$
f. $(3m^2 - n^2)(n + m)(n - m)$ **9. a.** straight charge
b. if more than 12 cheques a month
10. a. $5(3x + 2)(3x - 2)$ **b.** $(2p - 5)(2p + 3)$
c. $(8a + b)^2$ **d.** $(7m^2 + 4n)(7m^2 - 4n)$
e. $(6u + 5v)(u - 2v)$ **f.** $3(4 - 3c)^2$ **g.** $2a(3a - 2)(a + 4)$
h. $(2k - 1)(6k - 7)$ **i.** $(m^2 + p^2 + 2q)(m^2 - p^2 - 2q)$
j. $(4x^2 + 5)(x^2 - 5)$ **k.** $4(2p + q)(p - 6q)$
l. $(3ab + 8c^3)(3ab - 8c^3)$ **m.** $4(x + 4)(x + 7)$
n. $(12m + 5n)(m + n)$ **11.** zero **12.** *Digits* @ $0.76
(not number, otherwise 124 is one number and
would cost $0.76). **13.** 195 m³ **14. a.** $10\,000 - 4$,
9996 **b.** 9775 **c.** 9375 **d.** 997 500 **e.** 3575
Page 102 **1. a.** ± 6 **b.** 9 **c.** $\pm 12x$ **d.** 121
2. a. $(x + 5)^2$ **b.** $(4a + 3)^2$ **c.** $(x - 1)^2$ **d.** $(8x + 1)^2$
e. $(7y - 4)^2$ **f.** $(3x + 8)^2$ **g.** $(5x + 2y)^2$ **h.** $(3x - 10z)^2$
i. $(2a + 9c)^2$ **j.** $(6ab - 1)^2$ **k.** $(4 + 5pq)^2$ **l.** $(3x - 5yz)^2$
3. a. $2(x + 4)^2$ **b.** $3(a - 3b)^2$ **c.** $y(x + 5)^2$
d. $2a(3x + 4)^2$ **e.** $-2(x + 1)^2$ **f.** $6(x - 6y)^2$

g. $-2(5x + 2)^2$ **h.** $3(6 - 5p)^2$ **4.** $3x + 7$ **5.** 2
6. a. 200, 4, 2704 **b.** $(25 + 2)^2 = 625 + 100 + 4 = 729$
c. $(30 + 6)^2 = 900 + 360 + 36 = 1296$
d. $(100 + 12)^2 = 10\,000 + 2400 + 144 = 12\,544$

Page 103 **1. a.** -576 **b.** -3072 **c.** 3136 **d.** -1728
e. 6080 **f.** 882 **2. a.** \$183.04 **b.** \$276.00 **3.** Add 9,
divide by 2. **4. a.** 292 **b.** 226 **c.** 166 **d.** -66 **e.** 2
f. -17

Pages 104-105 **1. a.** $\dfrac{4xy}{3}$ **b.** $\dfrac{4a^3}{7b^2}$ **c.** $-2x^2yz$ **d.** $\dfrac{4b^2}{3a^2}$
e. $\dfrac{-3}{2p}$ **f.** $\dfrac{6z^3}{5xy^2}$ **g.** $\dfrac{7b^3}{3a}$ **h.** x^2 **i.** $2m^2$ **j.** $-5u^2v^2$ **k.** $\dfrac{-3t^3}{s}$
l. $4a^2$ **2. a.** $x - 2$ **b.** $x - 3$ **c.** $x^2 + 4x - 2$
d. $2a + 5b - c$ **e.** $a^2 + 8a - 5$ **f.** $2x^2y - 5x$
g. $3a^2b^2 - 2b$ **h.** $2x + 6y^2 - 1$ **i.** $2x^2 + 5xy - 3y^2$
j. $6p - q - 15pq$ **3. a.** $\$(6x^2 + 11x - 10)/\text{km}$
b. $(4x^2 + 16x + 15)$ **4. a.** $(6x - 5)$ **b.** $(2x + 5)$
c. $(2x + 3)$ **d.** $(3y - 5)$ **e.** $(x^2 + 2x + 4)$
f. $(4a^2 + 6a - 7)$ **g.** $(8x^2 - 22x + 5)$ **h.** $(x^2 - 2)$
i. $(2x^2 + 1)$ **j.** $(2x^2 + 1)$ **k.** $(m^2 - m)$ **l.** $x^3 + x^2 - x - 1$
5. $x^2 + 4x + 1$ **6.** 107 **7.** $(4x - 3)$ **8.** $(4x^2 - 11x - 3)$
9. 4 **10.** $(x + 12)$

Pages 106-107 **1.** The product of two numbers is
zero if and only if at least one of the numbers is
zero. **2.** zero **3. a.** 16 **b.** 0 **c.** -8 **d.** -8 **e.** 0 **f.** -5
zeros are -2, 4 · **4. a.** $p = -2$ **b.** $p = 0$ **c.** $p = 0$
d. $p = 0$ **e.** $p = 3$ **f.** $p = -\dfrac{2}{5}$ **5. a.** -6, 3 **b.** 5, -1
c. 0, -10 **d.** $\dfrac{7}{2}$, -5 **e.** $\dfrac{3}{4}$, $-\dfrac{2}{5}$ **f.** -6, $-\dfrac{8}{5}$ **g.** 0, 5
h. 6, $-\dfrac{1}{2}$ **i.** $\dfrac{-5}{6}$, $\dfrac{8}{3}$ **j.** 0, $\dfrac{3}{5}$ **6. a.** -2, 0 **b.** 1, 5 **c.** 6,
-6 **d.** 0, $\dfrac{10}{3}$ **e.** 3, $-\dfrac{1}{2}$ **f.** -3 **g.** $\dfrac{4}{5}$, $-\dfrac{4}{5}$ **h.** 2, $-\dfrac{1}{4}$
7. a. 4, $\dfrac{5}{3}$ **b.** 8, $\dfrac{-1}{5}$ **8.** 3 s and 1 s **9.** 8, 13 **10.** 29
11. a. 4 **b.** 4, -4 **c.** -2, 5 **d.** 1, 8 **e.** -3, $\dfrac{5}{4}$ **f.** $-\dfrac{2}{3}$,
$\dfrac{7}{2}$ **12. a.** $x = \dfrac{5}{2}$ or $y = -2$ **b.** $x = 6$ or $y = -\dfrac{1}{2}$
13. 25 **14.** Container A: 26 L; Container B: 12 L
15. $(100 - 2x)(50 - 2x) = 864 \therefore x = 56.79$ or
$x = 18.21$

Pages 108-109 **1.** $36x^2 + 3x - 5$ **2.** $(3x - 2)$
3. $4x^3 - 15x^2 + x + 6$ **4.** 6
5. a. $A = (2x + y)(2x + 2y) + (7x + 4y)(x - 4y) +$
$(3x + 5y)(4x - y) = 23x^2 - xy - 19y^2$
b. $26x + 14y = P$ **c.** $A = 489$ cm², $P = 158$ cm
6. $V = 30x^3 - 79x^2 + 43x + 12$,
$S.A. = 62x^2 - 94x + 10$
7. $V = [2(x + 2)]^3 - \dfrac{4}{3}\pi(x + 2)^3 = (x + 2)^3(8 - \dfrac{4}{3}\pi)$
8. 26, 33 **9.** 3 **10.** No, she is getting half as much as
she should. **11.** $6n^2 + 13n - 8$ **12.** $21x^2 + 5xy - 4y^2$
13. $r = \dfrac{3x}{2}$, $A_s = \dfrac{1}{2}\pi r^2 = \dfrac{9\pi x^2}{8}$,

$A_t = \dfrac{9\pi x^2}{8} - x^2 = \left(\dfrac{9\pi}{8} - 1\right)x^2$ **14.** 18 cm **15.** $9y$
16. 39 have both black and white fur.
17. $8x^2 + 22x - 21$

Page 110 **1.** because of x^2 **2. a.** 20 **b.** 40 **3.** to see
the polynomial (and try a better guess) **4.** 30
5. The computer will print the sentence in quotes
followed by the value of the polynomial *at* your
guess. **6.** -9 **7.** Computer continues asking for
input of guesses (indefinitely). **8.** 80 **9.** Finds the
zeros, X $\wedge$ 2 + X − 2, 0, X, X, End. **10.** To loop
through values of x to check for zeros (roots).

Page 111 **1. a.** binomial, 2nd, $x^2 + 5x$
b. trinomial, 3rd, $-8x^3 + 12x - 5$ **c.** monomial, 5th,
$15x^4y$ **d.** trinomial, 2nd, $-2x^2 + 8xy + 3y^2$ **2. a.** 22
b. -11 **c.** 18 **d.** 20 **3.** 84 cm² **4. a.** $16x + 3y$
b. $4a^2 + 6a - 4$ **c.** $5xy - 18yz + 4xz$
5. a. $-2x^2 + 6x - 17$ **b.** $-7ab + 3bc + 4ac$
6. a. $3a^3 - 12a^2 - 6a$ **b.** $-20x^2 + 15x^3 - 5x^4$
c. $-6x^2 - 12x - 41$ **d.** $15x^2 + 30x + 6$ **e.** $-3x^2 - x + 6$
7. a. $x^2 + 13x - 30$ **b.** $x^3 + 3x^2 - 2x - 6$
c. $3x^3 - 16x^2 - 4x + 3$ **d.** $x^3 + 4x^2 - 11x - 30$
e. $3x^2 + x - 34$ **f.** $-7x + 34$ **g.** $5x^2 + 6x - 16$
8. a. -34 **b.** -21 **9. a.** $D = P_o - P_n$,
$D = 16x - 4y - 17z$ **b.** $E = IR$,
$8x^4 + 4x^3 - 26x^2 - 3x + 15$ **10. a.** $12x$ **b.** $7ac$
11. a. $-x$, $-12x$ **b.** $4x$, $-2x$ **c.** $-12x$, $4x$ **d.** $21x$, $-3x$
12. a. $(x + 8)(2x - 1)$ **b.** $(3x - 1)(4x - 1)$
c. $4a(2a + 7)$ **d.** $(6p + 5)(6p - 5)$ **e.** $(2x + 1)^2$
f. $2m(m - 3)(2m + 5)$ **g.** $6x(2x^2 + 5y^2 + 1)$
h. $(5x + y + 3)(5x + y - 3)$ **i.** $(2a + 7b)^2$
j. $3(5x - 2m)^2$ **k.** $(4x^2 + 3)(x^2 - 5)$ **l.** $(ab - 4)(ab - 6)$
m. $(2x + 5)(6y - 1)$ **n.** $(5x^3 + 2y)(2x^3 - y)$
13. a. $A = \pi r(r + 2h)$ **b.** $A = 2(wl + wh + hl)$
c. $A = p(1 + rt)$ **d.** $A = \pi(R + r)(R - r)$
e. $A = \dfrac{1}{2}h(a + b)$ **f.** $a_n = a_1 + (n - 1)d$
14. a. $x(2x - 5) + 8$, 11 **b.** $x(x + 2) - 4$, 11
c. $x\{x[x - 4] + 5\} - 6$, 0 **d.** $x^2\{x^2[2x - 5] - 1\} - 18$, 54

Page 112 **1.** -1 **2.** fourth, $16b^4 - 3ab^2 - a^2b + 5a^3$
3. a. -12 **b.** -4 **c.** 20 **d.** 28 **4. a.** $18x^2 - 20xy + 8y^2$
b. $13p^2 + 3p - 15$ **5. a.** $3x^2 + 25xy - 2y^2$
b. $-23pq - 14qr - 13pr$ **c.** $-4m^2 + 2m - 7$ **d.** $-k^2 + 13$
6. a. $12x^4y^3z^2$ **b.** $28a^4b - 42a^3b^4$ **c.** $x^2y^2 + 5xy - 24$
d. $8m^2 - 42mn + 27n^2$ **e.** $6x^3 + 29x^2y - 23xy^2 + 3y^3$
f. $a^4 + 2a^3 - 11a^2 - 12a + 15$ **7. a.** $17x^2 - 15x - 5$
b. $24y + 2$ **c.** $10x - 24$ **d.** $8x^2 - 24x + 36$
e. $4x^2 + 7x - 22$ **f.** $73x^2 - 12x - 21$ **g.** $5p^2 - 7p - 49$
8. a. 5, -5, 4, -4 **b.** 1, -1, 5, -5 **c.** 4, -4 **d.** 9, -9,
12, -12, 21, -21 **9. a.** $4a(2a^2 - 3)$ **b.** $(x - 8)(x + 3)$
c. $(7s + 2t)(7s - 2t)$ **d.** $(2a + 5b)^2$ **e.** $(3x - 2)(6x - 1)$
f. $(2x + 1)(1 + 2y)$ **g.** $6(x - 3)^2$
h. $2(2x^2 + 5y)(2x^2 - 5y)$ **i.** $(2t + 5)(t - 4)$
j. $(5x - 4)(3x + 2)$ **k.** $(2x - y)(3a + 5b)$
10. a. $(2x + 5)(x - 5)$ **b.** $-(2x + 1)^2$

c. $(4x - 3)(4x + 3)$ d. $(x - 1)(x + 3)$ e. $(x + 1)(x - 1)$
11. a. $(2x + 3y)(2x - y)$ b. $5(m - 1)(m + 5)$
12. a. $7xy^2 - 4$ b. doesn't divide evenly,

$3x^2 - 4x + 1 - \dfrac{2}{x+1}$ c. $2x^3 + 3x^2 - 4x - 6$ 13. a. 0,
$\dfrac{8}{3}$ b. $\dfrac{1}{6}, \dfrac{-1}{6}$ c. $\dfrac{-5}{4}, \dfrac{3}{2}$ d. -5 14. $4x + 8$ where x
is the shortest side 15. $6x + 13$ 16. 65π
17. 7 quarters, 11 dimes

Chapter 5

Page 113 1. a. $7m^2 - m - 12n$ b. $13a^2 + 6b^2 + 4ab$
c. $9p - 5pq + 3q^2 + 10p^2$ 2. a. $-12c - 51d$
b. $10x^3 - 4x^2y$ c. $5r^2 + 27rs - 18s^2$
d. $16u^2 + 24uv + 9v^2$ e. $4x^3 - 3y^3 + 7x^2y - 16xy^2$
3. a. $10a - 9b$ b. $8m - 21n + 2$ c. $22x^2 - 19xy$
d. $-2a^2 - b^2 - 27ab$ 4. a. $t(5t - 8)$
b. $3mn(2m^2 - mn - 8n^2)$ c. $(p - 2q)(p + 7q)$
d. $(6x + 1)(6x - 1)$ e. $(4y + 3)^2$ f. $(3a - 8)(a + 2)$
g. $(4 - 3x)(2 + x)$ h. $2(n + 6)(2n - 3)$ 5. a. $6a$ b. $4p$
c. c d. $(a + 2b)$ e. $(3x + 2)$ f. $(m + 2)$ g. $(k + 4)$
6. a. $18pq$ b. $15x^2y^2$ c. $10m(m - 1)(m + 2)$
d. $(3p - 5)(p + 2)$ e. $(2a + b)(a - 3b)(2a - b)$

7. a. $\dfrac{15ab}{8c}$ b. $\dfrac{16mn^2}{15p}$ c. $\dfrac{9x^2}{4}$ d. $\dfrac{3y^2}{2u}$ 8. a. $\dfrac{5 + 9a}{6}$

b. $\dfrac{72 - 35x}{30x}$ 9. a. $x = -1$ b. $x = \dfrac{17}{3}$ c. $x = 29$

d. $x = 14$ e. $x = \dfrac{26}{45}$ f. $\dfrac{-106}{3}$ 10. a. F b. T c. F
11. Answers may vary.

Pages 114-115 1. a. $x \neq 0$ b. $x \neq 9$ c. $x \neq 0, 4$

d. $x \neq -2, -7$ e. $x \neq 1, 2$ f. $x \neq -1, \dfrac{5}{3}$ 2. a. $\dfrac{9}{5}$

b. $\dfrac{-4}{3}$ c. $\dfrac{b^2}{8a}$ d. $\dfrac{7mp}{3n^3}$ e. $8x + 2$ f. $\dfrac{4}{3x - 8}$

3. a. $\dfrac{4x + 5}{3x - 1}$ b. $\dfrac{x - 2}{3x + 5}$ c. $\dfrac{3x + 8y}{3(2 + y)}$ d. $\dfrac{3(b + 3c)}{4(a + c)}$

e. $\dfrac{3q^2 - 5p}{3q(p + 2q)}$ f. $\dfrac{2n(m^2 + 2n)}{3m(3n - 2m)}$ 4. a. $\dfrac{-(x + 3)}{x + 2}$ b. $\dfrac{x + 5}{x - 1}$

c. $\dfrac{x + 6}{3x}$ d. $\dfrac{x - 4}{x + 3}$ e. $\dfrac{a - 5}{a + 8}$ f. $\dfrac{y - 2}{x + 3}$ 5. a. $\dfrac{2x + 5}{x + 4}$,

$x \neq -4, 3$ b. $\dfrac{3x - 2}{x - 5}, x \neq \dfrac{-3}{2}, 5$ c. $\dfrac{2x - 1}{x + 2}, x \neq -2,$

$\dfrac{3}{4}$ d. $-\dfrac{5x - 1}{x + 3}, x \neq -3, \dfrac{1}{5}$ e. $\dfrac{5t + 4}{2t + 1}, t \neq \dfrac{-1}{2}, \dfrac{4}{5}$

f. $\dfrac{4p + 1}{4p - 3}, p \neq \dfrac{3}{4}, \dfrac{-1}{2}$ g. $\dfrac{c + 5}{3c + 2}, c \neq \dfrac{2}{3}, \dfrac{-2}{3}$

h. $\dfrac{-(2s + 5)}{s + 3}, s \neq -3, \dfrac{4}{3}$ 6. a. $\dfrac{2a - b}{a - 3b}$ b. $\dfrac{2x + 5y}{x + y}$

c. $\dfrac{m - 6n}{2m + n}$ d. $\dfrac{5y + 4x}{3y - x}$ e. $\dfrac{p - 4q}{2p + 3q}$ f. $\dfrac{3a + 2b}{a - 6b}$

7. a. $\dfrac{5x + 3}{x + 3}, x \neq -2, -3$ b. $\dfrac{x + 1}{-2x}, x \neq 0, \dfrac{4}{3}$

c. $\dfrac{x - 3}{2x - 3}, x \neq \dfrac{3}{2}, 3$ d. $\dfrac{6x + 1}{x - 4}, x \neq 4, 5$

8. a. $\dfrac{x - 5}{x + 4}, x \neq -4$ b. $\dfrac{x(3x + 2)}{5}, x \neq \dfrac{-2}{3}$

c. $\dfrac{5(x - 2)}{3x + 1}, x \neq -6, \dfrac{-1}{3}, 0$ d. $\dfrac{a + 6b}{5a + b}, a \neq \dfrac{-b}{5}, -3b$

e. $\dfrac{3(7p + 4q)}{5p + 2q}, p \neq \dfrac{2q}{5}, \dfrac{-2q}{5}$ f. $\dfrac{m(3m + 5n)}{n(m - 8n)}, n \neq 0,$

$m \neq \dfrac{8n}{m}, \dfrac{n}{6}$ 9. 36 10. average speed = 9.6 km/h

Pages 116-117 1. a. $\dfrac{4}{15}$ b. $\dfrac{3}{10}$ c. a d. $\dfrac{-1}{5y}$ e. $\dfrac{16}{15n}$

f. $\dfrac{-27}{20}$ 2. a. $\dfrac{20}{9}$ b. $\dfrac{-4}{9}$ c. $\dfrac{10}{9xy^2}$ d. $\dfrac{-9ab}{40}$ e. $\dfrac{n}{m}$

f. $\dfrac{7}{4ab^5}$ 3. a. $\dfrac{9b^2}{20a}$ b. $\dfrac{z^3}{12x^2y}$ c. $\dfrac{2}{b}$ d. $\dfrac{16xy}{3}$

4. a. $\dfrac{4}{x - 2}$ b. $\dfrac{(x + 2)(x - 3)}{x + 3}$ c. $x + 4$ d. $\dfrac{-5x}{x - 3}$

e. $\dfrac{-5x}{x + 4}$ 5. a. $\dfrac{a^2 - b^2}{24ab}$ b. 0.09 cm² 6. a. $\dfrac{a + 2}{3a - 2}$,

$a \neq -3, \dfrac{2}{3}$ b. $\dfrac{-4}{x}, x \neq 0, 4$ 7. a. $\dfrac{3x - 5}{-3}$

b. $\dfrac{10x}{3(x - 1)(x - 5)}$ c. $\dfrac{5(x + 4)}{6(x + 2)}$ d. $\dfrac{x + 3}{2}$ e. $-\dfrac{x + 5}{6x}$

f. $\dfrac{x(x + 4y)}{8y}$ g. $\dfrac{2a(a + 3b)}{3b(a + b)}$ 8. a. $\dfrac{3(x + 5)}{2}, x \neq -2, 0, 5$

b. $\dfrac{x - 4}{x + 2}, x \neq -2, \dfrac{-1}{6}, 3$ c. $-(x + 2), x \neq 2$

9. base $= \dfrac{2(x + 1)^2}{(2x + 1)(2x + 3)}$ 10. time $= \dfrac{(x + 2)(x - 1)}{2}$

Pages 118-119 1. a. 48 b. $90xy$ c. $60a^2b^3$ d. $27x^3y^2$

e. $60xy$ f. $24x^2y^2$ g. $12abc$ h. $30x^2y$ 2. a. $\dfrac{15x^2y}{5xy}$

b. $\dfrac{10x^2}{5xy}$ c. $\dfrac{15xy + 5x^2y + 5xy^2}{5xy}$ d. $\dfrac{10x^2y - 40xy^2}{5xy}$

3. a. $\dfrac{12x + 15y}{10}$ b. $\dfrac{7a}{8}$ c. $\dfrac{29x}{36}$ d. $\dfrac{7x}{15}$ 4. a. $\dfrac{20a - 15b}{6}$

b. $\dfrac{5x}{18}$ c. $\dfrac{-23x}{30}$ d. $\dfrac{15x - 12}{20}$ 5. a. $5xy^2$ b. $3x^2 + x$

c. $4x^3$ d. $x^2 - 1$ e. $6y^2 + 12y + 6$ f. $2(x + 1)^2$

6. a. $\dfrac{15a + 20}{6a^2}$ b. $\dfrac{15 - 14x}{20x^2}$ c. $\dfrac{8m - 15n}{36m^2n^2}$ d. $\dfrac{2c^2 + 3b^2}{abc}$

e. $\dfrac{18yz + 20xz - 27xy}{24xyz}$ f. $\dfrac{10bc - 3c^2 + 2ab}{abc}$

7. a. $\dfrac{11x + 17}{12}$ b. $\dfrac{27a - 10}{10}$ c. $\dfrac{9x + 10}{12}$ d. $\dfrac{17x + 40}{60}$

e. $\dfrac{24a + 13}{20}$ 8. a. $1, x \neq \dfrac{-3}{2}$ b. $\dfrac{2x - 3}{x + 4}, x \neq -4$ c. 3,

$x \neq -5$ d. $\dfrac{2x^2 + 13x + 2}{2x + 1}, x \neq \dfrac{-1}{2}$

9. a. $\dfrac{8x^2 + 15x - 12}{24x^2}$ b. $\dfrac{20a^2 + 24ab + 15b}{15ab}$ c. $\dfrac{x^2 + 1}{5x}$

d. $\dfrac{24a^2 - 11ab + 20b}{12a^2b}$ e. $\dfrac{6x + 4y^3 + 5x^3y}{6x^2y^2}$

f. $\dfrac{75q + 18p - 20}{30pq}$ g. $\dfrac{4m^2 + 21mn + 27n + 6}{18mn}$

h. $\dfrac{35x - 8}{24}$ 10. $\dfrac{5x^2 - 9x - 16}{x - 3}$ 11. a. 2 b. $x - 3$

c. $\frac{3x+1}{x+2}$ d. $\frac{x+8}{x-2}$ e. $\frac{x-3}{2x+5}$ **12. a.** $2x - 3, x \neq -6$

b. $\frac{x+20}{30x^2}, x \neq 0$ **13.** Area of circle $= \pi r^2$ ∴ radius

of larger pipe $= \frac{\text{diameter}}{2} = 12$ cm

∴ $A = \pi(12)^2 \doteq 452.4$ cm². Area of two smaller
pipes $= \pi(6)^2 + \pi(6)^2 \doteq (113.1 + 113.1)$ cm² $\doteq$
226.2 cm² ∴ the two smaller pipes are not the
equivalent of the larger one.

Pages 120-121 **1. a.** $2x(2x-3)$ **b.** $(x-6)(x+4)$
c. $15(x-3)$ **d.** $(2x+1)(2x-1)$
e. $(x-4)(x+8)(x+7)$ **f.** $(x+2)(x-3)(4x)$
g. $(x+5)^2(x-5)$ **h.** $3x(3x+4)(x-2)$
i. $2(x-1)(x+1)$ **2. a.** $4x(x+5)$ **b.** $(x-3)(x+2)$
c. $4x(x-2)$ **d.** $(x+1)(x-4)(x+4)$
e. $(x+3)(x+2)(x-2)$ **f.** $6x(3x+5)$ **3. a.** $\frac{5x+5}{4x(x+5)}$,

$x \neq 0, -5$ **b.** $\frac{19-3x}{(x-3)(x+2)}, x \neq -2, 3$ **c.** $\frac{-(17x+2)}{4x(x-2)}$,

$x \neq 0, 2$ **d.** $\frac{11x-4}{(x+4)(x-4)(x+1)}, x \neq 4, -4, 1$

e. $\frac{8x^2+14x}{(x+3)(x+2)(x-2)}, x \neq -3, -2, 2$ **f.** $\frac{36x+40}{6x(3x+5)}$,

$x \neq 0, \frac{-5}{3}$ **4. a.** $\frac{50x-4}{(3x+2)(x-4)}$ **b.** $\frac{-(3x+2)}{(x-2)(x-6)}$

c. $\frac{37x-110}{(5x+2)(2x-7)}$ **d.** $\frac{24x+12}{(4x-1)(4x+1)}$

e. $\frac{63x+42}{(5x-6)(4x+5)}$ **f.** $\frac{6x-6}{(3-x)(3+x)}$ **5. a.** $\frac{6(x+2)}{x(x+3)}$

b. $\frac{15x^2+11x-4}{2(5x+1)}$ **c.** $\frac{2(4x^2-3x-4)}{x(3x+4)}$ **d.** $\frac{6x^2+35x-4}{5x(x^2+1)}$

e. $\frac{3x^2+2x-14}{2(x+2)}$ **f.** $\frac{2x^2-7x-11}{4(5x-1)}$

6. perimeter $= 2l + 2w =$

$\frac{2x+10}{(x-1)(x-2)} + \frac{4x}{(x-2)(x+2)} = \frac{6x^2+10x+20}{(x-1)(x-2)(x+2)}$

7. a. $\frac{7x^2+6x+4}{(x+3)(x-4)}$ **b.** $\frac{5x^2-2x+25}{(x+5)(3x-1)}$

c. $\frac{3x^2+x+13}{(x-4)(2x+5)}$ **d.** $\frac{11x^2+72x+4}{8x(x-2)}$ **e.** $\frac{x+6}{(x+2)(x-2)}$

f. $\frac{2x^2+15x-15}{(2x-3)(2x+1)}$ **8. a.** $\frac{2x^2+7x-6}{x+3}$ **b.** $\frac{31-8x}{x-2}$

c. $\frac{3x^2-15x-8}{2x+5}$ **d.** $\frac{9x+8}{10x+3}$ **9.** $\frac{5x^2-6x-35}{x^2-2x-8}$

10. a. $\frac{18x+5}{4(x+3)}$ **b.** $\frac{33}{6(x-4)}$ **c.** $\frac{4x-1}{6(3x-4)}$

d. $\frac{16x^2+163x+132}{6(5x+6)(2x+5)}$ **11. a.** $\frac{11x+6}{(x-6)(x+2)(x+3)}$,

$x \neq -3, -2, 6$ **b.** $\frac{x^2+14x+16}{(3x+4)(3x-4)(x+2)}, x \neq -2, \frac{-4}{3}$,

$\frac{4}{3}$ **c.** $\frac{9}{x(2x+5)(2x-3)}, x \neq \frac{-5}{2}, 0, \frac{3}{2}$

d. $\frac{7x+34}{(3x+1)(x-2)(x+2)}, x \neq -2, \frac{-1}{3}, 2$ **12.** sum is

34 **13. a.** $\frac{9x^2-5x-5}{(4x-1)(x+2)(x-2)}$ **b.** $\frac{8x^2-x-9}{(3x+1)^2(2x-1)}$

c. $\frac{2x-2}{(5x-2)(x+2)(x+1)}$ **d.** $\frac{10x^2-4x+19}{(x+2)(4x+3)(3x-2)}$

Pages 122-123 **1. a.** $24(x-3)$ **b.** $(2k-3)(2k+3)$
c. $(n-8)(n-2)(n+4)$ **d.** $(t+6)(2t+3)(t+4)$
e. $(5x-1)(5x+1)(2x+5)$ **f.** $6b(b+5)(3b-4)$

2. a. $\frac{4(x+5)}{(2x-1)(x+5)}$ **b.** $\frac{2x(2x-1)}{(2x-1)(x+5)}$

c. $\frac{\frac{3}{x}(2x-1)(x+5)}{(2x-1)(x+5)}$ **d.** $\frac{2x^2(2x-1)}{(2x-1)(x+5)}$

3. a. $\frac{x^2+3x-7}{(x-4)(x+4)}, x \neq 4, -4$ **b.** $\frac{-7x^2+14x-1}{(x-1)(x+2)}$,

$x \neq -2, 1$ **c.** $\frac{x^2-10x+48}{3(x+8)(x-3)}, x \neq 3, -8$

d. $\frac{15x^2+3x-3}{x^2-1}, x \neq 1, -1$ **e.** $\frac{5x^2+26x-24}{(2x+3)(x-4)(x+4)}$,

$x \neq -4, 4, \frac{-3}{2}$ **4. a.** $\frac{10x^2+2x-3}{x(10x-3)}, x \neq 0, \frac{3}{10}$

b. $\frac{14x^2+17x-8}{(x+2)^2(3x-1)}, x \neq -2, \frac{1}{3}$

c. $\frac{16x-9}{3(2x-3)(x+6)(x+1)}, x \neq -6, -1, \frac{3}{2}$

d. $\frac{16x+19}{2x(4x+1)(x-1)(x+1)}, x \neq 0, 1, -1, \frac{-1}{4}$ **e.** 0

5. a. $\frac{4x+5}{(2x-1)(x+3)}$ **b.** $\frac{6a^2-8a-29}{(6a+1)(a-9)}$

c. $\frac{3x-2}{(x+3)(2x-5)}$ **d.** $\frac{13p^2+39p-24}{(2p+5)(p+6)}$

6. a. $\frac{-4(x+3)}{(x+2)(x+4)}$ **b.** $\frac{-33y}{(x-5y)(2x+y)}$

c. $\frac{y^2-6y-1}{3(y-1)(2y+1)}$ **d.** $\frac{5a^2+2ab-3b^2+6a-6b}{6(a+b)}$

7. a. $(3)(9)(5)$ **b.** $2x(x-4)(x+1)$
c. $(x+3)(x-3)(2x+7)$ **8.** 55 min

9. a. $\frac{15x^2+11x-91}{(x+4)(2x+5)(x-3)}$ **b.** $\frac{30x^3-23x^2+20x-3}{5x(3x-1)(3x+1)}$

c. $\frac{-9x^2-107x+10}{(x+4)(2x+1)(x-3)}$ **d.** $\frac{20x^2-19x-105}{(x-3)(x+3)(2x-5)}$

e. $\frac{5x^3-15x^2-61x-16}{(x+1)(x-4)(x+2)}$ **10.** $\frac{4x^2+26x+40}{(x+3)(x+5)}$

11. a. $R = \frac{rs}{r+s}$ **b.** $r = \frac{Rs}{s-R}$ **c.** $s = \frac{Rr}{r-R}$

Pages 124-125 **1.** Answers may vary. **2. a.** 6
b. 12 **c.** $2x(x-5)$ **d.** $(4x-1)(x+3)$ **e.** $5x(x+2)$

3. a. $x = \frac{36}{5}$ **b.** $x = \frac{12}{13}$ **c.** $x = \frac{15}{2}$ **d.** $x = \frac{10}{11}$

e. $x = \frac{-11}{5}$ **f.** $x = \frac{-26}{25}$ **4. a.** $x = \frac{-1}{4}$ **b.** $x = \frac{-2}{5}$

c. $x = \frac{6}{7}$ **d.** $x = \frac{8}{17}$ **e.** $x = \frac{-3}{2}$ **f.** $x = \frac{9}{10}$

5. a. $x = -4$ **b.** $x = \frac{-1}{2}$ **c.** $x = \frac{10}{19}$ **d.** $x = \frac{6}{5}$

e. $x = \frac{-1}{11}$ **f.** $x = \frac{1}{3}$ **6.** 32 **7.** 12, 18 **8.** Jan drove
230 km and Mike drove 280 km. **9.** 16, 40 **10.** 16
11. 24 students **12.** no solution **BRAINTICKLER**
The manager already owned the camera.

Page 126   **1.** calculated numerator, calculated denominator   **2.** Change the plus sign in lines 60, 80 to a minus.   **3.** $\frac{17}{20}$ **4.** Change lines 60, 70 to the following: P1 = A * C, P2 = B * D, Q1 = A * D, Q2 = B * C.   **5.** Answers may vary.   **6. a.** 90 **b.** 20 **c.** 150 **d.** 520   **8.** 12 is the LCD of 6 and 4.

Page 127   **1. a.** $x \neq 8$ **b.** $x \neq 0, -3$ **c.** $x \neq -1, 5$ **d.** $x \neq \frac{-3}{4}$ **e.** $x \neq 0, -3$ **f.** $x \neq \frac{9}{2}$ **2. a.** 80 **b.** $-24x^2y$ **c.** $2x(2x-5)$ **d.** $(x-1)^2$ **e.** $12(x+2)(x-2)$ **f.** $(x+3)(x-3)(x-2)$ **3. a.** 12 **b.** $6(x-2)$ **c.** $(x-2)(x+2)(x-5)$ **d.** $3x(x+3)(x-3)$ **e.** $4x(x-2)$ **4. a.** $\frac{4x}{5}$ **b.** 5 **c.** $\frac{x+3}{3x-5}$ **d.** $\frac{-1}{x+1}$ **e.** $\frac{6m}{m-4}$ **f.** $\frac{-(2x+5)}{2x}$ **g.** $\frac{-(x+4y)}{2x+y}$ **h.** $\frac{-(5a+3b)}{4a+b}$ **5. a.** $16p^4$ **b.** $x(x+2)$ **c.** $\frac{a}{3b}$ **d.** $\frac{4(x+7)}{x+4}$ **6. a.** $\frac{8y-5}{12}$ **b.** $\frac{3-2x}{2}$ **c.** $\frac{23a+7}{(a+2)(6a-1)}$ **d.** $\frac{8x^2+11x}{(2x+7)(4x-3)}$ **7.** 108   **8.** 9 mL   **9. a.** $\frac{16x-23}{(x+10)(x-3)(2x-1)}$ **b.** $\frac{x^2+6x+5}{(3x+5)(3x-5)(x+2)}$ **c.** $\frac{2y-14}{(y-4)(y-6)}$ **d.** 1 **e.** $\frac{2x^3+2x^2-32x+10}{(5x-1)(x+4)(x+2)}$ **f.** $\frac{9x^3-27x^2+18x+10}{x(2x+1)(x-5)}$ **g.** $\frac{24a^2+25a-18}{3(4a+3)}$ **h.** $\frac{2a-b}{(a+2b)(a-2b)(a+b)}$ **10. a.** $x = \frac{13}{3}$ **b.** $x = \frac{19}{4}$ **c.** $x = -\frac{39}{4}$ **d.** $x = \frac{22}{7}$ **e.** $x = \frac{34}{7}$ **11. a.** $\frac{3000}{l}$ **b.** $\frac{3000}{w+x}$ **c.** 25 cm

Page 128   **1. a.** $x \neq 0$ **b.** $x \neq -5$ **c.** $x \neq -1, 8$ **d.** $x \neq \frac{-1}{3}, \frac{1}{2}$ **2. a.** -120 **b.** $30xy$ **c.** $20abc$ **d.** $x(x-2)$ **e.** $(3x+1)(3x-1)$ **f.** $(x-y)(x+y)$ **g.** $a-b$ **h.** $15(x-2)$ **3. a.** 24 **b.** $2x(2x+1)$ **c.** $24x$ **d.** x^2+2x **e.** $x(x+2)(2x+5)$ **4. a.** $\frac{-3a^2}{4b}$ **b.** $\frac{3x^2}{2y}$ **c.** $\frac{5-x}{2}$ **d.** $\frac{4}{3}$ **e.** $\frac{x-2}{x+4}$ **f.** $\frac{3x}{x+1}$ **g.** $\frac{-1}{5}$ **h.** $\frac{-(3+x)}{2x+5}$ **5. a.** $\frac{3a^2b}{2}$ **b.** $\frac{-8}{5p^2}$ **c.** $\frac{10a}{3c}$ **d.** $\frac{5}{a^2b}$ **e.** $\frac{3y}{2}$ **f.** $\frac{5n(m+4n)}{4m(m+n)}$ **g.** $\frac{y(2x+y)}{4(x+4y)}$ **h.** $\frac{-2}{5x^2+1}$ **i.** $\frac{4p}{3p-5}$ **6. a.** $\frac{15}{2x}$ **b.** $\frac{b-8a}{ab}$ **c.** $\frac{73}{15c}$ **d.** $\frac{17x-3}{12}$ **e.** $\frac{m-74}{36}$ **f.** $\frac{13y+2}{40y}$ **7.** 16, 24   **8.** $f = \frac{d_o(d_o-2)}{2d_o-2}$ **9. a.** $\frac{4}{2x-3}, x \neq \frac{3}{2}$ **b.** $\frac{12x^2+32x+1}{x+3}, x \neq -3$ **c.** $\frac{4x^2-12x-4}{(x-2)(x-4)}, x \neq 2, 4$ **d.** $\frac{16a+119}{(a-1)(a+8)}, a \neq 1, -8$ **e.** $\frac{48y^2+70y-12}{(y-3)(2y+1)(5y)}, y \neq 0, \frac{-1}{2}, 3$ **f.** $\frac{8x^2-16x-1}{(2x-1)(2x+1)}, x \neq \frac{1}{2}, \frac{-1}{2}$

10. a. $a = \frac{26}{17}$ **b.** $x = 105$ **c.** $x = \frac{19}{2}$ **d.** $x = -5$ **11.** $\pi(R_2 - R_1)(R_2 + R_1)$

Chapter 6

Page 129   **1.** Answers may vary.   **2. a.** 2 **b.** 3 **c.** 4   **3.** Answers may vary.   **4.**

$$\xleftrightarrow{\quad \overset{X}{\bullet} \quad \overset{A}{\bullet} \quad \overset{Y}{\bullet} \quad}$$

5. Answers may vary.   **6. a.** Sum is 90. **b.** Sum is 180.   **7. a.** 55 **b.** 27 **c.** 33 **d.** 1 **e.** 78 **f.** 41 **g.** $(90-x)$ **h.** $(75+2x)$ **8. a.** 105 **b.** 60 **c.** 177 **d.** 2 **e.** 91 **f.** 53 **g.** $(180-x)$ **h.** $(115-x)$ **9. a.** all angles less than 90 **b.** one angle equal to 90 **c.** one angle greater than 90 but less than 180 **d.** exactly two equal angles   **10. a.** 3 sides of different lengths **b.** 2 sides equal in length **c.** 3 sides equal in length   **11. a.** no angles equal **b.** two angles equal **c.** all angles equal

Pages 130-131   **1.** less than 90°; greater than 90°; 180°; greater than 180°   **2.** Answers may vary.   **3. a.** $x = 22.5°$ **b.** $x = 20°$ **4. a.** $x = 130°$ **b.** $x = 5°$ **c.** $x = 6°$ **d.** $y = 49°$ **5.** Sum is 180°.   **6. a.** $x = 134°$ **b.** $x = 36°$ **c.** $x = 32°$ **d.** $x = 15.6°$ **7.** Answers can vary. **a.** $\angle POQ$ **b.** $\angle POS$ **c.** $\angle POT$ **d.** $\angle QOR$ and $\angle UOS$ **e.** $\angle UOT$ and $\angle TOS$ **f.** $\angle UOQ$ and $\angle QOR$ **g.** $\angle UOP$ and $\angle POR$ **h.** $\angle POU$ and $\angle UOT$

Pages 132-133   **1.** Supplementary angles; Subtraction property; Subtraction property; Transitive property   **2.** Opposite pairs of angles formed by the intersection of two lines are congruent.   **3. a.** addition, division, multiplication **b.** substitution **c.** reflexive **d.** transitive   **4.** Answers may vary.   **5.** Opposite angle theorem; 73°, Substitution; Supplementary angles; 180°, Substitution; 107°, Subtraction   **6. a.** $a = c = 44°$, $b = 136°$ **b.** $x = 18°$ **7. a.** $\angle POR = 126°$ **b.** 100° **c.** 48° **d.** 51°   **8.** 03:12 and 03:20   **9. a.** 119° **b.** 125° **c.** 39° **d.** 43°   **10.** Joe, Ali, Ayube, Ellen

Pages 134-135   **1.** Answers may vary.   **2. a.** equilateral triangle **b.** square   **3.** Column 2: quadrilateral, pentagon, hexagon, septagon; Column 4: octagon, nonagon, decagon, dodecagon   **5. a.** T **b.** square **c.** T **d.** equiangular **e.** T **f.** T **g.** equilateral (polygon) **h.** rectangle, square **i.** T **j.** trapezoid   **6. a.** parallelogram, rectangle, square, rhombus **b.** square, rhombus **c.** square, rectangle **d.** parallelogram, rectangle, square, rhombus **e.** parallelogram, rectangle, square, rhombus   **7.** Column 3: 9, 4, 14, 5, 20; Column 4: 6, 27, 7, 35, $\frac{n(n-3)}{2}$ **8.** rhombus   **9.** 8

Pages 136-137 **1. a.** $\overline{AB}$ and $\overline{DE}$, $\overline{BC}$ and $\overline{EF}$, $\overline{AC}$ and $\overline{DF}$, $\angle A \cong \angle D$, $\angle B \cong \angle E$, $\angle C \cong \angle F$, **b.** $\overline{KL}$ and $\overline{KN}$, $\overline{KM}$ and $\overline{KP}$, $\overline{LM}$ and $\overline{NP}$, $\angle K \cong \angle K$, $\angle KLM \cong \angle N$, $\angle KML \cong \angle P$ **2.** $\dfrac{300}{900} = \dfrac{500}{CD}$ **3. a.** 16
b. $\dfrac{125}{18}$ **4.** $x = y = z = 12.25$ **5.** \$1208.09
6. $\angle C = 180 - \angle A - \angle B$; $\angle F = 180 - \angle D - \angle E$ but $\angle D \cong \angle A$ and $\angle E \cong \angle B$; therefore, $\angle F \cong \angle C$
7. Answers may vary. **8.** 161.11... m **9.** 66.1 m

Pages 138-139 **1.** Answers may vary. **2. a.** 1, 2, 7, 8, a, b, g, h **b.** 3, 4, 5, 6, c, d, e, f **c.** 1, 5; 3, 7; 2, 6; 4, 8; a, e; c, g; b, f; d, h **d.** 3, 6; 4, 5; c, f; d, e **e.** 4, 6; 3, 5; c, e; d, f **f.** 1, 4; 2, 3; 5, 8; 6, 7; a, d; c, b; e, h; f, g
3. Yes; line through any two lines is a transversal.
4. Always constant. **5.** Alternate interior angles are equal. **6.** Consecutive interior angles are supplementary. **7. a.** If the sum of the interior angles is 180°, then lines are parallel. **8.** Answers may vary. **9.** consecutive interior angles — substitution property **10.** tetrahedron **11.** double tetrahedron

Pages 140-141 **1.** alternate interior angles; opposite angles; $\angle 7$; if a transversal intersects two parallel lines, the corresponding angles are equal
2. alternate interior angles; subtraction; substitution; $x = 20$ **3.** $\angle e = \angle d = 130°$, $\angle a = \angle c = 50°$, $\angle f = \angle g = 82°$ **4. a.** 70° **b.** 95°
5. a. $\angle a = 85°$, $\angle b = 41°$, $\angle c = 54°$ **b.** $\angle a = 56°$, $\angle b = 38°$ **6.** $\angle 1 \cong \angle 4$, $\angle 4 \cong \angle 2$
7. $\angle BAC = \angle DAE = 60°$, $\angle ABC = \angle ADE = 48°$, $\angle ACB = \angle AED = 72°$ **8.** $\angle 1 + \angle 2 + \angle 3 = 180°$, $\angle 1 \cong \angle 4$, $\angle 3 \cong \angle 5$ $\therefore \angle 4 + \angle 2 + \angle 5 = 180°$

Pages 142-143 **1.** To avoid incorrect generalizations. **2.** Answers may vary. **3.** Answers may vary. **4.** Angle bisectors are congruent.
5. The line is parallel to the third side. **6.** The angle bisector of the vertex formed by two congruent sides of an isosceles triangle is perpendicular to its base. **7.** "Ortho" means right angle. **8.** If the midpoint of the sides of any quadrilateral are joined, the resulting figure is always a parallelogram. **9.** Answers may vary. **10.** around

Pages 144-145 **1. a.** 106° **b.** 47° **c.** 66° **d.** $x = 50°$, $y = 59°$ **e.** 63° **f.** $a = 55°$, $b = 75°$, $c = 50°$ **2. a.** 77° **b.** 6° **c.** 43° **d.** 64° **e.** $180 - 8x°$ **f.** $200 - 3x°$ **3.** 63° **4. a.** $a = 72°$, $b = 52°$, $c = 52°$, $d = 56°$ **b.** $a = 70°$, $b = 75°$, $c = 35°$, $d = 70°$ **c.** $x = 36°$, $y = 54°$, $z = 36°$ **d.** $a = 61°$, $b = 40°$, $c = 40°$ **5. a.** $x = 20°$ **b.** $a = 32°$ **c.** $c = 8°$ **d.** $x = 17°$ **6.** $\angle ABX = 47°$, $\angle CBX = 47°$
7. two congruent triangles **8.** 18°, 72°, 90°
9. $a = 18°$, $b = 32°$ **10. a.** 360°; $180n - 360°$
b. $180(n - 2)$ **c.** 180°; 360°; 540°; 720°; 900°; 1080°; 1260°; 1440°; 1800°; $180(n - 2)°$ **BRAINTICKLER**

S = 9, E = 5, N = 6, D = 7, M = 1, O = 0, R = 8, Y = 2

Pages 146-147 **1. a.** $\angle ABD$, $\angle D$, $\angle C$ **b.** $\angle KLM$, $\angle N$, $\angle M$ **2. a.** 110° **b.** 125° **3.** A.S.T.T.; S.A.T.; Transitive; Subtraction **4. a.** $x = 30°$ **b.** $x = 25°$
c. $x = 10°$ **d.** $x = 20°$ **5. a.** $a = 105°$, $b = 30°$
b. $x = 30°$, $y = 40°$, $z = 20°$, $v = 50°$ **c.** $k = 100°$, $l = 40°$, $m = 20°$ **6.** Exterior angle cannot equal one interior opposite angle. **7.** S.A.T.; $\angle 1$; $\angle 3$; Parallel lines; Substitution; $\angle 4 = \angle 1 + \angle 2$; Substitution **8.** If the exterior angle is equal to the sum of the interior opposite angles then it must be greater than any of them. **9. a.** $\angle S$, $\angle R$ will be acute; $\angle T$ will be obtuse. **b.** $\angle S$, $\angle R$ will be acute; $\angle T$ will be 90°. **c.** $\angle S$ or $\angle R$ could be obtuse; $\angle T$ will be acute. **d.** not possible
10. a. 85° **b.** 80° **c.** 80° **d.** 155° **e.** 165°
11. Column 1: 120°, 72°, 60°, 45°, 36°; Column 2: 360° **12.** 17.4%

Pages 148-149 **1. a.** $\overline{AB} \cong \overline{SV}$, $\overline{AC} \cong \overline{SW}$, $\overline{BC} \cong \overline{VW}$, $\angle A \cong \angle S$, $\angle B \cong \angle V$, $\angle C \cong \angle W$, $\triangle ABC \cong \triangle SVW$ **b.** $\overline{EA} \cong \overline{DI}$, $\overline{ER} \cong \overline{DM}$, $\overline{AR} \cong \overline{IM}$, $\angle E \cong \angle D$, $\angle A \cong \angle I$, $\angle R \cong \angle M$, $\triangle EAR \cong \triangle DIM$ **2. a.** $\triangle ABC \cong \triangle JHI$
b. $\triangle PQR \cong \triangle XZY$ **3. a.** $\triangle RST \cong \triangle RVQ$
b. $\triangle DEF \cong \triangle HGK$ **4. a.** $\overline{AB} \cong \overline{KL}$, $\overline{AC} \cong \overline{KM}$, $\overline{BC} \cong \overline{LM}$, $\angle A \cong \angle K$, $\angle B \cong \angle L$, $\angle C \cong \angle M$
b. $\overline{RS} \cong \overline{PQ}$, $\overline{RT} \cong \overline{PR}$, $\overline{ST} \cong \overline{QR}$, $\angle R \cong \angle P$, $\angle S \cong \angle Q$, $\angle T \cong \angle R$ **c.** $\overline{EF} \cong \overline{EH}$, $\overline{EG} \cong \overline{EG}$, $\overline{FG} \cong \overline{HG}$, $\angle E \cong \angle E$, $\angle F \cong \angle H$, $\angle G \cong \angle G$
5. a. 120 cm **b.** 16 m **c.** 86° **d.** 65°
6. a. $\triangle BKE \cong \triangle SRI$ **b.** $\triangle ISR \cong \triangle KPL$
c. $\triangle QWE \cong \triangle UOJ$ **d.** $\triangle CVX \cong \triangle TYX$ **7.** $\angle L$, $\angle K$, $\angle J$, $\overline{LK}$, $\overline{LJ}$, $\overline{KJ}$ **8.** $\overline{DE} \cong \overline{KL}$, $\overline{DF} \cong \overline{KM}$, $\overline{EF} \cong \overline{LM}$, $\angle D \cong \angle K$, $\angle E \cong \angle L$, $\angle F \cong \angle M$
9. triangles congruent by definition **10.** $\overline{AB} \cong \overline{AC}$, isosceles triangle **11.** $\overline{AB} \cong \overline{AC}$, $\overline{AC} \cong \overline{BC}$, equilateral triangle **12. a.** 2 **b.** 4 **c.** 16, 32, 2^{n-1}
13. yes

Page 150 **1. a.** 30° **b.** 540° **c.** 360°
d. $S = 180(n - 2)$ **2. b.** Find the sum of the interior angles. **c.** It is the number of vertices. **d.** It is the number of degrees in a triangle. **3. a.** 20 number of sides of the polygon; 30 sum of the interior angles (720°); 40 prints the sum; 50 prints the measure of each interior angle (120°); 60 prints the measure of each exterior angle (60°); 70 prints the sum of the exterior angles (360°) **b.** 20 FOR N = 3 TO 10; 97 NEXT

Page 151 **1.** A line segment has endpoints.
2. $\overline{AB}$, $\overline{BC}$, $\overline{AC}$ **3. a.** $x = 20$ **b.** $p = 17$ **4. a.** $x = 24$
b. $z = 10$ **5. a.** square or rhombus **b.** all quadrilaterals **c.** all quadrilaterals **d.** trapezoid
e. square, rectangle **f.** parallelogram, rectangle,

rhombus, square **g.** square **6. a.** $x = 10$, $a = 150°$, $b = 30°$, $c = 150°$ **b.** $a = 65°$, $b = 74°$, $c = 41°$ **7.** Perpendicular bisectors are concurrent in squares and rectangles. **8. a.** $74°, 68°, 38°$ **b.** $86°, 46°, 132°$ **9.** Answers may vary. **10.** $64°, 32°, 84°$ **11.** 80 bubblegums, 18 pops, 2 bars **12.** $\overline{AB} \cong \overline{YZ}$, $\overline{BC} \cong \overline{ZX}$, $\overline{AC} \cong \overline{YX}$, $\angle A \cong \angle Y$, $\angle B \cong \angle Z$, $\angle C \cong \angle X$

Page 152 **1. a.** yes **b.** yes **c.** no **d.** yes **2. a.** $34°$ **b.** $93°$ **c.** $38°$ **d.** $31°$ **e.** $(90 - 5x)°$ **f.** $(110 + 2x)°$ **g.** $38°, 78°, 64°$ **3. a.** $x = 22.5°$, $y = 90°$ **b.** $x = 10°$, $y = 20°$ **4. a.** F **b.** T **c.** T **d.** F **e.** T **f.** T **5. a.** $x = 70°, 90°, 20°$ **b.** $x = 28$ **6.** Answers may vary. **7. a.** $a = c = 40°$, $b = d = 55°$, $e = 85°$ **b.** $a = 105°$, $b = d = 75°$, $c = 30°$ **8.** $\dfrac{AO}{OM} = \dfrac{2}{1} = \dfrac{BO}{ON} = \dfrac{CO}{OP}$ **9.** $70°, 110°$ **10.** $150°, 30°$

Cumulative Review Chapters 4 - 6

Pages 153-156 **1. a.** $3, -x^3 + 5x^2 + 2$ **b.** $4, -3x^4 + 19x^2$ **c.** $4, -x^4 + 4x^3 + 8x^2 - 12x - 15$

2. a. -52 **b.** -8 **c.** 35.5 **d.** $\dfrac{7}{6}$

3. a. $-4xy - 3yz + 14xz$ **b.** $7a^2b^2 - 12a^2b - 2ab^2$ **c.** $7m^2 + 5mn - 5$ **d.** $2v^2 - 7u^2 + 10u$ **e.** $4a^2 - 18ab - 24b^2$ **4. a.** $14u^2 + 50uv$ **b.** $-p - 13q$ **c.** $6x^3 - 35x^2 + 52x - 5$ **d.** $10y^2 + 20y - 13$ **e.** $5k^2 - 4k - 17$ **f.** $-x^2 + 16x - 18$ **g.** $14p^2 + 16p + 48$ **h.** $12m^3 + 29m^2 + 7m - 6$ **5. a.** $2a(5a + 8b)$ **b.** $(2m - 5)(m + 3)$ **c.** $(3k + 8)(k - 1)$ **d.** $(4x - 1)^2$ **e.** $2x(x - 3)(x - 2)$ **f.** $3(x - 5y)(x + 5y)$ **g.** $(4p - 3q)(p + 4q)$ **h.** $2(3r - 5t)(3r + 5t)$ **i.** $(4a + b)(2a + 5b)$ **j.** $-4xy(2y - 3 + 6x)$ **k.** $(4a - 3)(2b - 1)$

6. a. $a^2 + 4b$ **b.** $2x$ **c.** $a^2 + 5$ **7. a.** $\dfrac{4}{3}$ **b.** $x = 0$ or $x = 4$ **c.** $m = 3$ or $m = -\dfrac{1}{4}$ **d.** $k = \dfrac{-5}{2}$ or $k = 4$ **e.** $a = 8$ or $a = -1$ **f.** $t = \dfrac{-5}{2}$ or $t = -1$

8. $12x^2 + 56x + 60$ units^2 **9.** $P = 26m + 18n$ units; $A = 40m^2 + 36mn - 36n^2$ units^2 **10. a.** $S = 10a - 9b$ **b.** $P = 10a^2 - 26ab + 13b^2$ **11.** $6x - 4y$ units **12.** $12p^3 - 12p^2 + 3p$ m **13.** Row 1: $3a^2 - 9ab - 7b^2$; Row 2: $2a^2 + 3ab - 5b^2$, $-2a^2 - 5ab - 4b^2$; Row 3: $a^2 - 8ab - 3b^2$, $-3a^2 + 7ab - 2b^2$ **14.** three 23's, two 15's, one 12 **15.** $16a^3 + 16a^2b + 4ab^2$ **16. a.** $x \neq 0$ **b.** $n \neq 2$ **c.** $x \neq -3$ **d.** $a \neq \pm 3$ **e.** $y \neq -3$, $y \neq 1$

17. a. $\dfrac{3m^2}{8n^3}$ **b.** $\dfrac{6a - 5b}{2(4c + b)}$ **c.** $\dfrac{x - 8}{x - 2}$ **d.** $\dfrac{m - 4}{2m + 1}$ **e.** $\dfrac{2p + 3q}{6p - q}$ **f.** $\dfrac{5k + 6t}{3k}$ **18. a.** $\dfrac{16p^3}{3q^2}$ **b.** xy^2z **c.** 3 **d.** 5 **19. a.** $60ab^2$ **b.** $2q(p - 2q)$ **c.** $2x + 6$

d. $(x + 1)(x - 1)(x + 2)$ **20. a.** $\dfrac{6b + 3a}{4ab}$ **b.** $\dfrac{6qr - 5pr + 9q}{3pqr}$ **c.** $\dfrac{14m + 3}{24}$ **d.** $\dfrac{12b^2 - 3}{10ab}$ **21. a.** $\dfrac{5m - 2}{4m(m + 2)}$ **b.** $\dfrac{6x - 20}{(x + 4)(x - 2)(x - 4)}$ **c.** $\dfrac{4k^2 - 3k - 12}{(k + 1)(k - 4)}$ **d.** $\dfrac{-10s^2 + 10st + 11t^2}{(4s + t)(s + 2t)}$ **22.** $\dfrac{5a + 19}{(a - 4)(3a + 1)}$ **23. a.** 2.25 **b.** $15.333...$ **c.** 34.5 **d.** 3 **e.** $\dfrac{-1}{22}$ **f.** $0.545\,4...$ **24. a.** $\dfrac{160}{h}$ **b.** $\dfrac{160}{h - n}$ **25. a.** 73.333 min **b.** $\dfrac{95m + 15n}{m^2 + mn}$ h **26.** 1; didn't add 3 to get the next number **27.** 3 of clubs, 10 of diamonds, queen of spades **28. a.** less than 90° **b.** sum to 180° **c.** greater than 90° **d.** sum to 90° **29.** $132°$ and $48°$ **30. a.** O.A.T. **31.** $130°$ **32.** A square is a special rectangle. **33.** All sides and angles equal. **a.** equilateral triangle **b.** square **34.** $x = 52.5$, $y = 33.2$ **35.** one **36. a.** 3 and 6 **b.** 2 and 4 **c.** 1 and 8 **37.** Congruent angles: $\angle 1, \angle 7$; $\angle 2, \angle 8$; $\angle 3, \angle 5$; $\angle 4, \angle 6$; $\angle 1, \angle 3$; $\angle 2, \angle 4$; $\angle 6, \angle 8$; $\angle 5, \angle 7$; Supplementary angles: $\angle 1, \angle 8$; $\angle 1, \angle 2$; $\angle 2, \angle 7$; $\angle 7, \angle 8$; $\angle 2, \angle 3$; $\angle 6, \angle 7$; $\angle 3, \angle 6$; $\angle 3, \angle 4$; $\angle 4, \angle 5$; $\angle 5, \angle 6$ **38.** $e = 70° = d = c = h$, $a = 110° = f$, $b = 40°$, $g = 140°$ **39.** $72.5°$ **40.** Answers may vary. **41.** Answers may vary. **42.** Set the 2 min one and the 5 min one together. When the 2 min timer goes off, start the dinner leaving 3 min on the 5 min timer. **43.** Use parallel lines. **44.** $10°, 30°, 20°$ **45.** three congruent angles and sides **46.** No, angles don't match. **47.** $1050 **48.** Answers may vary. **49.** No, two parallel lines have 180°. **50. a.** No sides equal in length. **b.** Three sides equal in length. **c.** Two sides equal in length.

Chapter 7

Page 157 **1. c.** 1 unit **d.** 90° **e.** square **f.** $(0, 0)$ **g.** I, II, III, IV **2. a.** two lines in a plane that never intersect **b.** two lines intersect at 90° **c.** ratio of rise to run **d.** a closed plane figure **3. a.** both the same **b.** first **c.** no difference **4.** equilateral parallelogram **5. a.** $\dfrac{-3}{4}$ **b.** 1 **c.** undefined **d.** $\dfrac{-5}{3}$ **6.** $\sqrt{(x^2 + y^2)^2}$ **7.** 17 km **8. a.** 2 **b.** -19 **c.** 1.4 **9.** Diagonal does not bisect a trapezoid.

Pages 158-159 **1. a.** $(4, 1)$ **b.** $(-4, -1)$ **c.** $(-4, 1)$ **2.** $(0, -1), (-2, -4), (2, -4), (-4, 3), (4, 3)$ **3.** $A(-2, 2), B(5, 3), C(-3, -2)$ **4.** $(0, 1), (0, 3), (-2, 1), (-3, 0), (3, 0), (-2, -1), (2, -1)$ **5.** Answers may vary. **6.** $A(1, 0), B(2, 30), C(3, 60), D(4, 90), E(3, 120), F(2, 150), G(1, 180)$ **7.** Answers may vary.

Pages 160-161   **1. a.** 1 **b.** 0 **c.** $-\frac{3}{4}$ **2.** Answers may vary. **3. a.** $\frac{5}{3}$ **b.** $\frac{4}{5}$ **c.** $\frac{2}{7}$ **d.** 0 **4.** Answers may vary. **5.** $-3, -1, -\frac{3}{5}$ **6.** Answers may vary. **7. a.** (3, 3) **b.** (1, 1) **c.** (1, −5) **8. a.** yes, constant slope **b.** no, slope inconsistent **9.** Answers may vary. **10.** Answers may vary. **11.** Answers may vary. **12. a.** $\frac{1}{6}$ **b.** 3.5 m, 7 m, 10.5 m **c.** $\frac{2}{15}$ **13. a.** $\frac{q}{p}$ **b.** Answers may vary. **c.** Find slope using (0, 0). **14. a.** −9 **b.** 2 **c.** 3

Pages 162-163   **1.** Perpendicular: 1, 2; 2, 8; 3, 9; 5, 10, Parallel: 1, 8; 6, 7; 4, 10 **2.** Parallel sides have a slope of $\frac{4}{3}$. **3.** no **4. a.** Possible answers: **a.** (1, 2), (4, 2) **b.** (0, 9) **c.** $\left(4, \frac{11}{4}\right)$ **d.** (0, 0), (1, −4) **e.** (1, 3), (1, 6) **f.** (0, −3) **g.** (9, 17) **h.** (5, −5) **i.** $\left(\frac{29}{4}, -3\right)$ **5. a.** (1, 2), (4, 2) **b.** (−1, 2), (2, −4) **c.** (−1, −5), (1, −5) **d.** (0, 4), (3, 9) **6.** $-\frac{b}{a}$ **7.** Answers may vary. **8. a.** $\frac{20}{11}$ **b.** $\frac{1}{2}$ **c.** (0, 3) **d.** $\left(\frac{3}{2}, 0\right)$ **9.** $D(−1, 1)$ **10.** 11 **11.** Answers may vary.

Pages 164-165   **1. a.** 5 **b.** 5 **c.** 8 **d.** approx. 9.9 **e.** approx. 12.47 **f.** approx. 25.18 **g.** 4.5 **h.** 9.21 **2.** Answers may vary. **3. a.** 2, −2 **b.** approx. 40 units **c.** isosceles **4. a.** $\sqrt{(d−b)^2 + (c−a)^2}$ **b.** 25 **c.** $2\sqrt{10}t$ **d.** $\sqrt{5a^2 − 2a + 10}$ **5.** $\overline{PQ} = 4\sqrt{5}$, $\overline{QR} = 4\sqrt{5}$, $\overline{PR} = 4\sqrt{10}$ **6. a.** $\overline{PQ} = 2\sqrt{5} = \overline{QR} = \overline{RS} = \overline{PS}$ — rhombus **b.** $\overline{QS} = 6\sqrt{2}$, $\overline{PR} = 2\sqrt{2}$ **7.** (0, 0) to (3, −3) to (5, 3) to (2, 4); distance approx. 4119 m

Pages 166-167   **1. a.** T **b.** F **c.** F **d.** F **2. a.** (5, 10.5) **b.** (1.5, 7) **c.** (3, 3) **d.** (−2.5, −1) **e.** (0.5, −4) **f.** (−1.6, 2.55) **3.** 12 units² **4. a.** (0, 0), (1, 0), (1, 2), (−2, 2), (−2, −2), (3, −2), (3, 4), (−4, 4), (−4, −4), (5, −4), (5, 6) **b.** (0, 0), (1, 1), $\left(-\frac{1}{2}, 2\right)$, (−2, 0), $\left(\frac{1}{2}, -2\right)$, (3, 1), $\left(-\frac{1}{2}, 4\right)$, (−4, 0), $\left(\frac{1}{2}, -4\right)$, (5, 1) **5.** (0, 0) **6. a.** (6.75, 11.25), (10.5, 17.5), (14.25, 23.75) **b.** (−5.5, 1.5), (−3, 13), (−0.5, 24.5) **c.** (−9.5, 22.75), (−7, 12.5), (−4.5, 2.25) **d.** (−10.25, −13.75), (−8.5, −19.4), (−6.75, −25.05) **e.** (1.2, −29.55), (2.4, −19.7), (3.6, −9.85) **f.** $\left(\frac{3a+c}{4}, \frac{3b+d}{4}\right), \left(\frac{a+c}{2}, \frac{b+d}{2}\right),$ $\left(\frac{a+3c}{4}, \frac{b+3d}{4}\right)$ **7.** Answers may vary. **8. a.** $\left(\frac{3}{2}, -2\sqrt{3}\right)$ **b.** $\frac{\sqrt{201}}{2}$ **9.** $\overline{NT} = \sqrt{18}$, $\overline{TP} = \sqrt{18}$, $\overline{MT} = \sqrt{13}$, $\overline{TO} = \sqrt{13}$ **10.** $\overline{PQ} = \sqrt{10}$

11. Distance from vertex to point of intersection M is twice the remaining distance to the opposite side: for example $|\overline{MK}| = 6$, median $K = 9$ ∴ $\frac{6}{9} = \frac{2}{3}$. **12.** Answers may vary. **13.** Answers may vary. **14.** $\angle MTA \cong \angle WMB, \angle TMA \cong \angle MWB, \overline{TM} \cong \overline{MW}, \triangle TMA \cong \triangle MWB$

Pages 168-169   **1. a.** $\overline{AD} = \sqrt{5}$ **b.** slope $\overline{AD}$ = slope $\overline{BC}$ = −2, slope $\overline{AB}$ = slope $\overline{CD}$ = $\frac{3}{4}$ **2.** Slopes are negative reciprocals. **3.** $\overline{DF} = \overline{EF} = 7.8$ **4.** Opposite sides are equal and parallel. **5.** Opposite sides are equal and parallel. **6. a.** $\overline{PS} = \overline{PT} = 2\sqrt{13}$ **b.** $\overline{YZ}$ is bisected. **7. a.** parallelogram **b.** (−5, 5) and (5, −5) **c.** $x = \pm 5$, $y = \pm 4.5$ **8.** Answers may vary. **9.** 750 m **10. c.** $\overline{PQ} = \sqrt{a^2 + b^2}$ **d.** $\overline{QR} = \sqrt{c^2 + d^2}$, $\overline{PR} = \sqrt{(a−c)^2 + (b−d)^2}$ **e.** $\sqrt{a^2 − 2ac + c^2 + b^2 − 2bd + d^2}$ **f.** $ac = −bd$ **11.** one pair $\sqrt{p^2 + r^2}$, other pair $\sqrt{p^2 + q^2}$; one slope is undefined and the other is 0 **12. a.** $\overline{AB} = 4$, $\overline{LM} = 8$, $\overline{BC} = 3$, $\overline{MN} = 6$, $\overline{AC} = 5$, $\overline{LN} = 10$ **b.** 6 units², 24 units²

Page 170   **1.** points on the same straight line **2.** Check if the slopes between the two sets of points are the same. **3.** 41 LET A = X1 − X • 42 LET B = X2 − X1 • 43 LET C = X2 − X • 44 IF A = B = C THEN 99 • 45 IF A = 0 THEN 85 • 46 IF B = 0 THEN 85 • 47 IF C = 0 THEN 85 • 99 PRINT "ALL POINTS LIE IN A VERTICAL LINE" **4.** 10 INPUT "FIRST POINT "; X; Y • 15 INPUT "SECOND POINT "; X1; Y1 • 20 LET D = SQR((Y1 − Y) ∧ 2 + (X1 − X) ∧ 2) • 25 PRINT "DISTANCE BETWEEN POINTS "; D • 30 END **5.** 26 LET P = (X1 + X) / 2 • 27 LET Q = (Y1 + Y) / 2 • 28 PRINT "MIDPOINT IS ("; P; ", "; Q; ")" **7.** 30 INPUT "SECOND VERTEX " X1; Y1 • 40 INPUT "THIRD VERTEX "; X2; Y2 • 60 LET B = SQR((Y1 − Y) ∧ 2 + (X1 − X) ∧ 2) • 70 LET C = SQR((Y2 − Y) ∧ 2 + (X2 − X) ∧ 2) • 100 LET AREA = SQR(S * (S − A) * (S − B) * (S − C)) • 110 PRINT "AREA IS "; AREA **a.** calculating the lengths of sides **b.** solve for S **c.** to help the user understand the program **d.** no multiplication signs

Page 171   **1.** Answers may vary. **2.** (5, 1.4), (5, −1.4) **3. a.** $\frac{1}{3}$ **b.** $\frac{1}{4}$ **c.** $\frac{1}{9}$ **d.** $-\frac{1}{11}$ **e.** 0 **f.** undefined **g.** approx. 0.24 **h.** 0 **4.** Examples: **a.** $\left(-\frac{1}{2}, 2\right)$ **b.** (9, −5) **c.** $\left(\frac{19}{8}, -1\right)$ **d.** (6, 6) **5.** Example: (1, 150) **6.** Example: (120, 3) **7.** Example: (0, 4) **8. a.** $x = 2.5$ **b.** $y = \frac{140}{3}$ **9.** First coordinate is a. **10.** Slopes are not the same.

11. a. 10 **b.** 6.32 **c.** 12.2 **d.** 3.16 **12. a.** (5, 5)
b. (6, 6) **c.** (0, 0) **d.** (1.65, −1.15) **13.** a, c, e; b, d
14. Answers may vary. **15.** Examples: **a.** (−3, 1)

b. (−1, 7) **c.** (5, 0) **d.** (27, 6) **16.** 1, −1 **17.** 11, $-\dfrac{1}{11}$

Page 172 **1. a.** $\dfrac{7}{6}, -\dfrac{41}{27}, -\dfrac{6}{57}$ **b.** no **c.** scalene

d. $\left(-3, \dfrac{3}{2}\right)$, (2.7, 0.9), (−0.3, −2.6) **e.** $\dfrac{7}{6}, -\dfrac{41}{27}, -\dfrac{6}{57}$
f. $\sqrt{32.85}, \sqrt{21.25}, \sqrt{24.10}$ **g.** parallel **h.** Answers
may vary. **i.** (2.7, 0.9) **j.** (−0.6, −10.2) **k.** Example:
(0.6, 1.2) **2.** Answers may vary. **3.** Answers may
vary. **4. a.** 0 **b.** undefined **5.** Answer may vary.
6. Answers may vary. **7.** 5 units² **8.** Answers may
vary. **9. a.** Pick a point and calculate the necessary

lengths. **b.** M(6, 7), slopes are −2 and $\dfrac{1}{2}$ **c.** 1, −1

10. Answers may vary.

Chapter 8

Page 173 **1. a.** (4, 12), (5, 15), (6, 18) **b.** (4, 16),
(5, 25), (6, 36) **c.** (4, 7), (5, 9), (6, 11) **2. a.** −1, −2,
−3, −4, −5, −6 **b.** −9, −5, −1, 3, 7 **c.** 7, −5, 7, 43,
103 **3. a.** 13, 4, 1 **b.** 5, 5, 19 **c.** 19, 16, 7, 8 **4. a.** 4, 2
b. −13, 23 **5.** ratio of change in y to the change in x
6.

x	x^2	x^3
3	9	27
5.7	32.49	185.193
11	121	1331
13.5	182.25	2460.375

7. $a \leq c < b$, where a and b are real numbers

8. $x = \dfrac{2r}{\sqrt{5}}$ **9.** $36

Page 174 **1.** a set of ordered pairs where one term
is a function of the other term **2. a.** $n \longrightarrow 5n$; $(n, 5n)$

b. $n \longrightarrow 100n$; $(n, 100n)$ **c.** $n \longrightarrow \dfrac{n(n+1)}{2}$; $\left(n, \dfrac{n(n+1)}{2}\right)$
3. a. (9, 94.50) **b.** (12, 126) **c.** (35, 367.5)
4. Answers may vary. **5. a.** $5.50 **b.** $10.75
c. $18.10 **6.** Answers may vary. **7. a.** (1, 41),
(2, 41), (3, 43), (4, 47), (6, 61), (7, 71) **b.** $n = 91$
8. *many-to-one:* each x-value has the same y-value;
one-to-one: each x-value has exactly one y-value;
one-to-many: some x-values have more than one
y-value. **9.** A function is a relation such that for
every x-value there is exactly one y-value.

Page 175-177 **1. a.** relation **b.** linear **c.** constant
d. non-linear **2. a.** isolated **b.** continuous **3.** As
the length of the side approaches zero, so does the
perimeter. **4. a.** 14, 5.29, 75.69 **b.** no,
$3.1 \times 4 = 12.4$ **c.** Example: (1.3, 5.2) **5. a.** 11.18,

16.92, 23.98, 26.83, 35.78, 58.14 **c.** linear
6. Answers may vary. **7. a.** 119.38 cm

b.

Revolutions	Distance (m)
100	119
300	358
740	883
1000	1193
1250	1492

8. (0, 0), (2, 2), $\left(-2, \dfrac{2}{3}\right)$, $\left(3, \dfrac{3}{2}\right)$ **a.** numbers whose
sum and product are equal **9. b.** yes **c.** $(r, \pi r^2)$;
non-linear because of squared term **10.** Answers
may vary. **11.** Answers may vary. **12. b.** Rate of
growth increases each decade. **13. c.** non-linear
d. Graph has a maximum and a minimum.
14. Larger diameter is $\sqrt{2}$ times the smaller.
15. y-value is constant for all x-values. **16.** x-value
is constant for all y-values. **17. a.** approximately
15 m **b.** approximately 4 m **HISTORICAL NOTE**
a. 59 **b.** 17 **c.** 25 **d.** 42.02

Pages 178-179 **1.** a, d **2.**

Units	Income
1	170
2	190
3	210

3. a. linear **b.** constant **c.** (0, 0) **4.** b, c **5. a.** linear
b. There is a constant part not equal to 0. **6.** c, d
7. a. linear **b.** decreases **c.** constant **8. a.** direct
b. direct **c.** direct **9.** partial **10. c.** no; (x, x^3)
non-linear because of cubed term.

Pages 180-181 **1. a.** direct **b.** constant of
proportionality **2.** 3 **3. a.** 2325 km **b.** 6.5 h
c. 59 520 km **d.** 5 431 200 km **e.** for a 30 d month,
446 400 km **4. a.** 28 **b.** 33.2 **c.** 21.9 **d.** 48 **5. a.** 7;
95 **b.** (9, 42.75), (17.3, 82.33), (52, 247), (130, 617.5)

d. yes, 4.75 **6.** a, d **7. a.** $\dfrac{2}{5}$ **b.** $-\dfrac{4}{5}$ **8.** 12 N
9. (19, 59.7), (21, 65.9), (17.7, 55.5), (29, 91.1);
direct, $k = \pi$ **10. b.** yes **c.** Cost = Price × Amount
11. $\dfrac{A}{r^2}$ **12.** $\dfrac{V}{r^3}$

Pages 182-183 **1. a.** constant **b.** constant **c.** a
relation with a fixed part and a constant part
2. a. 4000 m **b.** yes **3. a.** 5.20; 7.80; 15

b. Examples: $\dfrac{3.90}{4} = 0.975$; $\dfrac{3.25}{3} = 1.083...$ **c.** $3.25
4. b. yes **d.** constant increase of 10¢/letter and a
fixed charge of $8/deck **5. a.** Examples:
(1200, 422), (1500, 440) **b.** $w = 350 + 0.06s$

6. a.

End of Month	1	2	3	...	12
Gas	59.997	59.994	59.991	...	59.964

b. partial variation **c.** $g = 60 - 0.003m$ **7. b.** $45.50,
$27.00, $15.90, $13.13, $12.20 **8. b.** partial, partial,

direct, other **c.** Emerson **BRAINTICKLER** TO = 16, AGE = 784, TWO = 196, NOT = 361, TWO + TO + TOO = 378 = NAG

Pages 184–185 **1. a.** increases **b.** product **c.** One quantity increases at a constant rate as the other decreases. **2.** Product sd is constant. **3. a.** 360 **b.** inversely **4. a.** Examples: (1, 12), (2, 6), (3, 4), ... **b.** Product is constant. **c.** $tv = 12$ **5. a.** $11 500 **b.** $4600 **c.** $va = 23\ 000$ **d.** No, product must be greater than zero. **6. a.** Examples: (1, 100), (2, 50), (4, 25), ... **b.** Product is constant. **d.** non-linear **7. a.** $15.60 **b.** Examples: (4, 19.5), (6, 13), ... **8. a.** no **b.** yes **c.** yes **9.** Example: $xy = 1600$ **10. a.** $td^2 = 0.01$ **b.** 0.5 cm

Page 186 **1.** < 375, then Company A; $375 < x < 800$, then Company B; > 800, then Company C **2.** 7200 units **3.** $d = km$ **4. a.** $c = 735 + 0.26k$ **5.** 487.5 km **6. a.** Weekly wage varies directly as the number of hours worked. **b.** Atomic weight varies inversely as the specific heat capacity. **c.** Frequency varies inversely as the wavelength. **d.** Mass varies directly as the square of r. **7.** 500 Hz

Page 187 **1. a.** between **b.** beyond **2. b.** 11.3 m **c.** around 14 **3. a.** $p = 12$, $q = 2.75$ **b.** $w = 7.05$, $u = 63.333...$

Page 188 **1.** $S = 4\pi r^2$ **2.** Return to line 50 and increment R. **3.** (0, 0), (0.5, π), (1, 12.566 36), (1.5, 28.274 31) **4.** 72 IF R = 1 THEN K1 = S / R • 74 IF R = 2 THEN K2 = S / R • 85 IF K1 = K2 THEN PRINT "DIRECT" • 86 GOTO 90 • 87 PRINT "NOT DIRECT" **5.** 30 PRINT "RADIUS", "SURFACE AREA", "RADIUS SQUARED" • 70 PRINT R, S, R $\wedge$ 2 **6.** 75 PRINT "RATIO OF S:R $\wedge$ 2"; S / R $\wedge$ 2 **7.** constant ratio $\rightarrow$ direct variation **8.** Modify program of the display: 30 PRINT "RATIO OF S:R $\wedge$ 2" • 60 V = 4 / 3 * PI * R $\wedge$ 3 • 70 PRINT R, V

Page 189 **1. a.** straight **b.** constant **c.** non-linear **d.** infinite **e.** partial **f.** inversely **g.** (0, 0) **h.** between

2. a.

Size	20 cm	46 cm	60 cm
Cost	$5.00	$9.68	$12.20

b. Custom Pizza for 20 cm only. **3. a.** 7 **b.** 32 **4. a.** 1548; 8 **b.** −1.02, −0.51, −20.4 **5.** partial **6. b.** linear **c.** isolated **d.** yes **e.** yes **f.** direct **g.** 1.4 **h.** $h = 1.4d$ **7.** Answers may vary.

Page 190 **1. a.** straight **b.** constant **c.** product **d.** beyond **2. a.** inverse **b.** none of these **c.** partial **d.** direct **3. a.** 4, 3 **b.** 6.9, 0.7 **4. a.** continuous **b.** no common ratio; slope isn't constant; product of elements is not constant **c.** Answer may vary. **d.** Answer may vary. **5. a.** Examples: (0, 0), (2, 4),

(3, 9) **b.** no constant of proportionality or constant product **6.** 5.25 **7.** $a = \frac{95}{418}F$ **8. a.** (ten thousands of litres, cost in dollars); Examples: (1, 8.916), (2, 13.002) **c.** linear, constant increase in cost, partial variation **d.** $C = 4.83 \times 4.086L$ **9. a.** inverse variation **10.** 2.52 L^3 **11. b.** approx. 15.36 **c.** estimating a hand-drawn curve

Chapter 9

Page 191 **1. a.** $x = 9$ **b.** $x = \frac{2}{3}$ **c.** $x = -12$ **d.** $a = 10.4$ **e.** no solution **f.** $c = 1.2$ **2.** Possible answers: **a.** $(-3, -17)$, $(2, -2)$ **b.** $(0, 20)$, $(2, 15)$ **3. a.** $3n + 2 = n + 4$ **b.** $\frac{3a}{4} - 6 = a - 10$

c. $a + 6 = 2(a - 5)$ **4. a.** 1 **b.** $-\frac{6}{7}$ **c.** $\frac{1}{4}$ **d.** $\frac{76}{41}$ **6. i)** $y = 7$, $x = 7$ **ii)** $y = -8$, $x = 2$ **iii)** $x = 22.5$, $y = -1.5$ **iv)** $y = -2.4$, $x = 1.333...$ **7. a.** $a = \frac{(P - 2b)}{2}$ **b.** $y = \frac{5x}{4} - 3$ **c.** $n = -\frac{5m}{2} + 5$ **8. a.** $p = kq$ **b.** $vs = k$ **9.** Too short to reach top buttons.

Pages 192–193 **1. a.** $p = 4s$ **b.** $c = 3.25 + 0.015p$ **c.** $m = 85 + 1.5b$ **d.** $y = 230n$ **e.** $d = 365.25a$ **f.** $t = 2.75 + 0.1c$ **2.** i with d, ii with b, iii with a **3.** c **4. a.** $g = 60 + 5t$ **b.** (110, 10), (125, 13), (160, 20) **5. a.** $c = 3.60 + 0.96m$ **b.** $t = 128.64v$ **c.** $pv = 8$ **d.** $s = 180(n - 2)$ **e.** $m = C - 0.2C$

6. a. $p = 6w + 10$ **b.** $s = 1.35c$ **c.** $A = \frac{(3h^2)}{2}$ **d.** $v = 25q$ **e.** $I = 0.0925s$ **f.** $I = 300 + 0.06s$ **g.** $L = 14.95 + 0.27L$ **7. a.** $c = (6.95 - 0.05n)n$ **b.** $0.022s$ for $s \le 1000$; $c = (0.022 - 0.0001s)s$ for $s > 1000$ **8. a.** area of a trapezoid **b.** slant height **c.** diagonal of a prism

Pages 194–195 **1. a.** Perimeter of a square is four times the length of one side. **b.** Volume of a cylinder is π times the square of the radius times the height. **c.** Volume of a sphere is four thirds times π times the radius cubed. **2.** $x + y = 37$ **3.** 17 **4.** Area of a circle is π times the square of the radius. **a.** 9π **b.** $\sqrt{\frac{10}{\pi}}$ **c.** π **d.** no **5. b.** $d = vt$ **c.** $t = \frac{d}{v}$ **6.** interest formula **7. a.** The present age in 6 a will be the same as four times the present age. **b.** The present age in 12 a will be five times the age 8 a ago. **c.** Five years ago the age was one half of the present age. **9.** Column 2: x, $x + 1$; l, $\frac{1}{2}$; x, $2x$; $3k$, $2k$; Column 3: $x + y = 33$; $l = 2w$; $y = 2x$; $\frac{3}{2} = \frac{x}{y}$

411

3. c and h, degree > 1

7. a. Increases at constant rate. **b.** no change
8. From $x = 0$ to 20, increases of 5 result in increases of 6 in y-values from -4 to 14. **9. b.** One is linear, one is non-linear, one crosses both axes, the other does not. **c.** $(1, 1)$ **d.** $y = 0$ in first; y is undefined in second. **10. a.** $\{2\}$ **b.** $\{x > 0\}$
11. a. $\{y \mid y = 4\}$ **b.** $\{y \in R\}$ **12. a.** $\{-1 \le y \le 1\}$ **b.** y increases then decreases then repeats this cycle.

Pages 198-199 **1. a.** Slope from $(1, 1)$ to $(2, 2)$ is 1; $(2, 2)$ to $(3, 3)$ is 1. **b.** Slope is 0 through $y = 2$.

c. Slope from $(-3, 4)$ to $(0, 2)$ is $-\frac{2}{3}$; $(0, 2)$ to $(3, 0)$

is $-\frac{2}{3}$ **2.** $-\frac{1}{8}, (13, -1)$ **3. a.** $2, -12, (1, -6)$ **b.** 2,

$-8, (1, -4)$ **c.** $6, -2, \left(1, -\frac{5}{3}\right)$ **d.** $\frac{10}{3}, 5, \left(1, \frac{7}{2}\right)$ **4.** a,

b, d, and f are linear. **6. i)** Both are linear. **ii)** In both cases, the decimals do not determine linearity since they are simple fractions with denominator 100. **7. a.** $8.61, 0.38$ **b.** $600, 32.3$ **c.** yes **8.** Answers may vary. **9. b.** no, isolated points for natural numbers of oranges **c.** 6 kg

Pages 200-201 **1. a.** $\frac{4}{3}, (0, 0)$ **b.** $-2, (-2, 0)$

3. a. 4 **b.** 0 **c.** -1 **d.** $\frac{8}{3}$ **4. a.** 3, 2 **b.** $-4, 6$ **c.** $\frac{3}{5}$,

-2.5 **d.** $5, 0$ **e.** $0, -2$ **f.** undefined, no y-intercept
5. Find two points on the line. Example: **a.** From $(-3, -17)$ and $(4, 18)$ slope is 5 which equals the x-coefficient. The y-intercept is -2. **6.** Possible

answers: $(-8, 0), \frac{3}{8}$; $(6, 0)$, undefined slope; $(0, 3)$,

$-\frac{1}{2}$ **7. b.** Slope is 500. **8. b.** Slope is 15.

9. b. Slope is $-\frac{5}{2}$ indicating the loss of

2.5 kg/month. **BRAINTICKLER** 60

Pages 202-203 **1. a.** $y = 2x - 7$ **b.** $y = -7x - 1$

c. $y = \frac{1x}{2} + \frac{5}{2}$ **d.** $y = \frac{-3x}{4} + \frac{7}{4}$ **2. a.** $y = \frac{5x}{6}$

b. $y = x - 4$ **c.** $y = -\frac{1x}{9} + \frac{14}{9}$ **d.** $y = \frac{3x}{10} - \frac{9}{10}$

e. $y = \frac{4x}{7} - \frac{11}{7}$ **f.** $y = \frac{9x}{2} + \frac{35}{2}$ **g.** $y = \frac{7x}{2} - \frac{3}{2}$

h. $x = 4$ **i.** $y = 0$ **j.** $x = 0$ **k.** $y = 3$ **l.** $y = \frac{8x}{15} + \frac{2}{5}$
3. a. $y = x + 5$ **b.** $y = -3x - 7$ **c.** $y = -4$

d. $y = -\frac{1x}{2} - \frac{7}{2}$ **e.** $y = 3x - 3$ **f.** $y = 2x$ **g.** $y = 3.5$

4. a. $y = \frac{9x}{22} + \frac{161}{55}$ **b.** $y = \frac{-5x}{11} + \frac{45}{11}$ **c.** $y = x - 7$

d. $(y - y_1) = m(x - x_1)$ **5. a.** $y = 0$ **b.** $x = 0$
6. $p = 1.7m - 1.4$ **7. a.** $c = 19t + 100$ **b.** 404 cups
8. a. $c = 0.13k + 895$ **b.** 19 800 km

9. a. $c = 22.5p + 125$ **b.** \$552.50 **10.** $y = -\frac{2x}{3} + \frac{8}{3}$

Pages 204-205 **1. a.** slope **b.** slope **c.** slope
d. y-intercept **e.** y-intercept **f.** x-intercept

2. a. $y = 2x + b$ **b.** $y = -\frac{5x}{3} + b$ **c.** $y = b$ **d.** $x = a$
e. $y = mx - 4$ **f.** $y = mx$ **3. a.** $y - 1 = m(x - 2)$
b. $y - 1 = m(x + 3)$ **c.** $y - 3 = mx$ **d.** $y = m(x - 4)$

e. $y - \frac{1}{2} = m\left(x - \frac{11}{4}\right)$ **f.** $y = m(x + 1) - 1$ **4.** $y = b$

5. $x = a$ **6. a.** m(slope) **b.** m(slope) **c.** b(y-intercept)
d. a(x-intercept) **7.** Possible answers:

a. $y = -\frac{5x}{3} + 3$ **b.** $y = x - 1$ **c.** $y = 4x - 2$ **d.** $y = -7$

e. $x = 0$ **f.** $x + y = 7$ **8. a.** all lines passing through the origin **b.** parallel lines with a slope of -1
c. parallel lines with a slope of -2 **d.** lines with the

same y-intercept equalling $\frac{-13}{7}$ **e.** horizontal line

f. lines passing through $(-6, -8)$ **g.** lines passing through $(1, 5)$ **h.** lines passing through $(7, 0)$
9. a. $y = x + b$ **b.** $x = a$ **10. a.** $y + 3 = m(x + 2)$

b. $y + 1 = mx$ or $y = mx - 1$ **11.** $y = \frac{-5x}{6} + b$

12. $y - 3 = m(x - 4)$ **13.** $(3, 13), (1, 10), (3, 9), (3, 7),$
$(3, 4)$ **BRAINTICKLER** Missiles meet halfway between the planets.

Pages 206-207 **1. a.** $A = 5, B = -2, C = 9$ **b.** $A = 2,$
$B = 1, C = -3$ **c.** $A = 7, B = -3, C = 0$ **d.** $A = 1,$
$B = -1, C = 1$ **e.** $A = 2, B = 0, C = -5$ **f.** $A = 0,$
$B = 3, C = -17$ **2.** Answers may vary.
3. a. $3x - y - 7 = 0$ **b.** $-x - y - 7 = 0$
c. $5x + 3y - 2 = 0$ **d.** $x - y - 13 = 0$ **e.** $2x - 12 = 0$
f. $4y - 20 = 0$ **g.** $3x - 4y + 9 = 0$
h. $10x + 15y + 12 = 0$ **4.** All vertical lines pass through $(0, 0)$. **5.** All lines are vertical. **6.** All lines are horizontal. **7.** This results in a graph of the

x-axis. **8. a.** $-\frac{5}{2}$ **b.** 3 **c.** $\frac{7}{3}$ **9.** $-\frac{A}{B}$ **10. a.** -5 **b.** 4

c. $-\frac{5}{3}$ **11.** $-\frac{C}{B}$ **12. a.** -3.6 **b.** -5 **c.** 16 **13.** $-\frac{C}{B}$

14. $3m - 5s + 80 = 0$ **15. a.** $x - y + 3 = 0$
b. $x + y + 2 = 0$

Page 208 **1.** Slopes are $\pm\frac{3}{2}$. **2.** $2x + 5y - 7 = 0$

3. $7x + 5y - 20 = 0$ **5.** $12x + 5y - 39 = 0$ and
$5x - 12y + 26 = 0$ **6.** Equation of line through AD
is $8x + 7y - 34 = 0$; $(-1, 6)$ satisfies the equation.

Page 209 **1. a.** $(5, 5)$ **b.** $(-3, 4)$ **c.** $(2, 9)$ **d.** $(-2, -2)$
e. $(0, -4)$ **f.** $(-4, 1)$ **g.** $(2, 3)$ **h.** $(4, 1)$ **i.** $(4, 1)$
j. $(3, 1)$ **2.** d and f because same slope **3.** Possible answer: $y = 3x - 2$ **4.** Possible answer: $4x + 5y = 0$
5. Answers may vary. **6.** $(2, 3)$ and $(-2, 3)$ **7.** $(1, 1)$ and $(-1, 1)$

Pages 210-211 **1.** x and y **2.** Answers may vary.
3. x and y satisfy both equations. **4.** x and y are incorrect. **5. a.** $(3, 18)$ **b.** $(-12, -43)$ **c.** $(4, -1)$

d. $(-2, 4)$ **e.** $(2, 3)$ **f.** $(1, -5)$ **6.** $3x + 4y - 16 = 0$ and $x - 4y - 2 = 0$; intersect at $(4.5, 0.625)$ **7.** a and c
8. a. $\left(\frac{74}{3}, -\frac{35}{3}\right)$ **b.** $(1, -2)$ **c.** $(6, -3)$ **d.** $(2, 1)$
e. $(-2, -6)$ **f.** $\left(-\frac{11}{2}, 5\right)$ **9. a.** $(-2, 6)$ **b.** $(2, 2)$
10. a. $(2, 0)$ **b.** $(9, 7)$ **11. a.** $F = 315, R = 6$ **b.** 447
c. 74 h **12. a.** $(6, 8)$ **b.** $\left(\frac{3}{4}, \frac{25}{8}\right)$

Pages 212-213 **1.** b, c, d **2. a.** $(1, 1)$ **b.** $(1, 2)$
c. $(0, -2)$ **d.** $(12, 10)$ **3. a.** $8x + 24y = 72$
b. $8x + 32y = 4$ **c.** $8x - 12y = 16$ **4. a.** $(5, 1)$
b. $(-3, -2)$ **c.** $(-1, 4)$ **d.** $(4, -2)$ **5.** substitution,
graphically **6. a.** $\left(-\frac{76}{25}, -\frac{3}{25}\right)$ **b.** $(5, 3)$ **c.** $(-1, -4)$
d. $(-2, 3)$ **7. a.** $(2, 7)$ **b.** $\left(-\frac{49}{29}, \frac{86}{29}\right)$ **c.** $(2, 1)$
d. $(-3, 5)$ **8. a.** 7960 **b.** 3560 **9. a.** $(1, 8), (2, -3),$
$(-4, 2)$ **b.** Slopes are negative reciprocals.
10. $\left(5\frac{3}{4}, -1\frac{1}{2}\right)$ **11.** 4.5 h

Pages 214-215 **1.** Answers may vary. **2.** no
difference **3.** same slopes, two parallel lines **4.** if
the slopes are equal yet the equations are not
multiples of one another **5. a.** $(1, 1)$ **b.** $(4, 3)$
c. $\left(-\frac{1}{2}, 2\right)$ **d.** $\left(\frac{2}{3}, -\frac{1}{3}\right)$ **6. a.** $(4, 0)$ **b.** $(2, -1)$
c. $(-3, 1)$ **d.** $(-3, -3)$ **7.** $H = 4.75, F = 235.5, 37$
sticks **8. a.** $(3, 1)$ **b.** $(1, -4)$
9. b. $y = 350\,000 + 15\,000x, y = 40\,000x$ **c.** 14
10. a. $3x - y - 2 = 0$ **b.** $x + 3y - 11 = 0$ **11. d.** $(2, 2),$
$(-1, 0)$ **12. b.** $(2, 3), \left(\frac{22}{5}, -\frac{3}{5}\right), (12, 7)$ **c.** scalene
13. 9^9 **14.** 9^{-9}

Pages 216-217 **1.** $x - y = 8$ **2.** $x + y = 109$
3. $x + y = 12$ **4.** 20, 12; 59.5, 49.5; 7, 5 **5. b.** $x = 13,$
$y = 9$ **6.** 60, 45 **7.** 0.29, 2.64 **8.** 73 **9.** 150, 75
10. b. 40, 10 **11.** $x = 12.5$ kg, $y = 37.5$ kg **12.** 60
cashews, 40 nuts **13.** 26, 51 **14.** $8.85, $4.52

Pages 218-219 **1. a.** inconsistent **b.** dependent
c. consistent **d.** dependent **2.** lines intersect in a
consistent system; lines are parallel in an
inconsistent system; lines coincide in a dependent
system. **3. a.** $\left(-\frac{11}{4}, -\frac{1}{4}\right)$, consistent **b.** $(2, 1),$
consistent **c.** infinitely many solutions, dependent
d. no solution, inconsistent **4. a.** $v = 4, w = -5,$
consistent **b.** inconsistent **5.** the pair in d
6. Possible answers: **a.** $2x - 4y + 5 = 0$
b. $3x - 6y - 18 = 0$ **8. a.** The first company offers a
better deal. **b.** $h = 1, r = 38$ **9.** 8000 inside and 4000
outside **10.** $15.34 for landscaper; $8.10 for the
student **11. a.** 40 **b.** the second up to age forty,
then the first after forty

Pages 220-221 **1. a.** all points below $y = x$ **b.** all
points below $y = x + 2$ **c.** all points above and
including the line $y = -x + 2$ **d.** all the points to the
right and including the line $y = 4x - 3$ **e.** all the
points to the right of $y = -7x + 5$ **f.** all the points to
the left of $y = 3x - 1$ **2.** Answers may vary.
3. a. all the points above the line $y = x$ **b.** all the
points above and including the x-axis **c.** all the
points below and including the x-axis
4. a. $y \leq -3x + 6$ **b.** $y \geq -\frac{1x}{2} + \frac{3}{2}$ **c.** $y < -\frac{6x}{5} - 2$
d. $y < \frac{3x}{2} + \frac{11}{3}$ **5.** above because $7 > -3 - 4$
6. Answers may vary. **7. a.** all the points above the
line $y = \frac{1}{4}x$ and to the left of $y = x - 2$ **b.** all the
points to the right of $y = 3x - 2$ and above and
including the x-axis **c.** all the points below and
including the line $y = 1$ and to the left of $x = 7$ **d.** all
the points to the right of $y = -4x$ and to the left of
$y = -4x + 1$ **e.** all the points to the right of $x + y = 0$
and to the left of $3x - 5y = 4$ **8.** Answers may vary.
9. a. $y > -\frac{3x}{4} + 3$ **b.** $x \geq 2$ **10. a.** $y \geq 3x - 3$
b. $x \geq 1$ and $y \geq 2$ **11.** $y \leq \frac{4x}{5} + 4, x \leq 0, y \geq 0$
12. $x \geq 0, y \geq 0, x + y \leq 85, 90x + 250y \leq 10\,000$
13. $3x - 7y + 28 \geq 0, x + 2y - 14 < 0, x \geq 0, y \geq 0,$
and $x \leq 6$

Pages 222-223 **1.** 140 when $x = 28, y = 0$
2. a. $(0, 30), (5, 9), (10, 6)$ **b.** $(5, 9), P = 31$ **c.** We are
concerned only with extremes. **3.** 5000 door guards
and 4000 window trims cost $480. **4.** 27 kg nitrate
and 3 kg phosphate **5.** 1400 of discount and 300 of
gourmet **6.** $21\frac{1}{3}\%$ nitrate and $10\frac{2}{3}\%$ phosphate
7. 2000 *scribe* and 5000 *stylus* **8.** $333\bar{3}$ Super and no
Regular

Page 224 **1.** input the equations of the two lines
2. to check the case when two lines are parallel
3. Answers may vary. **4.** $S1 = 0, S2 = 3$ **5. a.** no
solution **c.** division by zero error

Page 225 **1. a.** $w = 22.5 + 6.35h$ **b.** $s = r - 0.15r$
2. Answers may vary. **3. a.** 3996 **b.** 67 359.60
4. a. $-19, -7, 3$ **b.** $-\frac{23}{5}, -4, -\frac{7}{2}$ **c.** $\frac{85}{8}, \frac{19}{2}, \frac{137}{16}$
d. $-52.2, -48, -44.5$ **e.** $-1398, -1310$ **f.** $\frac{145}{3}, 45,$
$\frac{380}{9}$ **5. a.** slope 1, y-intercept 3 **b.** slope -4,
y-intercept 4 **c.** horizontal through 2.8 **6. a.** 2, 7
b. $-4, 2$ **c.** 0.07, 1.5 **d.** 0, 7 **e.** $\frac{3}{7}, -5$ **f.** $\frac{3}{5}, \frac{1}{5}$
7. a. $y = 4x + 15$ **b.** $y = -3x + 3$ **c.** $y = -2x - 1.5$
d. $y = 42$ **e.** $y = -x + 1$ **f.** $5y = 3x$ **8. a.** $y = x$
b. $y = 5$ **c.** $x = -2$ **d.** $2x - y = 0$ **e.** $y = x + 0.75$

9. a. $3x - y + 2 = 0$ **b.** $0.5x - y - 7 = 0$ **c.** $6x - 3 = 0$ **d.** $12x + y - 8 = 0$ **e.** $x - 6y - 60 = 0$ **f.** $-x - 8y + 16 = 0$ **10. a.** lines through the origin **b.** parallel lines with slope 3 **c.** horizontal lines **d.** vertical lines **e.** parallel lines with slope -6 **f.** lines through (1, 2) **11. a.** $y = mx - 2$ **b.** $y = \frac{4x}{3} + b$ **c.** $y = a$ **d.** $(y + 1) = \frac{2}{3}(x - 9)$ **13.** a, c, e, f **14. a.** (1, 4) **b.** (0, 0) **c.** (0, -1) **d.** no intersection **15. a.** (-6, 2) **b.** $\left(\frac{13}{15}, \frac{7}{3}\right)$ **c.** no solution **d.** $\left(-\frac{3}{29}, -\frac{9}{29}\right)$ **e.** $\left(\frac{136}{409}, -\frac{4772}{409}\right)$ **f.** no solution

Page 226 **1.** $v = kt$ **2.** Possible answers: (-3, 0), (-2, 2), (-1, 4), (0, 6), (1, 8), (2, 10) **3.** -1.625 **4.** 2.5 and -5 **5.** slope -3 and y-intercept 2 **6.** -1 and 10 **7.** -0.12 and 4.8 **8.** $y = \frac{2x}{5} - \frac{4}{5}$ **9.** $5x + y - 14 = 0$ **10.** $-\frac{A}{B}$ and $-\frac{C}{B}$ **11.** all lines with slope 2 **12.** all lines passing through (0, 7) **13. a.** $y = mx$ **b.** $y = a$ **c.** $y - 1 = mx$ **d.** $y + 3 = m(x - 2)$ **14.** (1, 2) **15. a.** (4, 0) **b.** (90, 135) **16.** 8 juice and 13 soft drinks **17.** 1 at 19 km/h and 5 at 12 km/h **18.** Possible answers: (0, 0) and (2, 4) **19.** below and including the line $y = 2x + 4$ **22.** 200 food items and 800 papers

Cumulative Review Chapters 7-9

Pages 227-230 **1. a.** (-3, -1) **b.** (3, 1) **c.** (3, -1) **2. a.** $\frac{4}{3}$ **b.** $\frac{-3}{4}$ **c.** $\frac{5}{2}$ **d.** 0 **e.** undefined **f.** $\frac{y_1 - y_2}{x_1 - x_2}$ **3.** Answers may vary. **4.** pairs of slopes are equal, not collinear **5.** $a = -2$ **6.** $b = \frac{-36}{5}$ **7.** $c = 16$ **8. a.** one pair of parallel sides **b.** Slope AB = slope $CD = 2$. **9.** Each side has length $5\sqrt{2}$, slope PQ = slope $RS = 1$, slope RQ = slope $SP = -7$ **10.** midpoint of DE is $G\left(\frac{-5}{2}, \frac{7}{2}\right)$, midpoint of DF is $H(2, 5)$, slope of $\overline{GH}$ = slope of $\overline{EF} = \frac{1}{3}$; lengths are $\sqrt{90}$ and $\frac{\sqrt{90}}{2}$. **11.** 5 **12. a.** The y-coordinate is the sum of the previous x-coordinate and the next consecutive number. **b.** {(5, 15), (6, 21), (7, 28), (8, 36)} **d.** no, points cannot be connected with one straight line **f.** 2, 84.5 **13. a.** interpolation **b.** extrapolation **c.** abscissa ordinate **14. b.** direct variation **15. b.** non-linear **c.** no, no answer for 0 **d.** no, the larger the number, the smaller its reciprocal **e.** 0 **16.** Left Flanker—18, Left

Prop—20, Left Lock—24, Hook—20, Right Lock—20, Right Prop—27, Right Flanker—21, Left Wing—21, Eighth Man—30, Fullback—19, Right Wing—24 **17.** Answers may vary. **18.** Answers may vary. **19.** 60 h : 1 min **20.** $52.50 **21. a.** 80 cm **b.** 492 **c.** no **22. a.** $40.00 **b.** Cost varies directly with distance driven. **c.** $0.17/km **d.** $C = 0.17k + 40$ **23.** $y = \frac{5x}{12} + \frac{1}{4}$ **24. a.** $C = 3c$ **b.** $S = 5.35h + 12$ **25.** Total Cost equals number of d's at $10.00 plus number of q's at $25.00. **26.** Pick three points on the line and prove they are collinear, e.g., (0, 0), (1, 55), (2, 110). **27.** $y = \frac{-2x}{3} + \frac{2}{3}$ **28.** $y = 0$ **29.** $x = 3$, $y = \frac{1}{x}$ **30. a.** $\frac{-3}{4}$, 1 **b.** $\frac{-1}{3}$, 2 **c.** 0, 0 **31. a.** $y = x - 3$ **b.** $y = \frac{2x}{3} - 3$ **c.** $y = 2$ **d.** $y = 2x$ **e.** $y = \frac{-2x}{3} - \frac{1}{3}$ **f.** $y = 3x$ **g.** $y = \frac{-12x}{5} + \frac{47}{5}$ **32.** set of first elements of the ordered pairs of a relation; the set of second elements of the ordered pairs of a relation **34. a.** $\left(\frac{1}{4}, \frac{9}{4}\right)$ **b.** $\left(\frac{-27}{2}, -16\right)$ **c.** $\left(\frac{2}{11}, \frac{-24}{11}\right)$ **d.** $\left(\frac{21}{29}, \frac{-11}{29}\right)$ **e.** $\left(\frac{19}{28}, \frac{-41}{28}\right)$ **f.** $\left(\frac{50}{19}, \frac{22}{19}\right)$ **g.** (-1, -3) **h.** (-1, -2) **35.** (17, 8) **36.** $F = 70$, $R = 60$ **a.** $520 **b.** 12.2 h **37.** one solution, no solutions, infinitely many solutions **38. a.** inconsistent **b.** dependent **39.** Medians intersect at $\left(-\frac{4}{3}, \frac{16}{3}\right)$. **40.** ($-5$, 4) **41. a.** $\left(\frac{29}{132}, \frac{-135}{44}\right)$ **b.** (7, 1) **42.** $\{(x, y) \mid -2x + y \le -2, 6x + 5y < 30, y \ge -3, x \ge 0, x, y \in R\}$ **45.** 50 standard, 40 deluxe **46.** $0.43/kg **47.** 24

Chapter 10

Page 231 **1. a.** opposite angles **b.** corresponding **c.** alternate interior **d.** consecutive interior **e.** linear pair **f.** alternate exterior **3. a.** $\angle A = 56°$, $\angle B = 52°$, $\angle C = 72°$ **b.** $\angle X = 38°$, $\angle Y = 77°$, $\angle XZY = 65°$ **4. a.** $\angle A = \angle D$, $\angle B = \angle E$, $\angle C = \angle F$, $\overline{AB} \cong \overline{DE}$, $\overline{AC} \cong \overline{DF}$, $\overline{BC} \cong \overline{EF}$ **b.** $\angle P \cong \angle V$, $\angle K \cong \angle U$, $\angle W \cong \angle E$, $\overline{PK} \cong \overline{VU}$, $\overline{PW} \cong \overline{VE}$, $\overline{KW} \cong \overline{UE}$ **c.** $\angle A \cong \angle Y$, $\angle N \cong \angle F$, $\angle U \cong \angle L$, $\overline{AN} \cong \overline{YF}$, $\overline{NU} \cong \overline{FL}$, $\overline{AU} \cong \overline{YL}$ **5. a.** a quadrilateral, each pair of opposite sides is equal and parallel **b.** a parallelogram with 4 congruent sides **c.** a rhombus with four 90° angles **d.** a quadrilateral with exactly one pair of parallel sides **6. a.** $x = 75°$, $y = 105°$, $z = 75°$ **b.** $x = 111°$, $y = 69°$, $z = 111°$

Pages 232-233 **1. a.** all statements are always true **b.** conclusions made about all trees based on only a few **c.** yes; yes **d.** deductive **2. a.** If it is a parrot, then it is a bird. **b.** If you are a grade 10 student, then you are a brilliant mathematician. **c.** If it is a triangle, then it has an angle sum of 180°. **d.** If you drive in Saskatchewan, then you must wear a seat belt. **e.** If two lines are parallel in the same plane, then they will never intersect. **f.** If a person lives in Toronto, then he lives in Ontario. **3. a.** It has rained. **b.** Janelle's backyard is a quadrilateral. **c.** You are disintegrated. **d.** You will have a winning basketball team. **4. b.** *ABC* is a triangle. **c.** true **5. a.** If a figure is a trapezoid, then the sum of the interior angles is 360°. **b.** Sum of interior angles is 360°. **6.** pugnacity and tenacity **7.** complementary and 90° **8.** If you are here, then you are mad. **9.** 2 **10.** as another statement assumed to be true

Pages 234-235 **1. a.** If it shines at night, then it is the Moon. False. False. **b.** If you can make a snowman, then it has snowed. True. True. **c.** If $y < x$, then $x > y$. True. True. **d.** If you have planted flower seeds, then flowers grow. False. False. **e.** If people will like ice cream, then they will like candy. False. False. **f.** If you do well in physics then you will do well in mathematics. False. False. **g.** If two segments are congruent, then they have the same length. True. True. **h.** If consecutive interior angles are supplementary, then the lines are parallel. True. True. **2. a.** If it is a spider, then it has eight legs. **b.** If someone is a teenager, then they are between 13 and 19 inclusive. **c.** If a person is a chemist, then they study molecules. **d.** If children are under six, then they believe in the Easter bunny. **e.** If it is an equilateral triangle, then it has three congruent sides. **f.** If a figure has three or more sides, then it is a polygon. **g.** If you are driving from Winnipeg to Red Deer, then you will pass through Saskatchewan. **h.** If this is the way up, then it is the way down. **3. a.** If a triangle has two forty-five degree angles, then it is a right triangle. False. True. **b.** Every rectangle is a square. True. False. **c.** If it is vaporized water, then it is steam. True. True. **d.** Lines that are perpendicular intersect at right angles. True. True. **e.** If a balloon floats, it is filled with helium. True. False. **f.** Vancouver is on Victoria. True. False. **4. a.** If it has eight legs, then it is a spider. **b.** If someone is between 13 and 19 inclusive, then they are a teenager. **c.** If a person studies molecules, then he/she is a chemist. **d.** If children believe in the Easter bunny, then they are under six. **e.** If a triangle has three congruent sides then it is equilateral. **f.** If it is a polygon, then it has three or

more sides. **g.** If you pass through Saskatchewan, then you are going from Red Deer to Winnipeg. **h .** If this is the way down, then it is the way up. **5. b.** A person is a teenager if and only if they are between 13 and 19 inclusive. **e.** A triangle is equilateral if and only if it has three congruent sides. **c.** It is steam if and only if it is vaporized water. **d.** Lines intersect at right angles if and only if they are perpendicular. **6.** No, he only reversed the order of the statement, not the if and then statements. **7. a.** If two angles are supplementary, then the sum of their measures is 180°. If the sum of their measures is 180°, then two angles are supplementary. **b.** If Trish is my friend, then she will lend me her scarf. If Trish will lend me her scarf, then she is my friend. **c.** If a triangle is scalene, then the lengths of all the sides are different. If the lengths of all the sides are different, then the triangle is scalene. **d.** If $x + 3$ is an odd number, then x is an even number. If x is an even number, then $x + 3$ is an odd number. **8. a.** I see it if and only if I eat it. **b.** I like it if and only if I get it. **c.** I breathe if and only if I sleep.

Pages 236-238 **1. a.** perpendicular **b.** given and required **c.** sum of the angles of a triangle, perpendicular segments are congruent, transitive property **d.** If $a = b$ and $b = c$, then $a = c$. **e.** $\angle B$ and $\angle C$ **2.** $\angle BAD \cong \angle DAC$, $\overline{AD} \perp \overline{BC}$, $\angle ADB \cong \angle ADC$, $\angle BAD + \angle ADB + \angle B = 180°$, $\angle DAC + \angle ADB + \angle C = 180°$, $\angle B \cong \angle C$ **3. a.** A parallelogram has parallel sides; parallel sides produce congruent angles such as alternate interior angles and corresponding angles; a transversal is needed between parallel lines. **b.** $\angle BAC + \angle DAC$ and $\angle DCA + \angle BCA$ **c.** No, we need parallel sides.

Pages 239-240 **1. a.** $\overline{RT} \cong \overline{RP}$, $\overline{RA} \cong \overline{RB}$, $\overline{AT} \cong \overline{TP} \cong \overline{PB}$ **b.** $\triangle RAT \cong \triangle RBP$ **c.** $\triangle RAP \cong \triangle RBT$ **d.** 3 **e.** $\overline{TP}$ **2. a.** yes **b.** no **c.** no **d.** yes **3.** GIVEN: as shown; REQUIRED: To prove $\triangle RMN \cong \triangle STP$; PROOF: Use 3 given parts and $\triangle RMN \cong \triangle STP$ (S.S.S.) **4.** GIVEN: $\overline{GK} \cong \overline{JK}$, $\overline{GH} \cong \overline{JH}$; REQUIRED: To prove $\triangle KGH \cong \triangle KJH$; PROOF: $\overline{GK} \cong \overline{JK}$ (given), $\overline{GH} \cong \overline{JH}$ (given), $\overline{KH} \cong \overline{KH}$ (reflexive), $\triangle KGH \cong \triangle KJH$ (S.S.S.) **5.** GIVEN: as shown; REQUIRED: To prove $\triangle ACD \cong \triangle BCD$; PROOF: $\overline{CB} \cong \overline{CA}$ (given), $\overline{CD} \cong \overline{CD}$ (reflexive), D is the midpoint of $\overline{AB}$ (given), $\overline{AD} \cong \overline{BD}$ (definition of midpoint), $\triangle ACD \cong \triangle BCD$ (S.S.S.) **6.** GIVEN: $\overline{RZ} \cong \overline{VW}$, $\overline{ZT} \cong \overline{WS}$, $\overline{RS} \cong \overline{VT}$; REQUIRED: To prove $\triangle ZRT \cong \triangle WVS$; PROOF: $\overline{RZ} \cong \overline{VW}$ (given), $\overline{ZT} \cong \overline{WS}$ (given), $\overline{RS} \cong \overline{VT}$ (given), $\overline{RT} \cong \overline{VS}$ (addition of $\overline{ST}$), $\triangle ZRT \cong \triangle WVS$

(S.S.S.) **7. a.** $\overline{GH} \cong \overline{IJ}$, $\overline{GJ} \cong \overline{IH}$ **b.** $\overline{KL} \cong \overline{NM}$, $\overline{KM} \cong \overline{NL}$

Pages 241-243 **1.** Answers may vary.
2. a. $\overline{AB} \cong \overline{DE}$, $\overline{AC} \cong \overline{DC}$ **b.** $\overline{RQ} \cong \overline{UT}$, $\overline{RS} \cong \overline{UV}$
c. $\overline{AD} \cong \overline{CB}$, $\overline{AC} \cong \overline{CA}$ **d.** $\overline{XY} \cong \overline{XZ}$, $\overline{XW} \cong \overline{XW}$
3. $\overline{AO} \cong \overline{CO}$; $\overline{BO} \cong \overline{DO}$; $\triangle CDB$; (C.P.C.T.);
(C.P.C.T.); (reflexive); (S.A.S.); $\triangle ABD \cong \triangle CDB$
4. a. GIVEN: $\overline{RV} \cong \overline{TV}$, $\angle RVS \cong \angle TVS$;
REQUIRED: To prove $\triangle RSV \cong \triangle TSV$; PROOF:
$\overline{RV} \cong \overline{TV}$ (given), $\angle RVS \cong \angle TVS$ (given),
$\overline{SV} \cong \overline{SV}$ (reflexive property), $\triangle RSV \cong \triangle TSV$
(S.A.S.) **b.** GIVEN: $\overline{LM} \cong \overline{OM}$, $\overline{KM} \cong \overline{NM}$;
REQUIRED: To prove $\triangle KLM \cong \triangle NOM$;
PROOF: $\overline{LM} \cong \overline{OM}$ (given), $\overline{KM} \cong \overline{NM}$ (given),
$\angle LMK \cong \angle OMN$ (vertically opposite angles),
$\triangle KLM \cong \triangle NOM$ (S.A.S.) **5.** $\overline{MN}$ becomes 2
congruent segments, angles = 90° **6.** (given);
$\overline{QS} = \overline{QS}$; $\triangle PQS \cong \triangle RQS$ (S.A.S.); $\angle P \cong \angle R$;
$\triangle PQS \cong \triangle RQS$ and $\angle P \cong \angle R$ **7. a.** none
b. $\overline{AB} \cong \overline{OT}$ **c.** $\triangle MTO$ and $\triangle MBA$ **d.** Use the given
information plus $\angle M \cong \angle M$ and the two triangles
are congruent by S.A.S. **8.** GIVEN: $\overline{AB} \cong \overline{AE}$,
$\overline{BC} \cong \overline{ED}$, $\angle B \cong \angle E$; REQUIRED: $\triangle AED$, $\triangle ACE$,
$\angle ACD$; PROOF: **a.** $\overline{BC} \cong \overline{ED}$ (given); $\angle B \cong \angle E$
(given); $\triangle ABC \cong \triangle AED$; $\triangle ABC \cong \triangle AED$
b. (given); $\angle B \cong \angle E$ (given); (given); (reflexive);
$\overline{BD} \cong \overline{EC}$; $\triangle ADB \cong \triangle ACE$ (S.A.S.);
$\angle ADC \cong \angle ACD$; $\triangle ADB \cong \triangle ACE$ and
$\angle ADC \cong \angle ACD$ **c.** Same as **b.** **9. a.** $\overline{TV}$ **b.** S.A.S.
c. $\overline{XW} \cong \overline{ZY}$ (given), $\angle ZYV \cong \angle XWT$ (given),
$\overline{YT} \cong \overline{WV}$ (given), $\overline{YV} \cong \overline{WT}$ (addition of $\overline{TV}$),
$\triangle XTW \cong \triangle ZVY$ (S.A.S.) **d.** $\overline{XT} \cong \overline{ZV}$,
$\angle TXW \cong \angle VZY$, $\angle XTV \cong \angle ZVY$ **e.** $\overline{XW} \cong \overline{ZY}$
(given), $\overline{YW} \cong \overline{WY}$ (reflexive), $\angle ZYW \cong \angle XWY$
(given) $\therefore$ $\triangle XYW \cong \triangle ZWY$ **f.** C.P.C.T.
g. $\overline{YX} \cong \overline{WZ}$ (C.P.C.T.), $\overline{ZV} \cong \overline{XT}$ (C.P.C.T.),
$\overline{YT} \cong \overline{WV}$ (given), $\triangle WVZ \cong \triangle YTX$ (S.S.S.)
10. a. $\overline{AD} \| \overline{CB}$ (given), $\angle D \cong \angle B$ (alternate interior
angles), $\overline{AD} \cong \overline{CB}$ (given), $\overline{DE} \cong \overline{BE}$ (given),
$\triangle ADE \cong \triangle CBE$ (S.A.S.) **b.** $\overline{AE} \cong \overline{CE}$ (C.P.C.T.)
11. a. If the diagonals of a quadrilateral bisect each
other, then the quadrilateral is a parallelogram.
b. Hypothesis: the diagonals of a quadrilateral
bisect each other. Conclusion: the quadrilateral is a
parallelogram. **12.** Use the S.A.S. postulate to
prove two of the triangles formed by the diagonals,
congruent. Then use C.P.C.T. to prove that the
alternate angles are congruent and therefore the
opposite sides are parallel. Repeat the process to
prove that the other pair of opposite sides are also
parallel and the figure is a parallelogram.
BRAINTICKLER Six points form a regular

hexagon and the 7th point above the centre of the
hexagon.

Pages 244-246 **2. a.** $\angle B$ and $\angle D$, $\angle BCA$ and $\angle DCA$
b. $\angle R$ and $\angle M$, $\angle S$ and $\angle L$ **c.** $\angle A$ and $\angle D$, $\angle C$ and
$\angle F$ **d.** $\angle W$ and $\angle Y$, $\angle WXZ$ and $\angle YZX$ **3. a.** S.S.S.
b. S.A.S. or S.S.S. **c.** A.S.A. or S.A.S. **d.** A.S.A.
4. a. $\overline{AD}$ bisects $\overline{BC}$, $\overline{AD}$ is perpendicular to $\overline{BC}$
b. $\overline{AD}$ **c.** $\overline{AD}$ bisects $\overline{BC}$ (given), $\overline{BD} \cong \overline{CD}$
(definition of bisects), $\overline{AD}$ is perpendicular to $\overline{BC}$
(given), $\angle ADB \cong \angle ADC$ (both are right angles),
$\overline{AD} \cong \overline{AD}$ (reflexive property), $\triangle ABD \cong \triangle ACD$
(S.A.S.) **d.** $\overline{AB} \cong \overline{AC}$, $\angle B \cong \angle C$, $\angle BAD \cong \angle CAD$
5. b. $\angle KLP$ and $\angle PMN$ **c.** $\angle K \cong \angle N$ (vertically
opposite angles) **d.** $\angle KPL$ and $\angle MPN$ (sum of
angles is 180°) **e.** no, sides not necessarily
congruent **f.** $\angle L$ and $\angle M$ **g.** Use b, c, and the given;
$\triangle$'s congruent by A.S.A.; congruent triangles
6. b. $\overline{YV}$ **c.** Use A.S.A. **7.** $\angle D \cong \angle B$, $\overline{DC} \cong \overline{CB}$,
$\angle DCE \cong \angle ACB$ (opposite angles),
$\triangle DCE \cong \triangle ABC$, $\overline{DE} \cong \overline{AB}$ **8. a.** $\angle 1$ and $\angle 2$ **b.** $\angle 3$
and $\angle 4$ **c.** Yes, addition property **d.** $\angle 2 \cong \angle 3$
(given), $\angle BAD \cong \angle CDA$ (addition property),
$\overline{AD} \cong \overline{DA}$ (reflexive property), $\triangle ABD \cong \triangle DCA$
(A.S.A.) **e.** $\overline{BD} \cong \overline{CA}$ (C.P.C.T.) **9. a.** all the given
information **b.** Prove that $\triangle BAC \cong \triangle EAD$
(A.S.A.), $\overline{BC} \cong \overline{ED}$ (C.P.C.T.). **c.** $\overline{CD}$
d. $\angle BAD \cong \angle EAC$ (addition of $\angle CAD$), $\overline{AB} \cong \overline{AE}$
(given), $\angle B \cong \angle E$ (given), $\triangle ABD \cong \triangle AEC$ (A.S.S.),
$\overline{BD} \cong \overline{EC}$ (C.P.C.T.) **10.** Rewrite the theorem to
read "If the figure is a parallelogram, then the
diagonals bisect each other." GIVEN: $ABCD$ is a
parallelogram with diagonals of $\overline{AC}$ and $\overline{BD}$
intersecting at E. REQUIRED: To prove that $\overline{AC}$
bisects $\overline{BD}$, and $\overline{BD}$ bisects $\overline{AC}$. **e.** In $\triangle ABE$ and
$\triangle DCE$, $\overline{AB} \| \overline{CD}$ (definition of a parallelogram),
$\angle BAE \cong \angle DCE$ (alternate interior angles),
$\angle ABE \cong \angle CDE$ (alternate interior angles),
$\overline{AB} \cong \overline{CD}$ (definition of a parallelogram),
$\triangle ABE \cong \triangle DCE$ (A.S.A.), $\overline{AE} \cong \overline{CE}$ (C.P.C.T.),
$\overline{DB}$ bisects $\overline{AC}$ (definition of bisect). Similarly,
using $\triangle ADE$ and $\triangle CBE$, $\overline{AC}$ bisects $\overline{DB}$.
11. a. $\angle R \cong \angle M$ (given), $\angle S \cong \angle N$ (sum of angles in
triangle), $\overline{RS} \cong \overline{MN}$ (given), $\triangle RST \cong \triangle MNP$
(A.S.A.) **b.** In two triangles, if two angles and a
non-contained side of one are congruent to the
corresponding two angles and non-contained side
in the other, then the two triangles are congruent.
c. non-contained side
BRAINTICKLER

Page 247   **1.** In an isosceles triangle, the sides opposite the congruent angles are congruent. Use a proof similar to the one in the display but use the fact that $\angle B \cong \angle C$ (twice) and $\overline{BC} \cong \overline{CB}$, triangles are congruent by A.S.A.   **2.** $\overline{AB} \cong \overline{AC}$, $\overline{AD} \cong \overline{AD}$, $\overline{BD} \cong \overline{CD}$ **3.** Use A.S.A. with given $+ \angle B \cong \angle C$ (angles opposite = sides). Use S.A.S. with given $+ \overline{AD} \cong \overline{AD}$ (reflexive). In both cases, $\triangle ABD \cong \triangle ACD$, $\overline{BD} \cong \overline{CD}$ (C.P.C.T.)   **4.** Same as 2.   **5.** $\overline{NP} \parallel \overline{QR}$ (given), $\angle MNP \cong \angle Q$ (corresponding angles), $\angle MPN \cong \angle R$ (corresponding angles), $\overline{MN} \cong \overline{MP}$ (given), $\angle MNP \cong \angle MPN$ (angles opposite congruent sides), $\angle Q \cong \angle R$ (transitive property twice), $\overline{MQ} \cong \overline{MR}$ (sides opposite congruent angles)   **6.** Use S.A.S. **7.** Use S.A.A.   **8.** $\overline{AC} \cong \overline{AD}$ (given), $\angle ACD \cong \angle ADC$ (angles opposite congruent sides), $\angle BCA$ and $\angle ACD$ form a linear pair as do $\angle ADC$ and $\angle ADE$, $\angle ACB \cong \angle ADE$ (subtraction property)

Pages 248-249   **1. a.** Crows are not black. **b.** In $\triangle XYZ$, $\angle X \cong \angle Y$. **c.** In $\triangle HIG$, $\angle G$ is not a right angle. **d.** $a = b$ **e.** ℓ_3 is not parallel to ℓ_4 **f.** $\triangle RST$ is not equilateral. **g.** $ABCD$ is not a square. **h.** $\angle 3$ is an exterior angle.   **2.** (contradiction); (assumption); (angles of a triangle); 190° (addition property); $\angle P \neq 60°$ (indirect reasoning)   **3.** Either $\angle B$ is obtuse or $\angle B$ is not obtuse. Assume $\angle B$ is obtuse (assumption), $\angle A + \angle B + \angle C = 180°$ ($\angle$'s of $\triangle$), $\angle A > 90°$ (given & def'n of obtuse), $\angle B > 90°$ (def'n of obtuse), $\angle A + \angle B > 180°$ (addition property), $\angle A + \angle B + \angle C > 180°$ — contradiction, therefore $\angle B$ is not obtuse. Similarly, $\angle C$ is not obtuse. **4.** (contradiction); (assumption); (given); (factor of 2); (def'n of prime); $2n$ is not prime (indirect reasoning)   **5.** Either n is even or it's not. Say n is even. Even times even is even. $\therefore n \times n$ is even. $n \times n = n^2$ which is odd (given). $\therefore n$ is odd.

Pages 250-251   **1. a.** $\angle 2$ and $\angle 6$, $\angle p$ and $\angle s$ **b.** $\angle 1$ and $\angle 3$, $\angle m$ and $\angle r$ **c.** $\angle 6$ and $\angle 7$, $\angle p$ and $\angle r$ **2. a.** $\angle 4 = 68°$, $\angle 3 = 112°$ **b.** $\angle 3 = 130°$, $\angle 4 = 50°$ **3.** C.A.P. stands for corresponding angles with parallel lines; C.I.A.P. stands for consecutive interior angles with parallel lines. **4. a.** no **b.** not enough information **c.** yes **d.** yes **5. a.** $\overline{AC} \parallel \overline{EH}$ **b.** $\ell_1 \parallel \ell_2$ and $m_1 \parallel m_2$ **c.** $\overline{AB} \parallel \overline{CD}$ **d.** $m_1 \parallel m_2$ **6.** Answers may vary.   **7.** Using the diagram in the display, $\angle 4 + \angle 6 = 180°$ (given), $\angle 2 + \angle 4 = 180°$ (form a linear pair), $\angle 4 + \angle 6 = \angle 2 + \angle 4$ (transitive property), $\angle 6 = \angle 2$ (subtraction property), $\ell_1 \parallel \ell_2$ (C.A.P.)   **8. a.** $\angle R \cong \angle U$ or $\angle S$ and $\angle T$ **b.** $\triangle RSV$ and $\triangle UTV$ **c.** yes **d.** Use the two given statements plus $\angle RVS \cong \angle UVT$ (vertically opposite angles), $\triangle RSV \cong \triangle UTV$ (S.A.S.), $\angle R \cong \angle U$ (C.P.C.T.),

$\overline{RS} \parallel \overline{UT}$ (A.A.P.)   **9. a.** $\overline{CE}$ bisects $\angle BCD$ (given), $\angle 2 \cong \angle 3$ (definition of bisection), $\angle A \cong \angle 2$ (given), $\angle A \cong \angle 3$ (transitive property), $\overline{AB} \parallel \overline{CE}$ (C.A.P.) **b.** Same procedure as a, except, $\angle B \cong \angle 2$ (transitive property), $\overline{AB} \parallel \overline{CE}$ (A.A.P.).   **10.** converses **11.** $\overline{MN} \parallel \overline{QP}$ (given), $\angle N + \angle 2 = 180°$ (consecutive interior angles), $\angle 1 \cong \angle 2$ (given), $\angle N + \angle 1 = 180°$ (substitution property), $\overline{MQ} \parallel \overline{NP}$ (C.I.A.P.)   **12.** Draw a diagonal and prove two triangles congruent. It is possible to get a pair of alternate interior angles congruent to prove that the other pair of sides is also parallel.   **13.** Draw both diagonals. If diagonals are $\overline{AC}$ and $\overline{BD}$, use the two triangles where $\overline{AC}$ and $\overline{BD}$ are the hypotenuse to prove congruent triangles and $\overline{AC} \cong \overline{BD}$ (C.P.C.T.).   **14.** 11   **15.** Answers may vary.

Page 252   **1.** If the square of the length of the longest side of a triangle is equal to the sum of the squares of the lengths of the other two sides, then the triangle is a right triangle.   **2. a.** S.S.S. **b.** $\angle MVT + \angle TVW + \angle NVW = 180°$ (form a straight line), $\angle MVT + \angle NVW = 90°$ (two acute angles in a right triangle), $\angle TVW$ is 90° (subtraction property). Similarly, $\angle T$, $\angle Z$, and $\angle W$ are right angles and $TVWZ$ is a square. **c.** One way is:

$$(a + b)^2 = 4\left(\frac{1}{2}ab\right) + c^2, \; a^2 + 2ab + b^2 = 2ab + c^2,$$
$$a^2 + b^2 = c^2. \quad \textbf{3. a. } \overline{QP} = 30 \text{ cm and } \overline{RM} = 14.4 \text{ cm}$$

b. $\overline{QR} = 16$ cm and $\overline{RM} = 9.6$ cm

Page 253   **1.** Use S.S.S.   **2.** Form $\triangle$'s APQ and BPQ. They are congruent by S.S.S. $\angle APQ \cong \angle BPQ$ (C.P.C.T.) and they are right angles since they are congruent and form a linear pair.   **3.** Prove perpendicular as in 2, prove bisector by using only the triangles above $\overline{AB}$.   **4.** parallel by A.A.P. or C.I.A.P.   **5.** $\triangle ABD \cong \triangle ACD$ (S.A.S.), $\angle ADB \cong \angle ADC$ (C.P.C.T.), and therefore is perpendicular (same as 2).   **6. a.** Use S.S.S. **b.** Same as 5.   **7.** $\triangle CRS \cong \triangle BTS$ (S.A.S.), $RTBC$ is a parallelogram (opposite sides parallel and equal from C.P.C.T.), $\overline{RS} \parallel \overline{CB}$ (opposite sides of parallelogram)   **8.** Divide quadrilateral $ABCD$ into 2 triangles by drawing a diagonal. Then use proof of 7.

Pages 254-255   **1. a.** Draw radii from ends of chords (A.S.A.). **b.** Draw radii from ends of the chord (S.A.S.).   **2.** 90° **3.** 9.8 cm **4.** 8 cm **5. b.** Answers will vary depending on **a.** **6. a.** $\triangle RSO$ and $\triangle STO$ (S.S.S.) **b.** $\triangle STO$ and $\triangle SRO$ (A.S.A.)   **7.** the intersection of the perpendicular bisectors and the two chords   **8.** 38 **9. a.** 90° **b.** 90° **10.** $\overline{ON}$ intersects $\overline{KM}$ at X;

$\overline{KX} \cong \overline{MX}$ (corollary 1); $\angle LXM \cong \angle LXK$ (bisector); $\overline{LX} \cong \overline{LX}$ (reflexive); $\therefore$ $\triangle LKX \cong \triangle LXM$ (S.A.S.); $\overline{LK} \cong \overline{LM}$ (C.P.C.T.) **11. a.** $\overline{AO} \cong \overline{OB} \cong \overline{OC} \cong \overline{OD}$ (radii); $\angle AOD \cong \angle BOC$ (opposite); $\triangle AOD \cong \triangle BOC$ (S.A.S.); $\overline{AD} \cong \overline{BC}$ (C.P.C.T.) **b.** Show $\overline{AC}$ bisects $\overline{BD}$. **12. a.** Prove $\triangle ABC \cong \triangle COA$ using hypotenuse and one side. **b.** If two tangents to a circle intersect externally at a point, then the lengths of the tangents are equal. **c.** 50°

Pages 256-257

1. *centre angle*: angle formed by the centre of the circle and 2 points on the circle; *inscribed angle*: angle formed by 3 points on the circle; *subtend*: holds up an angle **2. a.** $\angle NBL$, $\angle NCL$ **b.** $\angle LRN$, $\angle LSN$, $\angle LTN$ **3. a.** 42° **b.** 64° **c.** 87.5° **d.** 100° **4. a.** 61° **b.** 54° **5. a.** 76° **b.** 81° **6. a.** 124° **b.** 108° **c.** 180° **d.** 210° **7. a.** If a central angle and an inscribed angle are subtended by the same arc, then the measure of the central angle is twice that of the inscribed angle. **b.** If two inscribed angles are subtended by the same arc, then the measures of the two angles are equal. **8.** 180°; AOB (inscribed angle); 90° (division of equals) **9.** angle; right **10. a.** $\angle D + \angle B = 180°$ **b.** 360°; $\angle y$ (inscribed angle); $2(\angle B + \angle D)$; 180°; angles; supplementary

Pages 258-259

2. a. 10.7 **b.** 5.25 **3. a.** 14.25 **b.** 3.2 **c.** 13 **5.** 19.2 **6. a.** 8.6 **b.** 12.5 **c.** 2.25 **7.** $\overline{RS} = 5$, $\overline{RT} = 20$ **9. a.** 8 **b.** 8 **10.** Answers may vary. **11.** Answers may vary. **12.** Answers may vary. **13.** 20 cm **14.** 1.6 m

Page 260

1. a. 6.4 km **b.** 2.6 km **c.** $a^2 + b^2 = c^2$ **d.** Subtract the crossing distance from the actual outside walking distance. **2.** 40 LET C = SQR(A ∧ 2 + B ∧ 2); THE RETURN DISTANCE IS 6.4 KM **3. a.** Finds the distance saved. **b.** $c = 6.4$, $s = 2.6$ **c.** THE RETURN DISTANCE IS EQUAL TO 6.4031242 KM • S = 2.596875763 KM **4.** 20 INPUT A • 30 INPUT B • 45 PRINT "THE DISTANCE SAVED IS "; A + B − C; " KM" • THE DISTANCE SAVED IS 216.90482 KM • THE RETURN DISTANCE IS EQUAL TO 583.09518 KM **5.** 3, 4, 5; 15, 8, 17; 5, 12, 13; 7, 24, 25; 9, 40, 41; answers may vary. **6.** Answers may vary.

Page 261

1. a. If it's a dog, then it's an animal. **b.** If a person travels to Germany, then they travel to Europe. **c.** If a figure is a quadrilateral, then the sum of the measures of the angles is 360°. **2. a.** If you see sharks and poisonous spiders, then you are in Australia. If you are in Australia, then you see

sharks and poisonous spiders. **b.** If today is July 1, then it is Canada Day. If it is Canada Day, then it is July 1. **3. a.** H.L. **b.** S.S.S. **4. a.** $\overline{HO} \perp \overline{OB}$ and $\overline{DB} \perp \overline{OB}$ (given), $\angle O \cong \angle B$ (definition of perpendicular), $\overline{OP} \cong \overline{BE}$ (given), $\overline{OE} \cong \overline{BP}$ (addition of $\overline{PE}$), $\overline{HO} \cong \overline{DB}$ (given), $\triangle HOE \cong \triangle DBP$ (S.A.S.) **b.** $\angle FPE \cong \angle FEP$ (C.P.C.T.), $\overline{FP} \cong \overline{FE}$ (sides opposite congruent angles), $\triangle FPE$ is isosceles (definition of isosceles triangle). **5.** Assume all four angles are obtuse. Then $\angle A + \angle B + \angle C + \angle D > 360°$ (addition property), but $\angle A + \angle B + \angle C + \angle D = 360°$ (angles of a quadrilateral), therefore, a contradiction. **6.** In $\triangle ART$ and $\triangle DST$, $\overline{RT} \cong \overline{ST}$ (given), $\overline{AB} \| \overline{CD}$ (given), $\angle A \cong \angle D$ (alternate angles), $\angle ART \cong \angle DST$ (alternate angles), $\triangle ART \cong \triangle DST$ (S.A.A.), $\overline{TA} \cong \overline{TD}$ (C.P.C.T.), $\angle ATB \cong \angle DTC$ (vertically opposite angles), $\angle A \cong \angle D$ (alternate angles), $\triangle ABT \cong \triangle DCT$ (A.S.A.) **7. a.** $\triangle BAD$ and $\triangle EAC$ **b.** S.A.S. **c.** yes **d.** yes **e.** S.A.S. **f.** yes **g.** addition of $\angle CAD$ **8.** $\overline{BC} \cong \overline{DA}$ (given), $\overline{BA} \cong \overline{DC}$ (given), $\overline{BD} \cong \overline{DB}$ (reflexive property), $\triangle ABD \cong \triangle CDB$ (S.S.S.), $\angle BCD \cong \angle DAB$ (C.P.C.T.), $\angle DCE \cong \angle BAF$ (division property), $\angle FBA \cong \angle EDC$ (C.P.C.T.), $\triangle AFB \cong \triangle CED$ (A.S.A.), $\overline{BF} \cong \overline{DE}$ (C.P.C.T.) **9.** Join P perpendicular to each of the four sides forming eight right-angled triangles. Using $\overline{PA}$, $\overline{PB}$, $\overline{PC}$, and $\overline{PD}$ as the hypotenuse, apply the Pythagorean Theorem four times. By adding two pairs of equations and using the transitive property, you will obtain the desired proof. **10. a.** $\angle y = 58°$ **b.** $\angle AOB = 84°$

Page 262

1. Answers may vary. **2. a.** Alternate interior angles are congruent. **b.** Corresponding angles are congruent. **3.** a and h (A.S.A.); e and d (H.L.); c, d, and e (S.S.S.); b and g (S.A.S.); d, e, and f (S.A.S.) **4.** $\angle B + \angle C = \angle CAD + \angle DAC$ (exterior angle of a triangle), since $\angle B \cong \angle C$ (angles opposite congruent sides) and $\angle CAD \cong \angle DAC$ (construction), $\angle C \cong \angle DAC$ (division property), $\overline{AD} \| \overline{BC}$ (A.A.P.) **5.** $\overline{OR} \cong \overline{OT}$ (radii of a circle), $\overline{OS} \cong \overline{OS}$ (reflexive property), $\angle ROS \cong \angle TOS$ (given), $\triangle ROS \cong \triangle TOS$ (S.A.S.), $\overline{RS} \cong \overline{TS}$ (C.P.C.T.) **6. a.** triangles congruent by S.A.S. **b.** perpendicular by angles congruent (C.P.C.T.) **7.** Expressing the area of the large square in two ways, $c^2 = 4(\frac{1}{2}ab) + (a - b)^2$, $c^2 = 2ab + a^2 - 2ab + b^2$, $c^2 = a^2 + b^2$. **8.** $\angle RSQ \cong \angle TQS = 90°$ (converse of Pythagorean Theorem), $\overline{QT} \| \overline{RS}$ (A.A.P.) **9.** Assume $\overline{RS} \cong \overline{UT}$, then prove $\triangle RQS \cong \triangle UQT$ (S.A.S.). $\angle RQS \cong \angle UQT$ (C.P.C.T.) and a contradiction. **10. a.** 10.8 **b.** 11.2, 15.5, 6.2

Chapter 11

Page 263 **1. a.** 1, $\frac{-3}{8}$, $-\frac{1}{2}$ **b.** $\sqrt{101}$, $2\sqrt{5}$, $\sqrt{41}$

2. a. -3 **b.** $\frac{1}{4}$ **c.** $-\frac{2}{5}$ **d.** $-\frac{1}{6}$ **3. a.** $-\frac{1}{8}$ **b.** $\frac{2}{3}$

5. (2, 3) **6.** 29 d **7. b.** $A'(3, 6)$, $B'(6, 0)$, $C'(-2, 2)$

Page 264 **1. a.** reflection **b.** rotation of 180°
counterclockwise about the origin **2. i)** (2, 2),
(5, 0), (6, 6) **ii)** (2, -2), (-5, 0), (-6, -6)

Pages 265-267 **1.** New points: (-3, 3), (0, 4),
(-2, 0), (2, -1) **2. a.** (2, 3) **b.** (-2, 1) **c.** (0, 1)
3. a. $(x, y) \longrightarrow (x + 5, y + 2)$ **b.** $(x, y) \longrightarrow$
$(x + 1, y - 9)$ **c.** $(x, y) \longrightarrow (x - 3, y - 8)$ **4.** $A'(6, -3)$,
$B'(8, 1)$, $C'(11, -4)$ **5. a.** x decreased by 4, y
increased by 3 **b.** x decreased by 1, y increased by 1
6. a. $(x, y) \longrightarrow (x + 2, y + 4)$ **b.** same, 3 **c.** same,
$\sqrt{26}$ **7. a.** $A'(2, 1)$, $B'(6, 3)$, $C'(5, 0)$ **b.** slope
$\overline{AA'} = \frac{1}{3}$, slope $\overline{BB'} = \frac{1}{3}$, slope of $\overline{CC'} = \frac{1}{3}$
c. same **d.** $|\overline{AA'}| = 2\sqrt{10}$, $|\overline{BB'}| = 2\sqrt{10}$,
$|\overline{CC'}| = 2\sqrt{10}$ **e.** same **8.** New coordinates:
$D'(-2, 0)$, $E'(0, 6)$, $F'(2, 4)$, $G'(4, -1)$
9. a. $A'(-5, -1)$, $B'(-2, -3)$, $C'(-7, -4)$ **b.** x
decreased by 3, y decreased by 1 **c.** slope
$\overline{AB} = -\frac{2}{3}$, slope $\overline{AC} = \frac{3}{2}$ **d.** 90° **e.** slope
$\overline{A'B'} = -\frac{2}{3}$, slope $\overline{A'C'} = \frac{3}{2}$ **f.** 90° **g.** same
10. a. (6, 4) **b.** $C'(11, 4)$, $D'(10, 1)$ **c.** $(x, y) \longrightarrow$
$(x + 5, y)$ **d.** 20 square units **11. a.** $A'(-3, 2)$,
$C'(-5, -1)$ **c.** 6.5 square units

Pages 268-270 **1.** yes, invariant **2. a.** $(x, y) \longrightarrow$
$(-y, x)$ **b.** $(x, y) \longrightarrow (-x, -y)$ **c.** $(x, y) \longrightarrow (y, -x)$
d. $(x, y) \longrightarrow (y, -x)$ Positive: counterclockwise;
Negative: clockwise **4. a.** $D'(2, 0)$, $E'(0, 4)$, $F'(5, 2)$
b. x' equals $-y$, y' equals x **c.** $(x, y) \longrightarrow (-y, x)$
5. a. $A'(-2, -1)$, $B'(-3, -3)$, $C'(-6, 0)$ **b.** $(x, y) \longrightarrow$
$(-x, -y)$ **6. a.** $M'(-8, -6)$, $M''(6, -8)$ **b.** $N'(-2, 3)$,
$N''(-3, -2)$ **c.** $P'(9, -1)$, $P''(1, 9)$ **7. a.** $A'(-2, 5)$,
$B'(0, 4)$, $C'(0, 2)$, $D'(-2, 3)$ **b.** $(x, y) \longrightarrow (y, -x)$
8. a. (-4, -5) **b.** (-10, 3) **c.** (0, 7) **9. a.** $A(8, 3)$,
$B(2, -3)$, $C(4, 0)$, rotation 270° **b.** $A(3, -8)$,
$B(-3, -2)$, $C(0, -4)$, rotation 180° **c.** $A(-8, -3)$,
$B(-2, 3)$, $C(-4, 0)$, rotation 90° **10. a.** $F'(4, 2)$,
$G'(2, 7)$, $H'(7, 4)$ **b.** $(x, y) \longrightarrow (-y + 5, x + 1)$
11. a. $U'(-2, 1)$, $V'(1, -1)$, $W'(-5, 0)$ **b.** $(x, y) \longrightarrow$
$(-x + 2, -y + 2)$ **12. a.** $A'(1, -4)$, $B'(-4, -3)$,
$C'(-2, 1)$ **b.** lengths invariant **13. a.** negative
reciprocals **b.** same **c.** negative reciprocals, same
14. a. $|PQ| = |P'Q'| = \sqrt{5}$, $|\overline{QR}| = |\overline{Q'R'}| = \sqrt{53}$,
$|\overline{PR}| = |\overline{P'R'}| = 2\sqrt{13}$ **b.** slope $\overline{PQ} = \frac{1}{2}$, slope
$\overline{P'Q'} = \frac{-1}{2}$; slope $\overline{QR} = \frac{-7}{2}$, slope $\overline{Q'R'} = \frac{7}{2}$; slope

$\overline{PR} = \frac{-3}{2}$, slope $\overline{P'R'} = \frac{3}{2}$
15. $|\overline{OR}| \cong |\overline{OR'}| = \sqrt{29}$, $|\overline{OS}| \cong |\overline{OS'}| = 5$,
$|\overline{OT}| \cong |\overline{OT'}| = \sqrt{37}$ **16. a.** yes,
$|\overline{DE}| \cong |\overline{D'E'}| = \sqrt{10}$, $|\overline{EF}| \cong |\overline{E'F'}| = \sqrt{26}$,
$|\overline{FG}| \cong |\overline{F'G'}| = \sqrt{5}$, $|\overline{DG}| \cong |\overline{D'G'}| = \sqrt{17}$ **b.** yes
17. a. $A'(-2, 6)$, $B'(-5, 1)$, $C'(-6, 7)$ **b.** equal,
$|\overline{PA}| \cong |\overline{P'A'}| = \sqrt{10}$, $|\overline{PB}| \cong |\overline{P'B'}| = 2\sqrt{5}$,
$|\overline{PC}| \cong |\overline{P'C'}| = 5\sqrt{2}$ **18. b.** The perpendicular
bisectors pass through the centre of rotation.
19. a. $P'(-1, -4)$, $Q'(-4, -7)$, $R'(-8, 2)$ **b.** (1, -1)
c. yes

Pages 271-273 **1. a.** (4, -4), (5, 7), (-3, -1)
b. $(x, y) \longrightarrow (x, -y)$ **2. a.** (1, -5), (-6, 2), (-3, -8)
b. $(x, y) \longrightarrow (-x, y)$ **3.** $P(10, -4)$, $Q(6, 3)$
4. b. (-4, 2), (-6, -3), (4, -1) **c.** $(x, y) \longrightarrow (-y, -x)$
5. a. $P'(-5, 1)$, $R'(-7, 4)$, $|\overline{PR}| \cong |\overline{P'R'}| = \sqrt{13}$
b. $P'(5, -1)$, $R'(7, -4)$, $|\overline{PR}| \cong |\overline{P'R'}| = \sqrt{13}$
c. $P'(1, 5)$, $R'(4, 7)$, $|\overline{PR}| \cong |\overline{P'R'}| = \sqrt{13}$
d. $P'(-1, -5)$, $R'(-4, -7)$, $|\overline{PR}| \cong |\overline{P'R'}| = \sqrt{13}$
6. Slope of the line segments are 0. **7. a.** $F'(-6, 4)$,
$G'(2, -2)$, $H'(-1, 1)$ **b.** slope $\overline{FG} = \frac{3}{4}$, slope
$\overline{F'G'} = -\frac{3}{4}$, slope $\overline{GH} = 1$, slope $\overline{G'H'} = -1$, slope
$\overline{FH} = \frac{3}{5}$, slope $\overline{F'H'} = -\frac{3}{5}$ **c.** Image slope is
negative of object slope. **8. a.** $M'(6, -8)$, $N'(9, 3)$,
$P'(-4, 0)$ **b.** midpoint $\overline{MM'} = (-1, -1)$, midpoint
$\overline{NN'} = (6, 6)$, midpoint $\overline{PP'} = (-2, -2)$; each set
satisfies $y = x$ **9. a.** $R'(3, 8)$, $S'(5, 1)$, slope $\overline{RS} = \frac{7}{2}$,
slope $\overline{R'S'} = -\frac{7}{2}$ **b.** $R'(-3, 8)$, $S'(-5, -1)$, slope
$\overline{RS} = \frac{7}{2}$, slope $\overline{R'S'} = -\frac{7}{2}$ **c.** $R'(8, -3)$, $S'(1, -5)$,
slope $\overline{RS} = \frac{7}{2}$, slope $\overline{R'S'} = \frac{2}{7}$ **d.** $R'(-8, 3)$,
$S'(-1, 5)$, slope $\overline{RS} = \frac{7}{2}$, slope $\overline{R'S'} = \frac{2}{7}$ **10.** $y = x$
11. a. midpoint $\overline{DD'} = (-4, 4)$, midpoint
$\overline{FF'} = (3, -3)$ **b.** $y = -x$ **c.** line of reflection
12. a. $A'(4, 4)$, $B'(-2, 8)$, $C'(-4, 0)$ **d.** Perpendicular
bisector of joining segments coincide to form line of
reflection. **e.** $y = x - 2$

Pages 274-275 **1. a.** reflection in $y = -x$ **b.** length,
angle measure **c.** reversed in orientation
2. translation **3. a.** $J'(2, 0)$, $K'(5, 4)$, $L'(0, 2)$
b. $|\overline{JK}| \cong |\overline{J'K'}| = 5$, $|\overline{KL}| \cong |\overline{K'L'}| = \sqrt{29}$,
$|\overline{JL}| \cong |\overline{J'L'}| = 2\sqrt{2}$ **c.** slope $\overline{JK} = \frac{3}{4}$, slope
$\overline{J'K'} = \frac{4}{3}$, etc. **4.** Line segment joining centre of
rotation and vertex and its image is invariant.
5. $\overline{PP'} \| \overline{QQ'}$, segments joining corresponding points

are parallel, $\overline{P'Q'} \| \overline{PQ}$, length preserved in translation **6.** $|\overline{BC}| \cong |\overline{B'C}| = 2\sqrt{5}$,
7. a. $A'(4, -2)$, $B'(2, 2)$, $C'(0, 0)$, $|\overline{AB}| \cong |\overline{A'B'}| = 2\sqrt{5}$, $|\overline{AC}| \cong |\overline{A'C'}| = 2\sqrt{5}$, $|\overline{BC}| \cong |\overline{B'C'}| = 2\sqrt{2}$ **b.** isosceles and congruent
8. rotation 90° about origin **9. a.** 1) reflection in y, translation; 2) reflection in $y = x$; 3) rotation 90°, reflection in x-axis **b.** indirect, indirect, indirect
10. a. rotation of 90° **b.** direct **11. a.** reflection
b. indirect **c.** 3 parts: rotation direct; 4 parts: reflection indirect, translation direct, rotation direct

Pages 276-277   **1.** same **2.** slope of $2x + 3y = 4$ is $-\frac{2}{3}$, slope of $8x + 12y = 2$ is $-\frac{2}{3}$ **3. a.** $6x - y = 6$
b. $6x - y = -15$ **c.** $6x - y = 35$ **d.** $6x - y = -2$
4. a. negative reciprocal **b.** $\frac{2}{5}$ **c.** $2x - 5y = 1$
5. negative reciprocals **a.** $y + 5x = -2$
b. $2x - 3y = 4$ **c.** $2x + 4y = 9$ **d.** $x - y = 10$
6. $x - 2y = -8$ **7. a.** additive inverse **b.** additive inverse **c.** reciprocal **d.** reciprocal **8. a.** $3x + 5y = 8$
b. slope of line is $-\frac{5}{3}$, slope of image is $-\frac{3}{5}$
9. a. $3x + y = -10$ **b.** $(0, -10)$ **c.** slope of line = 3, slope of image = -3 **10.** $2x + 6y = 5$
11. a. $4x - y = 19$ **b.** $x - 2$, $y + 6$ **12. a.** $(-a, -b)$
b. replace x with $-x$, replace y with $-y$ **13. a.** $(x, y) \longrightarrow (x, -y)$ **b.** $(a, b) \longrightarrow (a, -b)$ **c.** replace x with x, replace y with $-y$ **14. a.** $(x, y) \longrightarrow (y, x)$ **b.** y, x

Pages 278-279   **1.** Answers may vary.
2. a. $A'(0, -2)$, $B'(-3, -5)$, $C'(-1, -7)$ **b.** $A'(0, 2)$, $B'(-3, 5)$, $C'(-1, 7)$ **c.** $A'(0, 2)$, $B'(-5, 3)$, $C'(-7, 1)$
d. $A'(4, -5)$, $B'(-1, -6)$, $C'(-3, -4)$ **e.** $A'(6, 0)$, $B'(3, -3)$, $C'(1, -1)$ **4.** $P'(1, 4)$, $Q'(-1, 0)$, $R'(2, -2)$
5. a. $M'(-1, 4)$, $N'(-8, -3)$ **b.** $M'(-6, -2)$, $N'(1, -9)$
6. rotation of 180° about the origin **7.** When transformations are performed in reverse, image is same as in Exercise 6. **8. a.** $F'(5, 8)$, $G'(8, 1)$
b. $|\overline{FF'}| \cong |\overline{GG'}| = \sqrt{65}$ **c.** slope $\overline{FF'}$ = slope $\overline{GG'} = \frac{4}{7}$ **d.** $(x, y) \longrightarrow (x + 7, y + 4)$ **9.** $R'(4, 2)$, $S'(-2, -3)$, $T'(1, -6)$, slope $\overline{RS} = \frac{6}{5}$, slope $\overline{R'S'} = \frac{5}{6}$, slope $\overline{ST} = -1$, slope $\overline{S'T'} = -1$, slope $\overline{RT} = \frac{3}{8}$, slope $\overline{R'T'} = \frac{8}{3}$; lengths are invariant
10. Answers may vary.

Pages 280-281   **1.** $(-2, 14)$, $(-2, 2)$, $(-14, 8)$, $(4, 8)$
2. a. $(-6, 15)$ **b.** $(0, 9)$ **c.** $(24, -3)$ **d.** $(12, 21)$
3. a. $A'(-2, 6)$, $B'(6, 8)$, $C'(0, 2)$ **b.** no, length is not preserved **4. a.** $P'(0.5, 2)$, $Q'(2.5, 1.5)$, $R'(1.5, 0.5)$
b. $P'(-2, -8)$, $Q'(-10, -6)$, $R'(-6, -2)$ **c.** image reduced **d.** If $|k| > 1$ image expanded; if $|k| < 1$ image reduced; also image rotated 180° about the

origin **5.** $|\overline{MN}| = 3\sqrt{2}$, $|\overline{M'N'}| = 12\sqrt{2}$ **6. a.** 2
b. slope $\overline{AB}$ = slope $\overline{A'B'} = -2$ **7.** slope $\overline{AC}$ = slope $\overline{A'C'} = -\frac{1}{2}$ **8.** $k > 0$ — slope is preserved; orientation is preserved; $k < 0$ — rotation of 180° about the origin; orientation reversed; for both, ratio of corresponding sides and its image are the same; angle measure is preserved. **9.** $4\overline{RS} \cong \overline{R'S'}$
10. $(x, y) \longrightarrow (6x, 6y)$ **11.** $|\overline{UV}| = \sqrt{10}$, $|\overline{U'V'}| = 4\sqrt{10}$ **12. a.** quadrupled **b.** increased by 9 times **c.** increased n^2 times **13.** $3x - 7y = 6$

Pages 282-283   **6.** $0, 6\frac{5}{9}$ **8.** 17, 10, 19
BRAINTICKLER 3

Pages 284-285   **1. a.** length, slope, angle measure, orientation **b.** length, angle measure, orientation
c. length, angle measure **d.** Translation and Reflection — length, angle measure; Translation and Rotation — length, angle measure, orientation; Reflection and Rotation — length, angle measure.
e. $k > 0$ — slope, angle measure, orientation; $k < 0$ — angle measure **2. a.** 86 is divisible by 2.
b. $\angle PQR$ is 90°. **c.** $ABCD$ has four sides. **d.** $ABCD$ is a parallelogram with 4 equal sides. **e.** $\triangle KLM$ has two congruent sides. **f.** $\angle BAP \cong \angle PAC$ **3.** Step 1. Given $\overline{RP}$ perpendicular bisector of $\overline{ST}$. Step 2. Prove $\overline{RT}$ and $\overline{RS}$ are reflections in line RP. Length invariant under reflection. **4.** 1) perpendicular bisector of $\overline{ED}$. 2) length invariant 3) same as part 1 4) same as part 2 5) transitive property
5. $\overline{JK} \cong \overline{J'K'}$ length invariant, $\angle FKJ \cong \angle F'K'J'$ angle measurement invariant, $\overline{FK} \cong \overline{F'K'}$ length invariant, $\therefore \triangle JFK \cong \triangle J'F'K'$ (S.A.S.) **6.** $\overline{AB} \cong \overline{BA'}$ length invariant $\therefore \overline{AA'}$ bisected by ℓ_1 **7.** $\overline{AC} \cong \overline{CA'}$ length invariant, $\overline{BA} \cong \overline{BA'}$ length invariant, $\angle BAC \cong \angle BA'C$ angle measurement invariant $\therefore \triangle ABC \cong \triangle A'BC$ (S.A.S.) $\therefore \triangle ABA'$ is isosceles triangle **8.** $\angle P \cong \angle R$ (given) $\therefore$ triangle is isosceles $\therefore \overline{PQ} \cong \overline{QR}$ **9.** All sides are congruent because length preserved under rotation $\therefore$ quadrilateral must be a rhombus. **10.** $\overline{BA} \cong \overline{C'A}$ reflexive, $\angle B'AB \cong \angle C'AC$ angle invariant, $\overline{B'A} \cong \overline{AC}$ (given) $\therefore \triangle B'BA \cong \triangle BAC \therefore \triangle B'C'C$ is isosceles **11.** $\ell_1 \| \ell_2$, slope invariant under translation, $x = y$, corresponding angles F pattern **12.** Sides containing the angles are parallel $\therefore$ adjacent angles are supplementary (interior angle theorem)

Page 286   **1.** sets up graphics display **2.** Line 50 draws a vertical line from row 20 to 24 in column 28; line 70 draws a vertical line from row 0 to row 39 at column 20; line 80 draws a horizontal from column 12 to 15 at row 24; line 90 draws a vertical line from row 20 to row 24 at column 12.

4. Lines 10 to 50 are same as display. 55 REM DRAW CENTRE OF ROTATION • 60 COLOR = 10 • 70 PLOT 20, 20 • 75 REM DRAW THE IMAGE AFTER REFLECTION • 80 HLIN 12, 15 AT 16 • 90 VLIN 16, 20 AT 12 • 99 END **5.** centre of rotation **6.** 75 REM 90 DEGREES • 80 HLIN 20, 24 AT 12 • 90 VLIN 12, 15 AT 24 • 95 REM 270 DEGREES • 100 HLIN 16, 20 AT 28 • 110 VLIN 25, 28 AT 16 • 199 END **7.** Lines 10 to 50 are same as display. 55 REM DRAW IMAGE • 60 HLIN 17, 20 AT 20 • 70 VLIN 16, 20 AT 20 • 99 END

Page 287 **1. a.** $A'(-2, -3)$, $B'(2, 2)$, $C'(3, -2)$ **b.** $A'(0, -6)$, $B'(-5, -2)$, $C'(-1, -1)$ **c.** $A'(6, 0)$, $B'(2, 5)$, $C'(1, 1)$ **2. a.** $P'(3, 4)$ **b.** $Q'(5, -4)$ **3.** $A'(-1, 1)$, $B'(3, 4)$, $C'(6, 2)$; $|\overline{AB}| \cong |\overline{A'B'}| = 5$, $|\overline{BC}| \cong |\overline{B'C'}| = \sqrt{13}$, $|\overline{AC}| \cong |\overline{A'C'}| = 5\sqrt{2}$; slope $\overline{AB}$ = slope $\overline{A'B'} = \frac{3}{4}$, slope $\overline{BC}$ = slope $\overline{B'C'} = -\frac{2}{3}$, slope $\overline{AC}$ = slope $\overline{A'C'} = \frac{1}{7}$ **4. a.** $D'(5, -3)$, $E'(4, 2)$, $F'(0, 0)$ **b.** reflection in x-axis **c.** $|\overline{DE}| \cong |\overline{D'E'}| = \sqrt{26}$, $|\overline{EF}| \cong |\overline{E'F'}| = 2\sqrt{5}$, $|\overline{DF}| \cong |\overline{D'F'}| = \sqrt{34}$ **5. a.** $A'(1, -5)$, $B'(-3, 5)$, $C'(-2, 1)$, $D'(2, 1)$; $|\overline{AB}| \cong |\overline{A'B'}| = 4$, $|\overline{BC}| \cong |\overline{B'C'}| = \sqrt{37}$, $|\overline{CD}| \cong |\overline{C'D'}| = 4$, $|\overline{AD}| \cong |\overline{A'D'}| = \sqrt{37}$ **b.** slope $\overline{BC}$ = slope $\overline{B'C'} = 6$ **c.** yes **6.** $7x + 2y = 2$ **7.** $x + 3y = 2$ **8.** $3x - y = -2$ **9.** $2x - y = 9$ **10. a.** $A'(0, 0)$, $B'(4, 3)$, $C'(2, -4)$ **b.** $A''(0, 0)$, $B''(4, -3)$, $C''(2, 4)$ **c.** $(x, y) \longrightarrow (x - 2, y - 3)$ **d.** $|\overline{AB}| \cong |\overline{A'B'}| = 5$, $|\overline{BC}| \cong |\overline{B'C'}| = \sqrt{53}$, $|\overline{AC}| \cong |\overline{A'C'}| = 2\sqrt{5}$ **e.** angle measure, orientation, slope **11.** Rotation preserves orientation. **12.** $|\overline{FG}| \cong |\overline{GH}|$ (given); $|\overline{FG}| \cong |\overline{FG'}|$ (reflection); $|\overline{GH}| \cong |\overline{G'H}|$ (reflection) $\therefore |\overline{FG}| \cong |\overline{GH}| \cong |\overline{G'H}| \cong |\overline{FG'}|$ (transitive) $\therefore FGHG'$ is a rhombus.

Page 288 **1. a.** translation; $A'(1, 2)$, $B'(5, 5)$, $C'(11, 1)$ **b.** rotation of 180° about the origin; $A'(2, 4)$, $B'(-2, -3)$, $C'(-8, 1)$ **c.** reflection in $y = x$; $A'(-4, -2)$, $B'(3, 2)$, $C'(-1, 8)$ **2. a.** $A'(-6, 13)$ **b.** $B'(1, -4)$ **c.** $C'(5, -2)$ **d.** $D'(-3, 8)$ **e.** $E'(-2, 10)$ **f.** $F'(-2, 0)$ **g.** $G'(-5, 6)$ **h.** $H'(-6, -4)$ **i.** $I'(9, -8)$ **3. a.** reflection in line $y = x$ **b.** reflection in y-axis **4.** $|\overline{PQ}| \cong |\overline{P'Q'}| = 5$, $|\overline{QR}| \cong |\overline{Q'R'}| = 2\sqrt{10}$, $|\overline{PR}| \cong |\overline{P'R'}| = \sqrt{5}$, slope $\overline{PQ}$ = slope $\overline{P'Q'} = -\frac{3}{4}$, slope $\overline{QR}$ = slope $\overline{Q'R'} = -\frac{1}{3}$, slope $\overline{PR}$ = slope $\overline{P'R'} = \frac{1}{2}$ **5.** $A'(3, -1)$, $B(7, 2)$, slope $\overline{AB}$ = slope $\overline{A'B'} = \frac{3}{4}$, $|\overline{AB}| \cong |\overline{A'B'}| = 5$ **6.** $3x - 5y = 19$ **7.** $8y - 3x = 12$ **8.** $A''(-5, 2)$, $B''(-1, -2)$, $C''(2, 3)$

9. $5x + y = -5$ **10.** $|\overline{AB}| \cong |\overline{A'B'}| = \sqrt{17}$, $|\overline{BC}| \cong |\overline{B'C'}| \cong \sqrt{65}$, $|\overline{CD}| \cong |\overline{C'D'}| = \sqrt{13}$, $|\overline{DA}| \cong |\overline{D'A'}| = \sqrt{29}$ **11.** directly congruent **12. a.** $D'(-6, -4)$, $F'(-4, 4)$, $G'(-2, -2)$ **b.** slope $\overline{FG}$ = slope $\overline{F'G'} = -3$ **13.** $|\overline{A'B'}| = 28$ cm, $|\overline{C'D'}| = 72$ cm, $|\overline{BC}| = 14$ cm

Chapter 12

Page 289 **1.** People may not always tell the truth during a personal interview. **2.** Answers may vary. **3.** Arithmetic confusion, e.g., $\frac{1}{3}$ of 12 is 4 thus $\frac{1}{4}$ of people suffer from athlete's foot. **4.** random sample **5.** Answers may vary. **6.** Answers may vary.

Pages 290-291 **1.** Sunday **2.** afternoon **3.** they get lower **4.** Sunday **5.** they get higher **6.** low water — afternoon, high water — morning **7.** A — 210, B — 158, C — 158, D — 116, E — 77, F — 70, G — 70, H — 63, I — 61, J — 17 **8.** Answers may vary. **9.** Answers may vary. **10.** Queenstak, Que Sturg **11.** \$125 **12.** Prado ex o **13.** Princpl A **14.** \$72 750 **15.** Answers may vary. **16.** Answers may vary.

Pages 292-293 **1.** Lakeview students **2.** Lakeview, Oceanview, and Mountainview students **3.** 100 **4.** 150 **5.** Not everyone was surveyed. **6.** reduce peer pressure when answering; more thought about answers, etc. **7.** Not everyone responded. **8.** No. peer pressure **9.** Oceanview and Mountainview students **10.** Answers may vary. Suggestion: odd digit = boy, even digit = girl **11.** Answers may vary. **12.** Answers may vary. **13.** Read digits in groups of three. **14. a.** 10% **b.** 40% **c.** Sample biased by greater percentage of female respondents. There should be 8 females and 32 males in the survey. **15. a.** Answers may vary. **b.** North 3, East 3, West 1, South 5

Pages 294-295 **1.** Answers may vary. Example: cost and foreign language **2.** Answers may vary. **3.** Generally telephone survey is least expensive, personal interviews most expensive. **4.** Telephone survey is fastest, personal interviews are slowest. **5. a.** precise **b.** vague **c.** vague **d.** precise **e.** precise **f.** precise **6. a.** fact **b.** opinion **c.** fact **d.** opinion **e.** opinion **f.** opinion **7.** *anonymous:* no identification of respondent; *confidential:* respondents identified, but names not released in report **8.** no information about respondent **9.** people are more likely to respond; not able to compare with other people **10.** confidential **11. a.** response **b.** response **c.** coverage **d.** response **e.** process **12.** Answers may vary. **13.** Answers may vary. **14.** Answers may vary.

Pages 296-297 **1.** 40 **2.** 2.5% **3.** 1.25, 1.75, 2.25, 2.75 **4.** 2.00 **5.** 2.50

6. a.

Class	Freq.	% Freq.	Cum. % Freq.
$310 \le d < 320$	1	4	4
$320 \le d < 330$	1	4	8
$330 \le d < 340$	2	8	16
$340 \le d < 350$	3	12	18
$350 \le d < 360$	7	28	56
$360 \le d < 370$	5	20	76
$370 \le d < 380$	3	12	88
$380 \le d < 390$	2	8	96
$390 \le d < 400$	1	4	100

b. 350 - 360 **c.** yes

7. a.

Class (000s)	Freq.	% Freq.	Cum. % Freq.
$100 \le p < 200$	10	45	45
$200 \le p < 300$	5	23	68
$300 \le p < 400$	1	4.5	72.5
$400 \le p < 500$	0	0	72.5
$500 \le p < 600$	5	23	95.5
$600 \le p < 700$	1	4.5	100

b. 100 - 600 and 200 - 700 increment of 100
c. 121 - 657 **d.** 700 000 and 100 000 **e.** 96% **f.** 23%
g. 10

8.

Class	Freq.	% Freq.	Cum. % Freq.
$0 \le h < 150$	3	10	10
$150 \le h < 300$	3	10	20
$300 \le h < 450$	4	13.3	33.3
$450 \le h < 600$	5	16.6	50
$600 \le h < 750$	6	20	70
$750 \le h < 900$	7	23.4	93.4
$900 \le h < 1050$	2	6.7	100

a. 7 **b.** boundaries: lower 150, 300, 450, 600, 750, 900; upper 150, 300, 450, 750, 900, 1050; limits: 0 and 1050; range 137 - 971 **c.** 16.6% **d.** 70%

e. Friday, Saturday, or Sunday **f.** $13\frac{1}{3}$% or about 4 d **g.** between 450 - 600 hamburgers **h.** Answers may vary. **i.** Answers may vary.

9. a.

Class	Freq.	% Freq.	Cum. % Freq.
$100 \le n < 200$	6	6	6
$200 \le n < 300$	18	18	24
$300 \le n < 400$	46	46	70
$400 \le n < 500$	20	20	90
$500 \le n < 600$	5	5	95
$600 \le n < 700$	1	1	96
$700 \le n < 800$	1	1	97
$800 \le n < 900$	1	1	98
$900 \le n < 1000$	2	2	100

b. between 18 and 46 polling stations **c.** Answers may vary.

Pages 298-299 **1.** source of data **2.** 50 **3.** 125 **4.** 300, 250 **5.** Greater area of the bar distorts data's appearance. **6. a.** histogram **b.** bar **c.** histogram **d.** bar or histogram **e.** bar **7.** 200 - 299 km/h: 6; 300 - 399 km/h: 17; 400 - 499 km/h: 17; 500 - 599 km/h: 3; 600 - 699 km/h: 0; 700 - 799 km/h: 3; 800 - 899 km/h: 5; 900 - 999 km/h: 9 **8.** more likely that they are both blue **10.** 0 seeds (3 or 7.5%), 1 seed (5 or 12.5%), 2 seeds (8 or 20%), 3 seeds (10 or 25%), 4 seeds (7 or 17.5%), 5 seeds (6 or 15%), 6 seeds (1 or 2.5%)

Pages 300-301 **1. a.** 4 **b.** 1 **c.** 6 **2. a.** $10 \le p < 11$, $17 \le p < 18$ **b.** $13 \le p < 14$, $14 \le p < 15$ **c.** $11 \le p < 12$, $16 \le p < 17$ **d.** $8 \le p < 9$, $19 \le p < 20$, $20 \le p < 21$ **e.** $12 \le p < 13$, $15 \le p < 16$

4.

Stem	Leaf
9	0.7
10	0.3, 0.4, 0.7
11	0.0, 0.9
12	0.1, 0.4, 0.9, 0.9
13	
14	0.5, 0.8

5.

Stem	Leaf
-3	7
-4	1, 7, 9
-5	3, 4, 7, 7, 8, 9
-6	1, 3

6.

Stem	Leaf
2	9.6
3	2.4, 8.9
4	2.5, 2.8, 5.2, 6.6, 7.2, 9.0
5	3.4, 5.5, 8.9
6	2.3
7	3.6
8	
9	0.7, 6.6

a. 40 - 50 mm **b.** 273.3 m
7. 38

8.

National			American
Leaf		Stem	Leaf
		7	8
		8	
1		9	
5, 6, 9, 9		10	5, 8, 9, 9, 9
1, 6, 8, 9, 9		11	2, 2, 3, 4, 6, 7, 8, 8, 8, 9, 9
0, 0, 1, 1, 1, 1, 1, 5, 6, 7, 9, 9		12	1, 2, 2, 2, 3, 6, 6, 6, 6, 9
0, 0, 2, 6, 7		13	0, 3, 9, 9
1, 2, 2, 3, 8, 9		14	0, 2, 4, 5
3		15	

a. National 121, American 126 **b.** no **c.** National 91, 153; American 78

9.

Stem	Leaf
180	1, 2, 3, 3, 3, 4, 4, 7, 7, 8, 8, 8
181	1, 7, 7, 7
182	3, 5, 6, 8, 9
183	0, 9
184	3, 3, 5
185	
186	0, 1, 1, 3, 8
187	5, 8, 8, 9, 9, 9
188	5, 5, 6, 6, 6
189	4, 8, 8, 8, 8, 8, 9

a. 1800 - 1810 **b.** 1850 - 1860 **c.** 6 **10.** $4 \times 5 = 20$, $5 \times 6 = 30$, $6 \times 7 = 42$

Pages 302-303 **1.** mean = 24.63, median = 25, modes = 20, 23, 25, 26, 27, or 32 **2.** Answers may vary. **3.** Assuming even distribution about the measures, mean = 73.9, mode = 40, median = 40 **4.** median = 40, mode = 40, mean = 73.9 **5.** mean = 24.25, mode = 25, median = 25 **6.** Answers may vary. **7.** two modes **8.** 1 groove **9.** mean = 73.62, mode = 74, median = 73 **10.** mean = 126.65, bi-modal 127 and 132, median = 127.5 **11.** mean = 166.36, mode = 169.9, median = 168.705 **12.** Answers may vary. **13.** No change occurs.

Pages 304-305 **1.** no effect, lowered by $3.50 **2.** mean is lower ($296.64), median is the same, mode is the same **3.** group comparison: mean ($299.27), individual fare: median ($352) **4.** same **5. a.** 7% **b.** 48.1% **c.** 18.7% **d.** 26.2% **6. a.** 11.5% **b.** 56.5% **c.** 16.5% **d.** 15.4% **7. a.** weighted mean = 66.2, mode = 75 **b.** Answers may vary. **8.** weighted mean = 274.06, mode = 273

9. Answers may vary. **10.** weighted mean = $506.03, mode = $500 **11.** weighted mean = 7, mode = 7

Pages 306-307 **1.** Middle value is there. **2. a.** 5 **b.** 2 **c.** 10 **d.** 104 **3. a.** 14 **b.** 2.5 **c.** −4 **d.** 28 **4.** Divide range by number of desired individuals. **5.** CM column: 12.5, 17.5, 22.5, 27.5, 32.8; CM $\times$ F column: 12.5, 150, 250, 402.5, 540, 275, 130; % Freq column: 0.7, 8.5, 14.2, 22.8, 30.7, 15.6, 7.5; Cum % Freq column: 0.7, 9.2, 23.4, 46.2, 76.9, 92.5, 100.0; Total row: 106, 1760, 100; mean = 16.6, median = 16.85, modal class $20 \leq n < 25$ **6.** CM column: 15, 25, 35, 45, 55, 65, 75, 85; CM $\times$ F column: 510, 9840, 24 050, 12 565, 11 790, 12 210, 10 400, 10 275, 6290; % Freq column: 0.5, 10.0, 24.6, 12.8, 12.0, 12.5, 10.6, 10.5, 6.4; Cum % Freq column: 0.5, 10.5, 35.1, 47.9, 59.9, 72.4, 83.0, 93.6, 100.0; Total row: 2934, 97 930, 100; mean = 33.38, median = 22.635, modal class $20 \leq n < 30$ **7.** mean = 61, median = 63.58, modal class $60 \leq m < 70$ **8.** mean = 53.46, median = 70.5, modal class $70 \leq p < 80$ **9.** mean = −14.5, median = −9.465, modal class $-10 \leq t < 0$ **10.** mean = 66.09, median = 65.095, modal class $60 \leq w < 65$

Pages 308-309 **1.** mean = 51.129%; median = 55; bimodal 0 - 10, 90 - 100; none represents parking lot use on an average day; bath tub **2.** mean = 31.43°C; median = 31°C; no mode; uniform **3.** mean = 133.3 mm; median = 110 mm; mode = 0 mm; normal **4.** mean = 50.47, median = 50.5, modal class 50 - 59, normal; when distribution is symmetrical, central measures are close **5.** mean = 3.2 wins/week; median = 2.5 wins/week; mode = 8 wins/week; bath tub; none of the central measures represent the number of wins in an average week **6.** mean = 5.465 coliform/mL; median = 6 coliform/mL; bi-modal class 6 coliform/mL or 1 coliform/mL; normal distribution **7.** mean = 180.06 cm; median = 180.05; modal class 177.5 - 182.4 **8.** mean = 11:30; median = 11:21.75; modal class 12:30 - 13:00 **9.** Answers may vary.

Pages 310-311 **1.** mode **2.** median **3.** mean **4.** mode **5.** mean **6.** mean **7.** median **8.** 70 kg **9.** The mean is probably used to encourage older people to buy sportswear. **10.** mean = $86 279, median = $81 592 **11. a.** mean **b.** median or mode **12.** median **13.** 20 km/h **14.** For some reason the older members were unable to attend. **15.** mode **16.** 50% **17. a.** An increase in number at lower income level moves the median down. **b.** mean **18.** 15.5 a

Pages 312-313 1. Box and whisker plot also shows where 90% of data will be. 2. confident to a certain percent that data will be in a given interval; if no values are recorded at a certain frequency 3. Answers may vary. 4. 6 - 18, all data occurs in this interval 5. Bias affects results and thus confidence will be different. 6. Answers may vary. 7. Answers may vary. 8. Answers may vary. 9. a. confidence interval: for girls 150 - 161, for boys 144 - 158 b. 157 cm, 151 cm c. Girls are typically taller.

Page 314 1. sample is too small 2. reduces the range (add precision) 3. improves reliability 4. 11 of 100 is best 5. 75 hens, 50 cattle 6. no, biased in favour of those who enjoy swimming pools (fresh water) 7. a. A different riding may elect a candidate from a different party than the incumbent. b. No, because 2 of 3 ridings polled would vote against the incumbent. 8. Answers may vary. **BRAINTICKLER**
$1 + (2 \times 3 \times 4 \times 5 \times 6 \times 7 \times 8 \times 9 \times 0) = 1$

Page 315 1. sample too small 2. biased 3. biased 4. sample too small 5. biased 6. census, too time consuming, process errors may occur 7. stratified random sample 8. biased 9. biased, sample too small 10. Answers may vary.

Pages 316-317 1. {10, 12, 14, 16, 18} 2. a. yes b. yes c. no d. yes e. yes f. no g. no h. no 3. a. {T, H}; T; H b. all the cards in the deck; 13 diamonds; hearts, clubs, and spades c. 1 - 6; 3; 1, 2, 4, 5, 6 d. odd and even digits; 1, 3, 5, 7, 9; 0, 2, 4, 6, 8 e. C, H, A, N, C, E; A, E; C, H, N f. 1, 2, 3, 4, 5, 6; 1, 2, 3, 4, 5, 6; $\varnothing$ 4. a. $\frac{1}{2}$ b. $\frac{1}{4}$ c. $\frac{1}{6}$ d. $\frac{1}{2}$ e. $\frac{2}{6}$ f. 1 5. Answers may vary. 6. a. $\frac{1}{8}$ b. $\frac{2}{8}$ c. 0 d. $\frac{6}{8}$ e. $\frac{4}{8}$ f. $\frac{4}{8}$ g. $\frac{3}{4}$ h. $\frac{1}{2}$ i. 1 j. 0 7. a. $\frac{1}{4}$ b. $\frac{1}{2}$ c. $\frac{1}{2}$ d. $\frac{1}{4}$ 8. a. $\frac{3}{11}$ b. $\frac{6}{11}$ c. $\frac{1}{11}$ d. $\frac{8}{11}$ e. $\frac{2}{11}$ f. $\frac{10}{11}$ g. 1 h. $\frac{3}{11}$ i. $\frac{8}{11}$ j. $\frac{6}{11}$ 9. a. 75% b. 50% c. 15% d. 1%

Pages 318-319 1. 0.2; 0.1333 2. closer approximation as the number of rolls increase 3. Answers may vary. 4. a. $\frac{3}{4}, \frac{1}{4}$ b. - d. Answers may vary. 5. $\frac{1}{2}$ 6. 3 7. Answers may vary. 8. theoretical $\frac{1}{4}, \frac{1}{2}, \frac{1}{4}$ 9. a. 35% b. 58% c. 81% d. 89% e. 52% f. 61% 10. $\frac{7}{36}$

Pages 320-321 1. a. $\frac{2}{9}$ b. $\frac{4}{9}$ 2. $\frac{10}{21}$ 3. $\frac{5}{21}$ 4. a. F b. T 5. a. $\frac{1}{25}$ b. $\frac{3}{50}$ c. $\frac{9}{25}$ d. $\frac{27}{50}$ 6. Answers may vary. 7. different digits 8. a. $\frac{1}{9}$ b. $\frac{7}{45}$ c. $\frac{7}{75}$ d. $\frac{4}{25}$ e. $\frac{1}{15}$ f. $\frac{1}{15}$ g. $\frac{49}{225}$ h. $\frac{1}{25}$ i. $\frac{2}{9}$ 9. a. $\frac{3}{29}$ b. $\frac{14}{87}$ c. $\frac{14}{145}$ d. $\frac{41}{435}$ e. $\frac{2}{29}$ f. $\frac{1}{29}$ 10. a. $\frac{1}{20}$ b. $\frac{1}{20}$ c. $\frac{3}{20}$ d. $\frac{3}{20}$ e. $\frac{3}{20}$ f. $\frac{3}{20}$ 11. Answers may vary. 12. 10^{-9} 13. a. $\frac{27}{320}$ b. $\frac{21}{320}$ c. $\frac{63}{320}$ d. $\frac{189}{320}$

Page 322 1. to choose a random number between 0 and 1 2. If the random number is less then 0.5, the computer will return to the top of the loop. 3. to make the probability exactly one half 4. Answers may vary. 5. Dividing by number of "flips" gives average probability. 6. $\frac{1}{2}$ 7. more precision because more trials 8. change 30 FOR X = 1 TO 200 • 70 LET T = T + 1 • 75 NEXT X • 76 PRINT "NUMBER OF HEADS ROLLED IS "; H − 1 • 77 PRINT "NUMBER OF TAILS ROLLED IS "; T − 1 9. change 30 X = 1 TO 50 • 40 RLL = RND(1) • 50 IF RLL < = (5 / 6) THEN 70 • LET R3 = R3 + 1 10. change 30 FOR X = 1 TO 150 • 50 IF RLL < = (20 / 36) THEN 70 • 60 LET R8 = R8 + 1

Page 323 1. choose 10 of 100 sailboat owners; 20 powerboat owners 2. 20 3. Survey excludes certain members of a population (i.e., if they have no telephone). 4. Answers may vary. 5. Classes: 0 - 20, 20 - 40, etc.; Frequency column: 1, 2, 3, 5, 7, 10, 2; Percent Frequency column: 3.3, 6.7, 10, 16.7, 23.4, 33.3, 6.2; Cumulative Frequency column: 3.3, 10, 20, 36.7, 60.1, 93.4, 100

6.

Stem	Leaf
1	1, 2, 6, 9, 9
2	1, 4, 5, 8, 9
3	1, 5, 6
4	0, 1, 1, 5, 6
5	3, 5, 9
6	1, 8
7	2, 9
8	6, 8
9	9

7. a. mean = 71.8, mode = 70, 63, median = 76 b. mean = 61.72, mode = 59, median = 61 8. mean = 6.8, no mode, median = 6.95, normal, central measures grouped 9. a. HH, HT, TH, TT; $\frac{1}{4}$; HT, TH, TT b. all cards; $\frac{1}{4}$; hearts, diamonds, and clubs c. G, G, G, G, W, W, W; $\frac{1}{2}$; G, G, G, W, W, W, W d. Sunday, Monday, Tuesday, Wednesday,

Thursday, Friday, Saturday; $\frac{1}{7}$ **10. a.** equally likely **b.** not equally likely **c.** not equally likely **d.** equally likely **e.** not equally likely **11. a.** $\frac{13}{90}$ **b.** $\frac{299}{900}$ **c.** $\frac{7}{45}$ **d.** $\frac{169}{900}$ **e.** $\frac{7}{90}$ **f.** $\frac{221}{900}$ **g.** $\frac{13}{90}$ **h.** 0 **i.** $\frac{91}{900}$ **12. a.** $\frac{3}{29}$ **b.** $\frac{13}{87}$ **c.** $\frac{7}{87}$ **d.** $\frac{7}{145}$ **e.** $\frac{91}{870}$ **f.** $\frac{26}{145}$

Page 324 **1. a.** 15 **b.** 30 **c.** source of data **d.** 30 m **e.** 5 m **2.** 3 **3.** errors made in doing repetitive tasks

4.
Stem	Leaf
1	1, 2, 3, 4
2	2, 2, 2, 5, 7, 8
3	3, 4, 6, 7
4	5, 5, 5, 7, 9
5	2, 3, 4, 4, 6, 8

6. mean = 10.015 kg, mode = 10.07 kg, median = 10.025 kg **7.** 6.96°C **8.** mean = 203.2 mg/L, modal class $200 < c < 250$, median = 213 mg/L

9. 81.875 kg **10.** R, R, R, R, R, R, W, W, W, W, W, W; R; complement is 5 reds, 6 whites **11. a.** $\frac{2}{7}$ **b.** $\frac{1}{7}$ **c.** $\frac{3}{7}$ **d.** $\frac{4}{7}$ **e.** $\frac{1}{7}$ **f.** 0 **g.** 1 **h.** $\frac{5}{7}$

Cumulative Review Chapters 10-12

Pages 325-328 **1. a.** therefore, we will play golf; deductive **b.** therefore, 12 is not prime; deductive **c.** therefore, you will also hate math; inductive **2. a.** If $\angle 1 \neq \angle 5$ then ℓ_1 is not parallel to ℓ_2. **b.** If $\angle 3 + \angle 5 \neq 180°$ then ℓ_1 is not parallel to ℓ_2. **c.** If $\angle 3 \neq \angle 6$ then ℓ_1 is not parallel to ℓ_2. **3. a.** $\overline{AB} \cong \overline{DF}$ and $\overline{AC} \cong \overline{DE}$ **b.** $\overline{ML} \cong \overline{NO}$ and $\overline{KM} \cong \overline{NP}$ **4. a.** $\angle Y \cong \angle S$ **b.** $\angle L \cong \angle S$ **5. a.** S.A.S. **b.** A.S.A. **6.** $\angle G \cong \angle A$ (given); $\angle PZW \cong \angle TWZ$ (given); $\overline{GZ} \cong \overline{GW} + \overline{WZ}, \overline{AW} = \overline{AZ} + \overline{ZW}$ (addition); $\overline{GW} \cong \overline{AZ}$ (given); $\therefore \overline{GZ} \cong \overline{AW}$; $\therefore \triangle GPZ \cong \triangle ATW$ (A.S.A.) **7.** 8 **8. a.** "if" is hypothesis, "then" is conclusion **b.** "if" is given, "then" is required **c. i)** "triangle is isosceles" is given; "altitude" is required **ii)** triangle is given; longest side opposite largest angle is required **9. a.** $\angle AED \cong \angle BEC$ (O.A.T.); $\angle A \cong \angle C$ (parallel lines); $\angle D \cong \angle C$ (parallel lines) **b.** $\overline{AD} \cong \overline{BC}$; $\overline{AE} \cong \overline{EC}$ **c.** A.S.A. **d.** congruent parts of congruent triangles **10. a.** $\overline{AB} \cong \overline{AC}$ if and only if $\triangle ABC$ is isosceles **b.** $\triangle ABD \cong \triangle ADC$ **c.** that $\overline{AD}$ does bisect $\angle A$ **11.** line from the vertex to the midpoint of the opposite side; let $\triangle ABC$ be isosceles with $\overline{AB} \cong \overline{AC}$ and D is midpoint of $\overline{BC}$; $\overline{AD} \cong \overline{AD}$ (reflexive); $\overline{AB} \cong \overline{AC}$ (given); $\overline{BD} \cong \overline{DC}$

(median) $\therefore \triangle ABD \cong \triangle ADC$ (S.S.S.); $\therefore \angle ABD \cong \angle DAC$ and $\angle ABD + \angle DAC \cong \angle A$; $\therefore \overline{AD}$ bisects $\angle A$. **12.** $12^2 + 16^2 = 20^2$ **13. a.** $|\overline{OR}|^2 = 49 - 16 = 33$ or $|\overline{OR}| = \sqrt{33}$ **b.** $|\overline{PR}|^2 = 128$ so $|\overline{PR}| = 8\sqrt{2}$, chord $\overline{PQ} = 16\sqrt{2}$ **c.** $|\overline{PO}| = \sqrt{277}$ **14.** $x = 105°, y = 75°$ **15. a.** 18.75 cm **b.** 20 cm **16.** 141.4 m **17. a.** reflection in y-axis **b.** reflection in the origin **c.** dilatation **d.** translation **18. a.** $(-x, y)$ **b.** $(-x, -y)$ **c.** $(3x, 3y)$ **d.** $(x - 4, y - 1)$ **19. a.** $A'(-3, 8), B'(-5, 5), C'(3, 3)$ **b.** $A'(1, -4), B'(3, -1), C'(-5, 1)$ **c.** $A'(-4, 1), B'(-1, 3), C'(1, -5)$ **20. a.** $M'(-4, -2)$ **b.** $N'(-4, 1)$ **c.** $P'(-4, -1)$ **d.** $Q'(-3, 1)$ **21. a.** yes, yes, yes **b.** yes, no, yes **c.** yes, no, yes **d.** no, yes, yes **22.** reflections, rotations, translations **23. a.** $3x - 2y = 3$ **b.** $3x - 2y = -2$ **c.** $-2x + 3y = 14$ **24.** $5x + 3y = 17$ **25. a.** $|\overline{AB}| = \sqrt{58}, |\overline{A'B'}| = 2\sqrt{58}$, etc. **b.** area of $\triangle ABC = 13.5$, area of $\triangle A'B'C' = 54$ **26.** $3x + 2y = -20$ **28. a.** $A'(4, -3), B'(6, 0), C'(-2, 2)$ **b.** 180° **c.** $\left(\frac{3}{2}, \frac{1}{2}\right)$ **29.** 1.73 m from the boy **30.** King **31. a.** show slope $\overline{KR}$ = slope $\overline{MS}$ = 5 **b.** show slope $\overline{K'R'}$ = slope $\overline{S'M'} = \frac{1}{5}$

32.
Stem	Leaf
1	1, 1, 1
1	2, 2, 2, 2, 2, 2, 2, 2, 2
1	3, 3, 3, 3, 3
1	4, 4, 4, 4, 4, 4
1	5, 5, 5, 5, 5
1	6, 6

33. mean = 13.23, median = 13, mode = 12 **34. a.** 8 **b.** 7 **35.** Answers may vary. **36.** mean = 27.8 a, median = 24 a, and modal class $20 \leq a < 30$

Chapter 13

Page 329 **1. a.** 10 m **b.** 8.9 cm **c.** 11.7 cm **d.** 18.3 m **2. a.** 18 mm **b.** 12.1 m **3. a.** $8\sqrt{2} = 11.3$ **b.** $8\sqrt{3} = 13.9$ **4. a.** 5 cm **b.** 13 cm **c.** $4\sqrt{10}$ cm **5. a.** 8 **b.** 84 **c.** 4.5 **d.** 8.8 **6. a.** $x = -1, y = 3$ **b.** $n = -3, m = -2$

Pages 330-331 **1. a.** $\overline{AB}$ and $\overline{DF}, \overline{AC}$ and $\overline{DE}, \overline{BC}$ and $\overline{FE}$ **b.** $\overline{RS}$ and $\overline{TU}, \overline{RV}$ and $\overline{TV}, \overline{SU}$ and $\overline{UV}$ **c.** $\overline{HE}$ and $\overline{FG}, \overline{EF}$ and $\overline{FG}, \overline{FH}$ and $\overline{FI}$

2. a. $x = 30$, $y = 36$ **b.** $r = 22.5$, $q = 13.5$ **c.** $m = 5\frac{5}{6}$, $l = 9\frac{1}{3}$ **3.** 4.8 **4.** 9.3 **5.** 120 **6. a.** $x = 7.5$, $y = 6$ **b.** $x = 12.5$, $y = 17.5$ **7.** 25.3 **8. a.** $x = 10$, $y = 14$ **b.** $x = 1.5$, $z = 2.5$ **c.** $b = 5.6$, $c = 6.4$ **d.** $x = 18.2$, $z = 6.1$ **e.** $y = 2.6$, $z = 3.9$ **9.** 80 cm

Pages 332-334   **1. a.** 4.7046 **b.** 0.7002 **c.** 57.2900 **d.** 0.2126 **e.** 1.0355 **f.** 1.7321 **2. a.** 29° **b.** 49° **c.** 39° **d.** 14° **3. a.** 1.3270 **b.** 0.3057 **c.** 0.9657 **d.** 57.2900 **4. a.** 54° **b.** 22° **c.** 85° **d.** 7° **5. a.** 1.5774 **b.** 0 **c.** −0.2679 **d.** −0.0555 **e.** 3 **f.** 1 **6. a.** $\tan A = \frac{8}{6}$, $\tan B = \frac{6}{8}$ **b.** $\tan A = \frac{12}{5}$, $\tan B = \frac{5}{12}$ **c.** $\tan A = \frac{42}{40}$, $\tan B = \frac{40}{42}$ **d.** $\tan A = \frac{16}{30}$, $\tan B = \frac{30}{16}$ **7. a.** 14.0 **b.** 4.1 **8. a.** 7.57 **b.** 10.46 **9. a.** 38° **b.** 55° **10.** 29° **11.** 2.3° **12.** 66.8 m

Pages 335-337   **1. a.** 0.5878 **b.** 0.2924 **c.** 1.5399 **d.** 0.9998 **e.** 0.7314 **f.** 0 **2. a.** 27° **b.** 56° **c.** 83° **d.** 7° **e.** 18° **f.** undefined **3. a.** 0.7314 **b.** 0.9455 **c.** 0.8290 **d.** 0.8290 **e.** 0.5 **f.** 0.2079 **4. a.** 12° **b.** 69° **c.** 50° **d.** undefined **e.** 49° **f.** 82° **5. a.** 0 **b.** −0.4664 **c.** 1.6737 **d.** 0 **e.** 0.7071 **f.** 1 **g.** 0.5992 **h.** 1 **6. a.** $\sin A = \frac{3}{5}$, $\cos A = \frac{4}{5}$, $\tan A = \frac{3}{4}$, $\sin B = \frac{4}{5}$, $\cos B = \frac{3}{5}$, $\tan B = \frac{4}{3}$ **b.** $\sin A = \frac{15}{17}$, $\cos A = \frac{8}{17}$, $\tan A = \frac{15}{8}$, $\sin B = \frac{8}{17}$, $\cos B = \frac{15}{17}$, $\tan B = \frac{8}{15}$ **7. a.** $x = 14.0$ **b.** $x = 7.9$ **c.** $x = 15.5$ **d.** $x = 35.5$ **8. a.** 42.8° **b.** 65.4° **c.** 55.6° **d.** 36° **9. a.** 4.6° **b.** 6.8° **10. a.** $a = 21.7$ **b.** $b = 24.6$ **c.** $c = 8.2$ **d.** $c = 10.3$ **11. a.** 60° **b.** 45° **c.** 67° **d.** 36° **e.** $(90 - x)°$

Page 338   **1. a.** $\angle A = 45°$, $\angle B = 45°$, $b = 12$ **b.** $\angle P = 51°$, $\angle R = 39°$, $q = 5.0$ **c.** $\angle X = 69°$, $z = 9.2$, $y = 25.7$ **d.** $\angle C = 48°$, $c = 64.7$, $a = 58.2$ **2. a.** $\angle Q = 54°$, $\angle P = 36°$, $r = 28.6$ **b.** $\angle Q = 52°$, $p = 9.9$, $q = 12.6$ **c.** $\angle Q = 18°$, $p = 118.2$, $r = 124.3$ **d.** $\angle P = 43°$, $\angle Q = 47°$, $p = 27.3$ **e.** $\angle P = 51°$, $\angle Q = 39°$, $q = 14.2$ **f.** $\angle P = 42°$, $p = 60.0$, $q = 66.7$ **g.** $\angle P = 78°$, $p = 22.1$, $r = 22.6$ **h.** $\angle Q = 45°$, $q = 14.9$, $r = 21.1$ **3.** $a = 55.2$, $b = 19.9$, $c = 41.0$, $\angle A = 126°$

Pages 339-340   **1.** 410 m **2.** 32 m **3. a.** 77° **b.** 10.7 m **4.** 29 m **5.** 122.8 m **6.** 389 m **7.** 485 m **8. a.** 32° **b.** 15.3 cm **9. a.** 15.7 cm **b.** 17.5 cm **c.** 137 cm² **10. a.** 135 m **b.** 155 m **11.** 113 m **12.** 122 **13.** 16° **14.**

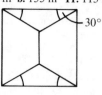

15. $450\sqrt{3}$
16. a. 7.2 m
b. 63.6 m

BRAINTICKLER

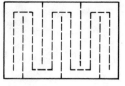

Cut along dotted lines.

Pages 341-343   **1.** A: 1×3; B: 4×4; C: 5×2; D: 2×2; E: 2×3; F: 1×4 **2. a.** $\begin{bmatrix} 2 & 8 & -11 \end{bmatrix}$

b. $\begin{bmatrix} 0 & 2 & -1 & 6 \\ -6 & 11 & -9 & 22 \\ -7 & 8 & 3 & 17 \\ 6 & 22 & 6 & 0 \end{bmatrix}$
c. not conformable
d. not conformable
e. not conformable
f. $\begin{bmatrix} -4 & -2 & 7 \end{bmatrix}$

g. $\begin{bmatrix} 0 & 8 & -13 & 10 \\ 2 & -1 & 3 & 0 \\ -7 & 2 & 3 & -25 \\ 10 & 28 & 6 & -8 \end{bmatrix}$
h. not conformable
i. not conformable
j. $\begin{bmatrix} 11 & 9 & -23 \end{bmatrix}$

k. $\begin{bmatrix} 0 & 9 & -9 & 20 \\ -14 & 27 & -21 & 55 \\ -21 & 21 & 9 & 30 \\ 20 & 69 & 18 & -4 \end{bmatrix}$
l. not conformable

3. a. $\begin{bmatrix} 2 & 8 & -11 \end{bmatrix}$ **b.** $\begin{bmatrix} 0 & 2 & -1 & 6 \\ -6 & 11 & -9 & 22 \\ -7 & 8 & 3 & 17 \\ 6 & 22 & 6 & 0 \end{bmatrix}$

4. the same, yes **5. a.** T **b.** T **c.** T **d.** Matrix addition is distributive. **6.** $\begin{bmatrix} 5 & -7 \\ -4 & 6 \end{bmatrix}$ **7. a.** $\begin{bmatrix} 1700 & 1200 & 1000 & 500 \\ 1300 & 1000 & 800 & 400 \end{bmatrix}$ **b. i)** 3000, sum of the first column **ii)** 3500, sum of the 2nd row **iii)** 7900, total matrix **8. a.** $x = 4$, $y = -5$, $z = 6$, $k = -3$, $m = 4$ **b.** $x = 6$, $y = -6$, $m = 7$, $n = 6$ **9.** $\begin{bmatrix} 0 & 1 & 1 & 0 \\ 0 & 0 & 0 & 1 \\ 1 & 0 & 0 & 1 \\ 1 & 1 & 1 & 0 \end{bmatrix}$

Pages 344-345   **1.** addition: same order; multiplication: number of columns in 1st matrix is the same as rows in the 2nd **2. a.** 5×3 **b.** sum of products of row 2 from 2nd matrix and column 1 from the 1st matrix **3. a.** 5×5 **b.** 4×4 **4.** $A \times B$ would not conform

5. a. $\begin{bmatrix} -17 & 21 \\ 10 & -3 \end{bmatrix}$
b. $\begin{bmatrix} -15 & -9 & -17 \\ -30 & 15 & -12 \end{bmatrix}$
c. $\begin{bmatrix} -10 & 14 & 2 \\ 20 & -7 & 10 \\ 5 & 1 & -3 \end{bmatrix}$
d. and **e.** do not conform
f. $\begin{bmatrix} -18 & 20 \\ -6 & -19 \\ 3 & 4 \end{bmatrix}$
g. $\begin{bmatrix} 35 & -13 & 17 \end{bmatrix}$
h. $\begin{bmatrix} -9 & -34 \end{bmatrix}$

i. $\begin{bmatrix} 33 & 0 \\ 0 & 33 \end{bmatrix}$ **j.** $\begin{bmatrix} -99 & -132 \\ -198 & 99 \end{bmatrix}$

6. no, no   **7.** $\begin{bmatrix} 1 & 0 & 0 \\ 0 & 1 & 0 \\ 0 & 0 & 1 \end{bmatrix}$

8. $AB = \begin{bmatrix} -1 & 0 \\ 0 & -1 \end{bmatrix} = BA$ **9.** $\begin{bmatrix} -5 & 4 \\ 2 & 3 \end{bmatrix}$ identity matrix

Pages 346-347

1. a. $\begin{bmatrix} -2 & \dfrac{-3}{2} \\ -3 & \dfrac{-5}{2} \end{bmatrix}$ **b.** $\begin{bmatrix} 1 & \dfrac{-3}{2} \\ 2 & \dfrac{-7}{2} \end{bmatrix}$

c. $\begin{bmatrix} -1 & 5 \\ 1 & -4 \end{bmatrix}$ **d.** no inverse

e. $\begin{bmatrix} \dfrac{1}{2} & \dfrac{1}{2} \\ 1 & 1 \end{bmatrix}$ **f.** $\begin{bmatrix} 9 & 10 \\ -6 & -8 \end{bmatrix}$

g. $\begin{bmatrix} \dfrac{-21}{50} & \dfrac{-1}{5} \\ \dfrac{3}{4} & \dfrac{-5}{6} \end{bmatrix}$ **h.** $\begin{bmatrix} \dfrac{2\sqrt5}{5} & \dfrac{3\sqrt{10}}{10} \\ \dfrac{\sqrt2}{2} & \dfrac{1}{2} \end{bmatrix}$

2. Inconsistent values for the variables.   **3. a.** $\begin{bmatrix} \dfrac{-1}{2} & \dfrac{-5}{2} \\ -1 & -6 \end{bmatrix}$

b. $\begin{bmatrix} -3 & 7 \\ -4 & 9 \end{bmatrix}$ **c.** $\begin{bmatrix} -4 & -21 \\ 4 & 18 \end{bmatrix}$

d. no inverse   **4. a.** $(-1, 3)$ **b.** $(4, 1)$ **c.** $(4, 1)$ **d.** no solution **e.** $\left(\dfrac{1}{4}, \dfrac{1}{2}\right)$ **f.** $\left(\dfrac{-1}{3}, \dfrac{1}{5}\right)$ **5. a.** inverse does not exist **b.** no solution for part d **6. a.** $(3, 4)$ **b.** $(4, -6)$ **c.** $(-6, -3)$ **d.** $\left(\dfrac{-1}{2}, \dfrac{3}{4}\right)$ **7. a.** no **b.** yes **c.** yes **d.** no **8. a.** $x + y = 11, x - y = 7$; solution: $(9, 2)$ **b.** $d + n = 29, 0.1d + 0.05n = 2.05$; solution: 17 nickels and 12 dimes **c.** $120 = 3(x - y)$, $120 = 2(x + y)$; solution: 50 km/h, 10 km/h **9.** for inconsistent values of the variables **10.** Only square matrices conform under multiplication in any order. **11.** Answers may vary.

Pages 348-350

1. a. $\begin{bmatrix} -5 \\ 2 \end{bmatrix}$ **b.** $\begin{bmatrix} 3 & -6 \\ -1 & 2 \end{bmatrix}$ **c.** $\begin{bmatrix} -1 & 5 & 1 \\ -1 & 0 & 3 \end{bmatrix}$

2. a. $\begin{bmatrix} 1 & 4 & 8 \\ 1 & -1 & -6 \end{bmatrix}$ **b.** $\begin{bmatrix} -4 & -1 & 3 \\ 10 & 8 & 3 \end{bmatrix}$

3. a. $A'(-3, -1), B'(2, 4)$ **b.** $K'(4, 2), L'(5, -2)$ **c.** $P'(-4, 1), Q'(3, -2)$ **4.** $\begin{bmatrix} -1 & 0 \\ 0 & 1 \end{bmatrix}$ $(-3, 2)$

5. a. $A'(-3, 0), B'(-4, 3), C'(1, 2)$ **b.** $K'(1, -1), L'(-2, -3), M'(-4, 1)$ **c.** $P'(-5, 3), Q'(2, -6), R'(-3, -1)$ **6. a.** $A'(4, -1), B'(-1, -5)$ **b.** $B'(-3, 2), F'(-1, 4), G'(3, 2)$ **7. a.** $(3, 2), (-6, -1), (9, -2)$, horizontal stretch **b.** $(1, 6), (-2, -3), (3, -6)$,

vertical stretch **c.** $(3, 6), (-6, -3), (9, -6)$, dilatation
8. a. $(-1, 1), (-1, 4), (-5, 1)$, 90° clockwise
b. $(-1, -1), (-4, -1), (-1, -5)$, 180° **c.** $(-1, 1), (-1, 4), (-5, 1)$, 90° counterclockwise
9. a. $\begin{bmatrix} 1 & 0 \\ 0 & -1 \end{bmatrix}$ **b.** $\begin{bmatrix} -1 & 0 \\ 0 & 1 \end{bmatrix}$ **c.** $\begin{bmatrix} 0 & 1 \\ 1 & 0 \end{bmatrix}$
d. $\begin{bmatrix} 4 & 0 \\ 0 & 4 \end{bmatrix}$ **e.** $\begin{bmatrix} 3 & 0 \\ 0 & 1 \end{bmatrix}$ **f.** $\begin{bmatrix} 1 & 0 \\ 0 & 2 \end{bmatrix}$
g. $\begin{bmatrix} 0 & 1 \\ -1 & 0 \end{bmatrix}$ **h.** $\begin{bmatrix} -1 & 0 \\ 0 & -1 \end{bmatrix}$ **i.** $\begin{bmatrix} 0 & -1 \\ 1 & 0 \end{bmatrix}$

10.

yes	yes	yes	yes	yes	yes	yes
yes	yes	yes	yes	no	yes	yes
yes	yes	yes	yes	no	yes	yes
no	yes	yes	yes	yes	no	yes
no	no	yes	yes	no	no	no

11. a. $A'(-1, -2), B'(-4, -2), C'(-4, -4), D'(-1, -4)$
b. $A'(1, 2), B'(4, 2), C'(4, 4), D'(1, 4)$ **c.** $A'(2, 1), B'(2, -4), C'(4, -4), D'(4, -1)$

Page 351   **1.** $10 \times 8 \times 3$ **2.** 405.92 m²
3. a. 160 cm³ **b.** 216 cm³   **4.** 30.375 cm³
5. a. increase 4 times **b.** increase 9 times **c.** n^2
6. 8 times; 27 times; n^3 **7.** 8 m²

Page 352   **1. a.** $V = 334$ cm³, $S.A. = 279$ cm²
b. $V = 5293$ cm³; $S.A. = 1685$ cm²   **2.** $1206.37
3. a. 37.5 **b.** 9425 m²   **4.** 22.4 m²   **5.** Volume column: 137, 550, 275, 1100, 1237; Surface Area column: 149, 377, 259, 597, 683   **6. a.** double height: volume $\times 2$, $S.A. \times 1.7$; double diameter: volume $\times 4$, $S.A. \times 2.5$; double both: volume $\times 8$, $S.A. \times 4$ **b.** triple height: volume $\times 3$, $S.A. \times 2.5$; triple diameter: volume $\times 9$, $S.A. \times 4.6$; triple both: volume $\times 27$, $S.A. = 9$ **c.** volume: $\dfrac{1}{8}$ as much, $S.A.: \dfrac{1}{4}$ as much   **7.** 7.7 m³

Page 353   **1.** $V = 7238$ cm³, $S.A. = 1810$ cm²
2. 57 m³   **3. a.** $V = 3054$ cm³, $S.A. = 1018$ cm²
b. $V = 4189$ cm³, $S.A. = 1257$ cm² **c.** $V = 4849$ cm³, $S.A. = 1385$ cm²   **4.** 1810 cm²   **5.** $8 : 3\sqrt3$ **6.** $2 : 3$
7. a. 43.1 m³ **b.** 28.7 m³ **c.** 21.5 m³ **d.** 3.4 m³
8. increases volume 8 times   **9.** $2 : 3$ **10. a.** sphere **b.** hemisphere **c.** cube

Pages 354-355   **1. a.** 145 cm³ **b.** 65 cm³   **2.** 94.2 m³
3. a. 594 cm³ **b.** 1178 cm³   **4. a.** 265 cm² **b.** 687 cm²
5. a. 10.3 cm **b.** 25.77 cm² **c.** 128.1 cm²
6. b. $S.A. = 397.6$ cm², $V = 453$ cm³   **7. a.** 58.4 cm²
b. 111.6 cm²   **8.** 484.6 cm²   **9.** 1130 mm²
10. 100.8π **11. a.** 114 cm² **b.** 422 cm²
12. a. 282.6 cm² **b.** 647.8 cm²

Page 356 **1.** Answers may vary. **2.** Answers may vary. **3. a.** 62.9 m² **b.** 1659 m² **4. a.** 796 cm³ **b.** 567 m³

Page 357 **1.** $330.33 **2. a.** 3375 cm³ **b.** 1470 cm², 1350 cm² **c.** cube **3.** sphere **4.** Answers may vary.

5. $(2r + 2h):rh$ **6. a.** $\frac{8}{3}:h$ or $8:r$ **b.** $3:h$ or $6:r$

c. $4:h$ or $4:r$ **d.** $3:r$ or $6:h$ **e.** $\frac{8}{3}:r$ or $8:h$ **f.** $\frac{5}{2}:r$ or $10:h$ **7.** f **8.** b

Pages 360-361 **1.** *rotational symmetry*: a shape that can be formed by rotating a 2-dimensional object around an axis, e.g., cylinder; *point symmetry*: a shape in which every point on the surface has a corresponding point equidistant from the centre, e.g., sphere; *plane symmetry*: a shape that can be sliced into two congruent halves, e.g., sphere **2.** No, a cone may have plane symmetry but not point symmetry. **3.** sphere **4.** slice through the middle of an object **5.** all **a.** 9 **b.** infinite **c.** infinite **6.** cone, sphere **7. a.** centre of cube **b.** centre of sphere **c.** none **10.** Answers may vary. **11.** $5000 **12. a.** 9 planes **b.** infinite, each containing the centre **13. a.** plane symmetry, from one end to the other **b.** plane symmetry, infinite vertical planes through centre **c.** plane symmetry, infinite vertical through centre **d.** plane symmetry, infinite vertical through centre

Pages 362-364 **1. a.** scalar **b.** vector **c.** vector **d.** scalar **e.** neither **f.** scalar **g.** scalar **h.** neither **i.** scalar **2. a.** N30°E **b.** S40°E **c.** due S **d.** S60°W **e.** N35°W **f.** N89°E **3. a.** 065° **b.** 160° **c.** 135° **d.** 090° **e.** 220° **f.** 335° **4. a.-d.** Answers may vary depending on scale chosen. **e.** Start at origin and have head of vector at (5, 3). **f.** Start at origin and head of vector at (−4, 3). **g.** Answers may vary depending on scale chosen. **5. a.** $2\sqrt{41}$ **b.** $3\sqrt{5}$ **c.** $\sqrt{17}$ **d.** 13 **6.** $\vec{a} = (4, 2), 2\sqrt{5}$; $\vec{b} = (3, 0), 3$; $\vec{c} = (0, 2), 2$; $\vec{d} = (-4, -4), 4\sqrt{2}$; $\vec{e} = (4, 3), 5$; $\vec{f} = (-1, -2), \sqrt{5}$; $\vec{g} = (-4, 4), 4\sqrt{2}$; $\vec{h} = (-2, 3), \sqrt{13}$; $\vec{i} = (4, -3), 5$ **7. a.** $\vec{KL}$ and $\vec{IJ}$ **b.** $\vec{EA}$ and $\vec{DB}$, $\vec{AB}$ and $\vec{ED}$, $\vec{FA}$ and $\vec{DC}$, $\vec{FE}$ and $\vec{BC}$ **c.** $\vec{RT}$, $\vec{TQ}$, and $\vec{VU}$; $\vec{VT}$, $\vec{SU}$, and $\vec{UQ}$; $\vec{RV}$, $\vec{VS}$, and $\vec{TU}$ **8.** Draw the diagonal, and a line from the diagonal, at 90°, to an open vertex **9. a.** $[-6, -4], 2\sqrt{13}$ **b.** $[-8, 6], 10$ **c.** $[10, -2], 2\sqrt{26}$ **d.** $[4, 0], 4$ **e.** $[6, 4], 2\sqrt{13}$ **f.** $[2, 4], 2\sqrt{5}$ **10.** $\Delta x = x_2 - x_1, \Delta y = y_2 - y_1$ $\therefore A = [(x_2 - x_1), (y_2 - y_1)]$ **11.** Answers may vary.

Pages 365-366 **1.** Head of one vector to the tail of the other gives the displacement. **2.** $\vec{AF}$ **3. a.** 13.9 km at 150° **b.** 510 km/h at 011° **4. a.** $\vec{DB}$ **b.** $\vec{CA}$ **c.** $\vec{AB}$ **d.** $\vec{DC}$ **e.** $\vec{KL}$ **f.** $\vec{LN}$ **g.** $\vec{PK}$ **5. a.** [8, 12]

b. [5, 3] **c.** [−1, −5] **d.** [1, 0] **e.** [−5, −11] **f.** [0, 0] **g.** [5, −12] **7. a.** [−8, 8] **b.** [0, −3] **c.** [0, 2] **8. a.** North $600\sqrt{2}$ N **b.** 10 km, 077° **c.** 14.9 km/h at 262° **9. a.** [−5, −2] **b.** [7, 3] **c.** [5, −3] **d.** [−x, −y] **10. a.** [4, 5] **b.** [−1, 18] **c.** [−13, 12] **d.** [9, −3]

Page 367 **1. a.** 200 N downwards **b.** 750 m/s at 070° **c.** 35 m at 15° **d.** [−25, 15] **e.** [35, 40] **f.** [−30, 0] **2. a.** [9, 12] **b.** [−10, 20] **c.** [−6, −8] **d.** [0, 20] **e.** [−16, −8] **f.** [0, 0] **3. a.** [−12, 4] **b.** [18, −6] **c.** [3, −1] **4.** reverses direction by 180° **5.** $|\vec{x}| = 3\sqrt{5}$ **a.** $6\sqrt{5}, 2\vec{x}$ **b.** $9\sqrt{5}, 3\vec{x}$ **c.** $4\sqrt{5}, \frac{4\vec{x}}{3}$ **6.** magnitude increased by absolute value of scalar **7. a.** $\vec{OB} + \vec{OH}$ **b.** $\vec{OB} + \frac{1}{2}\vec{OF}$ **c.** $\vec{OF} + \frac{1}{2}\vec{OB}$ **d.** $\frac{1}{2}(\vec{OB} + \vec{OF})$ **e.** $\frac{1}{2}\vec{OB} + \frac{3}{2}\vec{OF}$ **f.** $\frac{3}{2}\vec{OF}$

Pages 368-369 **1. a.** $\vec{DB} + \vec{BA}$ or $\vec{BC} + \vec{CA}$ **b.** $\vec{CB} + \vec{BD}$ or $\vec{CA} + \vec{AD}$ **c.** $\vec{CD} + \vec{DB}$ or $\vec{CA} + \vec{AB}$ **d.** $\vec{AD} + \vec{DB}$ or $\vec{AC} + \vec{CB}$ **e.** $\vec{DC} + \vec{CB}$ or $\vec{DA} + \vec{AB}$ **f.** $\vec{BD} + \vec{DC}$ or $\vec{BA} + \vec{AC}$ **2. a.** $\vec{n} + \vec{m}$ **b.** $\vec{n}$ **c.** $\vec{n}$ **d.** $-\vec{m}$ **e.** $-\vec{m}$ **f.** $-\vec{m} - \vec{n}$ **3. a.** $\vec{AD} + \vec{DN}$ **b.** $\vec{MB} + \vec{BC}$ **4.** $\vec{AD} + \vec{DN} \cong \vec{AN}$ (addition of vectors); $\vec{MB} + \vec{BC} \cong \vec{MC}$ (same); $\vec{AD} \cong \vec{BC}$ and $\vec{DN} \cong \vec{MB}$ (given); $\therefore \vec{AN} \cong \vec{MC}$ (transitive); $\vec{AN} \parallel \vec{MC}$ (equal vectors). **5.** In $\triangle AMN$, $\vec{MN} \cong \vec{MA} + \vec{AN}$ (add); in $\triangle ABC$, $\vec{BC} \cong \vec{BA} + \vec{AC}$ (add); $\vec{BC} \cong 3\vec{MA} + 3\vec{AN}$ (given); so $\vec{BC} \cong 3(\vec{MA} + \vec{AN})$; $\vec{BC} \cong 3\vec{MN}$ (substitution); $\therefore \vec{MN} \parallel \vec{BC}$ (one vector is multiple of the other). **6.** $\vec{EF} \cong \vec{ED} + \vec{DC} + \vec{CF}$ (add); $\vec{AB} \cong \vec{AE} + \vec{ED} + \vec{DC} + \vec{CF} + \vec{FB}$ (add); $\vec{AE} \cong -\vec{FB}$ or $\vec{AE} + \vec{FB} = 0$ (opposite); $\vec{EF} \cong \vec{AB}$ (transitive); $\therefore \vec{EF} \cong \vec{AB}$ and $\vec{EF} \parallel \vec{AB}$ (equal vectors). **7.** Quadrilateral $ABCD$ with $\vec{AB} \parallel \vec{DC}$; $\vec{AD} \cong \vec{AE} + \vec{ED}$ (add); $\vec{BC} \cong \vec{BE} + \vec{EC}$ (add); $\vec{AE} \cong \vec{EC}$ (given); $\vec{BE} \cong \vec{ED}$ (given); $\therefore \vec{AD} \cong \vec{BC}$ (substitution and transitive) so $\vec{AD} \cong \vec{BC}$, $\vec{AD} \parallel \vec{BC}$ (equal vectors), $ABCD$ is a parallelogram (opposite sides parallel and congruent). **8.** reverse of Exercise 7 **9.** Number of edges must be even because shared by two sides. But polyhedron has 41 edges. **10.** 27 **BRAINTICKLER** Will move in semicircles with respect to the ground.

Pages 370-371 **1. a.** 13 **b.** $\sqrt{30}$ **c.** $\sqrt{10}$ **d.** 6 **2. a.** $[4, -3, -7], \sqrt{74}$ **b.** $[-4, 0, -1], \sqrt{17}$ **c.** $[-8, 3, 6], \sqrt{109}$ **d.** $[-4, 3, 7], \sqrt{74}$ **e.** [4, 0, 1], $\sqrt{17}$ **f.** $[8, -3, -6], \sqrt{109}$ **3. a.** [17, 16, 34] **b.** [−6, 12, −4] **c.** [−26, −1, 17] **4.** [360, 520, 47]

428

Page 372 **1.** This program is correct to 6 decimal places. **2.** 30 FOR X = 47 TO 62; 70 NEXT X; delete 80 and 90 **3.** Answers may vary. **4.** Answers may vary. **5.** 10 REM SOLVE TRIANGLE • 20 LET A = 1 : AC = 90 • 30 LET B = 2 • 40 LET C = SQR(A ∧ 2 + B ∧ 2) • 50 LET X = A / C • 60 PRINT "CHECK SINE TABLES FOR RATIO" • 70 LET Y = B / C • 80 PRINT "CHECK SINE TABLES FOR RATIO" • 90 END **6.** Answers may vary.

Page 373 **1.** points are scattered around the graph **2.** one is in better condition than the other **3.** appropriate because ranges of each matches those on the chart **4.** yes, pattern of dots is up and to the right; faster you walk, the faster the heart rate

Pages 374-375 **1.** *negative correlation*: when one variable increases the other decreases; *positive correlation*: both variables increase together **2. a.** positive **b.** negative **c.** no correlation **3.** Answers may vary, e.g., players height, ice time. **4. i)** yes, years of education vs. salary, positive **ii)** yes, hours studied vs. mark, positive **iii)** yes, positive **iv)** no, no correlation **v)** yes, height vs. mass, positive **5.** Answers may vary. **6. a.** negative for *B*, positive for *A* **b.** *A* **c.** Answers may vary. **d.** Answers may vary, e.g., temperature outside population, amount of food. **7.** Possible answers: **a.** age of antiques vs. price of antiques **b.** age of car vs. resale value **c.** years employed vs. length of arm **8.** if all points follow the same pattern, i.e., if they all are on the same straight line

Pages 376-377 **1. a.** how one variable reacts as the other reacts **b.** line *b* appears to have as many points above as below **2.** a line drawn through the median extremes **3.** 120 by method 1 **4.** 27.5, method 1 **5.** *extrapolate*: estimate a value outside a known population; *interpolate*: estimate a value between known population values **7.** no, student who doesn't study will probably guess correctly or remember some of the answers **8.** $s = 3.2t + 50$ **9.** Answers may vary. **10.** yes **11.** Answers may vary. **12.** for 100% about 15 h; for 50% less than one hour **13. a.** 53% **b.** 52% **c.** 0 h **d.** 10 h **14.** Answers may vary. **15.** athletes are in better condition so there is less body fat

Pages 378-380 **1.** Possibly, if seasonally adjusted figures are high, on the average over a longer period, the outlook is bad. **2.** 7.44% **3.** yes **4. a.** trend **b.** cycle **c.** time series **d.** trend **5.** Answer will vary depending on argument presented. **6.** Possible answers: temperature, hours of sunlight **7.** mean = 30 mm/summer, median = 30.6 mm/summer; corn **8. b.** 241 km/h

c. 115 km/h **9.** trend, long term pattern, steady increase **10.** Possible answers: price of gold, price of fuel, stock prices up — sell; stock prices down — buy

Pages 381-382 **1.** Possible answer: case of oranges infected **2.** no, how good is the editor? **3.** yes **4.** yes **5.** no correlation; annual sales depends on advertising and promotion **6.** positive correlation, cars are getting faster **7.** positive correlation **8.** no correlation **9. a.** Possible answers: more graduates in work force, more non-university training needed for jobs **b.** more people smoke, more people diagnosed now than 100 a ago **10.** no, physiological limit

Pages 383-384

TRIGONOMETRY

1. a. $s = 21$, $t = 24$ **b.** $m = 8$, $p = 13\frac{1}{3}$ **2. a.** $x = 5.2$ **b.** 41° **3. a.** 42° or 48° **b.** $c = 18.3$, $\angle B = 55°$, $\angle C = 35°$ **4.** 18.8 m **5. a.** 393 m **b.** 829 m

MATRICES

1. a. 2×4 **b.** 3×1 **c.** 3×3 **d.** 3×2 **2. a.** $\begin{bmatrix} 3 & -1 \\ -1 & -3 \\ -5 & -4 \end{bmatrix}$ **b.** doesn't conform

c. $\begin{bmatrix} -4 & -12 & 4 \\ 7 & 0 & -7 \\ 5 & 0 & 1 \end{bmatrix}$ **d.** $\begin{bmatrix} -21 & 12 & -18 & -3 \\ 0 & -6 & 24 & -12 \end{bmatrix}$

e. $\begin{bmatrix} -7 & 12 & -5 \\ 7 & -15 & 11 \\ -1 & 0 & 7 \end{bmatrix}$ **f.** $\begin{bmatrix} -15 & 21 \\ 9 & 3 \\ -19 & 40 \end{bmatrix}$

3. $a = -6$, $b = 7$, $c = -3$, $d = 18$, $e = -5$

4. a. $\begin{bmatrix} 9 \\ 13 \end{bmatrix}$ **b.** $\begin{bmatrix} -1 & 16 \\ 25 & -24 \\ 27 & -42 \end{bmatrix}$ **c.** $\begin{bmatrix} -61 & 3 \\ 88 & -36 \end{bmatrix}$

d. $\begin{bmatrix} 30 & -20 \\ -70 & 50 \end{bmatrix}$ **e.** $\begin{bmatrix} -21 & 22 & -58 & 17 \\ 14 & -8 & 12 & 2 \\ -42 & 42 & -108 & 30 \end{bmatrix}$

f. $\begin{bmatrix} 50 \\ -6 \\ -12 \end{bmatrix}$ **g.** $\begin{bmatrix} -14 & 20 & 40 \\ 27 & -35 & -90 \end{bmatrix}$

h. and **i.** $\begin{bmatrix} -290 & 430 \\ 217 & -352 \end{bmatrix}$

5. Only square matrices have inverses.

THREE-DIMENSIONAL GEOMETRY

2. a. 372 cm² **b.** 1018 cm² **c.** 94 cm² **3.** $85.45 **4.** $330.50 **5. a.** 3.4 m³ **b.** 412 cm³ **c.** 11 494 cm³ **6. a.** object that can be divided into two congruent halves, e.g., sphere **b.** an object that is formed by rotating a 2-D shape around an axis, e.g., cylinder **c.** object such that every point on a surface has a corresponding point equidistant from the point of symmetry, e.g., sphere **7.** Answers may vary.

1. a. vector **b.** scalar **c.** vector **d.** neither
2. Answers may vary depending on the scale
chosen. **3. a.** and **b.** $\vec{a} = [-1, -2]$, $\sqrt{5}$; $\vec{b} = [2, -3]$,
$\sqrt{13}$; $\vec{c} = [-3, -2]$, $\sqrt{13}$; $\vec{d} = [5, -1]$, $\sqrt{26}$;
$\vec{e} = [-1, -2]$, $\sqrt{13}$; $\vec{f} = [-2, 3]$, $\sqrt{13}$; $\vec{g} = [-3, -2]$,
$\sqrt{13}$; $\vec{h} = [4, -1]$, $\sqrt{17}$; $\vec{i} = [3, 2]$, $\sqrt{13}$ **c.** c and g;
a and e **4. a.** $[-7, -5]$ **b.** $[1, -1]$ **c.** $[0, 0]$ **5. a.** 51,
$061°$ **b.** 5.6 m/s **c.** 3.1, $018°$ **6. a.** $[-4, 10]$
b. $[-15, -3]$ **c.** $[11, 13]$ **d.** $[-17, 2]$
7. a. $[-5, 11, -15]$ **b.** $[6, 5, 4]$

Pages 385-386

TRIGONOMETRY
1. $x = 11\frac{2}{3}$, $y = 9\frac{1}{3}$ **2. a.** $\sin A = \frac{9}{15}$, $\sin B = \frac{12}{15}$,
$\cos A = \frac{12}{15}$, $\cos B = \frac{9}{15}$, $\tan A = \frac{9}{12}$, $\tan B = \frac{12}{9}$
b. $\sin A = \frac{36}{39}$, $\sin B = \frac{15}{39}$, $\cos A = \frac{15}{39}$, $\cos B = \frac{36}{39}$,
$\tan A = \frac{36}{15}$, $\tan B = \frac{15}{36}$ **3.** 121 m **4.** 3800 m
5. $A = 3$ m, $B = 4$ m, $C = 4.7$ m, $D = 5$ m

MATRICES
1. a. $\begin{bmatrix} 9 & -10 & -13 \\ -4 & 8 & -15 \\ 18 & -21 & -1 \end{bmatrix}$ **b.** $\begin{bmatrix} -5 & 20 \\ 5 & -10 \\ 0 & -15 \end{bmatrix}$

2. a. 3×2 **b.** 3×3
c. 1×3 **d.** 4×2 **e.** 1×3
f. 1×2 **3.** $\begin{bmatrix} \frac{1}{6} & -\frac{1}{9} \\ 0 & -\frac{1}{3} \end{bmatrix}$

4. a. $\begin{bmatrix} 11 & -6 & 16 \\ 7 & 4 & 23 \\ 18 & -18 & 17 \end{bmatrix}$ **b.** $\begin{bmatrix} 1 & 24 & -4 \\ 6 & 17 & -14 \\ -9 & 27 & 14 \end{bmatrix}$

c. $\begin{bmatrix} 48 & -13 \\ -18 & -9 \\ -36 & 6 \\ 0 & -3 \end{bmatrix}$ **d.** $\begin{bmatrix} 10 & 1 & -2 \\ 7 & 17 & -2 \\ 3 & 6 & 4 \end{bmatrix}$ **e.** $\begin{bmatrix} -7 & 17 \end{bmatrix}$
f. $\begin{bmatrix} 12 & -52 \\ -18 & -6 \\ -18 & 6 \end{bmatrix}$

5. Find $EE^{-1} = \begin{bmatrix} 1 & 0 \\ 0 & 1 \end{bmatrix}$ **6.** no, yes

7. Show $XY = \begin{bmatrix} 1 & 0 & 0 \\ 0 & 1 & 0 \\ 0 & 0 & 1 \end{bmatrix}$.

THREE-DIMENSIONAL GEOMETRY
1. a. 1800 cm² **b.** 18 m² **c.** 640 m² **d.** 515 m²
2. a. 2121 m³ **b.** 1072 cm³ **c.** 1047 m³ **3.** 20 400 m³
4. 3551.8 m³

VECTORS
1. a. N65°E **b.** S45°E **c.** N70°W **2. a.** 085° **b.** 215°
c. 335° **3. a.** $[7, -4]$, $\sqrt{65}$ **b.** $[-7, 4]$, $\sqrt{65}$
c. $[-2, 1, 1]$, $\sqrt{6}$ **4. a.** $\vec{RN}$ **b.** none **c.** $\vec{SR}$ **d.** $\vec{KR}$
e. $\vec{MN}$ **f.** $\vec{KN}$ **g.** $\vec{KS}$ **h.** $\vec{KS}$ **5.** 22.4N **6. a.** 533, 148°
b. 104 m

Index